McGRAW-HILL PUBLICATIONS IN PSYCHOLOGY

J. F. DASHIELL, Ph.D., Consulting Editor

PHYSIOLOGICAL PSYCHOLOGY

McGraw-Hill Publications in Psychology

J. F. DASHIELL
CONSULTING EDITOR

Barker, Kounin, and Wright—CHILD BEHAVIOR AND DEVELOPMENT

Brown—PSYCHOLOGY AND THE SOCIAL ORDER

Brown—THE PSYCHODYNAMICS OF ABNORMAL BEHAVIOR

Cole—GENERAL PSYCHOLOGY

Crafts, Schneirla, Robinson, and Gilbert—RECENT EXPERIMENTS IN PSYCHOLOGY

Davis—PSYCHOLOGY OF LEARNING

Dunlap—RELIGION: ITS FUNCTIONS IN HUMAN LIFE

Gray—PSYCHOLOGY IN HUMAN AFFAIRS

Guilford—FUNDAMENTAL STATISTICS IN PSYCHOLOGY AND EDUCATION

Guilford—PSYCHOMETRIC METHODS

Hurlock—CHILD DEVELOPMENT

Lewin—A DYNAMIC THEORY OF PERSONALITY

Lewin—PRINCIPLES OF TOPOLOGICAL PSYCHOLOGY

McNemar and Merrill (Ed.)—STUDIES IN PERSONALITY

Maier and Schneirla—PRINCIPLES OF ANIMAL PSYCHOLOGY

Metfessel—STUDENT'S GUIDE FOR DEMONSTRATIONS OF PSYCHOLOGICAL EXPERIMENTS

Moore—PSYCHOLOGY FOR BUSINESS AND INDUSTRY

Morgan—PHYSIOLOGICAL PSYCHOLOGY

Pillsbury—AN ELEMENTARY PSYCHOLOGY OF THE ABNORMAL

Richards—MODERN CLINICAL PSYCHOLOGY

Ruckmick—THE PSYCHOLOGY OF FEELING AND EMOTION

Seashore—PSYCHOLOGY OF MUSIC

Seward—SEX AND THE SOCIAL ORDER

Stagner—PSYCHOLOGY OF PERSONALITY

Terman and Miles—SEX AND PERSONALITY

Wallin—PERSONALITY MALADJUSTMENTS AND MENTAL HYGIENE

PHYSIOLOGICAL PSYCHOLOGY

CLIFFORD T. MORGAN

*Associate Professor and Chairman, Department of
Psychology, The Johns Hopkins University*

FIRST EDITION
SIXTH IMPRESSION

McGRAW-HILL BOOK COMPANY, INC.

NEW YORK AND LONDON

1943

To

K. S. Lashley

and

C. P. Richter

PREFACE

This book is meant to be both a textbook for undergraduates who are preparing for psychology or medicine and a reference book for graduate students and workers in psychology, physiology, and medicine. To serve this twofold purpose, the author has taken time to explain the elementary facts of psychology, physiology, and anatomy and then has gone on to cover the more advanced aspects of research in the field, providing bibliographic references to the original papers used.

It was clear from the beginning that these two objectives could not be fully attained in every phase of physiological psychology, and, therefore, several principles were adopted in selecting the material to be taken up in the allotted space. The first principle embodied the conviction that the primary goal of physiological psychology is to establish the physiological mechanisms of normal human and animal behavior. On this principle several topics—for example, the effects of drugs and vitamin deficiency upon behavior—were not considered except as they are related directly to this goal.

The second principle was that the book should be factual and as free as possible from speculation and bias. Following this principle, experimental material obtained from animal studies has been emphasized at the expense of clinical observations on human individuals, for the animal experiments tend to provide more consistent and reliable information than do the clinical studies, which must in large part be based, unfortunately, upon subjective methods of observing behavior and upon accidental, often obscure, pathology. On this principle, too, the author has minimized "arm-chair" physiological psychology in which physiological mechanisms are deduced from purely psychological phenomena without corroborative evidence from physiology.

Nonetheless the reader will find interpretation and theory given some place in the book. A definite point of view, even if not explicitly stated, is implied in the organization of material and in the manner of describing results. An attempt has been made, too, to point out the significance of results to show how they favor or argue against theories that have been proposed. In certain places, the interpretation of results does not agree with the authors who report them or with others who have made reference to them. In several places a bias that the author cannot escape has been confessed, and in one chapter (XXII) there is a frank attempt

vii

to present a rather new theoretical approach to the physiological basis of motivation. In all cases, however, an endeavor has been made to separate facts and theories so that a reader, if he chooses, can reject a theory without denying the facts upon which it is based.

A third rule which has been followed concerns particularly the more sophisticated reader and experimenters in the field of physiological psychology. Since not every topic could be treated exhaustively, the exposition has been made most complete for topics that are not summarized in other readily available sources. For topics adequately considered elsewhere, the author has been content to present what seems to be a fair over-all picture of the material and to make sure to include the most recent and most significant studies. The same rule applies, also, in giving references to original papers. The listing of names and papers is not thorough where rather complete and up-to-date summaries of the literature already exist, as is the case in vision and hearing, but in other topics, a most notable example of which is mating behavior (XX), references are supplied for almost every statement. Furthermore, the rule is followed throughout that where there is a choice between references covering the same topic, the latest one is given. This rule, unfortunately, may occasionally have done injustice to the early and perhaps classic work of an author, but for the student who wishes to make use of the bibliography for more advanced work it should prove to be of advantage.

Two sorts of bibliographic references have been provided for the reader who wishes to do further reading on a topic or who would like to know the basis of the facts or conclusions that are presented. At the end of each chapter a few general references are given which cover topics considered in the chapter. At the end of the book, on the other hand, is a bibliography of titles for specific points in the text. With each reference is an indication of the page in the text to which it applies. Thus, the bibliography serves also as an author index. All names that appear in the text, whether within parentheses or not, refer to the general bibliography, not to the titles at the end of chapters. This system is used in order to provide a list of titles, particularly recent ones, in the field of psychology, without duplicating or dispersing titles among the various chapters.

Of the many fundamental concepts illustrated and documented in the book, the reader's attention is called to three. None of them is particularly new, yet all of them are given greater emphasis here than in most current works in psychology. The first is the *internal environment*. Although formulated 100 years ago by Claude Bernard, the concept of the internal environment has often been neglected by psychologists, particularly those of the conditioned-reflex variety. Research of recent years is showing us more and more how this concept must become an integral part of our theories of behavior.

The second concept is *interaction*. Though stressed by Gestalt psychologists and accepted by all, this concept is made particularly important by recent research in physiological psychology. Physiology tells us, for example, that the reflex, assumed by many to possess an elementary character, is a pattern of movement resulting from the interplay of many neurons and several aspects of their activity; and visual perception, formerly described quite inadequately by the camera analogy, can be better understood in terms of the interconnections and consequent interactions of various parts of the retina and visual pathways.

The third concept stressed in this book is related closely to the second and follows the trend of recent studies in physiology: *levels of organization of function*. In the various mechanisms of behavior, one sees not the localization of this or that item of behavior in a particular part of the nervous system, but rather the dependence of the behavior upon many levels of the nervous system, each level organizing some function or aspect of the behavior. This is particularly evident in the case of emotional and sexual behavior and applies, it would now appear, even to the phenomena of learning.

Now a few words about the preparation of the manuscript.

In this book, as in all others, there are many opportunities for misstatements of fact to creep into the exposition. The author has tried to guard against them by consulting original papers throughout the preparation of the manuscript, but despite this precaution errors will undoubtedly be found. The author will be greatly indebted to those readers who call such errors to his attention.

His indebtedness to those who have aided either directly or indirectly in the preparation of this book begins with Dr. P. E. Fields, of Ohio Wesleyan University, whose zeal for a sound biological basis of psychology first interested him as a student in going forward in the field. The debt to Drs. K. U. Smith, Leonard Carmichael, and E. A. Culler, his mentors in graduate work at the University of Rochester, is also great, for their teaching, research, and scholarship contributed more than can be estimated to the background of this manuscript. In particular, Dr. Smith's courses in comparative and physiological psychology, unparalleled in their coverage of the literature, have supplied invaluable notes. Dr. K. S. Lashley has contributed many ideas and has called attention to significant researches that might otherwise have been neglected.

The author is indebted also to his students of Harvard and Radcliffe colleges, who for two years used a short mimeographed edition of the book in a course in physiological psychology and supplied many valuable suggestions adopted in the final manuscript. Olaf Johnson, assistant in the course, and Eliot Stellar also read a considerable part of the manuscript, making suggestions for better exposition and catching errors of statement.   Dr. T. C. Ruch, of Yale University, read Chaps. XVII and XXI, added important material and contributed illustrations that add much to the book.   Robert McCleary prepared all the original drawings and thereby added greatly to the clarity of the illustrations. Mrs. Jeanette Galambos and Mrs. Ann Sanford typed parts of the manuscript.   The author's greatest debt, finally, is to his wife, Jane Morgan, who typed the principal part of the manuscript, offered many suggestions for content and exposition, lettered the drawings, read proof, and in various ways contributed the encouragement and cooperation necessary to the completion of the work.   The authors and publishers who have kindly permitted the use of their illustrations are acknowledged in the legends of the respective illustrations.

Clifford T. Morgan.

Cambridge, Mass.,
July, 1943.

CONTENTS

CONTENTS

PHYSIOLOGICAL PSYCHOLOGY

CHAPTER I

HISTORICAL INTRODUCTION

It is the living organism that we study in both physiology and psychology, but we do it in each case with a different purpose in mind. The aim of psychology is to understand the way in which physical stimuli govern the behavior of the organism. The purpose of physiology, on the other hand, is to understand the processes that go on within the organism. Obviously, however, these arise in part from external stimuli, and they determine the behavior which is observed in psychology. Therefore, neither the physiological events within the organism nor its conduct with respect to external stimuli can be fully comprehended independently of the other.

Definition and Scope.—From this statement we may go on to define physiological psychology. It is the study of the relation between the organism's physiological processes and its behavior; or, since behavior is the outcome of physiological events, we may say that physiological psychology is the study of the *physiological mechanisms of behavior.*

From this definition the scope of the present book may be foreseen. We shall not be interested in physiology of itself, nor in behavior of itself, but we shall look always for relations between the two. To be sure, it will be the known facts of behavior, as gleaned from present-day psychology, which will set the problems and tell us what to look for in physiology; but where we have neither physiological facts nor physiological theories to offer as mechanisms of behavior, there we shall have to pass the behavior by. The central problem will always be: What are the physiological mechanisms of behavior?

It is worth noting in advance where the study of this question will lead us, for its scope should not be underestimated. There is today a vast fund of knowledge concerning the behavior of the organism—not enough perhaps to answer many of our questions, but enough to be overwhelming at times. So it is also in physiology, and we shall have to review many of the facts of anatomy, chemistry, endocrinology, and various phases of physiology. In physiological psychology, therefore, we embrace several fields of science, not just one. For all that, however, what is relevant or not is more or less clearly established by its bearing upon the central problem—the nature of the physiological mechanisms underlying behavior.

One can always understand a problem better if he knows something of its history. For that reason we begin with a brief review of the historical background of modern physiological psychology. From such a review the reader may learn of the principal conceptions in the background of present-day research and of the men and methods through which our present knowledge has come. In addition, such a review can serve to introduce certain fundamental concepts and methods to which references will often be made in later chapters.

PHILOSOPHIC DUALISM

The ancients could see, as well as can the layman of today, the difference between the physical and mental aspects of man. From this observation the concepts of mind and body as separate entities readily developed. The question of obvious importance, then, was the nature of the relationship between the two. In the subsequent history of the question, four views of the mind-body relation can be distinguished: the double-aspect view, interactionism, parallelism, and the identity view. It is in this order, in general, that they appeared and exerted their influence upon physiology and psychology.

The Double-aspect View.—Aristotle (384–322 B.C.) forwarded the double-aspect view of the mind-body relation. For him body and mind were distinguishable, but nevertheless inseparable, aspects of one *substance*. Body was the *matter* and mind the *form* of that substance, which is always analyzable, said Aristotle, into these two aspects. Aside from differences in terminology, this view is closely comparable to the prevalent modern conception of mind as the function of the body. Between Aristotle and modern times, however, came more dualistic views in which the body and mind were credited with separate existences.

Cartesian Interactionism.—One such view, interactionism, was that of Descartes (1596–1650), who introduces the modern, though prescientific, era in psychology. For him there was a clean-cut dualism of mind and body, not just a logical distinction of two aspects, as Aristotle believed. Despite the separate identities of mind and body, said Descartes, the two influence each other's actions.

According to Descartes, the body is a machine which operates in a determined, lawful fashion. Animal spirits (which might today be read 'nervous impulses') flow in the nerve tubules to the brain and out again to the muscles. Physical principles govern their course; indeed, within the brain, the selection of pathways is made by the opening and closing of pores (today read 'synapses'). Through the pineal gland (see p. 76), however, operates the mind, which is aware of the activities of the animal spirits and intervenes on occasion to determine their course. Thus, although the body is a machine, it is a machine under the control of the mind.

Had this position met permanent acceptance, there would have been little hope of establishing a physiological psychology, for, if the mind were free, as Descartes claimed, we could study neither it nor the mechanistic processes of the body, since these too would be under the capricious control of the mind. Free agents do not behave according to scientific laws. Descartes's mechanistic scheme of the neural processes involved in sensation, thought, and behavior, however, represents a definite advance, though it was largely ignored by the philosophic psychology which followed him.

Parallelism in Philosophic Psychology.—That Descartes inaugurates the modern period in psychology has already been mentioned. This period may be divided into two phases: the *philosophic*, or rational, and the *experimental*. The former extended to the middle of the nineteenth century when the latter began, although there was, of course, temporal overlapping of the two movements, and modern psychology still has its philosophic aspects. Much of the philosophic phase and the first part of the experimental period were marked by another view of the mind-body relation, known as psychophysical parallelism.

Its first outstanding exponent was Leibnitz (1646–1716), the great mathematician-philosopher and the father of German psychology. Mind and body, according to his belief, were two independent and self-sufficient activities which did not interact but followed parallel courses. What occurred in one also took place in the other. They were not causally related in any way but were parallel because the same laws governed them both.

This view has some possibilities for the development of a physiological psychology, for, if mind and body are perfectly parallel, there is, for scientific purposes, no distinction to be made between their sets of causal laws, since one can study the activities of the body and know thereby the nature of the relationships within the mind. The view was not, however, interpreted in this way. Instead, with the subsequent adoption of the theory of psychophysical parallelism, attention was turned entirely to the study of mental processes, and every effort was made—consciously or unconsciously—to be rid of the body.

Although Leibnitz, a German, gave us psychophysical parallelism, it was the English school of philosophic psychology that was chiefly responsible for carrying it down to recent times. The founder of the English school, Locke (1632–1704), had little to say bearing directly upon parallelism, but his concern with the 'mind,' to the exclusion of the body, implicitly affirmed his belief in parallelism. Those who followed him, however, were more explicit. In Hartley (1705–1757) and later in Bain (1818–1903), a philosophy of mental association ('mental chemistry') was based on an unequivocal belief in parallel but separate processes of the mind and body.

Parallelism in Experimental Psychology.—We may turn now to experimental psychology. Its founder was Wundt (1832–1920); the place, Leipzig; the year, 1879. Wundt, though German, took much from English associationism, and in common with it held a parallelistic view of mind and body. He was not so thorough a parallelist as Leibnitz, however, for he believed the mind and the body to be quite independent of each other in many affairs and to be parallel only in certain special cases as, for example, in sensation. Although Wundt had previously been a physiologist, he obviously did not hope to derive any understanding of mental processes through a study of the nervous system. That mind had a lawful character, however, was his earnest belief, and he devoted his long and productive life to the analysis of its structure. But the study of mental life was, for him, something quite separate from the study of bodily processes.

In the light of this attitude, it is interesting that Wundt's great book should be entitled *Physiological Psychology*. Indeed, the experimental psychology which Wundt founded and whose influence was spread widely through his students and writings was called physiological psychology. This is the reason: Until Wundt, psychology had, with certain exceptions, been philosophical; the custom was to theorize freely without reference to experiment and with only unsystematic observations from personal experience as a guide. Just before Wundt, however, the experimental method had been firmly established in physiology (1830–1850). Because of his own training in physiology, he had been quite close to this development. Being of the firm opinion that the study of the mind should be experimental, and wishing to set off his new psychology sharply from that of the philosophic kind, Wundt styled it physiological psychology. His conception of experimental psychology was not, however, what we should today call physiological, for it consisted of introspection, *i.e.*, the systematic description of an observer's conscious experiences.

Modern Views.—In America after the turn of the twentieth century, we find psychophysical parallelism giving way first to a double-aspect view and later to an identity view of the mind-body relation. The former was espoused in the so-called *functionalism* of Dewey (1859–   ). In this new school of psychology, mind was regarded as the *adaptive* aspect of the biologic processes of the organism, the plastic or intelligent functions that looked after the survival of the organism. This view was a return to the Aristotelian perspective with new phrasing and perhaps a characteristically modern emphasis of the utility of mind.

Behaviorism, under Watson (1878–   ), took up the problem there. The functionalist's view did not, said Watson, go far enough, for it did not rid us of the conception of mind as something apart from the biological organism. We must recognize, he argued, that what we call mind is really the behavior of an organism, and when we do that, mind and body become identical, for behavior is only a special form of physiological event. In this recognition that mental processes can be scientifically available only as behavior, Watson and the behaviorists did a great service, for their formulation of the mind-body problem resolves it for the psychologist by allowing him to regard the 'mental' as a special type of organismic behavior which is in turn subject to a description in physiological terms.

EXPERIMENTAL METHOD

Although the important place of theory in the framing and interpretation of scientific observations is not to be gainsaid, the cornerstone of scientific knowledge is controlled observation, and this is the essential feature of the experimental method. Without it there is little that is science. Indeed, the founding of each of the departments of science has been marked by the adoption of the experimental method.

In almost no phase of science has this been more important than in physiological psychology. There is little or no relation between mind and body to be observed with the naked eye in the normal course of human affairs. One naturally sees only one or the other—not the relation between the two—and that is perhaps the reason why the mind-body dichotomy is so strongly entrenched in the thinking of the layman. It was the use of the experimental method which brought about the dissolution of the dichotomy. Let us briefly review, therefore, the history of this method in relation to physiological psychology.

Rationalism.—The Greeks made many valuable observations concerning the natural world, plants, animals, and man; Aristotle's writings abound with them. They were even implemented at times with experiments, some of which, in physics, are classics. It was the knowledge largely of the natural world, however, which benefited by observational and experimental methods, and the basic approach of the Greeks to the world was rationalistic—an attempt to reach conclusions through philosophic reasoning. It was this method which was chiefly employed in treating the mind-body problem.

The rational approach to the problems of mind, and of mind and body, was standard for the next twenty centuries. For the 200 years from

Locke (1690) until Wundt (1879) much was written about the mind, and 'laws of association' were even formulated, but all this was based, with few exceptions, upon the isolated observations and reflections of gifted individuals. Meanwhile, the other sciences, one by one, were becoming founded on experimentalism. This first took hold in physics and anatomy, then in chemistry, and finally in physiology. It was, as we have already seen, in experimental physiology that the experimental psychology of Wundt took its roots. For this reason, and also because our most valuable methods of study in physiological psychology came from physiology, its history is of especial interest to us.

Experimental Physiology.—When and by whom the first experiment in physiology was conducted are not easy to establish, but a great era of experimentalism certainly began about 1830. Like many other important events in scientific history, it came as a reaction to the confusion and controversy that had been brought by unbridled speculation. The chief offender in this case was phrenology, which burst into great prominence about 1800. Gall, its author, although a capable neuroanatomist for his time, displayed an unrestrained imagination in dealing with the functions of the brain. In his system of phrenology, of which we shall say more later, Gall more or less arbitrarily assigned different mental "faculties" to various ridges of the brain.

Precedents in experiment had already been set, and the younger physiologists thought it better to submit such notions as these to experiment. Realizing the model of exact knowledge which physics had by that time created through the use of the experimental method, they saw in such an experimental method the possibility of divorcing physiology as well from the mist and controversy of rational speculation.

The most influential proponents of the experiment in physiology were Johannes Müller (1801–1858) and Claude Bernard (1815–1878). Müller was noted as the writer of the first great *Handbook of Physiology*, published in several volumes between 1833 and 1840 and containing an exhaustive summary of the physiological facts of the time. He was also responsible for the formulation of the doctrine of specific nerve energies, which we shall discuss below and meet often in this book. With his discovery of the sugar-storing functions of the liver, Claude Bernard launched present-day endocrinology. Together, Bernard and Müller were the apostles of the experimental method; they lived what they preached, and their preaching and experiments made them the fathers of experimental physiology.

Hall and Flourens.—Of especial interest are two other men of this period, Marshall Hall (1790–1857) and Pierre Flourens (1794–1867). Their experiments are milestones in the history of experimental physiological psychology. Hall's contribution was the experimental study of the nervous basis of reflex behavior. Noticing that animals without a brain are responsive to sensory stimulation, he sectioned the spinal cord of a snake and observed its responses to various kinds of stimulation (1832). Upon such experimental observations he concluded quite correctly that reflex behavior depended upon the spinal cord, but more complex behavior (voluntary) upon the cerebrum of the brain. Here was a sound conclusion regarding a fundamental problem which was based upon the experimental method.

Even more exemplary, however, are the experiments of Flourens (1824). These contribute to an experimental physiological psychology in three important ways. (1) They introduce the *method of extirpation* of parts of the nervous system as a means of studying the physiological mechanisms of behavior. (2) They illustrate the use of *animal subjects*

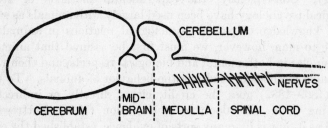

CEREBELLUM

NERVES

CEREBRUM   MID-   MEDULLA   SPINAL CORD
            BRAIN

Fig. 1.—Diagrammatic sketch of the six parts of the nervous system studied in Flourens's experiments.

as the basis for generalizing to man. (3) They suggest the concept of *levels of function* in the nervous system. All these principles are now an integral part of present-day physiological psychology.

Flourens's experiments may be summarized as follows (see Fig. 1). First he selected the principal anatomical divisions of the nervous system as they were then recognized: the cerebral hemispheres, the cerebellum, the midbrain, the medulla, the spinal cord, and the nerves (for terminology see Chap. V). Using pigeons, rabbits, and dogs, he performed operations in such a way that he could observe the effect upon the animals' behavior of the extirpation of each of these parts. From these observations he came to the following conclusions: Perceiving, willing, judging, and memory are functions of the cerebral hemispheres. The cerebellum, on the other hand, is the organ for the coordination of movements of locomotion. The midbrain functions in seeing. The medulla is concerned with the essential life processes of the organism, such as breathing and heartbeat. Through the nerves, the spinal cord and brain are excited, and the spinal cord conducts these excitations. So runs the original statement of the facts which are a fundamental part of modern physiological psychology, facts which we now include in the general concept of levels of function in the nervous system. Equally important, however, were the methods upon which these observations were based.

The Study of Animal Behavior.—The discussion of Flourens's experiments brings up the question of the use of animal subjects in the study of man. If one's object is to understand the physiological mechanisms of man's behavior, it is logical that man should be used for that study. Extirpation of the nervous system, and of other organs as well, however, has been one of the most fruitful methods at the command of the physiological psychologist; and it is hardly possible, of course, to apply this method to man. Occasionally one secures human individuals who, by chance, present the conditions that are to be studied, but one can hardly depend upon these for the development of a science of physiological psychology. Consequently, the experimental methods of study in physiological psychology have been used largely with animals as subjects.

For a knowledge of psychophysiological relations in animals to be applicable to man, however, we must first be assured that animals and man are similar in both mental and biological respects, and then we must have suitable methods of studying the behavior of animals. To Charles Darwin (1809–1882) goes the credit, either directly or indirectly, for contributing both. His doctrine of evolution (1859), buttressed and expanded as it now is by many sorts of evidence, established the essential continuity, both biological and behavioral, of man and animals. True, others before him had noted the similarity of human and animal behavioral characteristics, and physiology had already begun to apply its findings to human medicine, but the evolutionary doctrine was needed to establish firmly the premise that man could be studied through animals. In this way, therefore, the doctrine of evolution was a fundamental methodological contribution.

Out of the doctrine grew a wider interest in the mind and behavior of animals and eventually (about 1900) experimental methods of studying them. At first the purpose was purely psychological, to gain an insight into man's mind through animals. After all, animals could be studied under more favorable experimental conditions than man, and their mental processes were simpler and thus more easily understood. On this argument, methods of experimenting with animal behavior, highly developed in recent years, have greatly aided the study of the physiological mechanisms of behavior.

Clinical Methods.—Despite all that the study of animal behavior may contribute, however, the need for observations of a psychophysiological character on man is not to be denied. Man may be the kin of animals in all matters, yet he is, nevertheless, a distant kin. Even though both the differences and the likenesses between them are apparent, one cannot extend unquestionably to man conclusions based upon animals. With many of the experimental methods of animal study ruled out, however, we have only one choice—to make the best of the material that nature provides by studying, wherever possible, the psychological changes accompanying tumors or other injuries to the brain, glandular disfunctions, disorders of body chemistry, and other physiological abnormalities. The methods that one applies to these naturally occurring physiological disturbances are termed *clinical* methods, as distinguished from experimental methods, for they are applicable only to human individuals who come to the physician for care or treatment.

So far as physiological psychology is concerned, the classical instance of the use of the clinical method must be attributed to Broca (1824–1880). To him, in 1861, came by accident a man whose only behavioral difficulty was an inability to talk; Broca examined him thoroughly to make sure of that. Fortunately for Broca and for science, the man died shortly afterward and his brain could, therefore, be examined. An injury (or lesion), found in the third frontal convolution (see p. 528), appeared to be the cause of the man's inability to use words. Thus, by correlating a clinical symptom with an anatomical condition, Broca established a relation of great importance for physiological psychology. The region of the brain in which is 'stored' the memory for words, has subsequently become known as Broca's area.

Since Broca, many cases of brain injury have been studied, and more attention has been given to the possibilities of systematically investigating them. With the rise of experimental endocrinology and a better understanding of glandular disorders, the clinical method has been applied to these as well. Today there is an extensive collection of clinical reports available to the physiological psychologist, and, through the enlargement of clinical facilities, such methods are becoming more and more useful to him.

These methods have drawbacks, however, which should be recognized. In cases of brain injury, for example, the brain seldom becomes available for direct study and correlation with the psychological data previously obtained from the patient. When it is, the lesion which nature has made frequently lacks the precise size and position that it should have if unequivocal interpretations are to be made. Moreover, because the psychological methods customarily used in the clinic do not meet the standards of the experimental laboratory, clinical data are often lacking in precision. To some extent, of course, the best psychological methods available are still inadequate and must be further developed. Thus, although in the future more of the material of physiological psychology may be expected to be based upon man, today animal studies are its mainstay.

Physiological Methods.—We have seen above how experimental methods in physiological psychology came from physiology and that the first of these was the method of extirpation. In any general classification of the methods of obtaining physiological conditions to which to relate psychological processes, we might speak more generally of the *anatomical* method in which some aspect of the anatomical relations of the body is experimentally altered. In this category, we can include not only extirpation, but also instances, occasionally used, of the severance of connections of parts of the body from each other and of the transplantation and interchanging of parts. We may now note two other general methods, the *electrical* and the *chemical*.

ELECTRICAL METHODS

Of concern to us as students of physiological psychology are two kinds of electrical method, *stimulation* and *recording*. The latter is a relatively recent development, but the other is much older.

Immediately after Volta devised the first crude battery in 1800, thus making electric currents available for experimental use, Rolando (1770–1831) performed the first experiments on the stimulability of the brain, noting the now familiar fact that movements of various muscles can be elicited when electric currents are applied to the brain. Certain of Rolando's observations were in error, but his method has become important as a tool of modern physiological psychology.

Nearly 70 years elapsed before the method was put to further use. Then Fritsch and Hitzig, following closely upon the heels of Broca's discovery of the cerebral centers of speech, were able to establish definitely, by using electric stimulation, that motor functions are localized in a circumscribed area of the cerebral cortex. This area was in the anterior portion of the cerebrum (see p. 336), and within it they found different 'centers' for the movement of different groups of muscles. Today we have confirmed and extended their findings.

The method is also used now in several other aspects of physiology and psychology. For example, the areas of the cerebrum that mediate sensory experience have been mapped out by such electrical stimulation in conscious human patients. Moreover, because electric currents can be carefully regulated in respect to intensity and duration of application, and because they will excite all sense organs and nervous tissue, they may take the place of other kinds of stimuli and are consequently widely used as a standard laboratory tool.

Of more recent development are methods of recording electrical changes in the brain and body. As one might expect, these were contingent upon advances made in physics. Although such methods have been developed, for the most part, in the last 40 years, very crude methods of detecting electric currents were available throughout the nineteenth century. The first important modern technique was the Einthoven string galvanometer, devised in 1902, which allowed quite accurate recording of electrical changes in the body, if not too weak. A second step, of far-reaching significance, was the development of vacuum tubes for the amplification of very small electrical changes. Such advances have been made chiefly since 1920, in connection with the growth of radio, with the result that we are able today to measure and record electrical changes of the order of one-millionth of a volt.

That electrical changes occurred in nervous function, however, was known before the use of such refined recording devices. Before 1850 it was known that a difference in electrical potential existed between the nervous system and other tissues. In 1874, Caton discovered the spontaneous fluctuations in the electrical activity of the brain which are now familiarly known as 'brain waves.' Electrical changes in the visual cortex (see p. 138) upon stimulation by light were noted by Beck in 1890.

Thereafter, with the much more sensitive recording provided by the string galvanometer, the pace of research quickened. The systematic study of the nervous impulse was begun by Adrian and Lucas in 1912. Later, the activities of the various sense organs, particularly the eye and the ear, were studied to advantage by electrical recording. Finally, the proof that the brain has an electrical beat, furnished by Berger in 1934, ushered in the systematic study of 'brain waves' (Berger rhythms). Many are the facts which the electrical method has brought forth, and we shall utilize them often in later chapters.

CHEMICAL METHODS

Of chemical methods, mentioned above, only a word need be said. Although many of them are of importance to physiological psychology, their history is not particularly relevant. We have seen that Claude Bernard, by demonstrating the secretory functions of the liver, established the field of endocrinology. It is only recently, however, that endocrinology and physiological chemistry have reached a stage of usefulness for our problems. Of particular interest to us are the measurement of oxygen consumption, of acid, sugar, and other chemical states of the tissues, the establishment of the role played by the various glands in bodily function, and the availability of chemically pure glandular secretions (hormones) for use in conjunction with psychological studies. Although they are just now coming to the aid of physiological psychology, the late advances along these lines have been rapid.

Of the history of the experimental method, we may make in summary a few general observations. The periods of great advance in knowledge have always sprung from the use of new methods. With the introduction of the experimental method, as opposed to the philosophical, and the subsequent development of new types of experimental method, great increases in our knowledge have been brought about. In the particular case of physiological psychology, the extirpational method became its first tool. Later, electrical and chemical methods (in that order) have become more and more useful.

THE SENSES

It is in the study of the sense organs rather than the nervous system that psychology and physiology have had the most in common, and it is here that both the earliest and greatest advances have been made.

Aristotle was essentially correct in believing, as does the layman of today, that man has five senses. Despite all the receptors which have been described of late in histology, we have only subdivided his classification, not added to it, and that chiefly in respect to touch. Early in the nineteenth century it became clear that touch was really a complex of senses: temperature discrimination, touch, and pain; moreover, one was forced to distinguish between these and internal sense organs of the muscles, bones, and viscera. Also by that time many of the receptor organs of the body had been discovered and described by histologists. It remained only for these organs to be correlated with sensory functions.

The Doctrine of Specific Energy of Nerves.—Of central importance in the search for such correlations is the concept of the *specific energy of nerves*, formulated by Johannes Müller in his *Handbook of Physiology* (1833–1840). Around this concept, encountered in many phases of present-day physiological psychology, we must write the subsequent history of sensory physiology. Contained in it are two fundamental principles: (1) We are not directly aware of the world, but of our nerves (receptors), for these are intermediate between the external world and the brain. (2) Each sense organ possesses its own specific quality (energy) which determines the kind of sensation to which it will give rise.

Foreshadowing the first of these principles is the *doctrine of irritability*, laid down by von Haller (1708–1777). Before him, Descartes had taught that animal spirits (stimuli) in the external world could flow through the nerves to the brain and out to the muscle which thereupon contracted because animal spirits entered it. This notion was refuted, and a fundamental physiological concept, the doctrine of irritability, was established when von Haller showed that no matter how excitation came about, the energy for muscular contraction was supplied from within the muscle. Now the first principle of the concept of specific energies states, in effect, that the sense organs also supply their own energy, that their activity is only *released* by the stimuli exciting them.

The second principle, that of the *specificity* of the energies of receptors and nerves, was also anticipated in earlier writings, but to Müller goes the credit for explicitly formulating it. Through his influence this principle was destined to become a guiding light in later theories and investigations of sensory functions. Indeed, it is on it that the leading conceptions of sensory functions rest at the present time.

Largely responsible for this principle was Helmholtz (1821–1894). Psychologists know him for his theories of color vision and hearing, but these grew out of his belief in the doctrine of specific energy of nerves and from his extension of it. Not only must there be different specific energies in the different senses (modalities) to account for different sensations, asserted Helmholtz, but where there are different qualities of sensation in one sensory modality, as with the case of color in vision and tones in hearing, there also must the doctrine of specific energies apply.

On this argument is based in part the Young-Helmholtz theory (1852) of color vision, that the eye contains three sets of receptors, one responding to red, another to green, and another to blue, each possessing its own specific energy. From this argument also follows his "resonance" theory of hearing (1863), that different qualities of pitch depend upon the stimulation of different parts (nerve fibers) of the basilar membrane (see p. 249) of the ear. It is to be noted, however, that the doctrine of specific energies was only a guide for his researches. He was a great experimentalist—both in sensory physiology and in sensory psychology—and his researches are the classics in the field.

The concept of specific energies, as formulated by Müller and extended by Helmholtz, has guided later researches in other sensory fields. The discovery (1883–1884), of separate 'spots' for pain, cold, and warmth came about because it was thought that, since these sensations were independent of each other in consciousness, there must be different receptor endings to correspond. The current theories of four gustatory and six olfactory qualities (see Chap. VIII) are also outgrowths of the doctrine. In recent years, opposing theories have been offered to explain the qualities of sensory experience, but the concept of specific energies is still the most widely accepted. In later pages we shall see how the concept is important both as a problem and as an answer in physiological psychology—not only in the case of sensory processes but in other mental functions as well.

BEHAVIOR

Psychology began, as we have seen, with the study of the mind; it has subsequently become the science of behavior. In that change of viewpoint is contained a story of fundamental advance in the physiological approach to the mind-body problem.

The theme of the story is the *reflex*, and it begins with Descartes. According to him, animal spirits flowing into the brain from the sense organs were in many instances unaffected by the mind but were "reflected" out through the nerves to the muscles. An example of such "reflection," cited by Descartes, was the contraction of the pupil of the eye in response to light.

To the support of the reflex concept came about 1800 the *law of roots*, known commonly today as the Bell-Magendie law. This was the simple fact that the dorsal roots of the spinal cord are sensory in function, the ventral roots, motor (see p. 74). The proof of this law in the experiments of Sir Charles Bell (1774–1842) and Magendie (1783–1855) provided both an anatomical basis for the concept of the reflex and a direct demonstration that sensory activity enters the nervous system through one pathway and that motor activity leaves through another.

It remained, however, for Marshall Hall to perform the classic experiments in reflex action. As we have already seen, Hall demonstrated the basic role of the spinal cord in reflex action. Moreover, he went on to distinguish between reflex and voluntary action; one, he thought, was a spinal function largely independent of mind, whereas the other was carried out by the brain under the control of mind.

Around this distinction later grew a controversy in which the names of Pflüger (1829–1910) and Lotze (1817–1881) figured prominently. Hall had eliminated reflex behavior from the province of mental function, but to this Pflüger objected (1853). Mind, to him, was synonomous with nervous activity, and there was consequently no point in presenting mental functions as distinct from reflex action. In his view, both the spinal cord and the brain had mind, because they were both parts of the nervous system. Out of his belief came an intensive experimental study of reflex behavior, and it is, therefore, to be noted as an important step toward a behavioral and physiological conception of mind.

Against the view, however, Lotze argued (1853) that the reflex behavior of spinal animals was the consequence of previous experience acquired through mental function. He had noted that voluntary actions frequently became automatic through frequent repetition, and it was, he thought, the traces of these voluntary actions which were left in the spinal cord and observed in the spinal animal. Lotze's view of the relation of the mind to the nervous system was not particularly progressive, but his interpretation of reflex function foreshadows a modern notion, which we shall meet again, that as a learned act becomes deeply rooted in an individual's behavior it comes to be carried out by lower centers of the nervous system. It so turns out that this notion is false.

Two new developments marked the turn of the twentieth century. In 1906, Sherrington (1857–　　) published his now famous *Integrative*

Action of the Nervous System, in which he summarized his classic experiments on reflex action. In addition to providing a careful analysis of the varieties of reflex behavior, these experiments gave us a knowledge of the fundamental nervous processes concerned in the control of behavior. We shall meet with these often in the chapters that follow. Contemporary with Sherrington's contributions to the physiology of reflex action was a second great event, which also came from physiology, the discovery (1903) of the conditioned reflex by Pavlov (1849–1940). To find that reflexes could be conditioned to new stimuli threw an entirely new light on the nature of mental functions; indeed, it looked as though they might be understood entirely in terms of reflexes. The fundamental importance of the study of reflex action in understanding the mechanisms of behavior will be shown in later pages.

FUNCTIONAL LOCALIZATION IN THE BRAIN

For Aristotle, the seat of the soul (mind) was the heart, and the brain was a refrigerating apparatus for the fluids of the body, but to other Greeks the brain was an organ of mind. Anatomists of later centuries sometimes concurred in this belief, and one, Albertus Magnus, in the thirteenth century even ascribed different mental functions to different parts of the brain. But the preeminent role of the brain in mental functions was not given much attention until the nineteenth century. Then, in 1811, the question was brought to the fore by the phrenology of Gall (1758–1828) and Spurzheim (1776–1832).

The mind, said phrenology, is made up of many faculties—faculties of "destructiveness," "hope," "imitation," "benevolence," and so on— more than 30 in all. These faculties are to be found in different amounts and proportions in various people, but they are localized in the brain, and, indeed, in particular convolutions (see Chap. V). If one faculty is present in large degree, its convolution will be large, and that fact can be told from the corresponding 'bump' on the skull. Phrenology thus sponsored the most extreme form of localization.

The more levelheaded of the physiologists naturally questioned such a teaching as this. True, it correctly emphasized the fact that the brain was the organ of the mind, but in addition it drove them to experiments to check it. Of Flourens's classic studies we have already spoken, and these were in no small part a reaction to the teachings of phrenology.

The conclusions that Flourens reached were, in fact, directly opposed to the extreme localization held in phrenology. While admitting specific functions of different parts of the nervous system and himself outlining levels of function, Flourens saw *unity*, not diversity, as the great feature of neural functions. Within the cerebrum, one of the levels of the nervous system which he distinguished, he could find no differences of function.

His argument that it acted as a whole was readily accepted, because the reaction against phrenology had become quite general.

As a result, some time went by before attempts were again made to find functional localization. When in 1861, however, Broca described his famous case of word amnesia lacking a particular area of the cortex (see Fig. 2), interest in localization revived, but this time on a more experimental basis. Close upon Broca's discovery came the localization of motor functions in the cerebral cortex, established in 1870 by Fritsch

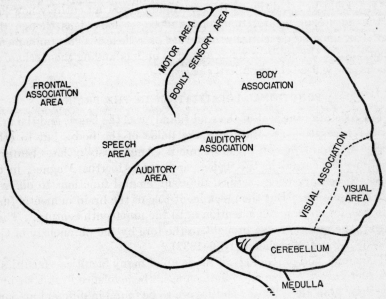

Fig. 2.—Side-view diagram of the human cerebral cortex showing localization of mental functions.

and Hitzig. These investigators, it will be remembered, made their finding by stimulating the cortex electrically. A little later (1881), the occipital lobes at the back of the head were shown by Munk to be visual in function. With these experimental facts was ushered in a new era of belief in the localization of mental functions in different parts of the brain.

The localization shown by these experiments was, however, of simple sensory and motor functions; the higher mental capacities, *viz.*, learning, memory, thought, and intelligence were another matter. For these three theories, each backed in some degree by experimental facts, had appeared by the end of the nineteenth century. (1) *Dynamic theory*, a name that characterizes Flourens's point of view, has been held by some through the latter part of the nineteenth century and again, after an intervening period, in recent years, particularly in the experimental work of Lashley (1890–   ) with which we shall meet later.   According to this theory, the higher mental functions are subserved by no particular part of the cerebrum but by all of it.   (2) According to the so-called *aggregation theory* (Munk, 1909), the interconnections between various sensory spheres, *i.e.*, between the localized areas for vision, hearing, touch, and so forth, carry out the higher 'associative' functions.   (3) According to a *localization theory*, however, not only are there primary receptive areas but also special 'associative' (or psychic) areas for each sensory modality and, according to some opinions, a localized general 'association' area in the frontal lobes (Fig. 2).   In later chapters we shall see how the available facts of the present day support these various theories of localization.

General References

BORING, E. G., 1929.   *A history of experimental psychology.*   New York: Appleton-Century.   Pp. xvi + 699.

BORING, E. G., 1942.   *Sensation and perception in the history of experimental Psychology.*   New York: Appleton-Century.   Pp. xv + 644.

FEARING, F., 1930.   *Reflex action.*   Baltimore: Williams & Wilkins.   Pp. ix + 350.

FULTON, J. F., 1930.   *Selected readings in the history of physiology.*   Springfield: C. C. Thomas.   Pp. xx + 317.

CHAPTER II

CELLULAR FUNCTIONS

As was pointed out in the last chapter, we must deal intimately with many of the facts of physiology in the course of our study. Moreover, it is better that many of these facts be considered at the beginning so that they will be clearly in mind when we meet directly with the problems of the physiological basis of behavior. We shall devote our attention in the next four chapters, therefore, to matters of biology. In this chapter the more general aspects of biological function will be treated, and in the three chapters that follow, the more specific facts of physiology and anatomy will be considered.

THE CELL

It was a discovery of great importance when Robert Hook first observed (1665) a very lowly organism, cork, to be made up of cells. Subsequently, many investigators observed cells in all kinds of tissues, and today we have come to recognize the *cell doctrine* (Schleiden and Schwann, 1838), that the cell is the unit of living organisms, as a fundamental concept of biology.

Even though the cell is the unit, however, we are now able to relate its functions in turn to the principles of physics and chemistry. It has been found, for example, that certain chemical compounds, the viruses, although they lack the structure of the cell, are nevertheless able to perform certain of its functions, most notably reproduction. We have been able to understand the cell itself to a considerable extent in terms of the chemical reactions taking place in its two principal parts, the cell membrane and the cytoplasm.

The Cell Membrane.—Mediating relations between the external world and the cytoplasm, the cell membrane functions in such a way that the cytoplasm will get the materials it needs and discharge into the environment the materials it cannot use. Governing this exchange of materials through the membrane is the *semipermeability* of the membrane and an *equilibrium* of physical energies.

1. The cell membrane is semipermeable by virtue of the fact that it allows only certain materials to diffuse through and holds the rest back. From this it follows, then, that the exchange of materials will not be completely free; instead, the equilibrium set up at the membrane will be one only of physical energies.

18

this when many kinds and numbers of ions are involved,
mental point has been indicated in this illustration.

sue two important properties of the cell membrane, *irrita-
nduction.* An appropriate stimulus can disturb the ionic
at a membrane and thereby cause a flow of ions through the
o restore it; this is irritability. Furthermore, through the fact
sturbance of the membrane equilibrium at one point can cause,
lancing processes that follow, a disturbance of equilibrium in an
region of the membrane, the cell is endowed with the property
ction.

plasm and Its Properties.—We may now turn our attention to
l events occurring within the protoplasm of the cell. Worth
first are the classes of chemical compounds of which cytoplasm is
up. The most important of these by bulk is *water*, which consti-
70 to 90 per cent of the cell's weight; water acts as a solvent for
compounds and enters into chemical reactions with them. These
be divided into four main groups: carbohydrates, which consist
ively of carbon, hydrogen, and oxygen; fats, also made up of these
elents but often combined with phosphorus, nitrogen, and sulfur;
proeins, whose important characteristic is the presence of nitrogen; and
mineral salts, chiefly those of calcium, phosphorus, potassium, and magnesium. These groups are merely listed here, but we shall have occasion
to refer to them again from time to time.

Chemical reactions within cells are customarily divided into two types,
anabolic and catabolic, the former referring to processes in which chemical
materials are built up and stored. Even these, however, are the result of
catabolic processes, *i.e.*, reactions in which energy is expended, for according to the law of conservation of energy one compound cannot gain
energy without another's losing it. The catabolic processes of energy
expenditure are, therefore, the basis of chemical activities in the cell.
On them depend, as we shall see, the activities of the organism in which
we are chiefly interested.

One may think of energy expenditure in the chemical activities of
cytoplasm as an *oxidative* reaction. This may take one of several forms,
only two of which are of consequence to us. (1) The more important
is the breakdown of carbohydrates, fats, or proteins through reaction
with oxygen. In this breakdown, oxygen is used up and carbon dioxide
is commonly produced, although other intermediate compounds may
also occur. The complete oxidation of carbohydrates, for example,
gives carbon dioxide, but incomplete oxidation may cause the breakdown
to stop at lactic acid, alcohol, or some related compound. (2) An
oxidative reaction may also be one in which electrons are lost. In this
case the chemical reaction may not require oxygen but may simply

2. Three kinds of physic... which the membrane will be... temperature on both sides of th... The pressure will also reach an... that chemical materials in soluti... environment and cytoplasm of livi... (osmotic) against a membrane; in orde... nor 'explode,' the pressure on each side m... maintain such a state, various materials... membrane. (c) A similar equilibrium of i... membrane will also obtain.

Since such an ionic equilibrium is of con... understanding nervous and sensory function, it... some detail. First, we must note that many of th... found in living organisms are *electrolytes; i.e.*, they... carrying positive and negative charges. Next, the m... able to some ions and not to others, but—and this is... equilibrium established will be only of those to which th... permeable, *i.e.*, of the diffusible ions. The law governing t... is that *the product of the concentrations of the diffusible ions on... membrane shall be equal* (Donnan, 1924).

Out of this fact comes a very important phenomenon,... which may be explained and illustrated (Bodansky, p. 22)[1]... Consider two electrolytes, NaCl and NaR, on the respective... membrane thus:

(a)	(b)
Na^+	Na^+
R^-	Cl^-

Assume now that the membrane is impermeable to R^-. The... equilibrium must be established with Na^+ and Cl^-, and the concentr... of b is higher than that of (a). Na^+ and Cl^- ions will move, there... through the membrane from b to a, thus making the number of Na^+ i... greater on the side a than on the side b. Less than half, however,... the Na^+ and Cl^- ions of b will diffuse through, because the Na^+ io... originally present at a contribute to the equilibrium. The net result a... equilibrium will be that the Na^+ ions will be greater at a than at b, and... the Cl^- ions will be greater at b than at a. a will therefore be positive and... b negative; in other words, the membrane will be polarized. Thus in... terms of the principles of ionic equilibrium comes a disequilibrium or... polarization of the membrane. The situation is, of course, much more...

[1] In the bibliography and author index, which appears at the end of the book is to be found the title and source of all references appearing in the text.

involve a recombination of molecules in which electrons are released from some of the atoms. The electrons represent energy (electrical) expended, and their loss is seen, when measured with the appropriate instruments, as a flow of electrical current. Energy expended in this way is, however, usually compensated for later by a primary oxidative reaction, *i.e.*, one in which oxygen is consumed. Such is the case, for example, with the nervous impulse which, consisting of the release of electrons, can be elicited in the absence of oxygen, but which ultimately requires oxygen for the building up of the energy released as electrons.

Resulting from oxidative processes with the cytoplasm of cells are several properties of the cell which are of concern to us. (1) Through very complex chemical processes, the nature of which is not well understood, arises the ability of a cell to *reproduce*. We know that chemical conditions affecting oxidative reactions materially influence reproductive processes. (2) Through breaking down materials in the cytoplasm and resynthesizing, the cell *secretes* substances that may be important in other phases of its activities, or—in the case of multicellular organisms— in the processes of other cells. (3) In some oxidative reactions, molecules move or change in shape, thus causing the cytoplasm and the cell itself to change shape or to *contract*.

In viewing the functions of the cell as a whole, we must note that, although a rough separation of the properties of the membrane and cytoplasm can be made, the activities of the cell membrane and cytoplasm are closely interrelated. Depolarization of the membrane may, for example, cause the cytoplasm to contract or to secrete, and chemical conditions in the cytoplasm naturally affect the equilibrium and exchange of materials at the membrane. The present summary brings out, however, the important features of the cell in which we shall later be interested.

Cellular Differentiation.—We have been discussing a 'typical' cell, one that shows all the features of all the cells we know in the human body. Although such unicellular animals as the amoeba typically exhibit these features, no such 'typical' cell is to be found in the multicellular animals higher in the phylogenetic (evolutionary) scale. There we find certain of the properties described above accentuated in one cell and others emphasized in other cells. *Differentiation* has taken place: the chemical composition of cells has been specialized, the functions or kinds of chemical reactions which they perform have been narrowed down, and the structures have also changed correspondingly. It is through such differentiation of cells that multicellular organisms like man have evolved their complex biological structures and capacities.

Primary Germ Layers.—The more general aspects of the differentiation of cells in evolution can be seen by comparing the principal features of the lower invertebrate and vertebrate animals. These have been represented diagrammatically in Fig. 3. The most primitive multi-cellular organisms are merely collections of cells, each of which possesses the same essential structure and functions. In the first differentiation, the cells of the organism divide into two layers, the *endoderm* and *ecto-derm*, and within them is a cavity, which throughout the later evolution is the digestive tract. Subsequently, a third layer, the *mesoderm*, appears between the other two layers, and within it is another cavity, the coelom, which later becomes the main body cavity. When this appears, the mesoderm is divided into two parts, an inner splanchnic portion and an outer somatic mesoderm adjacent to the ectoderm. From these

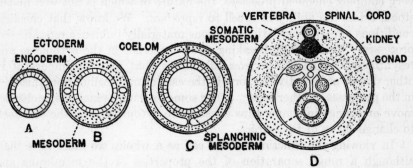

FIG. 3.—The evolution of organs of the body from the three primary germ layers. (*After M. F. Guyer, 1941. Animal biology. New York: Harper, p. 37. By permission of the publishers.*)

three primary germ layers, the ectoderm, mesoderm, and endoderm, proceed all further differentiations.

In evolutionary development and in the embryological growth of an individual, we can relate the various organs of the body, and their functions, to these three primary layers.

1. From the ectoderm emerge the skin, the sense organs, and the nervous system. These structures, it will be noted, serve much the same functions as did the membrane of the unicellular animal; *i.e.*, they mediate relations between the external world and the rest of the organism. The sense organs have specialized in the property of irritability, for it is their principal function to react to stimulation. Differentiated for conduction, the nervous system is also quite irritable, because of the nature of the physical relation of irritability to conduction.

2. From the mesoderm arise those tissues which are important chiefly in the movements of the organism and in the maintenance of its mechanical structure. The somatic mesoderm gives rise to the skeleton and to the muscles outside the body cavity, *i.e.*, the peripheral musculature. The splanchnic mesoderm, on the other hand, is the source of the visceral

muscles of the digestive and urogenital tracts. In these differentiations of muscle from mesoderm, it is to be noted, the contractile property of the cell has been especially emphasized. Associated with it, however, has been the development of irritability. It may be pointed out, in addition, that differentiation has proceeded farther in the case of somatic mesoderm than in splanchnic; peripheral musculature is more irritable, contracts more quickly and more powerfully than does visceral musculature.

3. From the endoderm develop the epithelial cells and the mucosa of the alimentary tract. Beyond this, however, the distinction between mesoderm and endoderm is hard to draw, at least briefly, for the two seem to be interrelated in the differentiation of the organs and glands located in the body cavity. These appear, in general, to subserve the basic functions of making use of the materials taken into the organism for maintenance and reproduction. The special functions of the cell accentuated in this case are growth, secretion, and reproduction.

Thus, in brief outline, has been presented the picture of the way in which the various properties emerging from the chemical activities of the single cell have been assigned in varying degrees to different tissues of the body through the differentiation of cells in both structure and function.

RECEPTOR-ADJUSTOR-EFFECTOR MECHANISMS

Because of the special importance of the receptors, nerve cells, and effectors in physiological psychology, it is well to consider the differentia-

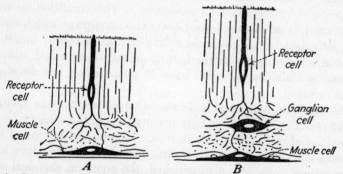

Fig. 4.—Diagram of primitive response mechanisms. *A*, a simple receptor-effector mechanism; *B*, a receptor-adjustor-effector mechanism. (*From G. H. Parker, 1919. The elementary nervous system. Philadelphia: Lippincott, pp. 201–202. By permission of the publishers.*)

tion of these in somewhat greater detail. It has become established that they differentiated in a definite order in phylogenetic development (Parker). The first to appear in differentiation is the muscle effector cell; it is the result of the specialization of the functions of irritability and contractility (Fig. 4). Then the function of irritability is further developed in the receptor cell, and this is the first instance of true neural tissue. Finally irritability and especially conduction are further developed in the formation of adjustor cells, thus completing the differentiation of the essential structure of the physiological mechanisms for responding to stimulation.

The Receptors.—Although the primitive receptor was primarily a nerve cell differentiated from the ectoderm, its further development has been so elaborate that, for the sake of presentation, receptors should be considered first from the functional point of view and then from the structural aspect.

1. As a result of differentiation with respect to the stimuli to which they are sensitive, receptors come to be of three classes, thermal, mechanical, and chemical. To these we may add a fourth class, the visual receptors, but it should be noted that these arise through the differentiation of special chemical materials in the cell which are responsive to light. In none of these specializations, however, does a receptor completely lose sensitivity to any kind of energy change; its development results only in a special increase in one type of sensitivity. Thus the thermal receptors are only *more* sensitive to changes in temperature than are other receptors; for the mechanoreceptors, a mechanical stimulus is simply *more* effective; likewise with the chemoreceptors.

Also worthy of note is the fact that, in all such differentiation, sensitivity to electrical stimulation is not lost or significantly diminished. The reason for this is to be found in the nature of the condition at the membrane which determines its sensitivity. This condition, as we have already noted, is an ionic polarization of the membrane which obviously can be disturbed by an electrical stimulus. To account, however, for differential sensitivity to thermal, mechanical, or chemical stimuli, we must assume that the chemical basis of polarization has developed in different fashions.

2. Along with functional differentiation go changes in histological structure (see Fig. 5). These may occur either in the sensory neuron or in the epithelial cell upon which it ends. A good illustration of both of these cases is to be found in the chemoreceptors. Of the three kinds of chemoreceptors ordinarily distinguished, the common chemical receptor is the most primitive, in that in it neither the sensory neuron nor the sensory epithelial cell is specialized; the divided fibers of the neuron simply end upon the relatively undifferentiated epithelial cell. In the more sensitive and efficient taste receptors, on the other hand, the epithelial cell has been specialized for heightened sensitivity to particular kinds of chemical stimuli; in the smell receptors, the third class of chemoreceptors, not epithelial cells, but the sensory neurons, have been differentiated in structure and also most certainly in chemical composition.

The structures serving other sensory modalities show a similar divergence in direction of structural differentiation. The visual receptors, like the olfactory, are simply highly specialized neurons. The mechanoreceptors, however, follow as a class the other line of differentiation.

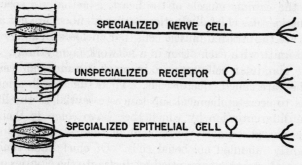

Fig. 5.—Types of specialization of sensory neurons and epithelial cells. (*After Parker.*)

Those mediating simple pain, like the common chemical receptors, are nerve cells ending freely among epithelial cells. But the auditory and the touch receptors are characterized by the very special character of the epithelial cells associated with them.

Adjustors.—The differentiation of nerve cells is, of course, of central importance to us, but a full discussion of that topic will be deferred to later chapters. Worthy of brief note at this point, however, is the fact that in nerve cells both structural and functional differentiation has proceeded in such a manner as to emphasize the conductive properties of cells. Thus, nerve cells have become greatly elongated into fibers whose sole function is to conduct a disturbance originated by stimulation of the membrane.

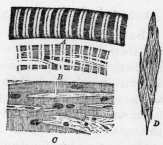

Fig. 6.—Types of muscle cells. *A* and *B*, striped-muscle fibers; *C*, heart-muscle fibers; *D*, smooth-muscle fibers. (*From M. F. Guyer, 1941. Animal biology. New York: Harper, p. 405. By permission of the publishers.*)

Effectors.—The effectors, those cells and groups of cells by means of which the organism behaves, are composed of two main classes, the muscles and the glands. The muscles we divide, in turn, into three types, according to the amount and the kind of differentiation. The most primitive, or least differentiated, of the muscle effectors is the nonstriated, or *smooth*, muscle cell (see Fig. 6). Typically a spindle-shaped cell, it contains within it a special substance, the fibrillae, upon which its contractile properties depend. *Striated* muscle cells, however, are more elaborate in form. They are much more elongated than are smooth muscle cells and are enclosed in a special elastic membrane, the sarcolemma. In them the contractile fibrillae are differentiated into two substances, one darker than the other, the regular alternation of which throughout the length of the fiber gives the muscle cell its striated appearance. A third type of muscle, the *cardiac* muscle of the heart, is actually a special kind of striated muscle. Its chief distinction is that its fibers are not arranged in parallel, as are the striated muscle cells, nor enclosed in a membrane, but branch and unite with each other in a network (syncytium).

Because glandular cells receive, in most instances at least, effector neurons, they are called effector cells. Their function in a multicellular organism is to secrete chemical substances essential to the life of other cells. The differentiation by which they have come to their secretory functions is not particularly prominent in their structure, for they are merely slightly modified epithelial cells. Of chief importance to us is whether their secretions are emptied by *ducts* into the cavities of the body, as in the case of the duct glands of the digestive tract, or whether their secretions empty directly into the blood. These *ductless* glands are of more interest to us because their secretions affect the body as a whole and the nervous system in particular. The functional differentiation of ductless gland cells, through which they come to manufacture different secretions, will be discussed in greater detail later in the chapter.

INTERCELLULAR FUNCTIONS IN EMBRYOLOGICAL DEVELOPMENT

So far, we have looked only at individual cells, their basic properties, and their differentiated functions, but we have not considered how cells influence each other. In coming now to this question, we meet the problem with which we shall have to deal throughout the rest of our study. Obviously, physiological activities in man are made up of the complex interactions of the different functions of various cells. These interactions, particularly as they occur in the nervous system, we shall subsequently study in considerable detail. First, however, let us consider them in their more general aspects.

One of the best sources of information concerning intercellular influences is to be found in the facts of experimental embryology. Here these influences have been studied as they operate in the development of the organism from a single cell, and here also have they been investigated as they pertain to the differentiation of the nervous system. Let us, therefore, briefly review the most important aspects of the embryological development of the organism.

The growth of the organism begins with the fertilization, by a spermatocyte, of an egg, which then becomes the *zygote*. In this unicellular form, the organism shows a differentiation of structure comparable to that of endoderm and ectoderm. At one end of the zygote, known as the *vegetal* pole, is collected the food material of the cell; such material is absent at the other end, the *animal* pole. The line drawn between these two poles is the chief *axis* of the zygote. Along this axis is made the first division of the zygote into daughter cells, or *blastomeres;* in subsequent cleavage of these cells, and of their daughter cells in turn, this axis is maintained, for the food material continues to remain concentrated at the vegetal pole.

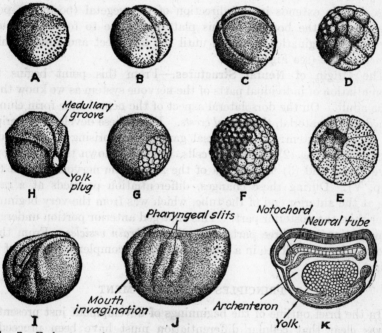

Fig. 7.—Early stages of growth in the frog. *A*, one cell; *B*, two cells; *C*, four cells; *D*, blastula, many cells; *E*, section of *D* showing internal cavity; *F*, late blastula; *G*, early gastrula; *H*, formation of medullary plate; *I*, formation of neural tube and elongation of the body; *J*, beginning of tail; *K*, median section of *J*. *(From R. H. Wolcott, 1940. Animal biology. New York: McGraw-Hill, p. 378.)*

Gastrulation.—The division of cells goes on for some time until a ball of cells, the *blastula,* is formed, and in it a cavity, the *blastocoel.* Then begins a series of specific differentiations known as *gastrulation* (see Fig. 7). First there is an invagination of the blastula near its vegetal pole, and this is enlarged until it forms a second cavity, later to become the digestive tract. The two layers of cells formed by this invagination are the endoderm and the ectoderm. Soon the third primary layer, mesoderm, is differentiated from the cells bordering on the opening of the second cavity. Thus are the three germ layers differentiated in the early stages of embryological development.

Neural Differentiation.—Shortly afterward, there is a dorsal thickening of the ectoderm along the median line of the embryo; this thickening is called the *presumptive medullary plate*, because from it the nervous system will subsequently develop. It lies, it is to be noted, along the polar axis of the organism. Soon it is transformed into the true medullary plate by the differentiation of the epidermal cells, of which it consists, into growing nerve cells, or *neuroblasts*. The medullary plate takes the form of a spoon whose ladle is at the animal (anterior) end of the organism and whose handle extends in the direction of the vegetal (posterior) pole. Subsequently, the borders of this plate evaginate to form the *neural groove*, and evagination proceeds until the lips meet and fuse, forming the *neural tube* (see Fig. 7).

The Origin of Neural Structures.—From this point begins the differentiation of individual parts of the nervous system as we know them in the adult. On the dorsolateral aspect of the neural tube form clumps of medullary material, the *neural crests*. From these develop the peripheral nervous system: (1) the dorsal ganglia, comprising the cell bodies of sensory nerves, (2) the sheath cells, which lay down the coverings of nerve fibers, and (3) the ganglia of the autonomic nervous system (see Chap. V). During these changes, differentiation proceeds at a rapid pace at the anterior end of the tube, which was from the very beginning larger than the posterior part. This enlarged anterior portion undergoes segmentation into three parts, the *primary brain vesicles*. From these develops, as we shall see in a later chapter, the complex structure of the brain.

PRINCIPLES OF DEVELOPMENT

In the brief outline of the beginnings of development just presented, it was clear that cellular differentiation must have been proceeding 'according to plan.' For the intricate features of adult structure to be elaborated in embryonic growth, differentiation in various cells must be delicately coordinated to occur in just the right part of the organism at just the right time. How is this timing and organization of embryonic growth accomplished? Because the external environment of the organism is usually relatively constant, the answer to this question must lie in the interrelations of the differentiating cells themselves. To these, therefore, let us now turn our attention.

Equipotentiality.—One of the classic experiments on this problem was reported by Driesch in 1891. After he had completely separated from each other the first two blastomeres (daughter cells) of a zygote, he observed that each blastomere developed into a normal embryo. Under normal conditions, of course, the two blastomeres would have collaborated in the formation of a single embryo. In later experiments Driesch has been confirmed, and, in addition, the partial separation of blastomeres has been observed to give rise to a partial duplication of the parts of an embryonic organism. From these observations it is clear that normal differentiation proceeds from the mutual influences of the blastomeres upon each other, but that in the absence of these influences development begins in each blastomere as it normally does in the zygote.

Derived from these facts is the concept of *equipotentiality*, in which Driesch concluded that: an organism is a system of parts, each of which has equal potency or ability to function as the other. Such a concept applies, as we shall see (Chap. XXIV), not only to embryonic growth but also to the interaction of cells in the adult organism. Lashley has shown (1929), for example, that, although various adjacent nerve cells in the brain may influence each other's functions, when by extirpation some of them are removed, those which remain will come to carry out the functions formerly subserved by all. To this fact, Lashley has also given the name *equipotentiality*.

Self-differentiation.—Equipotentiality is not by any means, however, the usual thing in either embryonic development or in adult cellular functions. One can obtain Driesch's results only when the separation of blastomeres is done in the early stages of their division. Later on, the cellular capacities and hence the intercellular influences are no longer equal, but instead some cells come to play a dominant role in differentiation and others become quite dependent upon them. The former are said to undergo self-differentiation, for changes in them go ahead without respect to influences from other cells. Most notable of the primary germ layers in this respect is the mesoderm; its differentiation tends to be quite independent of changes in other germ layers.

Induction.—Those cells, however, which are capable of self-differentiation influence those which are not, thereby *inducing* differentiation. Such induction is well illustrated by the formation of the nervous system: Although mesoderm does not appear in gastrulation until after ectoderm and endoderm (see above), once it appears, further differentiation is greatly influenced by it. Thus it induces the medullary plate out of which the nervous system develops, and it later determines to some extent certain features of the nervous system. Then despite its dependence upon the mesoderm, the embryonic nervous system itself induces other changes. For example, the primitive retina of the eye, which is embryologically a part of the brain, induces differentiation in the epithelial ectoderm of a lens to form part of the eye. Thus changes in one cell group, while being induced by influences from other cells, may in turn induce changes in still other groups of cells.

Reaction Potency.—Cells whose differentiation depends upon inductive influences from other cells are not, however, entirely at the mercy of those influences. Through some self-differentiation of their own or through development induced in them previously, the kind of changes and the influences that will induce them are restricted. Thus they are predisposed in a greater or lesser degree to certain kinds of differentiation, a fact which has been termed *reaction potency*.

In surveying these general aspects of intercellular influences in development we see, although without understanding the specific details, that the organization of the structure and functions of an organism is a matter of the mutual influences, dependent and independent, of cells upon each other. In this respect, the course of development illustrates well the conditions that obtain in the adult organism.

THE NATURE OF INTERCELLULAR INFLUENCES

We have seen how cells influence each other in embryonic differentiation. Now the question is: what is the nature of the intercellular influences, or by what specific means do cells influence each other? The answer to this problem, as we are able to give it in general terms, affords general insights into the nature of the forces at work in the integration of the normal activities of the organism.

Chemical Factors.—One of the most important clues to the nature of intercellular influences comes from the facts of induction summarized above. This influence, it was found (Mangold and Spemann), did not depend upon the cells of the inductor being alive. Upon further investigation the influence of cells in producing differentiation was found to be due, in some instances at least, to a special chemical substance (Holtfreter), and to this the name *organizer* (or evocator) was given.

Subsequent experiments (see Spemann) with all sorts of materials, living and dead, cooked, ground, and treated in a variety of other ways, have revealed many organizers which will induce organs of various kinds in different regions of the embryo. Sometimes the organs have been imperfectly formed, but in other cases differentiation has been complete. Of many known organizers those which are most potent are: tissues with a high metabolism (see below); certain acids, these being particularly potent in inducing nervous differentiation; and secretions of glandular cells. So far no one chemical substance has been found to be responsible for the differentiation of any one organ—the nature of chemical influences appears to be more complex than that—but the primary importance of the chemical aspects of cell function has been clearly demonstrated. Undoubtedly these go back to the nature of the genes which govern inheritance, for only through the processes of embryologic development can hereditary influences appear.

Metabolic Factors.—Although metabolic factors exert only a particular kind of chemical influence, they deserve to be considered separately. As we do this, it should be remembered that metabolism can be considered, so far as we are concerned, as the breakdown of chemical materials through oxidation. The energy expended in such oxidation can take the form of heat or of mechanical or electrical work.

Credit for emphasizing metabolic factors in embryonic development goes to Child (1924). His contribution emphasizes the fact that in all stages of development an organism possesses a metabolic gradient extending from its animal (anterior) pole to its vegetal (posterior) pole. This Child demonstrated in four different ways: (1) The respiratory rate (*i.e.*, the rate of consumption of oxygen) is greater at the anterior pole than at the posterior pole. (2) Correlated with this difference in respiratory rate between the two poles is a difference in electrical potential, due to the fact that where oxidation is greater, more energy is expended in the form of electrons. (3) The anterior end of a growing organism is more susceptible to destruction by toxic agents than the posterior. This, he points out, arises from the fact that a toxic agent will take effect most quickly where there is the highest rate of oxidation. (4) Finally, the anterior end stains more readily than does the posterior pole, and this is also an indication of a metabolic gradient.

On the basis of this *physiological gradient,* Child gives an account of differentiation in embryonic growth in which he assumes that the metabolic rate of a cell is an influence that is extended to other cells and shapes the course of their differentiation. He points particularly to the possibility that the basic axial physiological gradient of the nervous system may give rise successively to other gradients. For example, a gradient perpendicular to the axial gradient may be set up through the fact that the nervous system as a whole has a higher metabolic rate than neighboring tissues.

Child is no doubt right in believing that the metabolic rates of cells can influence each other, but the chemical factors in differentiation and the specific nature of the changes involved are certainly not accounted for in terms of oxidative rate alone. As proof one may cite experiments in which disturbances of the metabolic gradients have been experimentally produced without leading to abnormalities of development (Gilchrist).

Electrical Factors.—Besides varying in metabolic rate, cells may influence each other in differentiation through their electrical activity. This, of course, must be determined by their chemical reactions, because, in the living organism, there is no other source of electrical change than oxidative chemical reactions. Electrical factors have, therefore, generally been recognized as derived factors and have been suggested as important only for certain kinds and phases of differentiation, particularly of the nervous system.

Emphasis on the importance of electrical effects in neural differentiation is provided in the theory of neurobiotaxis offered by Kappers.

He states that nerve cells are galvanotropic: they respond to electrical stimulation by migrating and sending fibers in the direction of the source of the electrical stimulation. Evidence for such neurobiotaxis was given in an experiment in which neuroblasts, cultivated in an artificial medium, were observed to grow when subjected to electrical stimulation (Ingvar). Other experiments (see Weiss), however, have repeated this procedure and obtained negative results. So it is not certain how much reliance can be put on the principle of neurobiotaxis. The theory, however, has been widely applied both to embryological and evolutionary development of the nervous system (Kappers, Huber, and Crosby) as well as to learning.

Mechanical Factors.—In addition to chemical and electrical influences there is also evidence that the mechanical stresses and strains which must arise in the relations of cells to each other may be of importance in differentiation. In a specific experiment designed to test this possibility, Weiss cultivated neuroblasts in a medium outside of the body and then subjected them to specific stresses and strains, which, he found, determined the direction in which the fibers of the neuroblasts grew. Similar evidence has come from the direct observation by Speidel of neuroblasts growing in the body. The fibers of neuroblasts, he reports, follow paths (of least resistance) laid down by blood vessels, connective tissue, and other structures. It may be concluded, therefore, that among the factors determining structural differentiation is the mechanical relation of cells to each other.

The Field Concept.—Despite a great deal of progress in recent years, much yet remains to be learned about the details of intercellular influences in development. Some observers, aware of the shortcomings of our present understanding and impressed by the essential 'unity' of developmental processes, have attempted to formulate a viewpoint which, pending the outcome of more specific analysis, will give us a more general and effective understanding of developmental processes. For these observers, the most prominent of whom is Weiss, the *field concept* does that.

In this concept Weiss emphasizes the interdependence of the many events taking place simultaneously and successively in embryological development. Differentiation occurs, says Weiss, in a field of action or organization, somewhat analogous to the magnetic field; the whole field is organized into subordinate fields; and many or all of these operate together in determining any specific event in development. Thus the field concept summarizes the fact that the influences of cells upon each other are complex and may extend directly or indirectly to all cells of the organism.

It should be noted, in concluding this section, that the field concept and other statements of general relationships, which have been presented here, apply no better to embryological development than they do to the interrelations of cellular functions in the adult organism. After all, the changes and 'behavior' of cells in growth are simply the preparation for the integrated physiological activities of maturity. The relations of cell functions in nervous activity and in behavior are complex too, and events occurring in one part of the organism extend their influence to activities in other parts of the organism and are influenced by them in turn. It is this similarity between embryological growth processes and normal physiological functions which justifies the summary that we have just finished.

General References

CHILD, C. M., 1921. *The origin and development of the nervous system.* Chicago: Univ. Chicago Press. Pp. xiii + 296.

PARKER, G. H., 1919. *The elementary nervous system.* Philadelphia: Lippincott. Pp. 229.

SPEMANN, H., 1938. *Embryonic development and induction.* New Haven: Yale Univ. Press. Pp. 398.

WEISS, P., 1939. *Principles of development.* New York: Holt. Pp. xix + 601.

CHAPTER III

THE INTERNAL ENVIRONMENT

In the last chapter three points of fundamental importance were emphasized: (1) The cell and its properties constitute the fundamental basis of the activity of an organism. (2) Through the differentiation of cell structure and functions, the various organs of the body come to have their specialized functions. (3) Despite all their specialization, however, the cells of an organism have an essential unity of function because they continually influence each other's activities.

Now the organ of the body in which we are most interested is the nervous system, for behavior is based upon the individual and collective activities of its cells. The nervous system, however, is only one specialized part of the organism, and it is open to influences of various kinds from other cells of the body. These influences are an *internal environment* of the nervous system and determine the nature of nervous activities just as much as do stimuli of the external environment which affect the nervous system through the sense organs. Before one can understand nervous functions and their immediate importance in behavior, one must turn first to a consideration of the influences of the internal environment to which these functions are subject.

Aside from certain stimuli that affect the nervous system through internal receptors, which will be considered more conveniently later in the book, the immediate internal environment of the nervous system is the blood. By means of blood vessels, with which the nervous system is unusually well supplied, every nerve cell is constantly supplied by the blood with the materials upon which the nervous system depends for carrying out its essential functions, and, indeed, for life itself. The chemical constitution of the blood, the factors determining this constitution, and to some extent the factors influencing the distribution of blood to the nervous system make up, therefore, the major part of the study of the internal environment.

THE ENDOCRINE GLANDS

Of fundamental importance both as constituents of the blood and as regulators of blood chemistry are the hormones. These are chemical substances secreted by the cells of the ductless (endocrine) glands and emptied directly into the blood (see Fig. 8). They are not used as fuel in the body but influence other chemical reactions of an oxidative nature, thereby determining in many instances, through their effects on permeability of cell membranes, the distribution of chemical materials in the blood and various tissues. They may be treated in turn.

Insulin—the Hormone of the Pancreas.—Situated just posterior to the stomach and attached by a duct to the intestinal tract is the pancreas (see Fig. 9). Through the duct it delivers a pancreatic secretion into the digestive tract, thereby aiding digestion; in addition, the pancreas also manufactures a hormone, insulin, which it pours directly into the blood.

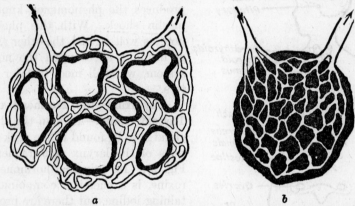

a   *b*

Fig. 8.—Diagrams of endocrine glands. (*a*) Gland composed of irregular sacs (heavy black lines) surrounded by tissue and blood vessels (*e.g.*, thyroid and ovary); (*b*) gland simply consisting of epithelium (black) penetrated by networks of blood vessels (white). Most glands belong to this type (adrenals, pancreas, parathyroids, hypophysis). (*From A. A. Maximov and W. Bloom. A textbook of histology, 4th ed., p. 291. Philadelphia: Saunders, 1941. By permission of the publishers.*)

Insulin appears to exert its influence in the body by increasing the permeability of cells to sugar (glucose) in the blood. Thus, when present in normal amounts in the blood, insulin ensures that the various tissues of the body get enough glucose as fuel for the work they have to do. Because the nervous system, particularly the brain, consumes glucose almost exclusively for its activities, insulin is of primary importance in nervous functions. When the supply of insulin is below normal (hypoinsulinism), as is the case in diabetes (d. mellitus), the blood-sugar level mounts, because the sugar can get neither into the liver, where it is normally stored, nor into the tissues where it is burned. Consequently in hypoinsulinism the nervous system is deprived of its essential fuel, with the result that its metabolic rate and general level of activity fall.

When, on the other hand, insulin is present in the blood in abnormally large amounts (hyperinsulinism), the sugar diffuses into the cells of the body, especially into the liver, muscles, and nervous system, in an excessive amount and the blood sugar consequently falls. The effect upon the nervous system is to raise its metabolic rate and increase the amount of nervous activity. Should the hyperinsulinism become very acute, however, the effect is the opposite—for this reason: nerve cells cannot store a very large supply of sugar but depend largely upon the blood for their supply. In insulin excess, however, the blood sugar has been withdrawn mostly into the liver and the muscles, and the nerve cells, when they exhaust their supply, can get no more. The result in this case is a starvation of nerve cells, which reduces their activity to a very low level and produces the phenomenon known as insulin shock. With this phenomenon, as well as with the other aspects of insulin's effect upon the nervous system, we shall meet in later chapters.

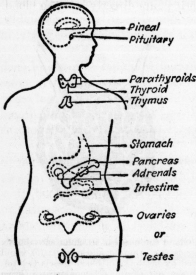

FIG. 9.—Silhouette of the human figure showing the location of the endocrine organs. (*From R. G. Hoskins. Tides of life, p. 19. New York: Norton, 1933. By permission of the publishers.*)

Thyroxine—the Hormone of the Thyroid Gland.—In man the thyroid gland is to be found in the neck at the sides of the larynx and trachea (see Fig. 9). Its principal hormone, thyroxine, is a chemical compound containing iodine, but there are probably other related hormones secreted by it. Their function and that of thyroxine is to aid the oxidation of materials within the cells of the various tissues. Whereas insulin regulates the amount of sugar getting into the cells, thyroxine regulates its use after it is in the cells. The role of thyroxine is not limited to the oxidation of sugars, however, but includes all sorts of metabolic reactions, including the processes of development. This control is well illustrated by the fact that tadpoles will not change into frogs in the absence of the thyroid gland, and, on the other hand, will metamorphose prematurely after the administration of thyroxine (Gudernatsch). Through its effect upon metabolic rate, the thyroid hormone also influences the amount of heat produced in the body and thus is an important part of the body's temperature-regulating mechanism.

Parathormone—the Hormone of the Parathyroid Glands.—Located in the vicinity of, or imbedded in, the thyroid gland are two pairs of very small glands, the parathyroids. Their hormone, parathormone, is concerned primarily in regulating the amount of calcium in the blood, probably through the removal of it from the bones. The relationship is a direct one; the more parathormone, the higher the blood calcium.

Because of the great importance of the ionic equilibrium at the membrane of nerve cells, the calcium level of the blood, as controlled by the parathyroid glands, is of considerable importance. Calcium ions have been shown to depress the excitability of nerve cells (see Bishop), and when they are reduced below the normal level, as in parathyroid deficiency, the excitability of nerve cells is consequently increased. This condition may be created by removal of the parathyroid glands, and it will be expressed in the behavior of an animal as extreme excitability, hypertonus of muscles, and sometimes, if calcium deficiency is acute, in convulsions.

Adrenalin—the Hormone of the Adrenal Medulla.—On top of each kidney is another gland, the adrenal. When it is examined in cross section, it may be seen to consist of two distinct parts, an external *cortex* and an internal *medulla*. From the latter is secreted one of the adrenal hormones, adrenalin (or epinephrine). It has several important functions.

1. In its effect upon blood-sugar level and the distribution of sugar to the cells of the body, it is the antagonist of insulin. Adrenalin releases sugar from the liver where it is stored and puts it into the blood, thus raising the blood-sugar level. In doing this, it supplies more sugar to nerve and muscle cells. This has the net effect of raising the rate of oxidation in these tissues, an effect which is expressed in greater neuromuscular excitability and in a greater production of heat.

2. Adrenalin raises metabolism, however, not only through the regulation of sugar, but also through increasing the oxygen-carrying capacity of the blood. Adrenalin causes the release of red corpuscles into the blood from the spleen, and, since it is the hemoglobin of red corpuscles which transports oxygen in the blood, the amount of oxygen reaching the tissues is thereby increased.

3. Related to these two functions in stimulating metabolism is the action of adrenalin upon smooth muscle cells, causing some to contract and others to relax, but functioning in both cases to raise neuromuscular metabolism. Thus adrenalin relaxes the smooth muscles of the intestine and constricts those of the blood vessels going to them, with the result that fuel is not consumed there but is diverted to the striped muscles and the nervous system. In its effects upon smooth muscles, upon the fuel made available to the tissues, and upon the oxygen-carrying capacity of the blood, adrenalin exerts its influence toward increasing activity in nerve and muscle cells.

Cortin—the Extract of the Adrenal Cortex.—The cortex of the adrenal glands probably secretes several hormones. These are found together in

the extract of the cortex, known as cortin. Although certain of them
have been isolated, it is most convenient here to consider them together.

Cortin has a slight effect upon sugar metabolism, similar to that
exerted by adrenalin, but its chief effect is upon mineral and water
metabolism. Especially significant is its relation to sodium. When the
adrenal cortex is extirpated, the sodium level of the blood falls and sodium
is excreted by the kidneys. Accompanying this is a loss of water from
the tissues and an increased excretion of it. This dehydration appears to
be the result of changes in sodium metabolism, for it can be ameliorated
by the feeding of sodium. Cortin apparently regulates the excretion of
sodium from the body, and in its absence sodium is excreted more freely,
thus producing all the secondary effects of sodium deficiency. Among
these, it may be noted, is a reduction of nervous excitability, for sodium,
unlike calcium, is required for normal nervous excitability. Largely as a
result of this fact, animals suffering from cortical deficiency are inactive
and, in severe stages, may go into a coma.

The Gonadal Hormones.—Besides cortin, the adrenal cortex secretes,
in small amounts, so-called androgenic hormones with the same physiological action as certain gonadal hormones secreted by the glands of sex.
Cortin is itself closely related chemically to these hormones and is
derived from the same tissues in embryological development.

Of the sex, or gonadal, hormones there are, of course, two classes, male
and female. There are several closely related female hormones, but of
these two are most important, *estrin* and *progesterone*. Both of these are
secreted by the female ovaries. Estrin is responsible for the physiological changes associated with ovum development and sexual receptivity,
whereas progesterone has to do especially with pregnancy. Of the male
hormones there are also several of closely related chemical composition,
but those of principal significance are *testosterone,* which is secreted by the
testes, and *androsterone,* an androgen which is found in male urine.
These hormones, as well as the female gonadal hormones, appear to
raise the metabolic level of the nervous system; in what manner, however, it is not known. They do, nevertheless, affect nervous activity,
as will be discussed more fully in a later section on sexual behavior.

The Hormones of the Pituitary Gland.—The most important of all the
endocrine glands is the pituitary, for not only does it secrete several
hormones of its own but it also controls the activity of other glands. It
is to be found immediately beneath the brain, to which it is connected by
nerve fibers. Although its structure is very complex, for our purposes
only two parts need to be distinguished, the anterior and posterior lobes.
It is this latter part which is connected to the brain and which is affected
directly by nervous impulses arising there; the anterior lobe appears to be
free of nerve cells.

Extracts of the posterior lobe are known as *pituitrin*. The chemical nature of pituitrin is not well understood, but of its several probable hormones only one is of direct concern to us: the *antidiuretic factor*. This regulates the amount of water excreted by the kidneys and thus the water balance of the organism. Without it a condition known as *diabetes insipidus* occurs in which water is excreted in large amounts (polyuria) and a great thirst for water is created (polydipsia).

There are a number of hormones secreted by the anterior lobe of the pituitary body. Of these the growth hormone, *phyone,* is best known. Deficiency of phyone causes *dwarfism* or *infantilism* in which there is an underdevelopment of the bones of the body and of the sexual organs. An excess of phyone expresses itself in overgrowth of the long bones of the body and of the jaw and cheek bones; if it occurs during growth, the result is *gigantism,* but if it should occur after adolescence, the result is *acromegaly,* a condition in which the jaw undergoes excessive growth.

The anterior pituitary (prehypophysis) also produces a hormone which exerts an influence similar to adrenalin in raising blood-sugar level and in antagonizing the effects of insulin; this hormone is known as the *diabetogenic* hormone. More important, however, are the hormones that regulate the secretion of other glands, the *tropic* hormones of the anterior pituitary. Of these there is one which stimulates each gland. Thus a *pancreatropic* hormone aids the growth and secretion of the pancreas; an *adrenotropic* hormone stimulates the adrenal glands; a *thyrotropic*, the thyroid; a *parathyrotropic*, the parathyroids; and *gonadotropic* hormones, the male and female gonads. Through these hormones the pituitary exercises the role of a 'master' gland, controlling indirectly all the functions dependent upon the other glands. If, for example, the prehypophysis is removed, these glands undergo degeneration, or atrophy, and their secretions are much reduced. The tropic hormones of the prehypophysis also aid in normal development of these glands.

HOMEOSTASIS

As we saw in the last chapter, the cell tends to maintain an equilibrium with its environment by exchanging materials through its semipermeable membrane. Indeed, equilibrium is the fundamental condition of the cell's existence. When materials in its environment are increased, these diffuse through the membrane and are oxidized within it; then the by-products of the metabolism of these materials diffuse out through the membrane with the result that equilibrium is maintained in respect of them. When, on the other hand, materials are withdrawn from the environment and the membrane equilibrium is disturbed, materials from inside the cell diffuse outward to restore it. A tendency toward equilibrium, then, is a basic phenomenon of the cell.

This is true not only of the cell but also of the organism as a whole. When cells differentiate to perform special functions, they thereby give up some of their ability to maintain an equilibrium with their environment. This ability, as a consequence, can be ensured only through the collaboration, and to some extent the specialization, of cells to see that their environment—*i.e.*, the internal environment—is kept relatively constant. The equilibrium of the cells comes to depend, then, upon the equilibrium of the internal environment, which is distinguished from the former by the special name *homeostasis* (Cannon).

Instrumental in maintaining such a homeostatic equilibrium are several different but interrelated mechanisms. The hormones are one. There is a long list of others: the lungs through which carbon dioxide is excreted and oxygen taken in; the circulatory system which controls the distribution of blood to the various tissues; the kidneys through which various products of metabolism, particularly those from the breakdown of proteins, are excreted; the digestive tract by means of which essential materials are brought into the body; and finally the nervous system which takes part, directly or indirectly, in regulating the other homeostatic mechanisms.

Not only are there several mechanisms for maintaining homeostasis, but there are many aspects of the internal environment which must also be regulated. Of these we shall consider only a few which are of greatest importance for nervous functions: sugar, hydrogen-ion concentration, and oxygen.

Sugar.—Of the three principal sources of energy, the proteins, fats, and carbohydrates, the latter are most important in the activities of nerve and muscle cells. Carbohydrates, as eaten, are in several forms, chief of which are starches and complex sugars. In the intestinal tract and before they are absorbed into the blood, however, they are broken down into the simple sugar *glucose* (dextrose), the form in which carbohydrates are circulated in the blood. When glucose comes to be stored, however, it is converted into a special form known as *glycogen*. This is deposited for the most part in the liver and in the muscles, from which it is liberated as the body needs it.

Most in need of glycogen are the nervous system and muscles, which can use little else for their fuel. Both can derive energy temporarily from other complex chemical materials, but for them to continue to function this energy must always be repaid through the oxidation of sugar. For this reason the means of supplying sugar to muscle and nerve, as well as the conditions influencing its utilization, are of special interest.

Several factors are important in sugar homeostasis. Insulin is responsible for the storage of sugar in the liver where it is converted into·

liver glycogen. This is reconverted to glucose and released into the blood under the influence either of adrenalin or of nervous impulses to the liver. It is largely through the antagonistic effects of adrenalin and insulin that the level of blood sugar is kept relatively constant. When the level is too high in the blood passing through the pancreas (hyperglycemia), the production of insulin is increased, thus causing more to be stored in the liver. In hypoglycemia, on the other hand, adrenalin is liberated and this mobilizes sugar from the liver.

For the sugar in the blood to enter the cells of the nervous system and muscles in adequate quantities, the cells must be made permeable to it by insulin. Once there, its rate of oxidation is largely determined by thyroxine and the concentration of oxygen. Resulting from the oxidation are water and several oxidation products, the first and most important of which is lactic acid. This may diffuse out of the cell into the blood and be transported to the liver, there to be resynthesized into glycogen, or it may undergo further oxidation within the cell. In the latter case, pyruvic acid and carbon dioxide (carbonic acid) are the result, and these must be removed by the blood and excreted.

Hydrogen-ion Concentration.—The products of sugar metabolism which have been mentioned, it will be noted, are nearly all acids, as indeed are most of the products of oxidation in the body. Besides lactic acid, pyruvic acid, and carbonic acid, the end products of sugar oxidation, other acids formed in appreciable amounts in the body are hydrochloric, sulfuric, and phosphoric.

Now acids are chemical substances that dissociate in water to give a large number of hydrogen ions (H+), and the effect of acid metabolites upon the blood, therefore, is to raise its hydrogen-ion concentration. This, however, disturbs cell functions, for an important aspect of the cell's relation to its environment is the equilibrium of ions established at the membrane. This is particularly true of the nerve cell, whose special functions are dependent upon ionic polarization of its membrane. It is necessary, therefore, that the internal environment remain stable with respect to its hydrogen-ion concentration.

For the accomplishment of this the body has three principal mechanisms: (1) In the blood is carried a number of chemical materials, called *buffers*, which are capable of 'binding' or taking up acid ions. Such buffers are usually carried in excess and can be used temporarily to neutralize acids coming into the blood from metabolism in the tissues. (2) Many of the acids resulting from the metabolism of proteins, although buffered temporarily in the blood, are excreted by the kidneys. (3) Carbon dioxide, however, which is produced in greater quantities in metabolism than any other acid, is removed from the body through the lungs.

Concerning this last point there is more to be said, particularly about the way in which carbon dioxide brings about changes leading to its removal through the lungs. This removal, one may note, can be expedited in two ways: by increasing the breathing rate and thus the rate of diffusion into the air of the lungs, and by increasing the rate of flow of blood to the lungs. The carbon dioxide in the blood brings about both of these results by direct stimulation of the nervous system. It does the first by exciting the respiratory center in the hind part of the brain and the second by exciting vasomotor centers in the brain. As a result of the latter, blood vessels are constricted in size and the flow of blood through them is speeded. Thus, through direct action upon the nervous system, an increase in the hydrogen-ion concentration of the blood brings about effects that will return the concentration to a normal level.

Before leaving the question of hydrogen-ion concentration, a word should be said concerning the way in which it is usually specified in physiological terminology. It is customary to use a logarithmic scale in which low values represent high acidity; high values denote the opposite state, alkalinity; the neutral point is 7. Values on this scale are known as the pH. To illustrate: a pH of 7 is neither acid nor alkali, whereas one of 8 is slightly alkaline and one of 6 is slightly acid. Because the scale is logarithmic, a pH of 8 is ten times as alkaline as one of 7; similarly, a pH of 5 is ten times more acid than one of 6. The reader should be clear about these matters, for it will later be more convenient to refer to hydrogen-ion concentration in terms of pH.

It may be noted in passing that the extreme limits of variation of the pH of the blood are 7.8 and 6.8. Above or below them, respectively, cell functions, particularly those of the nervous system, are so disturbed that death results. The normal pH of the blood is about 7.4, *i.e.*, slightly alkaline, and variations from this value are surprisingly small.

Oxygen.—The oxygen used in metabolism must be brought into the organism through the lungs. There it is absorbed through small arterioles into the blood where it combines with the hemoglobin of the red corpuscles. When the percentage of oxygen in the air is normal (about 21 per cent) and when breathing is at a normal rate, these corpuscles will absorb oxygen to about 95 per cent of their capacity. If, however, the oxygen available to the lungs is reduced, the oxygen saturation of the red corpuscles also falls, creating a condition of *anoxemia*. By means of the circulation of the blood, red corpuscles carrying oxygen are transported to the tissues where the oxygen is given up.

That oxygen be available in sufficient amounts to the cells of the body is of course a basic condition to be maintained in the homeostasis of the body. This is secured, it is interesting to note, not by the direct effects of oxygen deficiency, but by the pH of the blood, particularly as the pH is influenced by carbon dioxide and lactic acid. So far as the nervous system is concerned, the amount of oxygen it gets is determined by the pH of the blood in three different ways: (1) A rise in acidity increases breathing, as we have seen, by directly stimulating neural respiratory centers. This tends to raise the oxygen saturation of the red corpuscles leaving the lungs. (2) As was also stated, a lowered pH (raised acidity) increases, through neural excitation, the tonus of blood vessels and causes blood to be transported to and from the lungs and to and from the tissues more rapidly; consequently the efficiency of transportation of oxygen is increased. (3) Furthermore, carbon dioxide stimulates blood vessels of the nervous system directly and causes them to *expand*, thereby augmenting the amount of oxygen-carrying blood which nerve cells get.

It is indeed fortunate that oxygen deficiency and an excess of carbon dioxide usually go together. If breathing is retarded in rate or depth, the removal of carbon dioxide is reduced and so is the intake of oxygen. In the tissues, on the other hand, when carbon dioxide content is high usually the rate of flow of blood is slow and the supply of oxygen is consequently deficient. Thus is it possible for carbon dioxide to be the principal factor in maintaining an adequate supply of oxygen in the internal environment.

Since oxygen supply is such a fundamental condition of nervous function, let us note, finally, the circumstances under which the cells of the nervous system will be made anoxic. Four general kinds of anoxia have been distinguished: (1) Oxygen deficiency resulting from some interference with the ability of a cell to use oxygen is known as *histotoxic anoxia;* cyanide poisoning is a good example. (2) When the anoxia arises, however, from defective transportation of blood to the tissues, it is *stagnant anoxia.* This comes from any circumstances which retard circulation, for example, heart failure, low blood pressure, or the local obstruction of blood vessels. (3) *Anemic anoxia* is the result of a reduction of the hemoglobin content of the blood either through a deficiency of red corpuscles, as in anemia, or through a poisoning of the hemoglobin, as in carbon monoxide poisoning. (4) Finally, anoxia may be caused by a reduction in the amount of oxygen available to the lungs. This type of anoxia we call *anoxic anoxia.* Because oxygen is so important to nervous activities, it will be well to keep in mind these different causes of nervous anoxia.

General References

BODANSKY, M., 1938. *Introduction to physiological chemistry.* New York: Wiley. Pp. ix + 686.

BARCROFT, J., 1938. *The brain and its environment.* New Haven: Yale Univ. Press. Pp. vii + 117.

CHAPTER IV

THE PHYSIOLOGY OF NERVE CELLS

With a general sketch of the internal environment of the nervous system behind us, we come now to a consideration of the nervous system itself. We shall begin in this chapter with nerve cells and their functional relation to each other, and then, in the chapter that follows, we shall consider the more general features of the nervous system.

THE ANATOMY OF THE NEURON

The structural and functional unit of the body is the cell; similarly, the unit of the nervous system is the nerve cell, or *neuron*. In it are contained all the essential properties of nervous action, and only in the study of its activities can the more complex features of nervous function be understood.

General Structure.—The neuron has three parts: dendrites, a cell body (perikaryon), and an axon (see Fig. 10). The dendrites and the axon are extensions of the cell body and are known as nerve fibers. They may be distinguished from each other in several ways: (1) The dendrites are to be found in positions where they can be excited by environmental stimuli or by the activities of other cells, either sensory epithelial cells or other neurons. Thus the dendrite is the 'receiving' end of the neuron. The axon, on the other hand, is connected to muscle cells or other neurons to which it 'delivers' the nervous impulses carried by it. (2) The dendrite tapers off in size as it leaves the cell body so that one can hardly tell where the cell body ends and the dendrite begins. Where the axon leaves the cell body, however, is plainly marked by a small elevation of the cell body, the *axon hillock*, from which the nerve cylinder extends outward with uniform size. (3) A cell body usually has several dendrites, branching a great deal in treelike fashion; there is only one axon, even though this sometimes sends off collaterals at right angles to itself.

Internal Structure.—Certain aspects of the internal structure of a neuron are significant. Its cell body, like all cells, contains cytoplasm, and also within the cell body is a nucleus which appears to play the dominant role in the life processes of the neuron. The fibers of the neuron, on the other hand, represent the specialization of the membrane properties of a cell. In both the cell body and the fibers one can see

44

neurofibrils as very fine filaments streaming through the cytoplasm. These were once thought to be the basis of the neuron's special property of conduction, but that now seems improbable. Of more importance is the *chromidial substance* (Nissl's granules). This may be observed only in the cytoplasm of the cell body and in the dendrites for a short distance from the cell body. Its importance will be discussed below. There is, finally, the *Golgi apparatus*, a complex reticular network, which is confined to the cell body.

Myelin Sheath.—Closely affiliated with the nerve fiber, although not a part of it, is the myelin sheath. Not all nerve fibers are myelinated, but when they are, the myelin covers the main portion of the axons and dendrites and stops near the perikaryon. Of the utmost importance is the fact that the myelin is white, whereas neurons are gray. From it one may usually determine quite easily where, in the nervous system, cell bodies lie and where only fibers are present. Thus we are able to speak, in dealing with the gross structure of the nervous system, of *gray matter* and *white matter*, referring to cell bodies and fibers, respectively.

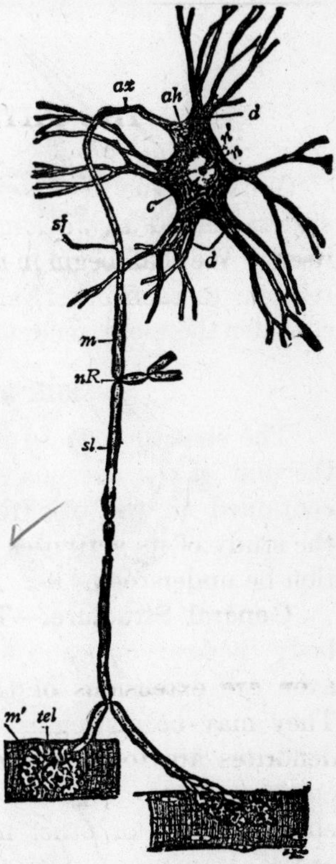

Little is known concerning the exact function of the myelin sheath. There are, however, certain functional differences between myelinated and unmyelinated nerve fibers. Fibers, for example, which are a part of a diffusely conducting system, as are 'pain fibers' and fibers delivered to smooth muscles of the blood vessels and intestines, usually are not myelinated. Where the functions of individual fibers are important, as in the neurons of the eye or of touch, they tend to be myelinated. In addition to these differences there are others, which, however, are best discussed below.

Fig. 10.—Diagram of a motor neuron. A typical cell from the ventral gray matter of the spinal cord: *ax*, axon; *d*, dendrites; *m*, myelin sheath; *m'*, striated muscle fiber; *sf*, collateral branch of axon; *tel*, motor end plate. Axon, dendrites, end plate, collaterals, cell body, all are parts of a single neuron. (*From C. J. Herrick. Introduction to neurology, 5th ed., p. 43. Philadelpia: Saunders, 1931. By permission of the publishers.*)

Physiological Anatomy.—The microscopic structure of the neuron and its sheath, as detailed above, is of considerable importance. By using various dyes to stain different parts of the neuron, the neuroanatomist has learned much concerning the structural relation of neurons to each other in the nervous system. Dyes which stain the chromidial substance tell him where the cell bodies are. Also, dyes which stain the myelin

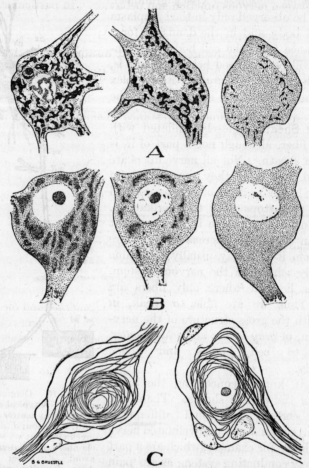

Fig. 11.—The principal structures in a neuron of the spinal cord and the changes which result in them from injury. (*A*) Golgi apparatus: left, normal cell; middle, retispersion 1 week after section of the axon; right, retisolution after section of the spinal cord (after Penfield, 1920). (*B*) Nissl substance: left, a normal cell; middle, moderate chromotolysis from fatigue; right, extreme retrograde chromotolysic degeneration (after Dolley, 1913). (*C*) Neurofibrils in living cells of 8-day chicks cultivated 1 week in culture (after Weiss and Wang, 1936). (*From J. F. Fulton. Physiology of the nervous system, p. 42. New York: Oxford*, 1938. *By permission of the publishers.*)

sheath, or nerve fibers themselves, reveal the course that fibers follow and the connections they make with each other. In this way, the knowledge of gross neuroanatomy has been advanced by the study of the structure of the neuron.

Such a study may also shed light upon whether or not neurons are properly performing their functions. This knowledge is, of course, of great point in physiological psychology, where one wishes to know the relation between nervous function and behavior. In particular, one may want to know whether certain cells are alive, and this can be told by noting any one of several signs.

One consists of the disintegration and disappearance of chromidial substance in cells which are fatigued, dying, or dead (see Fig. 11). If, for example, one examines the brains of animals that have been kept awake for very long periods of time, many of the neurons will be found to have lost their chromidial substance (Dolley). If the damage is slight, this occurs only in the dendrites, but if more severe, it extends through the entire cell. Such a disintegration of the chromidial substance is known as *chromatolysis* and is employed often as an index of the ill health or death of a neuron. Death may also be signified by changes in the Golgi apparatus, in which case the Golgi material first moves toward the periphery of the cell body and then undergoes fragmentation to disappear eventually with the rest of the cell.

Neuronal Degeneration.—The term *degeneration* applies not only to the death of a neuron but also to changes taking place in part of the neuron whether or not it dies. Three types of degeneration may be distinguished. (1) If fibers are severed from their cell bodies, the part of the fiber distal to the place of the cut will degenerate and die. This is *Wallerian* degeneration, and occurs in all neurons. In fibers outside the central nervous system, however, the part of the fiber still attached to the cell body will begin to grow and will eventually replace the part that has degenerated. (2) In the brain and spinal cord, on the other hand, no such regeneration takes place. Instead, not only does the distal fiber degenerate, but the proximal fiber and indeed the whole neuron dies in what has been called *secondary* degeneration. By virtue of this fact, we may note in passing, it is possible to trace the pathways in the nervous system and to determine where cell bodies of the pathways are located. (3) Still a third type of degeneration, *transneural* degeneration, occurs only rarely and then only in certain parts of the central nervous system. In this case, because other cells have died and left them without their normal connections, cells undergo chromatolysis and death without having incurred any direct injury.

THE ACTION POTENTIAL OF NERVE FIBERS

As we already have noted, an important aspect of the equilibrium of a cell is the polarization of ions at its membrane. In this function the nerve cell has specialized, as one might judge from the neuron's fibers, since these are nearly all membrane. Polarization is easily disturbed by various kinds of stimuli, and its disturbance at one point of the membrane readily affects polarization at neighboring points; thus is the neuron specialized for *irritability* and *conduction*. Both of these processes consist of chemical changes at the membrane, in which ions or the electrical charges carried by ions diffuse through the membrane. Although such chemical changes involve all kinds of work—chemical, thermal, mechanical, and electrical—their electrical aspects are the most conspicuous;

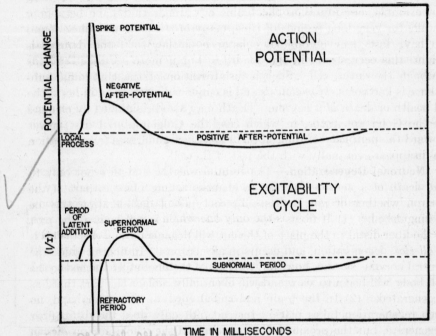

Fig. 12.—The action potential and excitability cycle of a typical sensory neuron following a stimulus sufficiently intense to produce a "nervous impulse" (spike potential). There are four parallel phases in each: local process and period of latent addition, spike potential and refractory period, negative after-potential and supernormal period, positive after-potential and subnormal period. The duration of the first two phases has been exaggerated in proportion to the length of the second two phases.

for the electrical currents can be picked up by electrodes and recorded by means of highly sensitive instruments developed for this purpose in recent years. Consequently the greater part of our information concerning nervous activity has come from the study of the electrical properties of nerves.

When a nerve fiber is excited by an electrical stimulus, as is the custom in research with nervous tissues, a series of four electrical potentials, one following the other in quick succession, can be recorded (see Fig. 12). These are (1) a local or subthreshold potential, (2) a spike potential or nervous impulse, (3) a negative after-potential, and (4) a positive after-potential. Together these make up the *action potential* of a nerve fiber subjected to stimulation.

Local and Spike Potentials.—When a nerve fiber is stimulated, the first reaction is a local potential[1] at the point of stimulation, *i.e.*, at the electrode (Hodgkin, Katz). If the stimulus is weak, the potential remains small and is restricted to the region of the electrode. When the stimulus is increased a little in intensity, however, the size of the local potential increases and is propagated a short distance along the membrane of the fiber, there to die out. With a still greater intensity of stimulation, there appears suddenly a vary large potential, the spike potential, following closely and merging with the local potential. Unlike the local potential, however, the spike potential does not change in magnitude with any further increases in the strength of the stimulus and is propagated the entire length of the nerve fiber. Thus it follows an all-or-none law with respect both to its size and its propagation, even though it depends upon the building up of a local potential which is graded in both respects.

Of these potentials, the spike potential was the first to be recognized and measured. Because it is the basic phenomenon of nervous activity, it has come to be called the nervous impulse. The largest of the potentials arising from nerve fibers, it is the only one which is propagated through the fiber without decrement, *i.e.*, at all-or-none intensity. Consequently, when the nerve fiber is stimulated, it is the spike potential that will travel through the dendrites and cell body to the end of the axon and stimulate the next neuron or muscle fiber connected to it.

The Membrane Theory of Nerve Conduction.—That the nervous impulse arises from the depolarization of the neuronal membrane has been realized for some time and is formally referred to as the *membrane theory* of nervous conduction (Lillie). We do not yet, however, fully understand the processes occurring at the membrane, but the best conception of them which present knowledge affords may be summarized as follows (see Gasser).

The neuronal membrane is normally polarized with positive ions on the outside and negative ions on the inside (see Fig. 13). This fact one may establish experimentally by recording from electrodes placed on a severed nerve, one on the outside of the nerve and another on the inside at the place of the cut. A stimulus applied to a nerve removes the external positive ions and upsets the membrane equilibrium; the negative ions diffuse through the membrane to the outside. In this way is set up a

---

[1] The local potential has been recorded only in special conditions of experimentation, but many facts lead to the belief that it is characteristic of all healthy and sensitive nerve fibers.

local bioelectric current of which the local potential is probably the recordable aspect.

So long as this local current remains small, as it will when the stimulus is weak and the nerve only partially depolarized, it will not be propagated. When, however, the local current is increased in strength, it spreads along the membrane and neutralizes external positive ions in the region adjacent to the point of stimulation. Here the effect is the same as at the point of stimulation, *viz.*, a depolarization of the membrane and

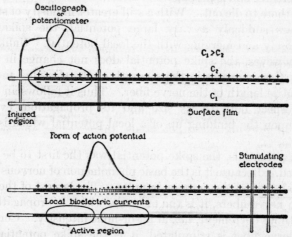

Fig. 13.—Illustrating the membrane theory of nervous conduction. The upper part of the diagram indicates how a potential will be registered between normal and injured regions of a nerve fiber. The lower part shows how a transient change produced in the stimulating electrodes at the right and traveling toward the injured portion will be registered in recording electrodes placed as indicated in the upper part of the figure. (*From H. S. Gasser. Electrical signs of biological activity. J. Appl. Physics, 9, 89, 1938. By permission of the American Institute of Physics.*)

a flow of current through the membrane from inside to outside. So on it goes, with the result that the depolarization of the membrane perpetuates itself in progressively adjacent regions and the local current becomes a self-maintaining spike potential traveling the whole length of the nerve.

In this scheme the relation between the local potential and the spike potential is clear. It is when the local potential becomes intense enough to stimulate adjacent regions of the nerve that it is transformed into a self-exciting spike potential traversing the nerve without decrement. Such a theoretical relation is clearly borne out by experiments (Hodgkin), in which the local potential, when sufficiently large, has been observed to blend in with the spike potential which immediately follows it.

The Size of the Nervous Impulse.—The nervous impulse is always as large as the region of the membrane in which it appears will permit, and to this fact we give the name *all-or-none law.* There are, nevertheless, several factors related to the size of the nervous impulse permitted by the membrane. Indeed, any change in the equilibrium of the membrane, whether chemical, thermal, or mechanical, will alter the amount of the potential. Of more general importance, however, is the relation of almost direct proportionality between impulse size and the diameter of a nerve fiber (Gasser and Grundfest). Its significance lies in the fact that fibers in the nervous system are of widely different sizes and therefore have characteristically different impulse sizes. Moreover, the diameter of nerve fibers is not constant for any given neuron, for at their ends neurons break up into a number of small filaments. As a result there is a reduction in the size of the nervous impulse, a fact which becomes of consequence, as we shall see, in the problem of transmission of nerve impulses across a synapse.

After-potentials.—Both the local and spike potentials are registered on recording instruments as negative potentials because they represent the loss or neutralization of positive ions at the point of stimulation of the membrane. Following these potentials, there occurs another negative potential, and then a positive potential, both of which are called after-potentials because they follow the spike potential (nervous impulse). In the typical mammalian nerve, the spike potential lasts 0.4 millisecond, but the after-potentials take about 100 msec. to run their course. Of this time the negative after-potential takes about 14 msec. and the positive after-potential lasts about 85 msec.

Not yet clearly determined is the cause of the after-potentials. Their presence, however, is known to be correlated with the production of heat in the nerve fiber, and it is thought that they represent fundamental metabolic processes connected with the repayment to the membrane of the energy expended in the nervous impulse. This would undoubtedly involve diffusion through the membrane and the rearrangement of ions at the surface of the membrane. The principal significance of the after-potentials rests in their correlation with changes in the excitability of the neuron.

THE EXCITABILITY CURVE

Out of the experimental neurophysiology of the last three decades has grown a rather clear conception of the important aspects of neuronal excitability. What we know today is certainly not the whole story, but it nevertheless provides a good basis for understanding the more complex aspects of the integrating functions of the nervous system. To see the essential facts in clear relief, we may trace the changes that occur in the sensitivity of a nerve fiber from the time a stimulus is first applied to it until the nerve fiber returns again to a resting state. This series of changes is known as the *excitability curve* and consists of four parts: the period of latent addition, the refractory period, the supernormal period, and the subnormal period.

Before discussing these, however, we should define a few terms. *Subthreshold stimulation* will refer to a stimulus that is insufficient to produce a spike potential (nervous impulse) in a nerve fiber; a *threshold stimulus*, on the other hand, is one that is intense enough to excite the fiber. A fiber is said to be *excited* when a nervous impulse is evoked, except in the case where 'subliminal excitation' refers only to the arousal of a local potential. Also, by *excitability*, in reference to a neuron, will be meant the strength of a stimulus required to excite a nervous impulse; when this is low, the nerve fiber is more excitable than when it is high. We may note that *nerve* means a bundle of nerve fibers outside of the brain or spinal cord but leading to (sensory) or away from (motor) them.

The Period of Latent Addition.—It is a local potential, we have seen, which must be built up to some 'threshold' value before it will turn into a spike potential. To do that a stimulus must be of a certain intensity and last for a minimal time, for the reason that opposed to the local potential is an antagonistic process, a *decay* process, which tends to destroy it. If the intensity is not great enough, the local process, which the potential represents, will—even though the stimulus continues to be applied—deteriorate and the nerve fiber will become accommodated, with the result that, in order to excite it, the stimulus strength must be raised to a higher value than would have been required in the beginning.

The decay of the local potential responsible for accommodation will naturally proceed at a faster rate when the stimulus is withdrawn, and the excitability of the fiber will quickly return to normal. In the meantime, however, if a second stimulus is applied, its intensity can be less than the normal threshold value and yet excite the fiber. In other words, two stimuli, each of subthreshold strength, if presented within an interval shorter than the time of decay of the local potential following the first stimulus, will *summate.* From this property the period of latent addition gets its name. This period, it is important to note, is extremely short; in a typical neuron it lasts only 0.5 msec. or less. The decay of the local potential is, therefore, an extremely rapid process.

The Refractory Period.—Most well known of the changes in neuronal excitability is that occurring during the so-called refractory period. Following the period of latent addition, it consists of two parts: one in which a stimulus, no matter how intense, will not excite the nerve, the *absolute* refractory period; and one in which a stimulus to be effective must be more intense than the normal threshold strength, the *relative* refractory period. Throughout this refractory period, however, the excitability gradually approaches normal again. In a typical large nerve fiber, these two phases of the refractory period last about 0.5 msec. and 3 msec., respectively (Gasser and Grundfest). It is of note that the absolute refractory period coincides very closely to the duration of the spike potential, whereas the relative refractory period fills the period of transition between the spike potential and the negative after-potential.

The Supernormal Period.—Though the excitability returns to normal during the relative refractory period, it does not stop there but proceeds to overshoot the mark, so to speak, and become greater than normal. Then, the stimulus required to evoke an impulse need be considerably less than when the nerve has been resting. This period of supernormal excitability, it is interesting to note, coincides with the negative after-potential (Gasser, 1939); in the typical large nerve fiber, it appears between 3 and 15 msec. after the nervous impulse has been discharged.

The Subnormal Period.—The last phase of the excitability curve is a period of subnormal excitability; this occurs between 15 and 100 msec. in the so-called typical nerve fiber and is coextensive with the positive after-potential already described. In this period a stimulus of above-normal intensity is required for excitation; in this respect, although it lasts much longer, it is like the relative refractory period.

Potentials and Excitability.—As remarks above have indicated, there is a very clear correlation between the potentials of a nerve fiber and its excitability. For each phase of the excitability cycle there is a parallel in one of the four distinguishable potentials. This fact is a convenient aid in research, for it is usually much easier to record changes in potential than to work out the thresholds of excitability. In many different studies which have been conducted under different conditions with nerve fibers both inside and outside the nervous system, this parallelism has been maintained. The reader should see clearly, however, that it is not simply a parallelism of excitability with negative and positive potentials. In the period of latent addition where excitability is enhanced, the local potential is negative, yet it is also negative in the case of the spike potential which is accompanied by absolute refractoriness. Then again, the augmented excitability of the supernormal period parallels the negative after-potential, while the positive after-potential represents subnormality of excitability. It is, therefore, the distinct phases of the potential cycle, rather than their signs which parallel the phases of the excitability cycle.

FACTORS AFFECTING EXCITABILITY

Tetanus.—The facts that have been discussed thus far in this section have been drawn from the study of isolated impulses in nerve fibers. To gain a better idea of how neurons behave in the intact organism, however, one should study the effects of rapidly *repeated* stimulation, or tetanus, upon nerve-fiber action. From such a study have come some facts of importance concerning the excitability curve (Gasser, 1939; see Fig. 14): after a tetanus, the negative after-potential tends to disappear along with the supernormal period of excitability; the positive after-potential, on the other hand, is greatly augmented and with it appears a great depression of excitability. Of note also is the lengthening of the period of the positive after-potential and of the coincident subnormality of excitability. The amount to which this period is lengthened depends upon the length and severity of the tetanus. In some cases it may last seconds or even a minute or longer (Gasser and Grundfest, 1936). Its significance for central nervous function will be seen later.

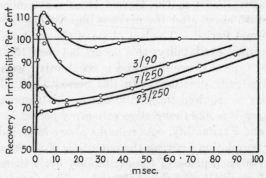

Fig. 14.—The effect of tetanus on the excitability cycle of neurons. The highest curve is a normal cycle following a single stimulus applied to a normal resting neuron; the next curve is that obtained following three stimulations delivered at the rate of 90 per second; the next, following seven shocks delivered at the rate of 250 per second. (*From H. S. Gasser and H. Grundfest. Action and excitability in mammalian A fibers. Amer. J. Physiol.,* **117,** *113–133, 1936. By permission of the American Journal of Physiology.*)

pH.—One of the important aspects of the internal environment is, as we have seen, the acid-alkaline balance, or pH, of the blood: since the homeostatic mechanisms of the body do not succeed in keeping the pH completely constant, the effect of changes of pH upon nerve-fiber excitability is a consideration of consequence in the understanding of normal nervous functions.

The general relationship between pH and nerve excitability is a direct one (see Fig. 15); the lower the pH, the lower the excitability, and conversely (Lehmann, 1937). To this generalization we may add some details by looking at the effect of pH on the excitability curve (Fig. 16). At normal pH, 7.4, the curve is that which we have already described. Raising the pH to 8.0, however, brings about some remarkable changes. Almost completely gone is the normal negative after-potential and supernormal period, and the nerve goes immediately into a subnormal period; but following it there appears an oscillation of negative and positive after-potentials and of excitability between supernormal and subnormal levels. There is, moreover, during the oscillation of excitability, a spontaneous discharge of spike potentials. This oscillation, as we shall see later in this book, is very much like the nervous discharge that accompanies epileptic behavior.

Upon returning the pH from 8.0 to the normal value of 7.4, the oscillation between super- and subnormality disappears, but for the first few minutes an augmented and prolonged supernormality appears in its place. Then, before the nerve finally returns to normal it passes through a period of depressed excitability (Fig. 15).

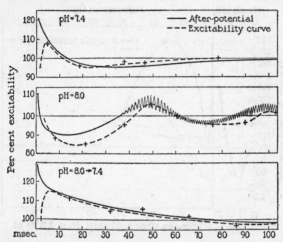

Fig. 15.—Relation between excitability curves and after-potentials in a phrenic nerve of the cat at pH 7.4 and 8.0 and during a shift from pH 8.0 to 7.4. The spontaneous discharge in the after-potential at pH 8.0 is represented schematically. (*From J. E. Lehmann. The effects of changes in pH on the action of mammalian A nerve fibers. Amer. J. Physiol.,* **118**, 609, 1937. *By permission of the American Journal of Physiology.*)

Oxygen.—As already stated in the last chapter, the amount of oxygen available to nerve cells is a basic aspect of the internal environment of the nervous system; changes in this supply alter neural excitability. The effect of anoxia, and subsequently of the restoration of oxygen, upon nerve excitability is shown in Fig. 16. Oxygen deprivation first causes excitability to rise and then, afterward, to fall markedly to a low level, at which no potentials of any sort can be evoked. Here excitability stays until oxygen is restored. Thereupon it rises quickly for a brief period but then passes again through a period of depression before it finally settles at the normal level. All these changes in excitability with alteration in oxygen supply are paralleled, when they occur in the intact organism, by behavioral effects. Of these, more later.

Mineral Balance.—Several mineral salts are known to be concerned both in the ionic equilibrium of the cell membrane and in certain phases of the metabolism of nerve fibers. Of these, calcium and potassium appear to be the most important (Lehmann), and their relations to nerve excitability are therefore of some consequence. [A high calcium content of the environment is like a low pH; it depresses nerve excitability.] The withdrawal of calcium, on the other hand, is accompanied by all the changes in the excitability and action potential characteristic of a pH of 8.0. Thus an oscillation of negative and positive after-potentials occurs together with oscillations of excitability and spontaneous discharges of spike potentials. This effect is due to the absence of *ions* of calcium rather than calcium itself, for if the calcium content of the nerve's environ-

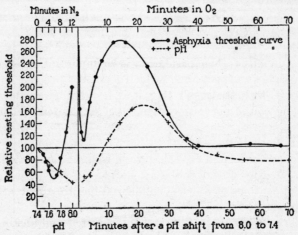

FIG. 16.—The effects of change of pH and of lack of oxygen upon the threshold of nerve fibers. The dotted line in the left-hand section shows the lowering of threshold with gradual increase in pH; the dotted line in the right-hand portion indicates the rise and fall of threshold in the course of an hour, following change of pH from 8.0 back to the normal level of 7.4. The solid line in the left-hand section shows an initial fall followed by a rise in threshold when a fiber is subjected to oxygen lack, and in the right-hand part the solid line shows that, after oxygen is restored, there is an initial drop in threshold back toward normal level, but after that there is another period of depressed excitability (raised threshold) in the course of a half hour before the normal resting threshold is reached. (*From J. E. Lehmann. The effects of asphyxia on mammalian A nerve fibers. Amer. J. Physiol.*, **119**, 113, 1937. *By permission of the American Journal of Physiology.*)

ment is left high but the number of calcium ions reduced by the addition of citrates, the effect will be obtained just the same.

An opposite relation obtains between potassium and neuronal excitability; the concentration of potassium is directly proportional to excitability. Without potassium the thresholds of fibers are quite high and they are lowered hardly at all, as they are in normal circumstances, by raising the pH to 8.0. Indeed, when potassium is low, no matter how high the pH is raised, one does not observe the oscillating excitability and spontaneous discharge characteristic of normal nerve fibers in a like situation.

All these factors—pH, oxygen, calcium, and potassium—are obviously interrelated in their effects upon neuronal excitability. There is, in fact, reason to believe that the effects of pH and oxygen are exerted through changes in calcium and potassium ion concentration (Lehmann). However this may be, the basic factors in each case are clearly a matter of ionic balance at neuronal membranes. Later we shall encounter instances of disturbances of behavior which arise from disturbances of such factors as pH, oxygenation, and mineral balance.

TEMPORAL ASPECTS OF NEURONAL ACTIVITY

It seems quite probable that the carrying of 'messages' in the nervous system is done entirely by the spike potential, or so-called nervous impulse, yet, as we have just seen, there are fluctuations in the excitability of nerve fibers which markedly influence whether or not spike potentials will arise. Obviously, then, periodicity is an important aspect of neuronal functions. It is an aspect about which more has become known in the last few years, with the result that it is fast becoming the key to the understanding of the nervous system. Let us, therefore, consider it in some detail.

Neuronal Periodicity.—So far we have paid attention only to fluctuations in after-potential and excitability following the evocation of nervous impulses. We may go beyond that, however, to a more fundamental periodicity of neurons, of which such fluctuations are apparently only one kind of expression.

When nerve fibers are in a normal environment and unstimulated, we find in our records no evidence of rhythms of excitability or potential. Periodicity is probably there, however, even though we are unable to record evidences of it. For when the irritability of a nerve fiber is increased by lowering the calcium concentration (or raising the sodium chloride concentration, spontaneous oscillations of potential and excitability appear (Arvanitaki). To these oscillations all that has been said above applies; during their negative phase, the fiber is more excitable, whereas in the positive phase of the cycle, the threshold is increased. From this fact we might presume that rhythms of excitability are a fundamental aspect of the resting, as well as of the excited, nerve fiber.

Credence is given this belief by the fact that the cell bodies of neurons in a normal environment usually present rhythmic oscillations of potential and of excitability. Cell bodies in all parts of the nervous system, whether they are left in the organism or studied outside of the body, appear to show this effect (Jasper, Bishop). The 'brain waves' recorded from the cerebral cortex and the spontaneous rhythms of neural activity controlling breathing and heartbeat are examples. Moreover, when such rhythmic fluctuations in potential and excitability become very great, spontaneous 'firing' of spike potentials occurs in the negative phase of the oscillation. It is in this way that respiration and heartbeat are normally carried out; when this same phenomenon is found in recorded 'brain waves,' as a result of some abnormal condition, we observe epileptic discharges. On this topic it will be enough to note here that rhythmic oscillation is a basic characteristic of neurons and upon it depends excitability.

Conduction Rates.—We have already seen that nerve fibers of the nervous system differ in size and that the size of the nervous impulse corresponds with the fiber size. This is not all, however. With fiber

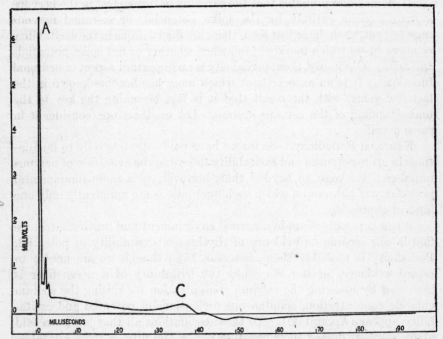

Fig. 17.—Action potential from the saphenous nerve of the cat, showing elevations of the *A* and *C* types of fibers. (*From H. S. Gasser. The classification of nerve fibers. Ohio J. Sci.*, 1941, **41**, 145–149. *By permission of H. S. Gasser.*)

size are also correlated several other important factors. One is myelination; the largest fibers are thickly myelinated, smaller fibers are more thinly myelinated, and the smallest fibers often have no myelin at all. Another is excitability; the larger the fiber, the more excitable is it, *i.e.*, the weaker may be the stimulus which excites it. Finally there is velocity of conduction; fibers of larger diameter conduct much faster than smaller ones.

Fiber Types.—These relations introduce us to another fact of considerable significance: nerve fibers in the various nerves of the body can be divided into several distinct types on the basis of their differences in speed of conduction, myelinization, fiber size, and impulse size (see Fig.

17).   Each of many different nerves of the body has been found to have a limited number of fiber types (Bishop *et al.*)*;* the optic nerve has two, the nerves to the skin, three, and other nerves a similarly small number. With the different fiber types have been correlated differences in function, elaborated in detail in later chapters.   Here we are interested in the general case, which may be illustrated by taking as an example the fiber types in a cutaneous nerve.

There we find three types which, for the sake of convenience, have been labeled *A*, *B*, and *C*.   Their existence has been demonstrated by the grouping of them which occurs naturally in respect to thresholds of excitability and velocity of conduction.   If a relatively weak stimulus is applied at one point to the bundle of nerve fibers and the nerve impulses are recorded at another point on the nerve, the result is a flock of impulses that pass the recording electrodes at about the same time.   Upon raising the intensity of the stimulus a little, however, one observes not only the original group (*A*) but shortly after they pass, another group (*B*). Finally, upon still more intense stimulation, after *A* and *B* impulses have passed in their turn a third group (*C*) appears at the recording electrodes.

Combining this information with a microscopic study of nerve fibers of various sizes and their amounts of myelination, one comes to the conclusion that there are three different groups of nerve fibers with the following properties:

Fibers	Size	Myelinization	Conduction rate	Impulse size	Sensitivity
A	Large	Thick	Fast	Large	Great
B	Medium	Thin	Moderate	Medium	Medium
C	Small	None	Very slow	Very small	Poor

How such fiber types suggest an explanation of the specific energy of nerves will be seen later.

Fiber Types and Excitability Curve.—Related to differences of fiber types in respect particularly of velocity of conduction are characteristic differences in the excitability curve, which may be noted in the records of *A* and *C* fibers presented in Fig. 18.   The excitability curves of both the *A* and *C* fibers have the typical form that has been described earlier, but they differ chiefly in respect of the duration of the curve.   That of the *A* fibers is less than 100 msec., whereas the subnormal period of *C* fibers may not end until a minute has passed.   From this fact it is easy to see that *A* fibers can respond much more frequently than the *C* fibers.   In repetitive discharges, of course, the excitability curve does not run its full course, but each spike potential tends to come in the period of supernormality after which the curve begins again.

Recruitment.—Also related to the periodicity of nerve fibers and to their excitability curve is the phenomenon of recruitment. By this term we refer to a gradual increase in the number of nerve fibers giving nervous impulses, as one continues to stimulate a nerve in rapid succession. For a number of years, recruitment was thought to be a phenomenon restricted to the central nervous system, for it was observed

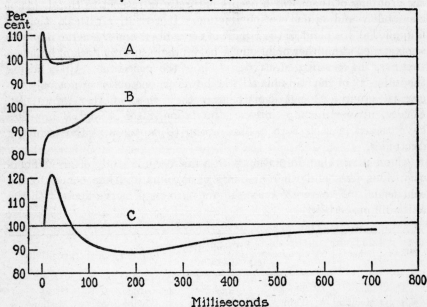

Recovery of excitability after a single response

Fig. 18.—Excitability cycles in *A*, *B*, and *C* types of fibers. The *B* fiber in this case is considered to be an autonomic motor fiber, whereas the *A* and *C* fibers are cutaneous sensory nerve fibers. (*From H. S. Gasser. Axons as samples of nervous tissue.* J. Neurophysiol., **2**, 361–369, 1939. *By permission of C. C. Thomas, publisher.*)

only in reflex behavior. When, for example, a sensory nerve was stimulated with an electric current of high frequency, the reflex response gradually became stronger, thus indicating that more and more impulses were going down the motor nerve. Only recently has it been shown that the same phenomenon may be observed in nerve fibers outside the central nervous system. In this observation are several points of significance.

The experiment (Gasser) was conducted by stimulating the fibers of a nerve with alternating current at a frequency slightly above the threshold of the nerve's most sensitive fibers. From another point on the nerve the resulting spike potentials were recorded, their height indicating the number of fibers responding at any one time. At the beginning of stimulation only a few fibers responded on each cycle of the alternating current, but as the stimulation continued, more and more fibers 'came in' and thereafter continued to respond until a large percentage of the fibers of the nerve had been enlisted.

Such recruitment appears to depend upon a fact that has not been mentioned before—a subthreshold excitability curve. It seems that at first the stimulus applied to the fibers does not evoke a spike potential, but only the first local potential. This is followed, however, by changes in excitability paralleling the usual excitability cycle, first a period of depression comparable to the refractory period, and then a period of supernormality. In this period the nerve fiber becomes excitable to a strength of stimulus which at the beginning is insufficient, and, consequently, upon stimulation it gives a spike potential. Subsequently, of course, the cycle repeats itself with another period of supernormality, and thus, if the frequency of the stimulus is optimal, the nerve fiber is permanently recruited.

Although this account is theoretical, there is good evidence for it. We know, of course, about the presence of the local potential. Also, it has been shown that following a subthreshold stimulus there is a period of depression paralleling the refractory phase in an excited nerve (Erlanger and Blair). From such evidence, and also from the fact that there is little difference between the local and spike potential except in capacity for propagation, there is good basis for believing that excitability cycles may result from subthreshold stimuli.

SYNAPTIC FUNCTIONS

Until now we have been dealing with individual nerve fibers as they are found in nerves outside of the brain and spinal cord. Not individual neurons, however, but myriads of them connected with each other in diverse ways make up the nervous system which we wish to understand, and it is a question whether our knowledge of individual neurons will provide the basis for that understanding. One of our most distinguished modern neurophysiologists, Keith Lucas, thought so, and much research of the last decade has tended to support him. In this section, therefore, let us consider how far and in what ways the properties of individual nerve fibers may help us understand the functions of the nervous system.

The Synapse.—Neurons are, of course, never connected anatomically, for they are each individual cells with their own membranes, but their fibers do interlace to form a functional juncture, the synapse. This has two characteristics of note: (1) The fibers of the axon are divided into many small terminals at the end of which are, characteristically, small bulbous enlargements, known as terminal bulbs, or *boutons* (see Fig. 19). These end upon dendrites, or, in some cases, upon the cell body of another neuron. (2) By virtue of the fact that each cell has several axon collaterals and usually many dendrites, one neuron has terminal connections, both afferent and efferent, with many others. It is these two characteristics which most clearly distinguish the nervous system from the individual nerve fiber, and to them let us, therefore, address our attention.

Synaptic Transmission.—A question that has been much discussed in recent years is how a nervous impulse in one neuron causes an impulse

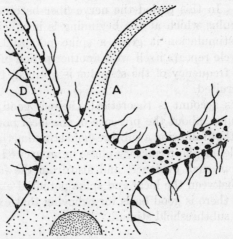

Fig. 19.—Part of a ventral horn cell from the rabbit showing normal synaptic terminals on the lateral surface of its cell body and dendrites *D*, but not upon its axon *A* except at the base. Each terminal makes an individual synapse with the ventral horn cell; such synaptic junctions are characteristic of most of the synapses in the central nervous system. (*After Cajal. From J. F. Fulton. Physiology of the nervous system, p. 58. New York: Oxford,* 1938. *By permission of the publishers.*)

in the dendrite of a neuron with which it makes synapse. In other words, what is the mechanism of synaptic transmission? Answers to this question fall into two general classes, which may be called the *humoral* and *electrical* theories, respectively.

According to the humoral theory, an impulse arriving at the terminal bulb of an axon causes a chemical substance to be secreted or released into the synaptic space, and this substance diffuses across the synaptic gap to stimulate the dendrite. The evidence for this theory is, for the most part, indirect, being drawn from facts about synaptic transmission at the juncture of autonomic nerves and smooth muscle. There, many researches of recent years show (Cannon and Rosenbleuth) that chemical materials are partly, if not wholly, responsible for transmission. By analogy, it has been supposed that the same sort of situation exists in synapses of the central nervous system. Some experiments have been conducted to see whether this supposition is correct, but so far they have not proved conclusive (see Fulton, p. 73).

According to the electrical theory, the action potential of one neuron directly stimulates the adjacent neuron without the intervention of chemical processes. The spike potential is the largest component of the action potential of a nerve fiber, and the amount of energy in it, according to calculation, is quite sufficient for the excitation of a fiber across the synaptic gap. When other aspects of synaptic transmission are also considered, they too are harmonious with an electrical theory of transmission, but we need not consider the details here.

At present there is no way of making a satisfactory decision between these two alternative theories. The changes in ionic equilibrium that occur at the membrane of nerve fibers during their activity have, we know, both chemical and electrical aspects. Ions, it should be remembered, are by definition chemical groupings carrying electrical charges. Where ionic changes are the basis of a phenomenon, therefore, it is exceedingly difficult to determine whether the electrical or the chemical aspects of the changes are the crucial factors in the phenomenon. So it is in the case of synaptic transmission. It seems, however, that when the solution to this problem is obtained, it will take account of both electrical and chemical factors in transmission and will assign some properties of synaptic transmission to electrical and others to chemical properties of nervous activity.

For the purposes of the present discussion, it is most convenient to regard transmission as electrical, for we are better acquainted with the electrical phenomena of nervous activity than with the chemical, and it is easier, perhaps, to think in electrical rather than chemical terms. Our policy in this respect, however, should not be taken as a prejudgment of the problem of synaptic transmission, but rather as one of convenience in exposition.

Synaptic Summation.—Whatever the basis of synaptic transmission may be, the synapse introduces a factor, which might be called resistance, into the activities of the nervous system. This is the result of two special conditions peculiar to the synapse: (1) The nervous impulse at the terminal boutons is of comparatively small intensity, (*a*) because spike potentials are not very intense stimuli for nerve fibers, and (*b*) because the diminishing size of the fiber at the synapse tends to reduce the intensity of the impulse still further. (2) The synaptic space is responsible for some loss of efficiency in transmission. The amount of current crossing the space to the other dendrite will be somewhat less than that found at the membrane from which it arises.

From synaptic resistance comes the fundamental characteristic, if not requirement, that synaptic transmission involves a *spatial summation* of impulses. If one impulse alone comes to the synapse, it excites only a local potential in the adjacent dendrite, and this potential, although it may propagate a short distance along the dendrite, is of insufficient intensity to become a spike potential. If, however, at the same time, another impulse also arrives at the synapse and excites a similar 'subthreshold' local potential, the two local potentials may *summate*—provided that they are near enough to each other in the dendrites or cell body of the receiving neuron—to a size adequate for self-propagation and thus for the spike potential to occur. That such summation is actually the case, if not the rule, in the central nervous system, has been amply proven by the careful experiments of Lorente de No.

Such summation appears to depend upon two conditions. One is that the summating impulses shall arrive within the period of latent

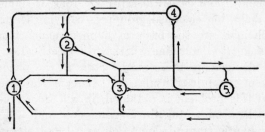

Fig. 20.—Diagram of neurons and their synaptic connections illustrating the principle of recurrent (reverberatory) nerve circuits as seen in the IIIrd nerve nucleus. (*After Lorente de No.*)

addition; *i.e.*, the local potential generated by one impulse must not have died away before the second impulse arrives or there can be no summation of local potentials. Since the period of latent addition is short, usually less than 0.5 msec., this means that impulses to summate must arrive practically simultaneously. The second condition is that the summating impulses must stimulate neighboring parts of a neuron. Since the local potentials are really 'local,' two such potentials cannot summate if two impulses arrive at quite disparate points on the neuron. This is apparently a matter of some importance in determining the selection of pathways of conduction in the central nervous system.

Recurrent Nervous Circuits.—In a moment we shall consider the various phenomena for which the synaptic nervous system is responsible, but before that, let us look at what happens when neurons are synaptically joined in a recurrent circuit. This term is illustrated in Fig. 20 and implies essentially that neurons are joined in circuits such that nervous impulses initiated in neuron 3 travel through neuron 5, and perhaps even more neurons, back again eventually to neuron 3. The important feature of this arrangement is that once an impulse is started at any point in the circuit it is thereafter self-perpetuating; nervous activity in the circuit, as a consequence, may continue indefinitely, or at least for a long time, without any further stimulation from outside of the circuit.

C.E.S. and C.I.S.—Before the excitability curve or the recurrent circuit or the facts of synaptic summation were known, Sir Charles Sherrington performed his classic experiments upon reflex action (1906). From them and from similar studies conducted later came many facts about the functions of a synaptic nervous system which could not be explained by the known properties of individual nerve fibers. The most distinctive properties of the synaptical nervous system seemed to be: (1) the relatively long duration of events occurring there—of the order of seconds and minutes rather than thousandths of a second as in individual nerve fibers; (2) states of facilitation and inhibition which could not be found in nerve fibers alone.

To account for these properties, Sherrington postulated two processes characteristic of the synapse, a central excitatory state (c.e.s.) and a central inhibitory state (c.i.s.), both of which could be built up and broken down over long periods of time. The c.e.s. and c.i.s. were conceived as the accumulation of ions at the synapse which, respectively, facilitated or inhibited synaptic transmission. Today, with our knowledge of the excitability cycle of nerve fibers, of the conditions of synaptic transmission, and of recurrent circuits, we are able to deal much more effectively than could Sherrington with the phenomena of the synaptic nervous system.

Speed of Conduction.—One of the conspicuous aspects of conduction in the central nervous system is that it is much slower than conduction in a peripheral nerve. From this it might appear that much delay was entailed in synaptic transmission. We know now, however, that synaptic delay may be very short (Lorente de No) and that the delay, when it is long, is due to several internuncial neurons (see p. 311) being intercalated, in the path of conduction through the spinal cord or brain, between sensory and motor nerve fibers.

One-way Conduction.—If one stimulates a nerve fiber at any point except at its ends, impulses will travel in both directions from the point of stimulation. Across the synapse, however, impulses are conducted in one direction only. To explain such one-way conduction we now have the fact that transmission at the synapse often, if not always, requires the spatial summation of impulses (McCulloch). Such summation, it appears from anatomical evidence, can occur in one direction and not the other because the dendrites or parts of the cell body upon which axons end are closer together, and thus more capable of summation of local potentials, than are the axon branches which end upon them.

Spatial Summation.—Sherrington observed that, in certain instances, one could stimulate either of two sets of nerves without obtaining synaptical transmission of the effects, but that stimulating two simultaneously would cause synaptic transmission. This Sherrington conceived to be due to the overlapping of the central terminals of the two groups of nerve fibers and to the resulting summation of the c.e.s. produced by each. Such a conception accords with present facts, except that the c.e.s. in this case appears to be the local potentials in the dendrites at the synapse.

Temporal Summation.—More important perhaps is the fact that whereas one excitation of a nerve might fail to pass the central synapse, a second stimulation of the same nerve within 15 msec. would bring about synaptic transmission. This phenomenon Sherrington thought to be accounted for by the summation of c.e.s. produced by the respective stimulations. If the c.e.s. is the local potential, as above, however, we know that it can summate only within a period of 0.5 msec. More attractive is the view recently offered by Lorente de No that the first stimulation sets up activity in the recurrent circuits which summates (spatially) with the impulses set up by the second stimulation. Thus, in this case, the c.e.s. appears to be the persistence of nervous impulses in internuncial recurrent circuits.

After-discharge.—Closely allied with the phenomenon of temporal summation is after-discharge. In this the effects of a single brief stimulation are continued for some time in motor nerve fibers emerging from the nervous system. Like temporal summation, after-discharge is now considered to be due to the persistence of the impulses initiated in the internuncial recurrent circuits by the original stimulus.

Successive Inhibition.—More extraordinary perhaps than the phenomena just described are those of inhibition, which Sherrington observed in reflex action. If, for example, one stimulus follows another by an interval of about 20 msec.—longer, that is, than the interval for temporal summation—its effects are very often inhibited. The central synaptic state created by the first stimulus apparently inhibits synaptic transmission of the nervous impulses initiated by the second stimulus. This state Sherrington called the central inhibitory state (c.i.s.), but beyond that he did not go.

Today, however, we can go a step further in believing that inhibition is, in this instance at least, the same phenomenon as the subnormal period found in peripheral nerve fibers. Upon finding that positive after-potential in nerve fibers goes along with subnormality of excitability, records have subsequently been taken of potentials in the spinal cord, and the inhibition which Sherrington observed is correlated with the appearance of positive after-potentials in internuncial neurons of the cord (Gasser and Graham). Inhibition is not, therefore, a property of the synapse, but of the nerve fibers; it is due to the subnormal phase of the excitability curve of central neurons.

Reciprocal Inhibition.—All inhibition, however, does not involve successive stimuli. More often one stimulus may directly inhibit the normal effects of another, as in limb movements, which normally depend upon the 'coordination' of antagonistic muscles—those which bend the limb (flexors) and those which extend it (extensors). By stimulating the appropriate sensory nerve fibers, one may cause the flexor muscles to contract and the extensor muscles to relax. If, however, a stronger stimulus is applied at the same time to certain other sensory nerve fibers, the flexor muscles will abruptly relax and the extensor muscles will contract. This effect we call *reciprocal inhibition* because it is inhibition reciprocally related to the excitation of an antagonistic muscle.

Although it is well illustrated by examples from reflex action, reciprocal inhibition is of much more general significance. There is hardly an aspect of the activity of the nervous system in which it does not play a role. Impulses in one set of neurons in the nervous system not only excite other neurons to activity but also inhibit still others. Indeed, we may say that the coordination or integration of activities of the central nervous system is brought about both through excitation and through reciprocal inhibition. Proof of this statement will be indicated by many of the phenomena of behavior which we shall later consider.

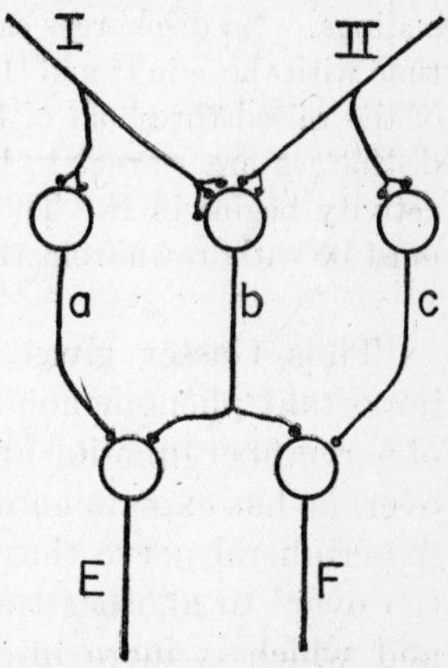

FIG. 21.—Diagram of neurons and synaptic connections involved in reciprocal inhibition (innervation). For explanation see text. (*After Gasser.*)

An important question, then, is how, through the interaction of neurons at synapses, reciprocal inhibition takes place. As an answer to this question, we have a theory recently proposed by Gasser. There is as yet little direct proof for it, but it can hardly be far wrong, because it is based upon the now relatively well-known facts of nerve-fiber and synaptic function (above), and it is not contradicted by any other known facts. Let us, therefore, examine it in some detail, making use of Fig. 21 for illustration.

Gasser postulates neurons disposed anatomically as shown in the figure and then assumes: (1) When two different neurons, I and II, are delivering impulses to a common neuron b, b will respond regularly to the discharging neuron (I or II) which has the greater number of endings, for that fiber will produce a greater summated local potential in the receiving neuron b and thus constitute a more intense stimulus capable of evoking an impulse in b throughout a greater proportion of b's excitability curve. (2) Whichever of I and II is lesser in this respect will seldom, if ever, elicit impulses in *b*, because it is more than likely to find *b* in a phase of poor excitability, either refractory or subnormal.

How, from these two assumptions, one can account for reciprocal inhibition, Gasser explains as follows (1937, pp. 188–189):

If a neuron *b* common to two pathways be switched out of one pathway when it is taken up by another, the necessary conditions for reciprocal innervation [inhibition] would be fulfilled. Let us suppose that rhythmic stimulation of fiber [II] is maintaining a flexor reflex. Neurons *b* and *c* are excited, and their discharges arriving synchronously at F cause it to respond. Then let us suppose that in the course of this response an extensor reflex is set up through stimulation of fiber [I]. The latter can excite *b* in the intervals between responses to I, because of the stronger excitation which it is able to deliver through its three endings. No discharges can result therefrom in F, as the impulses in *b* are out of time with those in *c*; and [II] is no longer able to excite *b* and *c* in unison, because of the raised threshold of the former. Neuron *b* is dominated by fiber [I]. Its discharges are caused to be synchronous with those in *a* instead of in *c*, and activity begins in E. Thus, when innervation of the extensor muscles starts it must be withdrawn from the flexor muscles.

Thus Gasser gives a very plausible explanation of an extremely important phenomenon and does it entirely in terms of the known facts of nerve-fiber function and of conditions of synaptic transmission. Moreover, he has experimentally demonstrated an essential part of the theory: A peripheral nerve that is responding to repeated shocks will, he finds, 'go over' to another train of stimuli which is interposed between them and which is more intense, thereupon ceasing to respond to the first weaker train. Thus the assumption that a neuron can be 'commanded' by whichever of two trains of stimuli is stronger is verified.

There are, of course, other conditions besides the number of endings which can give one neuron dominance over another. Its impulses may be larger; its endings may be closer together upon the receiving neuron and thus a greater summation of local potential can take place; or it may be that its frequency of impulses is more nearly optimal for the receiving neuron than is the frequency of the neuron competing for command of it.

The important point to be noted is that here is a mechanism by which complicated nervous processes may be organized into patterns—for organization can be nothing else but the excitation of certain neurons and the inhibition of others into some spatial or temporal pattern. Undoubtedly the specific details of such organizations are very complex and involve not only more detailed information concerning neurons but also more concerning their anatomical connections in the nervous system. Nevertheless, in the scheme presented here we can get a glimpse of how the more complex processes would appear to be organized, if we but had more information concerning them.

General References

ERLANGER, J., and H. S. GASSER, 1937. *Electrical signs of nervous activity.* Philadelphia: Univ. Penn. Press. Pp. x + 221.

FULTON, J. F., 1938. *Physiology of the nervous system.* New York: Oxford. Pp. xv + 674.

CHAPTER V

THE NERVOUS SYSTEM

From individual neurons we go now to the consideration of the nervous system as a system of parts, each of which is made up of many neurons. The general structural plan of the nervous system will be our chief interest, but some reference will be made to the function of the parts considered. Furthermore, since we shall review, for the most part, only the general facts about the nervous system, it makes little difference which of several different animals' nervous systems we use for illustration, for all vertebrate animals show the same general features. Lest there be a confusion, however, let us limit the statements in this chapter to the *human nervous system*. In the chapter that follows we shall have occasion to point out some of the differences in the nervous systems of various animals and the differences in psychological functions which are related to them.

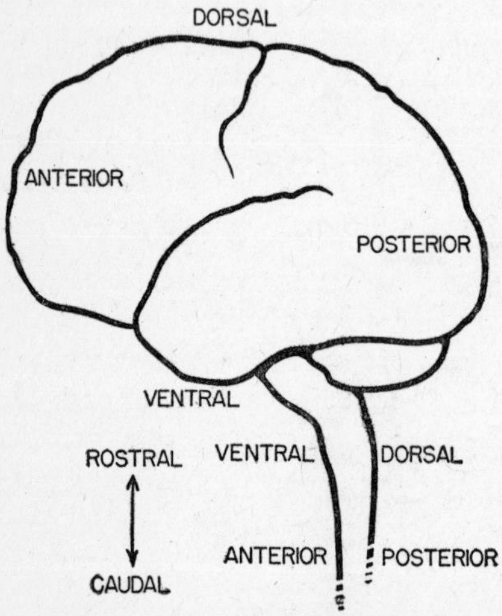

Definition of Terms.—To describe even the most general aspects of neuroanatomy is no simple matter. Indeed, it would be impossible if we did not have a number of convenient terms denoting directions in the nervous system, by means of which we can orient ourselves comparatively easily. (See Fig. 22.)

Fig. 22.—Side view of the human brain illustrating the various terms used in neurology to denote direction or position.

The use of the terms *anterior* and *posterior*, better limited to the brain only, refers to the front and back of the head, respectively. *Rostral* and *caudal*, on the other hand, we shall restrict to the spinal cord where they will mean headward and tailward, respectively. *Dorsal* refers to the top of the head or to the back of the spinal cord, whereas *ventral* is used to indicate the bottom of the brain and the side of the spinal cord nearest the abdominal cavity. *Medial* is in the direction of the midline of the body and *lateral* away from it. Finally, we use *proximal* and *distal* to indicate what is near to and far from, respectively, some given

70

position. All these terms indicate direction or relative position and do not in any way refer to a specific locus.

Gray and White Matter.—Certain other terms should also be made clear at this point. It has already been noted that nerve fibers, if they

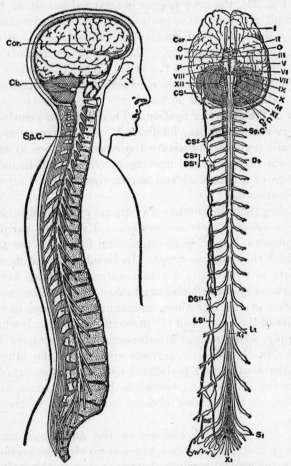

FIG. 23.—The nervous system as a whole. Left, lateral view; right, ventral view. *Cer.*, the cerebrum; *Cb.*, the cerebellum; *Sp. C.*, the spinal cord; *P*, the pons; *M*, the medulla. Numbers referring to the brain in the right-hand figure indicate cranial nerves; letters and numbers in lower part of this figure indicate ganglia and nerve trunks emerging from, or associated with, the spinal cord and concerned in somatic and autonomic functions. (*From J. R. Angell. Psychology, p. 30. New York: Holt, 1909. By permission of the publishers.*)

are myelinated, are white, whereas cell bodies, because they are never covered with myelin, are always gray. From this fact we are able to tell quite readily in looking at the nervous system just where cell bodies are collected and where bundles of nerve fibers are gathered together. To the nerve fibers in such bundles we give the name *tract* or *fasciculus;* clumps of cell bodies are referred to either as *nuclei* or *ganglia.*

Worth noting is the difference between the brain and spinal cord in respect of the position of white and gray matter. In the cerebral hemispheres (see Fig. 23), the gray matter is arranged mostly on the outside next to the skull, although other parts of the brain are of a more complex structure. In the spinal cord, on the other hand, there is a rather clear division of gray and white matter, with the white on the outside and the gray matter forming the core of the cord. What this means, of course, is that the pathways of the spinal cord constitute its peripheral portion and the cell bodies its central portion.

Divisions of the Nervous System.—There are two principal ways in which the nervous system may be divided. According to one, the brain and spinal cord together constitute the *central* nervous system as distinguished from the *peripheral* nervous system, which includes all the ganglia (groups of cell bodies) and nerves (nerve fibers) outside of the brain and spinal cord.

In classifying them in another way we may distinguish between the *somatic* and *autonomic* nervous systems. Each has peripheral and central components, but their distinguishing feature is the part of the body with which they are concerned. Included in the autonomic system are those parts of the central nervous system and those nerves of the peripheral nervous system which have to do with the responses of (1) the smooth muscles of the intestines, urogenital tract, and blood vessels; (2) the muscles of the heart; and (3) those endocrine glands which receive a nervous supply. In general, the autonomic system controls the internal environment. In the somatic nervous system, on the other hand, is included all the central and peripheral nervous system which conveys impulses from the sense organs, organizes them in the brain, and delivers motor impulses to the striated skeletal musculature of the body and limbs.

Although the peripheral endings of the autonomic and somatic nervous systems are quite distinct, there is no clear separation of them to be made in the central nervous system or even in the main trunks of peripheral nerves. In the latter, we can to some extent sort out the fibers into autonomic and somatic on the basis of known differences in fiber types and by tracing the fibers to their terminations. Some centers of the central nervous system, on the other hand, are concerned principally with autonomic functions or with somatic activities, although such divisions of function are always a matter of degree, and autonomic and somatic processes are always closely coordinated. That is to be expected, however, because adjustments of the internal environment of the nervous system must always be essential to somatic adjustments and vice versa, and the two mechanisms must, therefore, be thoroughly interlinked.

THE PERIPHERAL SOMATIC SYSTEM

Let us first consider the somatic nervous system, and specifically, the peripheral portion made up of nerves and ganglia. These are usually divided into *cranial* and *spinal* on the basis of the part of the central nervous system from which they take origin. Motor fibers of both cranial and spinal nerves have their cell bodies within the central nervous system, usually in the ventral region nearest the point of exit of the fibers. Sensory fibers, on the other hand, always have their cell bodies in ganglia outside of the central nervous system. Cranial ganglia are to be found here and there in the recesses of the skull near the several small holes in the skull which serve as entrances and exits for nerve fibers; but the spinal ganglia are, as we shall see, arranged much more regularly along the spinal column.

The Cranial Nerves.—One ordinarily distinguishes 12 sets of cranial nerves, the names and functions of which are summarized in Table 1.

TABLE 1.—THE NAMES, FUNCTIONS, AND ORIGINS OF THE CRANIAL NERVES

Number	Name	Functions	Origin or end in the brain
I	Olfactory	(s) Smell	Cerebral hemispheres (ventral part)
II	Optic	(s) Vision	Thalamus
III	Oculomotor	(m) Eye movement	Midbrain
IV	Trochlear	(m) Eye movement	Midbrain
V	Trigeminal	(m) Masticatory movements	Midbrain and pons
		(s) Sensitivity of face and tongue	Medulla
VI	Abducens	(m) Eye movement	Medulla
VII	Facial	(m) Facial movement	Medulla
VIII	Auditory vestibular	(s) Hearing	Medulla
		(s) Balance	
IX	Glossopharyngeal	(s) Tongue and (m) pharynx	Medulla
X	Vagus	(s) Heart, blood vessels, viscera (m)	Medulla
XI	Spinal accessory	(m) Neck muscles and viscera	Medulla
XII	Hypoglossal	(m) Tongue muscles	Medulla

The first two nerves, the olfactory and optic, are purely sensory in function. Neither of them is a true nerve, however, in the sense that nerves ordinarily consist only of fibers pushed out from the nervous system;

but, instead, these nerves represent portions of brain tissue which have migrated from the central nervous system to form the retina of the eye and the olfactory membrane but which, nevertheless, have maintained their connections with the brain. Three other nerves, the IIIrd, IVth, and VIth are made up entirely of motor fibers innervating the muscles of the eye and concerned with its movement. The central nuclei of these nerves make up an important center for the control of eye movements, later to be taken up in detail.

The Vth cranial nerve, the *trigeminal*, is the most important nerve for sensations and movements of the mouth. Innervating the majority of the taste buds of the tongue, it carries, in addition, tactile sensations from the face, tongue, and mouth; moreover, the trigeminal is the principal motor nerve for the control of chewing. Cooperating with the Vth nerve in respect of the sensations of taste and touch in the mouth and throat are the sensory portions of the *glossopharyngeal* (IXth) and the *vagus* (Xth). Its motor functions in chewing, tongue movement, and swallowing are augmented by the services of the glossopharyngeal and the *hypoglossal* (XIIth). In the trigeminal's control of facial movements, the *facial* (VIIth) nerve also takes a part. The VIIIth nerve (*auditory-vestibular*) is purely sensory, innervating the ear and the labyrinths which function in equilibration. Of the functions of the vagus nerve we shall see more later when we come to the autonomic system.

The Spinal Somatic Nerves.—Much more regularly arranged and more uniform in function are the spinal nerves. Of these there are 31 pairs (in man) disposed at regular intervals along the spinal cord, entering and leaving the spinal cord through the spaces between the spinal vertebrae. The spinal nerves may be classified into five groups according to the part of the spinal cord with which they are associated:

Name	Number	Position
Cervical	8	Neck
Thoracic	12	Chest
Lumbar	5	Loin
Sacral	5	End of spinal column
Coccygeal	1	End of spinal column

An important aspect of the spinal nerves is the *law of roots*, which was mentioned earlier in the historical introduction. Just before entering the vertebral column the spinal nerves divide into two roots. Of these the dorsal root is sensory in function and the ventral root motor (although there are exceptions). On each dorsal root there is a marked swelling, the *dorsal* spinal *ganglion*, which contains the cell bodies of the sensory fibers passing through it from the sense organs into the spinal cord. It is within the spinal cord itself, however, that the cell bodies of the motor fibers are to be found. Because these cell bodies form a mass of gray matter in the ventral part of the cord resembling a horn, they are frequently spoken of as the *ventral horn cells*.

The sensory portions of the spinal nerves come from the tactual, thermal, and pain receptors of the skin; from the receptors in the blood vessels; from pressure and pain receptors in the muscles, tendons, and joints; and to some extent from the internal receptors in the digestive tract and body cavities. As this list plainly indicates, the sensory roots of the nerves mediate sensitivity of most of the body except the face. Similarly, although each nerve has its distribution confined to a relatively small area of the body (dermatome; p. 274), the motor portions of the spinal nerves control all the striated muscles of the arms, legs, and body except for those of the head and neck.

THE CENTRAL SOMATIC SYSTEM

As already stated, the central nervous system consists of the brain and spinal cord, and since it is primarily concerned with the relation between the organism and the external world it may be regarded as somatic nervous system. The brain is, of course, the highest and most important center of integration. Impulses come to it and leave it to a considerable extent through the cranial nerves, yet sensory impulses from all of the body except the head, as well as the control of the actions of the body by the brain, must be carried out through the spinal cord. In it are to be found great conduction paths proceeding upward and downward between entrances and exits of the various spinal nerves and the brain. Conduction is, therefore, the first important function of the spinal cord. It also serves, however, as an integrating center of its own and mediates, as we shall see in later chapters, many complex reflex actions without very much help from the brain.

Let us turn first, however, to the structure of the brain, for it is much easier to discuss the pathways of the spinal cord after the significance of the parts of the brain to which, and from which, spinal pathways conduct has been made clear.

THE BRAIN

The most basic divisions of the brain have already been indicated in earlier references to the embryological growth of the brain. The first gross differentiation in development is into three primary vesicles, the *forebrain*, *midbrain*, and *hindbrain*, occupying the relative positions indicated by their names. Later in embryological differentiation, the forebrain divides into two parts, the *telencephalon* and the *diencephalon*; nothing happens to the midbrain (*mesencephalon*); but from the division of the hindbrain arise the *metencephalon* and *myelencephalon*. Thus the adult brain is composed of the five major divisions, tel-, di-, mes-, met-, and myelencephalon, in that order from front to back, as Fig. 24 shows. Let us now consider the structure and functions of each of these parts in turn.

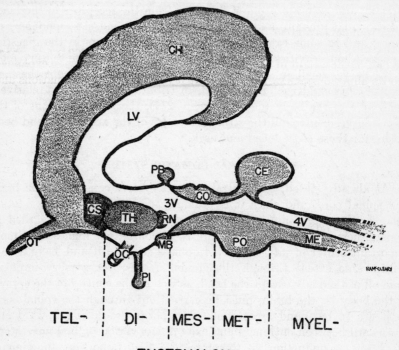

Fig. 24.—Schematic drawing of the brain of mammalian animals. *CH*, cerebral hemispheres; *LV*, lateral ventricles; *OT*, olfactory tracts; *CS*, corpus striatum; *OC*, optic chiasma; *PI*, pituitary gland; *TH*, thalamus; *PB*, pineal body; *3V*, third ventricle; *RN*, red nucleus; *MB*, mammillary bodies; *CO*, superior and inferior colliculi (corpora quadrigemina); *CE*, cerebellum; *PO*, pons; *4V*, fourth ventricle; *ME*, medulla. (*After Lickley.*)

The Telencephalon.—This consists of the olfactory bulb and olfactory tracts, the cerebral hemispheres, the lateral ventricles, and the basal ganglia.

The *olfactory bulbs* lie in the anterior region of the cranial cavity immediately above the olfactory receptors (see Fig. 24). They are made up principally of cell bodies which are connected with the brain by the fibers of the olfactory nerve terminating on the central surface of the brain.

The *cerebral hemispheres* consist of the cerebral cortex (meaning rind or covering) which is gray matter, of white fiber tracts which underlie the cortex and pass between it and lower parts of the brain, and of the corpus callosum, which is made up of fiber tracts passing between the cortices of the two cerebral hemispheres.

Of these the cerebral cortex will receive a large measure of our interest, for in it reside the complex psychological functions that distinguish man. In birds and lower animals the cortex is not very important; only the first signs of its development are present. In mammals, however, the cortex undergoes a great development compared with changes in the rest of the nervous system. Indeed, in man the cerebral cortex is about one-half of the weight of the entire nervous system, and it has so expanded into its allotted space in the skull that it shows many invaginations and

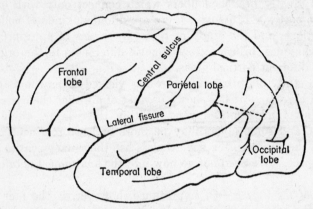

FIG. 25.—Lateral view of the human brain showing lobes and principal fissures and sulci used in denoting the position of various areas of the cerebral cortex. (*From A. Kuntz. Neuroanatomy, p.* 358. *Philadelphia: Lea and Febiger,* 1942. *By permission of the publishers.*)

ridges which thus greatly enlarge the amount of cortex. An invagination has the name *sulcus* or *fissure*, and the ridge between two of them is known as a *gyrus*.

To indicate various parts of the cerebral cortex, one makes use of certain sulci and gyri as landmarks. The most important of these are as follows. The cortex is divided into two symmetrical halves, or hemispheres, by the deep *longitudinal fissure* that runs along the mid-line. On the dorsal surface of the cortex and somewhat posterior to the center is the *central sulcus*, a deep furrow that runs laterally and slightly anteriorly from the median longitudinal fissure. On the lateral surface of the cortex the *lateral fissure* may be seen running posteriorly and dorsally.

Lobes of the Cortex.—On the basis of these three principal fissures, one may mark off four pairs of lobes in the cerebral cortex (see Fig. 25). The *frontal lobes* include all the cortex anterior to the central sulcus. The *parietal lobes*, occupying the dorsal surface of the hemispheres, extend

posteriorly from the central sulcus and laterally to the lateral fissure.
Lateral and ventral to the lateral fissure, one finds the *temporal lobes*.
A fourth pair of lobes, the *occipital*, are also distinguished, but they are
not marked off by any major fissures (Fig. 25).

Architectonic Structure.—The cerebral cortex can also be described
in terms of its histological, or cellular, structure. Although the cortex
is really a great ganglion, it is unlike most ganglia found elsewhere in
the nervous system in that, possessing as it does a great many connections
between its various cells, it also contains a great number of nerve fibers.
A large proportion of the cortical cells, in fact, possess comparatively
short and greatly branched fibers which connect only with other cells
within the cortex. Moreover, there are different kinds of cells, as well
as connections, and the study of these, by means of appropriate histological techniques, brings out systematic differences in the organization
of cells in different cortical areas.

Such a study of cytoarchitecture has yielded several facts of importance (see Fig. 26). It has shown us, first of all, that the cortex is composed of six fundamental layers. Within these layers there may be
subgroups, and some layers may be more or less prominent in certain
areas, but the entire cortex nevertheless has the same essential structure
in this respect. We need not go now into the anatomical details of these
layers.

Areas of the Cortex.—Of importance, however, is the fact that the
ridges of the cortex differ in cytoarchitectural structure and that these
differences are in some degree correlated with diverse functions. For
this reason and also for convenience in specifying precisely particular
areas of the cortex, systems of denotation of various cytoarchitectural
areas—*i.e.*, areas differing in the characteristics of the six layers—have
been worked out. A widely used system, developed by Brodmann,
is shown in Fig. 26 and will be the one used in this book whenever we
have need of such a system.

Let us briefly discuss the relation of the cytoarchitectural areas to
the four lobes described above and to their general psychological functions. Within the frontal lobes we may distinguish four principal areas
as we go from the central sulcus to the anterior pole of the hemispheres.
(1) The *precentral area*, immediately in front of the central sulcus, is
the electrically stimulable area discovered by Fritsch and Hitzig, often
called the *motor* area or Brodmann's area 4. (2) Immediately in front
of it is the *intermediate precentral area*, sometimes called the *premotor*
area or Brodmann's area 6, which is intimately concerned in motor functions. An area forming the lateral basal portion of this premotor area
has a somewhat different cytoarchitectural structure but is, nevertheless,
obviously a part of the premotor area. Its chief importance to us is

that it is the speech area, discovered by Broca, and today it is given the numbers 44 and 45 in Brodmann's system. Occupying the larger and anterior part of the frontal lobe are the (3) *prefrontal areas*, sometimes referred to as the frontal "association" areas because they seem to

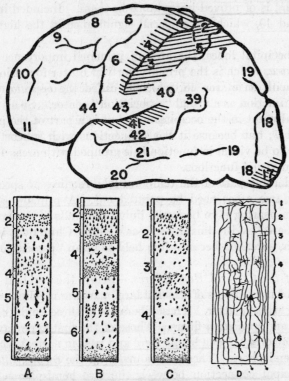

Fig. 26.—Upper figure is a schematic drawing of the lateral aspect of the human cortex showing the principal cortical areas of functional significance and the Brodmann numbers assigned to them. The lower figure presents representative cross sections of three areas and illustrates the histological differences among different areas. *A* is from area 4 and shows that the large motor cells of layer 5 are quite prominent, whereas layer 4 is proportionally very narrow. *B* is from area 17, which is the visual area of the cortex, and shows that layer 4 is highly developed, whereas layer 5 is quite thin. *C* is from the medial and ventral portion of the temporal lobe, which is made of olfactory cortex (paleocortex), and illustrates the fact that the primitive part of the cortex has only 4 layers. *D* is a diagram of synaptic relations in area 4 as seen in silver staining and indicates that synaptic connections are mainly radial, *i.e.*, from one layer to another, rather than horizontal, *i.e.*, from one part to another of the same layer. (*From S. Cobb. Foundations of neuropsychiatry, p. 72. Baltimore: Williams and Wilkins, 1941. By permission of the publishers.*)

have special importance in integrating mental activity. They are made up of a number of different architectural areas with their respective numbers (see Fig. 26). In the present study, however, we shall usually consider the areas as a whole by names rather than by number.

In the parietal lobe there is first the *postcentral area*, Brodmann's 3–1–2, which lies immediately posterior to the central sulcus. This is a sensory area, concerned primarily in sensations of touch. Behind it are several areas, which for our purposes may be considered together as the *posterior parietal area* or *lobule*. This includes Brodmann's areas 5 and 7 and receives fibers related indirectly to touch and kinesthetic functions and is of proved importance in them. Included in area 7 are areas 39 and 40, which have special significance in the higher thought processes.

In the occipital lobes, the area of principal importance is area 17, the *striate area*, which is the primary cortical center for vision. Closely associated with it is area 18, which is called the *occipital area* and is believed to function as a visual "association" center. So also is area 19, which is really not in the occipital lobe but is a part of the parietal lobe and of area 7; but because it has connections with subcortical centers which seem to be visual in function it is grouped with areas 17 and 18 as concerned in visual functions.

A considerable part of the temporal lobe requires no specific denotation. Only two areas need be pointed out. A primary sensory area concerned in hearing is to be found lining the walls of the lateral fissure and is numbered by Brodmann as areas 41–42. Close by it is the audiopsychic area, so called because it is held to be an "association" area for hearing.

Fibers of the Cerebral Hemispheres.—Below the cerebral cortex is a great mass of nerve fibers of which a large part are myelinated, therefore constituting white matter. These fibers are of three kinds: *commissural*, *association*, and *projection* fibers. Those of the first type have their cell bodies in the cortex of one hemisphere and pass in a great white sheet to the other hemisphere. These fibers make up the *corpus callosum* which is the principal connection between the two hemispheres, and forms the floor of the median longitudinal fissure as well as the roof of the lateral ventricles (see below). Besides the corpus callosum, there are other commissural fibers passing between the two hemispheres, but they are of little concern to us.

'Association' fibers are those which connect one part of the cortex to another. They were formerly thought to play a large part in the integration of activities of the cortex, but it now appears that they do not extend very far from the point of origin, and it is more probable that the relation of various areas to each other is conducted directly through the cortex or by way of the thalamus.

Of greatest functional importance are the projection fibers by which impulses get to and leave the cortex. Projection fibers are classified as *afferent* or *corticopetal* (those radiating upward from the thalamus and subcortical centers to the cortex) and *efferent* or *corticofugal* (those projecting downward to various subcortical centers). These latter fibers may end at any one of several points: the basal ganglia, thalamus, midbrain, hindbrain, or ventral cells of the spinal cord. Corticopetal fibers, on the other hand, take their origin, almost without exception, in the nuclei of the thalamus. How such nuclei are related to areas of the cortex will be considered in some detail below.

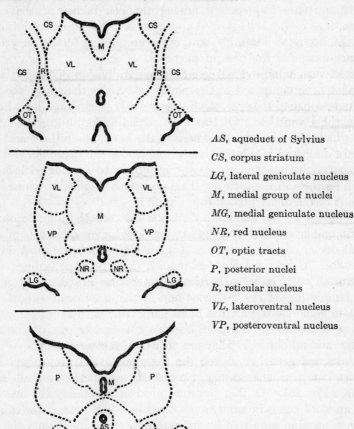

AS, aqueduct of Sylvius

CS, corpus striatum

LG, lateral geniculate nucleus

M, medial group of nuclei

MG, medial geniculate nucleus

NR, red nucleus

OT, optic tracts

P, posterior nuclei

R, reticular nucleus

VL, lateroventral nucleus

VP, posteroventral nucleus

Fig. 27.—Diagrammatic drawings of cross sections of the thalamus. Upper figure illustrates nuclei and tracts seen in anterior thalamus, the middle figure those in the middle thalamus, and the lower figure those in the posterior thalamus. (*After Fulton.*)

The Basal Ganglia.—The phylogenetically oldest parts of the telencephalon are the basal ganglia. These are a mass of gray matter lying below the cortex and, for the most part, above the thalamus or diencephalon, although certain small but important parts of them are lodged between the diencephalon and mesencephalon (midbrain). These latter, the *substantia nigra* and the *red nucleus* (Fig. 24), are of great significance in the maintenance of the posture of the organism and in certain aspects of the coordination of movement. Although properly a part of the cerebral hemispheres, they appear to have migrated, in phylogenesis, away from the main portion of the basal ganglia, which is the *corpus striatum.* This term means striped body and has its origin in the fact that projection fibers passing upward and downward between the cortex and thalamus are interspersed among the cell bodies of the corpus striatum, thus giving it its striped appearance. The corpus striatum is a fairly complex, as well as important, structure, but its further description is not necessary for the present purposes.

The Diencephalon.—The second principal division of the brain, the diencephalon, is composed of the pineal body, the thalamus, the optic tracts and retinae of the eyes, the pituitary body, the mammillary bodies, and the third ventricle. Of these the pineal and pituitary bodies are glands which are taken up elsewhere in the book, the retinae and optic tracts are discussed in a later chapter on vision, the mammillary bodies are a part of the autonomic nervous system to be considered below, as also will be the third ventricle. That leaves the *thalamus,* which is the main part of the diencephalon (see Fig. 27).

The thalamus, the great relay station between the lower centers of the brain and spinal cord and the cerebral hemispheres, consists of many different nuclei whose structure and interrelationships are most difficult to visualize. Briefly, we may distinguish three principal groups:

1. Nuclei with only subcortical connections are disposed mainly along the mid-line of the thalamus and in the anteroventral part; they connect in some cases with the basal ganglia or with other parts of the thalamus, but so far as is known they do not send or receive any fibers from the cerebral cortex. They are of little significance to us.

2. A second group of nuclei, the thalamocortical projection nuclei, otherwise known as the sensory relay nuclei, are of the greatest importance (see Fig. 28). Of this group we need mention only the ones with which we shall come in contact most often. The *lateroventral nucleus,* lying in a position indicated by its name, receives fibers from the cerebellum and sends projections to the frontal lobe, particularly the precentral gyrus. It functions, as one might suspect from its anatomical connections, in the coordination of the activities of the cerebellum and the frontal lobe in controlling muscular movements. The *posteroventral nucleus,* situated close to the lateroventral, is the major relay station for sensory fibers representing the skin and muscle senses and sends projections to the cortex, particularly to the postcentral gyrus, which is employed in somesthetic sensory activities. Besides these two parts of the ventral nucleus, there are two other thalamic relay nuclei of note, the *lateral* and *medial geniculate bodies,* which are slight enlargements on the lateral surface of the thalamus. The former is the station through

which impulses from the eyes are relayed to the cortex and to other visual centers, whereas the latter exercises a similar function in hearing. Of these two centers we shall hear much in the future.

3. The third group of thalamic nuclei are the 'association' nuclei which receive their impulses from within the thalamus but which send projections to the cerebral cortex (see Fig. 28). In general, nuclei of this type send their thalamocortical fibers either to the anterior part of the frontal lobes or to the posterior part of the parietal lobes. Thus

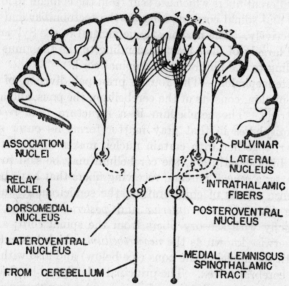

Fig. 28.—A. E. Walker's drawing of the projections of thalamic nuclei to the cerebral cortex. The association nuclei shown consist of the dorsomedial nucleus, the lateral nucleus, and the pulvinar. The relay nuclei shown are the lateroventral and postero-ventral nuclei. The visual and auditory projection systems are not included in this drawing. (*Drawn by T. C. Ruch. Based upon A. E. Walker's The primate thalamus. Courtesy of T. C. Ruch.*)

the *pulvinar*, which is a thalamic association nucleus thought to subserve visual functions, projects to Brodmann's area 19, *i.e.*, to the extreme posterior parietal lobe. The *lateral* nucleus of the thalamus, on the other hand, sends its fibers to the main part of area 7, the parietal lobe. To the prefrontal areas, however, go the projections of the *dorsomedial nucleus* which is related to several other thalamic nuclei.

The Mesencephalon.—The midbrain, or mesencephalon, forms the stalk that connects the forebrain and hindbrain. Dividing this stalk into dorsal and ventral portions is the Sylvian aqueduct, a part of the cerebrospinal system (see below). The dorsal part is known as the tectum (roof) or, since it is made up of four bodies, the *corpora quadri-gemina*, arranged in two pairs. One pair is a little in front of, and above, the other and is called the *superior colliculi;* the other is called the *inferior colliculi.* (1) The superior colliculi, supplied by fibers originating in or relayed from the retinae by way of the lateral geniculate bodies, are nuclei of the visual system.   (2) The inferior colliculi, on the other hand, are centers of the auditory system, the scheme of which will be detailed fully in another place (p. 226).   Worthy of note here is the fact that both the superior and inferior colliculi mediate some of the more reflexive aspects of behavior dependent upon vision and audition.   Significant, too, are the efferent fibers which are sent from the colliculi to lower centers of the brain and spinal cord, making up the tectobulbar and tectospinal tracts, respectively.   The nervous tissue ventral to the Sylvian aqueduct is composed largely of fiber tracts ascending to the thalamus and cortex and descending to the hindbrain and spinal cord.

The Metencephalon.—The fourth principal division of the brain, the metencephalon, consists of the cerebellum, the pons, and a part of the fourth ventricle.   The cerebellum is a structure that resembles the cerebral hemispheres in that gray matter forms its outer surface and white matter, together with certain nuclei, makes up its interior.   For purposes of brief description, the cerebellum may be said to be divided into four parts: a *ventral* portion, receiving fibers that have been relayed from the sense organs of equilibration, the semicircular canals, utricle, and saccule (p. 291); the *anterior* and *posterior* portions, which are supplied chiefly with sensory fibers from the spinal cord; and a *dorsal* portion, otherwise known as the *neocerebellum,* which has extensive connections with the nuclei of the pons (see below) and also with the frontal lobes of the cerebral cortex.   The principal role played by the cerebellum is a smoothing and coordinating of impulses leading to muscular movements; it is to be regarded, therefore, as an organ of motor coordination.

Forming the ventral portion of the metencephalon is the *pons.*   This consists (1) of transverse fibers emerging from one side of the cerebellum and traversing the ventral surface of the hindbrain to reenter the cerebellum on the opposite side; (2) of a complex of nuclei, the *pontine nuclei,* within this band of transverse fibers; and (3) of fiber tracts ascending and descending to various levels of the central nervous system.   In the pons, also, are to be found the nuclei of the trigeminal nerve (Vth) which is so important in sensations and movement of the mouth and face.

The Myelencephalon.—This is the term for the medulla, which joins the spinal cord and the brain.   Important as the locus of the nuclei of the majority of cranial nerves, it also contains autonomic nuclei concerned with breathing, heartbeat, and blood pressure, thus serving to maintain the basic life-preserving functions of the organism.   In addition, the tracts of conduction between the brain and spinal cord pass through the myelencephalon.

THE SPINAL CORD

The internal structure of the spinal cord is much simpler and more uniform throughout its various parts than is that of the brain. No matter where it is sectioned, it presents the same essential appearance. The interior is gray matter (cell bodies), so distributed as to present the picture of a butterfly whose essential form is the letter H (see Fig. 29). Outside the gray matter are great columns of white matter making up various fiber tracts passing up and down the cord. Dividing the cord

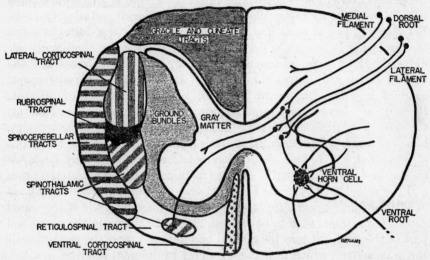

FIG. 29.—Schematic drawing of the principal connections and pathways of the spinal cord. The right-hand part of the figure shows endings of sensory fibers entering the cord, fibers crossing over from one side of the cord to the other, and connections of the motor horn cells; the left-hand part of the figure indicates the approximate size and position of tracts conducting upward and downward in the cord.

into two symmetrical halves are two median clefts, the dorsal and ventral fissures. Between them, in the central part of the cord, are two commissures joining the two halves of the cord; one is the crossbar of the H, composed of gray matter and called the gray commissure; ventral to it is the white commissure, which consists of fibers passing from one side to the other.

Gray Matter.—The central parts of the gray matter are concerned mainly with impulses crossing the mid-line in commissural fibers, for there are fibers as well as cell bodies in the gray matter. The cell bodies of the more peripheral gray matter are concerned, on the other hand, with sensory or motor functions or with projection functions. Thus the dorsal horns of gray matter extend outward toward the edge of the cord, to the point where the fibers of the dorsal sensory ganglion pass into the cord by way of the *dorsal root;* the dorsal horn is, therefore, in great part sensory in function. Although the ventral horn, on the other hand, is not so near the surface of the cord, it is plain that its functions are mostly motor, for from it stream fibers that emerge from the cord in the *ventral roots* and form the motor portion of the spinal nerves. Finally, the more lateral portions of the gray matter contain cell bodies whose fibers are found in the conduction paths of the spinal cord. One must remember, however, that such statements as these, and those which follow, are necessarily schematic.

Conduction Paths.—The white matter of the cord is divided into three pairs of columns by the median clefts and the dorsal and sensory roots. Between the dorsal roots and the dorsal fissure are the dorsal columns (or fasciculi); between the dorsal and ventral roots are the lateral columns; in the ventral region marked off by the ventral roots and the ventral fissure are the ventral columns. In general, the dorsal columns conduct impulses brainward and are, therefore, sensory or afferent; the ventral columns carry impulses downward and are motor or efferent; the lateral columns are mixed. Exceptions will appear in a moment, however, when a more detailed analysis of the functions of these columns is presented. A further distinction between pathways may be made on the basis of their length. Long tracts connect centers of the brain and the spinal cord, whereas the short ones, sometimes known as *ground bundles* or *intersegmental tracts*, only connect different levels of the spinal cord. Long tracts tend to be located, as Fig. 29 shows, in the peripheral part of the cord, whereas the ground bundles are nearer the cell bodies of the gray matter, which they must connect at different levels.

To understand the way in which these long tracts are named will make reference to them later more convenient. In conventional nomenclature, the name of each tract includes first the name of the center from which it arises and in which cell bodies of its fibers are usually located, and then the name of the place in which the fibers of the tract end. There are a few exceptions to this rule; tracts are sometimes assigned special names according to their significance or according to the persons who first described them. Some of the more important tracts are named and related to each other in Fig. 29. These tracts will be referred to from time to time in later chapters, and the illustration, thus, deserves special attention. There is, however, no need for their further description at this point.

THE PERIPHERAL AUTONOMIC SYSTEM

As already stated, the autonomic system is concerned principally with internal adjustments of the organism, whereas the somatic system mediates adjustments between the external world and the organism.

Correlated with the different roles played by these two systems are certain differences in their structure and activities. (1) The somatic system embraces both sensory and motor activities, but the autonomic is considered only as a motor system.[1] (2) All the synapses of the somatic system, except for the special cases of the retina and olfactory bulb, are to be found within the central nervous system; on the other hand, it is signally characteristic of the autonomic system that many of its synapses and its ganglia lie outside of the central nervous system. (3) In respect to organization of functions, the two systems differ in that the autonomic tends to function more as a whole and is less differentiated than the somatic system. (4) They differ also in distribution of fibers, for, as we have already seen, the autonomic system innervates the glands and smooth muscles of the viscera and blood vessels, whereas the motor somatic system is distributed to the striated muscles of the periphery.

DIVISIONS OF THE AUTONOMIC SYSTEM

We distinguish two channels of outflow of nervous activity in the autonomic nervous system (see Fig. 30): (1) The *orthosympathetic* (commonly known simply as the sympathetic) outflow takes place through the *thoracic* and *lumbar* regions of the spinal cord, and for this reason it is sometimes referred to as the thoracicolumbar system. (2) The *parasympathetic* division takes its origin in the *cranial* and *sacral* regions of the central nervous system, and it may accordingly be called the craniosacral system.

The two divisions are largely, although not completely, antagonistic in their effects. In general, the sympathetic system *mobilizes* the resources of the body for use in work and special emergencies, while the parasympthetic system *conserves* and stores bodily resources. In other words, the first helps *spend* bodily resources (catabolism) and the second helps *save* them (anabolism). This statement, although true in general, does not hold in certain specific instances. Naturally, too, these two systems never act independently of each other, but are brought into correlated activity in varying degrees depending upon the demands made upon the organism by the external world. Through their antagonistic, yet coordinated, action, a comparatively stable equilibrium of the internal environment is maintained under many different conditions of work and rest. How that is done will be illustrated in the more detailed treatment of the two systems which follows.

The Orthosympathetic System.—Spinal paths of conduction exist for the autonomic system just as in the somatic motor system. The motor

---

[1] It is somewhat unfortunate that such has become the custom, for it would make better sense to include also in the autonomic system many sensory fibers which innervate the viscera and are plainly related to autonomic motor functions.

cells of the autonomic system tend, however, to be found in the lateral parts of the spinal gray matter rather than in the ventral horns as are the somatic motor neurons. In the thoracicolumbar segments of the

TABLE 2.—AUTONOMIC PATHWAYS AND THEIR FUNCTIONS

Organ	Origin	Nerve	Effector	Function
Eye:				
Para......	Midbrain	III (Oculomotor)	Ciliary muscle	Accommodation
			Iris	Contraction
Ortho.....	Spinal cord	Ciliary nerve	Eyeball	Exophthalmos
			Iris	Dilation
Cerebral arteries:				
Para......	Medulla	VII (Facial)	Carotid artery and	Dilation
			blood vessels of	
Ortho.....	Spinal cord	Various	brain	Contraction
Heart:				
Para......	Medulla	X (Vagus)	Heart and coronary vessels	Inhibition and coronary constriction
Ortho.....	Spinal cord	Various	Heart and coronary vessels	Acceleration and dilation
Stomach and small intestine:				
Para......	Medulla	X (Vagus)	Gastric musculature	Contraction and secretion
Ortho.....	Spinal cord	Splanchnic	Gastric muscles and glands	Inhibition of contraction and secretion
Genitourinary tract:				
Para......	Spinal cord	Sacral	Genitourinary muscles and blood vessels	Urination, defecation, vasodilation, erection
Ortho.....	Spinal cord	Hypogastric	Genitourinary muscles and blood vessels	Contraction of sphincters, prostate, and seminal vesicles, inhibition of rectum and bladder
Arteries of body:				
Para......	Spinal cord	Various	Blood vessels	Dilation
Ortho.....	Spinal cord	Various	Blood vessels	Contraction

spinal cord, the axons of autonomic cells pass out the ventral roots with the somatic motor axons and make up part of the ventral roots. Just outside the spinal cord, however, these sympathetic axons leave the main nerve root and enter a *sympathetic ganglion* where they end upon the cell bodies of other neurons.

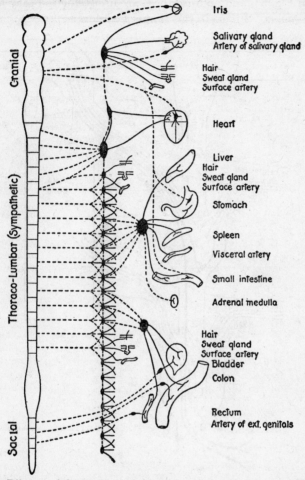

FIG. 30.—Diagram of the structure of the autonomic nervous system. On the left are represented the brain and spinal cord and on the right the autonomic ganglia, autonomic nerves, and the organs of the body upon which the nerves end. The corresponding part of the autonomic system on the left has been omitted. The dashed lines between the central nervous system and the row of ganglia represent preganglionic fibers; the dashed lines between the ganglia and the peripherally located organs of the body represent postganglionic fibers. (*From W. B. Cannon. Bodily changes in pain, hunger, fear and rage, 2d ed., p. 23. New York: D. Appleton, 1929. By permission of the publishers.*)

There are 22 sympathetic ganglia (in man) arranged regularly along the spinal cord and constituting the so-called sympathetic chain, or ganglionic cord. In the ganglia of this cord end the fibers originating in the spinal cord as just described. These fibers we call *preganglionic* fibers. Because they are mostly myelinated, the bundle which they make up after leaving the spinal nerve is called the *white ramus*. The cell bodies in the ganglion send axonal fibers back to the spinal nerves as shown in Fig. 31, and because these are unmyelinated they are known as the *gray ramus*. Fibers in this ramus we know as *postganglionic* fibers.

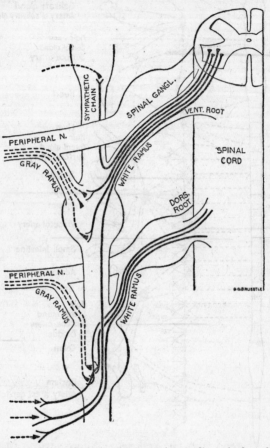

Fig. 31.—Diagram of the relations of autonomic ganglia, spinal cord, and peripheral nerves in the sympathetic system (thoracicolumbar outflow). Preganglionic fibers, making up the white rami, leave the lateral columns of the spinal cord and proceed by way of the ventral nerve roots to the sympathetic chain, where they terminate at various levels. The postganglionic fibers, making up the gray rami, join the peripheral nerves or blood vessels and thence are distributed to the peripheral organs, which they innervate. (*After Edinger. From J. F. Fulton. Physiology of the nervous system, p. 208. New York: Oxford University Press, 1938. By permission of the publishers.*)

Not all the fibers leaving the sympathetic ganglion go back to the spinal nerve, nor do all the preganglionic fibers from the spinal cord end in the nearest ganglion of the sympathetic cord. As shown in Fig. 31, they may pursue any one of three courses: (1) They may end upon the cell bodies in the nearest sympathetic ganglion as described above. (2) They may pass through that ganglion into the bundles of fibers which connect the various sympathetic ganglia with each other, thus forming a cord; in this case they end finally upon the cell bodies of ganglia above or below the segment from which they came. (3) They may pass out through the sympathetic ganglion in an autonomic nerve to the distal part of the body and there end in *collateral ganglia* located in the vicinity of the muscles or glands which are to be innervated. These collateral ganglia are another part of the autonomic system not yet mentioned and are peripheral centers for distribution of sympathetic effects although, as we shall see below, they do receive some parasympathetic innervation.

A final aspect of the structure of the peripheral orthosympathetic system to be noted is that, although preganglionic fibers leave the spinal cord in only the thoracic and lumbar regions, sympathetic ganglia are to be found in the cervical regions as well. The cervical sympathetic ganglia are three in number: superior, middle, and inferior (see Fig. 30). These receive their fibers by way of connecting pathways to the thoracic and lumbar sympathetic chain. Thus, for a preganglionic fiber to reach the cervical ganglia it must leave the spinal cord in the thoracic region and enter the thoracic sympathetic cord and then turn upward to the cervical ganglia.

Despite this somewhat roundabout way in which preganglionic fibers get to them, the cervical ganglia are the most important in the sympathetic chain. Their postganglionic fibers innervate the blood vessels and sweat glands of the head, the dilator fibers of the pupils, the blood vessels of the heart, and the heart itself. The principal control of the blood supply of the brain is, in fact, vested in the sympathetic outflow of the cervical ganglia, although there is in this respect an antagonistic action of the parasympathetic system (see below).

The distribution of both the cervical and the thoracicolumbar divisions of the sympathetic cord is summarized in Table 2. From this and Fig. 30 it can be seen that the thoracicolumbar chain innervates all the other organs of the viscera below the heart: the liver, stomach, intestines, bladder, urogenital organs, and adrenal glands. In the vicinity of these organs are three ganglia, bearing the names of, and distributed to, the organs indicated in the figure.

Turning now to the more functional aspects of the sympathetic system, we may refer again to the general fact that the sympathetic system mobilizes rather diffusely the resources of the organism. Because this is of particular importance when the organism is threatened with danger and has strenuous work to do, the sympathetic system has been thought of as subserving *emergency* functions (Cannon). In the light of this generalization, the significance of the principal effects of sympathetic activity becomes clear: widening of the pupils, constriction of visceral blood vessels so that blood is directed to the muscles and brain, acceleration of the rate of heartbeat, inhibition of intestinal and gastric activity, the secretion of adrenalin with the result that blood sugar is raised and tissue metabolism increased—all these effects prepare the organism to deal with an emergency situation.   Further details concerning the sympathetic system and its functions may be found in Table 2.

The Parasympathetic System.—As we have already seen, the sympathetic system has ganglia either in the region of the spinal cord or in the vicinity of the organs that it innervates.   Only the latter situation is true, however, of the parasympathetic division.   This has long preganglionic fibers arising either in the brain or in the sacral division of the spinal cord and extending to the parasympathetic ganglia which are always close by the tissues to which their fibers are distributed.   Thus there is no chain of parasympathetic ganglia by which nervous effects can be interrelated.   From such a structural difference in the two systems one may surmise a characteristic functional difference, *viz.*, that the sympathetic division tends to act more diffusely and as a whole, whereas the parasympathetic division is a more highly differentiated system which is more capable of independent activity in each of its parts.

One may distinguish three principal outflows of the parasympathetic division: tectal, bulbar, and sacral.

1. The cell bodies of the preganglionic fibers in the *tectal* outflow are found in the floor of the midbrain in connection with the nuclei of the IIIrd and IVth cranial nerves.   The tectal preganglionic fibers leave the brain along with the fibers of the IIIrd and IVth nerves and travel to their endings on the ciliary ganglion cells, which in turn send postganglionic fibers to the iris and the muscles of accommodation of the eye. These effectors are, therefore, under the control of tectal parasympathetic fibers just as the striated ocular muscles concerned in eye movements are innervated by the IIIrd and IVth somatic cranial nerves.

2. Located in the medulla, the preganglionic cell bodies of the *bulbar* outflow send their fibers together with the somatic components of the VIIth, IXth, and Xth nerves to the face, mouth, throat, and many organs of the viscera.   The preganglionic fibers separate from the somatic fibers in the viscera and make synapses with postganglionic fibers in the parasympathetic ganglia.   As one can see from Fig. 30, these innervate many of the same organs as do the sympathetic fibers, and the effects of the two kinds of fibers are, in general, antagonistic.   Thus, the parasympathetic fibers of the vagus (Xth) nerve inhibit heartbeat, whereas the cervical sympathetics accelerate it.   The former tend to cause dilation of blood vessels and the latter to constrict blood vessels. Moreover, whereas sympathetic activity releases adrenalin to raise

blood sugar, the parasympathetic fibers stimulate insulin production which lowers blood sugar. And so it is with other effects (see Table 2).

3. Preganglionic cells of the *sacral* outflow of the parasympathetic system lie in the gray matter of the sacral spinal cord. Their fibers emerge in the ventral roots along with somatic fibers but soon leave them to go to the ganglia associated with the lower viscera—especially the bladder and lower intestine. The postganglionic fibers distributed to them produce effects antagonistic to the sympathetic fibers which innervate the same organs.

The general functions of the parasympathetic system are those of the conservation of bodily resources and the building up of the body. Thus the parasympathetic outflow causes constriction of the pupil, a response that serves to protect the eye from excessive light. It inhibits the heartbeat and causes vasodilation, in this way lowering blood pressure, which reduces the utilization of fuels throughout the body. It participates in digestion, definitely a constructive process, in several ways: by increasing the rate and amount of salivary secretion, by increasing contractions of the stomach, by causing digestive juices to be secreted into the stomach. Through the sacral outflow, moreover, the parasympathetic division frees the body of unwanted, and perhaps even poisonous, materials by causing emptying of the bladder and colon.

Neurohumoral Transmission.—At synapses in the central nervous system there seems to be nothing other than the electrical aspects of the nervous impulse required for synaptic transmission. In the autonomic system, on the other hand, particularly at the neuroeffector synapse between the postganglionic fiber and the smooth muscle or gland, a considerable array of evidence (Cannon and Rosenbleuth) indicates that there is a chemical substance mediating synaptic transmission. We cannot go into this evidence in detail, but its general nature may be illustrated by the classic experiment performed by Loewi (1921). This investigator filled the heart of a frog with Ringer's solution and stimulated the vagus nerve (which inhibits the heart), and then found that the Ringer's solution was capable of inhibiting another frog heart in the absence of any nervous stimulation. In this way he demonstrated that the inhibitory action of the vagus nerve upon the heart was accomplished through the liberation of some inhibiting chemical mediator. This was later discovered to be acetylcholine, one of the two substances of principal importance in synaptic transmission from autonomic nerves to effectors.

By procedures similar to Loewi's it has been further demonstrated that at some of the sympathetic nerve endings a substance very much like adrenalin is liberated, and it is this which accumulates at the juncture of the nerve fiber and effector and induces response in the effector.

Furthermore, it is only in this way that an autonomic nerve can have inhibitory effects. Sympathetic nerves to the stomach and intestine, for example, inhibit motility of the smooth muscles by liberating the adrenalinlike substance which has the property of inhibiting certain types of smooth muscle. By such chemical mediation we have in the autonomic system a *peripheral* mechanism of inhibition, whereas in the somatic nervous system, in contrast, all inhibition, so far as we have yet been able to ascertain, occurs only at *central* synapses.[1]

Of significance also are the relations between the two chemical mediators and the two divisions of the autonomic system. Acetylcholine is the mediator of the parasympathetic division, although it is also liberated by certain fibers of the sympathetic division. Most sympathetic fibers, however, release the adrenalinlike substance. For convenience of expression we are, therefore, accustomed to say that the parasympathetic system is *cholinergic* and that endings of the sympathetic system may be either cholinergic or *adrenergic*, these two words referring to the type of mediator produced. Cholinergic sympathetic fibers, it is to be noted, have effects very similar to the parasympathetic system. Although the typical effect of sympathetic activity is vasoconstriction, mediated by adrenergic fibers, these cholinergic fibers may cause dilation of some blood vessels—*e.g.*, those of striated muscles. It is important that the sympathetic system has both adrenergic and cholinergic fibers, but, having noted it, we may, nevertheless, think of the system as typically adrenergic, in contrast to the cholinergic parasympathetic system.

A further point in this connection is that the characteristic difference of the two autonomic divisions in respect to specificity of function is maintained in the chemical properties of the respective mediators. The sympathetic system is diffuse and tends to act as a whole. Its typical mediator, the adrenalinlike substance, is similarly a very stable chemical substance which, once liberated at an adrenergic sympathetic ending, can diffuse through the near-by fluids to other effectors, particularly adjacent smooth muscles, thus exciting them when they themselves have not been subjected to nervous impulses. As one can readily see, the result of this property is to make sympathetic effects diffuse to a degree even beyond that caused by the interconnections of sympathetic neurons. The parasympathetic division, on the other hand, is a more highly differentiated system, and its chemical mediator, acetylcholine, is a highly unstable substance, destroyed rather rapidly by other chemical substances near the site of its liberation and unable, therefore, to diffuse far to

---

[1] There is a type of inhibition, Wedensky inhibition, occurring at neuromuscular junctures of the somatic system, that results from stimulation at a high frequency, but this is not what we ordinarily refer to in speaking of inhibition with respect to somatic behavior.

stimulate other effectors. Thus, effectors excited by acetylcholine will respond for the most part only when the cholinergic fibers in direct connection with them are stimulated. This property, one can see, tends to localize parasympathetic effects and to aid in maintaining the comparatively great specificity of function which obtains in this system.

THE CENTRAL AUTONOMIC SYSTEM

As we have seen above, the preganglionic centers of outflow of the autonomic system are to be found in the midbrain, medulla, and through-

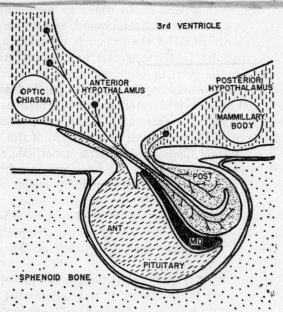

3rd VENTRICLE

OPTIC CHIASMA

ANTERIOR HYPOTHALAMUS

POSTERIOR HYPOTHALAMUS

MAMMILLARY BODY

POST

ANT

MID

PITUITARY

SPHENOID BONE

Fig. 32.—Sketch of the pituitary body, the hypothalamus, and their anatomical relations to each other. Note the nerve fibers from the hypothalamus to the posterior part of the pituitary body.

out the length of the spinal cord. These centers are comparable to the ventral horn cells of the spinal cord and the motor centers of the brain stem in that they are the last cell stations before nervous impulses leave the central nervous system. Above these preganglionic centers are others comparable to the higher levels of the somatic nervous system, and these higher centers normally control and organize autonomic activities in the intact organism. Although such higher centers are located in the midbrain, hypothalamus, thalamus, striate body, and cerebral cortex, for nearly every part of the brain has some connection with the autonomic outflow, the centers whose functions we know best and which are of greatest importance in organizing autonomic behavior are in the hypothalamus and cerebral cortex.

Autonomic Nuclei of the Hypothalamus.—Primary control of autonomic functions is vested in the hypothalamus; it is there that differentiation and organization of different patterns of autonomic reaction takes place. As one can see in Fig. 32, this center is rather clearly set off from the rest of the brain, lying in the ventral and medial part of the diencephalon. Associated with the hypothalamus is the pituitary gland and its stalk, the infundibulum, which projects from the floor of the hypothalamus. Also, protruding from the floor of the hypothalamus are the paired *mammillary bodies* and the *tuber cinerium*. Making up the hypothalamus proper are several nuclei which we may consider in two main groups: (1) the posterior and lateral nuclei, and (2) the medial and anterior nuclei. The function of the former is primarily sympathetic, whereas the latter organize, for the most part, parasympathetic functions.

If one stimulates the first, or posterior, group electrically, all the effects of sympathetic discharge are obtained: the pupils dilate, the heart is accelerated, blood pressure is elevated, gastric contractions and gastrointestinal activity are halted. Extirpation of this group of nuclei, on the other hand, presents all the symptoms of hypotonia of the sympathetic system and of a resulting dominance of parasympathetic activity: the pupils contract, the heart beats slower, the blood pressure drops. Moreover, the result of extirpation of the mammillary region of the hypothalamus, which makes up part of the posterior group of nuclei, is abnormal sleepiness or somnolence. As we shall see later (Chap. XVIII), sleep is demonstrably under the influence of the parasympathetic system, and it is, therefore, reasonable that extirpation of the sympathetic centers should serve to induce it.

The anterior and medial group of hypothalamic nuclei is predominantly parasympathetic in function. If it is stimulated electrically, the heart is slowed, blood sugar is lowered, and various other parasympathetic phenomena appear. To destroy the anterior group is to bring about an increase in blood sugar, a rise in heartbeat and blood pressure, vasoconstriction, and general sympathetic effects; these are the results to be expected if the sympathetic system were left without the antagonistic effect of the parasympathetic division.

General Functions of the Hypothalamus.—All the individual autonomic effects that can be produced by hypothalamic activity are controlled also by lower centers in the medulla and spinal cord; the distinctive importance of the hypothalamus is not in producing these autonomic effects but in its *integration* of them into patterns of activity which adjust the internal environment of the organism. Such integrating functions of the hypothalamus are derived from its relations to all the various neural and endocrine mechanisms for regulating the internal environment.

Receiving fibers from the cerebral cortex, it makes autonomic adjustments appropriate to the cortical events mediating somatic behavior. It sends efferent projection fibers downward to the bulbar mechanisms of respiration, heartbeat, and glandular regulation. Such projection fibers extend even farther downward to the preganglionic neurons of the spinal cord, thus regulating autonomic adjustments. Finally, the hypothalamus sends nerve fibers to the pituitary gland with which it is so closely associated and in this way controls certain of the activities of the pituitary gland and, because of the pituitary's control of other glands, hormonal secretions in general.

We may note in passing some of the general functions which the hypothalamus is able to subserve by these various means. Body temperature is crucially dependent upon this center. Whenever it is necessary for the body to lose heat, the hypothalamus causes vasodilation, increased sweating, increased respiration, and a lowering of metabolism. Through converse effects and, in addition, by inducing shivering, it causes heat to be conserved and the body temperature raised, whenever this is required. As the primary neural center regulating endocrine secretions, the hypothalamus plays a major role in regulating metabolism, particularly of fats, carbohydrates, and water. In addition, it is there that the control of blood pressure and thus of the distribution of blood to the brain is mainly, though not exclusively, vested. Sexual functions, which include complex autonomic effects (see Chap. XX) as well as certain somatic reactions, depend upon the hypothalamus and also, as we shall see later, upon part of the midbrain immediately behind it. Furthermore, physiological conditions associated with hunger and thirst are dependent in an important degree upon the activity of the hypothalamus. That it is also a center for emotional behavior will be shown in some detail in a later chapter (XVII). There is, therefore, a long list of important activities of the hypothalamus—more perhaps than one would expect to be contained in a neural center which is comparatively so small.

The list of these hypothalamic functions is, as the reader can see, one of motor functions. How, one may ask, is the hypothalamus informed of the duties it must perform? Or, in other words, what are the stimuli for its activities? The answer to this question is not at all clear at the present time, although we know, of course, that it receives fibers from many sources including some from the sense organs and the higher levels of the brain. These, however, are not enough to explain certain reactions, *e.g.*, sexual behavior, which seem to depend upon chemical conditions of the blood, and evidence has indicated that chemical and hormonal conditions of the blood can stimulate directly the cells located in the hypothalamus. Such a mechanism, of course, operates in addition to hypothalamic activation through other afferent and corticothalamic channels.

Autonomic Functions of the Cerebral Cortex.—We have previously observed that the nervous system is organized into different levels of function. This fact is apparent in the anatomical structure of the central nervous system as well as in the organization of somatic functions at spinal, bulbar, cerebellar, tectal, and corticothalamic levels. But nowhere is the concept of levels of function better seen than in the autonomic system. Autonomic effects of one or two types, which are confined to limited regions of the body, can be obtained at the spinal level, but definite coordination of autonomic reactions takes place in the medulla, where, for example, vasomotor effects and rate of heartbeat may be integrated so that a relatively constant blood pressure is maintained. At the hypothalamic level, furthermore, there occurs an integration of several kinds of effects into more general functions. Moreover, there are thalamic and striatal (corpus striatum) levels of autonomic function, although these are as yet poorly understood. Finally, in the cerebral cortex we find the highest and most delicate integrations of autonomic function. When, for example, muscular work is carried out under the influence of the cerebral cortex, there is a corresponding change in the distribution of blood to the muscles. We also find changes in sweating, in salivation, and in other kinds of autonomic behavior correlated with states of anxiety, mental work, and somatic behavior of cerebral origin. Such a close correlation of somatic and autonomic activities is, of course, demanded if the organism is to go about its work efficiently.

The basis of the correlation of autonomic and somatic functions at the cortical level is partly to be found in the overlapping of their representation in various cortical areas. Thus, in the motor cortex, where different parts of the motor area, autonomic control of the blood vessels and glands (where these are implicated) in one part of the body is vested in the same area as is the somatic control. For example, lacrimation of the tear glands is represented in the same region of the cortex as is the cortical control of eye movements. A similar relation holds between salivation and movements of the tongue and jaws. Other instances amply affirm this relation. Thus we see that, not only at the cortical level but also in lower levels, somatic and autonomic reactions are closely correlated anatomically and functionally.

THE INTERNAL ENVIRONMENT OF THE NERVOUS SYSTEM

We dealt in an earlier chapter with the general chemical characteristics of the internal environment and their importance for nervous function.

Now, having considered the general functions of nerve cells and the nervous system, we must come back once again to the internal environment. This time, however, we shall look particularly at the specific mechanisms by which the chemical constituents of the internal environment are made available to the nervous system. To do that, we must examine the circulation of blood in the brain, the cerebrospinal fluid, and their dependence upon nervous functions.

Blood Supply of the Brain.—From the top of the heart emerges one great blood vessel, the *aorta*, which runs in an *aortic arch*, giving off arteries to the head, and then proceeds downward to distribute blood to the trunk and lower parts of the body. Of the arteries to the head, two important trunks, the *internal carotid* and the *vertebral* arteries, are the principal sources of blood supply of the brain. In the internal carotid artery is an enlargement, the *carotid sinus*, in which there are chemical and mechanical receptors registering changes in the chemical condition, particularly of the amount of carbon dioxide, and the pressure of the blood going to the head. These carotid-sinus receptors are associated with the reflex mechanisms controlling blood pressure and respiration.

The internal carotid and vertebral arteries join at the base of the brain in a giant anastomosis, the *circle of Willis;* from it many smaller arteries arise and branch to various parts of the brain. The advantage of this circle, we may note, is that any one or two of the four major arteries that supply it may be cut off without seriously depriving the brain of blood. Thereby is the brain, whose circulation, above that of all other organs of the body, must remain relatively constant for the survival of the organism, given multiple protection against shortage of blood.

The various cerebral arteries divide into smaller *arterioles* and then finally into networks of capillaries. From the capillary networks, blood drains into the small venules and then into veins, finally to be collected in various venous sinuses located in the linings of the brain. It is the capillaries, however, which bring the blood into contact with nerve cells, for they form a bed of interconnecting channels which surrounds and entwines the nerve cells. Thus, every neuron comes in close proximity to the flow of blood and obtains from it, by the diffusion of certain of the elements of the blood through the capillary walls, the materials for its existence. The gray matter of cell bodies, we may note, receives a much richer supply of capillaries than does the white matter, a distribution which is reasonable in the light of the high metabolism of the cell body and the centralization of nutritive functions there. Certain parts of the gray matter, moreover, have a much richer blood supply than others, as, for example, the hypothalamus which has the densest capillary bed in the nervous system (Scharrer). This fact is to be correlated with the importance of the hypothalamus in the regulation of the internal environment and the consequent requirement that it respond most sensitively to changes in the condition of the blood.

Intracerebral Vasomotor Functions.—Innervating the arteries and veins of the brain are vasomotor nerve fibers which even supply certain capillaries. Some of these are vasoconstrictors from the sympathetic system and others are vasodilators of the parasympathetic system. They are most conspicuous on the surface of the cerebral cortex but also exist in subcortical blood vessels. Thus there are nervous mechanisms by which the flow of blood to different areas of the brain may be controlled. It happens, however, that the vasoconstrictor action of the sympathetic system upon the cerebral blood vessels is not great compared with that in other parts of the body, for it is offset by an accompanying vaso-constriction of blood vessels in the body which increases the pressure of blood in the head and may thus cause, through sheer mechanical force, vasodilation of cerebral vessels.

Besides vasomotor innervation of the cerebral blood vessels there are local conditions that may affect circulation in individual parts of the brain, and these, we shall see later, are of considerable importance in understanding certain psychological phenomena. For one thing, carbon dioxide in the blood, the product of the metabolism of nerve cells, causes vasodilation of the blood vessels, thus increasing blood flow. Probably dependent upon this effect is the vasodilation and accompanying increase in blood flow which follows nervous activity in a given region. It has been shown, for example, that blood flow increases in the visual area of the cortex when the eye is stimulated by light (Gerard). Other factors such as temperature, oxygen supply, sugar, and the potassium-calcium ratio in an area also influence local circulation.

It is important to note, finally, that sensory fibers, as well as motor nerve fibers, innervate many of the blood vessels of the brain, particularly the larger ones. Under what conditions such sensory fibers are stimu-lated is not at present fully understood, but it seems well established that excessive dilation of blood vessels for one reason or another will excite them. Indeed, certain kinds of headaches have been shown to arise in this way (see Chap. XVII). Sensory fibers innervating the cerebral blood vessels mediate such experience, providing, also, a reflex mechan-ism for the regulation of blood flow in particular areas of the brain.

Extracerebral Vasomotor Functions.—Although many of the adjust-ments of blood flow to the brain are made locally within the blood vessels of the brain and even in restricted areas, the more important vasomotor adjustments take place in blood vessels outside of, but leading to, the cranial cavity. The three most important mechanisms for such adjust-ments may be summarized as follows: (1) In the enlargement of the internal carotid artery, *i.e.*, the carotid sinus, are receptors sensitive to both chemical and pressure stimuli. These are represented in the medulla, and a rise in carbon dioxide or a lowering of blood pressure in the sinus causes the cardiac and vasomotor centers of the medulla to increase cerebral blood flow by increasing heartbeat and vasoconstriction throughout the body. (2) The aortic arch has in it pressure receptors which are responsive to changes in blood pressure and bring about reflexly compensatory reactions in pressure by depressing the heart and increasing vasodilation. (3) Finally, the carbon dioxide content of the blood directly affects the vasodilator and vasoconstrictor centers in the medulla, thus setting up autonomic motor impulses which increase or decrease cerebral blood flow depending, respectively, upon whether the carbon dioxide is too high or too low.

The Cerebrospinal Fluid.—All organs of the body are supplied with blood in greater or lesser amounts, and the nervous system, because of its crucial importance in the economy of the body, receives much more than most other organs. Peculiar to the nervous system, however, is another type of fluid supply, the cerebrospinal fluid. This is to be found in the *ventricular* and *subarachnoid* cavities of the brain and spinal cord. The ventricular system is within the brain and spinal cord, the subarachnoid spaces are in the external linings.

The ventricular system consists of four ventricles in the brain and a spinal canal in the spinal cord. Two ventricles, ordinarily called the lateral ventricles, are to be found in the cerebral hemispheres in a position indicated in Fig. 24. These communicate with each other and with the third ventricle which is located in the mid-line in the thalamus and hypothalamus. By means of the Sylvian aqueduct which passes through the midbrain, separating it into a floor and a roof, the third ventricle is connected with the fourth ventricle contained within the caudal pons and rostral medulla. This narrows down caudally to a small canal which runs the length of the spinal cord in the gray commissure.

The subarachnoid spaces are between layers of the external lining of the brain (meninges). One of them comes into close proximity with the fourth ventricle, being separated from it only by a thin membrane, which, however, has small openings in it through which fluid from the ventricular system can communicate with that in the subarachnoid spaces.

The cerebrospinal fluid is an almost colorless liquid very much like the blood in composition except that it has no red or white corpuscles and contains no blood proteins. Indeed, it appears to be rich in the food materials of the blood. Its function with respect to the nervous system is not clearly understood, although it is clear that it is partly nutritive. It is widely believed that this fluid is secreted or filtered from the blood in networks of arterial blood vessels (choroid plexi) found in the ventricles, and it appears to be absorbed by a similar net of venous vessels (arachnoid

villi) in the subarachnoid spaces.   The importance of the cerebrospinal
fluid in understanding nervous functions consists at present of certain
correlations between changes in its chemical constitution and changes in
nervous function and also in the effect of alterations in its pressure upon
nervous activities.

General References

CANNON, W. B., and A. ROSENBLEUTH, 1937. *Autonomic neuro-effector systems.*
New York: Macmillan. Pp. xiv + 230.

FULTON, J. F., 1938. *Physiology of the nervous system.* New York: Oxford. Pp.
xv + 674.

KUNTZ, A., 1942. *The autonomic nervous system.* 2d ed. Philadelphia: Lea and
Febiger. P. 697.

RASMUSSEN, A., 1941. *The principal nervous pathways.* 2d ed. New York:
Macmillan. Pp. ix + 73.

CHAPTER VI
PHYLOGENETIC DEVELOPMENT

As was evident in considering the historical development of physiological psychology, the experimental facts upon which we shall rely for conclusions concerning the physiological basis of behavior are derived in very large part from animals. Consequently, to be able to apply our conclusions to man we must be fully aware of the differences and similarities between man and animals in respect of both psychological capacity and biological structure. To the more important of these matters, therefore, we shall turn our attention in the present chapter.

Because we subsequently deal only with vertebrate animals and particularly with the mammals, it is upon these that the discussion will focus. Making up the vertebrate series in ascending order are the fishes, amphibia, reptiles, birds, and mammals. Upon all these, both psychological and physiological studies have been made in abundance. Psychophysiological work, however, has most frequently dealt with birds (mostly pigeons and chickens) and with certain members of the mammalian series. Most important of these in ascending phylogenetic order are rats, guinea pigs, and rabbits (rodents), cats and dogs (carnivora), and monkeys, apes, and man (primates). The psychophysiological differences in these various animals of the vertebrate scale will be considered under the headings of motor ability, sensory capacity, adaptive behavior, and the nervous system.

MOTOR ABILITY

Behavior which is concerned with the satisfaction of bodily needs does not undergo any remarkable development in vertebrate evolution. Naturally there are many differences between one species and another in the patterns of behavior with which the organism seeks food and water, and mating patterns are often quite elaborate even in the lowest animals. On the whole, however, such differences are not related to an animal's position in the phylogenetic scale. Thus, with certain minor exceptions which will be noted in subsequent chapters, one animal is about as representative as another for the study of the physiological mechanisms mediating motivated behavior.

Such is not the case, however, with other types of behavior. Both locomotor and manipulatory behavior undergo considerable develop-

103

ment in phylogenesis.   First to be differentiated is locomotor behavior, for by it an animal may adjust to his environment through changing his orientation and position with respect to it.   Without tracing all the various steps in this development we may note that appendages for loco-motion first appear in such amphibia as frogs and toads and become most highly developed in birds and certain of the lower mammals.   In birds of flight, for example, a great deal of the musculature has been given over to locomotion, and sensory mechanisms, particularly those of vision and equilibration, have been integrated with locomotor mechanisms to provide for the highly strenuous and complex adjustments of flight.

Later in evolution, emphasis on locomotor adjustment has given way to the development of manipulatory adjustments by which an animal may deal with his environment by manipulating it or moving it instead of shifting his entire body with respect to it.   Some of the inframam-malian animals are capable of using their limbs for manipulation; the rat, for example, can pull in strings and move objects with its limbs, but it is in higher animals that manipulation becomes really serviceable in adjust-ment.   Between the rat and the monkey, for instance, there are remark-able differences.   The monkey can use its hands for handling latches, sticks, and strings in a manner like that of man.   In the higher apes, more-over, manipulation is even more highly evolved, for here the thumb comes to be in apposition to the other fingers, and a great deal of control over individual digits appears.   The chimpanzee, for example, can use knives, forks, spoons, and other utensils, almost as well as can man.

Related to the development of manipulative motor ability in phylo-genesis are changes in visually determined behavior.   Nearly all verte-brate animals from fishes to man make reflex adjustments to visual stimuli.   The most notable and stable of these, as observed experi-mentally, is the movement of the head or eyes in following the horizontal movement of vertical stripes in the visual field.   Just as is the case with other kinds of motor dexterity, however, so is it also typical of lower animals that they move their heads in following the moving striations, whereas in the higher primates eye movements independent of the head become much more prominent.   Thus phylogenetic development entails in this case also the differentiation of behavior from general involvement of the whole body, or large parts of it, to the skilled use of only a few muscles.

In addition to showing the highest development of manipulatory ability, although by no means the best locomotor capacity, man has developed another motor facility—language.   The adjustments of the vocal cords required for language, although seen in rudimentary form in the other primates, are the gifts of man only.   These are very delicate in pattern, form, and sequential order, and man makes the most of them.

Related to such linguistic motor ability are corresponding changes in the nervous system, and these we shall consider in the section below.

SENSORY CAPACITY

Vision.—Along with phylogenetic changes in visuomotor behavior mentioned above, goes a change in the position of the eyes in the head, so that the *binocular* field increases in size. In fishes and in all animals up to and including the lower mammals, with but a few exceptions, the eyes are laterally placed in the head in such a way that the fields of the two do not overlap. Consequently, little coordination of either the movement of the eyes or the sensory impressions mediated by them is required. Indeed, in some cases the eyes seem to function quite independently of each other in both respects (Levine). In lower mammals, on the other hand, the eyes begin to be more frontally placed with the result that their fields overlap; and since the two then see, in part, the same things, their activities—and indeed their central visual processes—become more interrelated. Only through such interrelations, in fact, is it possible to achieve binocular depth perception. Of this capacity and changes in the nervous system related to it we shall see more later.

The essential characteristics of visual sensitivity do not seem to vary in any consistent way with phylogenetic development. The wave lengths of light to which different vertebrates are maximally sensitive, as well as the wave lengths which they can see at all, are roughly the same, so far as we can make out (Bridgman). There is some evidence that certain fishes have a slightly different distribution of visual sensitivity, but these seem to be special cases accounted for in terms of slightly different chemical substances participating in photochemical activities of the retina (Wald).

In color vision there appears to be no consistent change or improvement in phylogenesis. We have some difficulty in proving such a statement, because the technical difficulties of establishing the existence of color vision in an animal, let alone the degree of its refinement, are not easily surmounted. Such evidence as we have, however, indicates that ability to discriminate differences in wave length independently of brightness (color vision) exists in fish (Reeves) and in birds (Hamilton and Coleman). There is some question about the rat, but at present one can believe that it also is capable of at least crude color vision (Muenzinger and Reynolds). About the primates there can be little doubt (Nissen and McCulloch), for they appear to discriminate colors easily. We cannot, therefore, believe on the basis of the evidence at hand that color vision is a psychological capacity that has undergone any marked development in phylogeny.

Measurements of visual acuity, *i.e.*, the ability to resolve the details of the visual environment, give no indication of systematic phyletic differences. Precise measures have been made in several animals by observing the size of stripes which when moved will be attended by movements of the eyes or head, and considerable difference in visual acuity between various animals has been found, but these differences have little to do with phylogenetic status (Warkentin).

In the discrimination of differences in visual brightness, however, there does appear to be some improvement in phylogeny, but there it is possible that the differences are to be accounted for, not in terms of any improvement on the optical efficiency of the eye, but in the perceptual processes associated with vision and in the intelligence of animals in solving the problems by means of which an experimenter measures brightness discrimination (Mead).

Pattern vision, *i.e.*, the capacity to appreciate differences in the shape and contours of objects, exists even in such invertebrate animals as the insects (Verlaine). There is also every indication that birds and lower mammals are all quite able to perceive visual patterns, and it is possible that they are as capable as man in this respect (Munn, Fields, Lashley). There are, however, considerable changes in some aspects of visual capacity in phylogenetic development, but these concern "concept-formation" and higher intellectual processes *based* upon vision, rather than the fundamental perception of the shape and pattern of figures. Of these differences something will be said in another section.

Summarizing these various facts, we may make the general statement that little or no improvement is to be observed in visual mechanisms in the phyletic series. Whatever superiority man and the higher animals may possess in dealing with visual aspects of the environment must lie, therefore, not so much in a superior sensory capacity, but in other capacities of a higher order. For an evaluation of these, see the discussion below of adaptive behavior.

Hearing.—In hearing, as contrasted with vision, considerable phylogenetic development takes place both in the anatomical structure of the ear and in auditory capacity. In fishes, as the accompanying figure illustrates (33), there is no structure comparable to the cochlea of man, but only the rudimentary *lagena* from which the cochlea later differentiates. Whether or not this functions in hearing is not clear; we know only that fishes have relatively poor hearing in respect to both the intensity and the range of frequency of sounds heard by them. The frequencies that they hear are not nearly so high as those to which man and higher mammals are sensitive, and it is doubtful whether they can discriminate different tones (frequencies) from each other, although it has been reported that they can.

It is in the bird that the cochlea first becomes differentiated. There it appears as a drawn-out enlargement of the lagena and is usually slightly coiled to make part of a circle. What auditory capacity is possessed by birds is not known, but it may be supposed from indirect evidence (Wever and Bray) that it is quite good and corresponds in general respects with man's, at least with regard to the range of frequencies that can be heard. In mammals, the fundamental cochlear structure laid down in birds is further developed by the lengthening of the cochlea into a spiral coil of two or more turns.

The range of frequencies to which mammals are sensitive varies somewhat, but not particularly in relation to phylogenetic level. The guinea pig seems to hear about as well as man, but the cat, on the other hand,

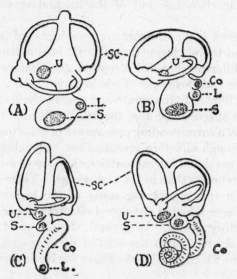

Fig. 33.—The evolution of the inner ear. (*A*) Fish, (*B*) frog, (*C*) bird, and (*D*) mammal. *SC*, semicircular canals; *Co*, cochlea; *U, S,* and *L*, otoliths of the utricle, saccule, and lagena. (*After von Frisch. From F. A. Moss, Ed. Comparative Psychology, p. 176. New York: Prentice-Hall, 1934. By permission of the publishers.*)

hears higher frequencies than man and has maximal sensitivity at a point one to two octaves (*i.e.*, between two to four times the frequency) above that of man's maximal sensitivity (Dworkin *et al.*). The rat, moreover, has a distribution of sensitivity much higher than that (Gould and Morgan). Notwithstanding our knowledge of auditory sensitivity in these animals, we still lack satisfactory information concerning their perception of pitch and their ability to discriminate different frequencies. It is quite possible that in the development from birds to mammals, the ear has become a better analyzer of sounds and therefore equips the animal for better appreciation of pitch. But from the anatomical structure of the ears of most mammals from rats to man, one may conclude that in them the ear has reached its highest development. As in vision, so here, however, must one distinguish between basic sensory capacity and the use of this capacity in higher intellectual processes.

Other Senses.—The sense organs for the maintenance of body equilibrium have not changed significantly in vertebrate phylogeny. Throughout the vestibular apparatus the essential structure remains unaltered (see Fig. 33), and no differences in behavior determined by it are noticeable. True, the importance of this mechanism is magnified in the flying birds, where so much depends upon equilibrium, and there are corresponding changes in the parts of the nervous system concerned with equilibrium; but these are developments, not of the sense organs or of the sensory mechanisms, but of the integrating centers related to them.

Of great interest is the comparative prominence of taste and smell at different levels of the phylogenetic scale. It is established that in fishes there are two different chemical receptors, the olfactory and gustatory receptors (Parker and Sheldon). Taste in particular is greatly developed. Instead of being limited to the mouth and tongue, there are taste receptors —in some fishes at least—all over the body. Related to this fact there is, as we shall see, a corresponding prominence of gustatory mechanisms in the brain. Although olfactory receptors are, throughout phylogeny, to be found in the nasal and buccal cavities, they are of greater importance in the lower vertebrates than in the higher ones. There are, however, no absolute rules in this regard, for many of the higher mammals, *e.g.*, dogs and deer, have a highly developed olfactory apparatus and possess very good olfactory acuity. In general, the extent of development of olfaction is closely related to the kind of life a species of animal leads and the extent to which smell is necessary for its preservation.

ADAPTIVE BEHAVIOR

Man is obviously better equipped to cope with environmental situations of all sorts than are animals below him; yet his superiority is due, in part, to his greater manipulative motor ability and not to any appreciable improvement in sensory capacity. Manipulative ability of itself, however, is not nearly enough to account for the complexity of his adjustments. Phylogenetic improvement must, therefore, have been in the "higher" mental processes—learning, reasoning, and thought. To these, then, we may turn in the expectation of finding important phylogenetic differences.

Learning.—If one considers first the performance of various vertebrate animals in learning simple adjustments such as the discrimination of various sensory stimuli, the running of a maze, or the solution of relatively easy problem boxes, one finds no consistent or significant differences attributable to phylogenetic status (Lashley). All birds and mammals that have been studied are quite capable of learning to manipulate strings, levers, or pedals in the solution of a problem box if they have such manipulations in their normal repertoire of adjustments. Mammals are uniformly capable of learning mazes. Moreover, there are no significant differences, it appears, in the rate at which different animals learn such problems. Indeed, in a study comparing the maze performance of rats and college students (Lathan and Fields) the rats were found to be superior in rate of learning. From this and many other studies in which various animals of different phylogenetic development have been compared, it has been concluded that "the rate of formation of simple habits has increased little, if at all, through . . . evolution" (Lashley, p. 467). We must turn, then, to other aspects of adaptive behavior for an understanding of the psychological differences so obvious in the phyletic scale.

Concept Formation.—Generalization, abstraction, concept formation, equivalence, similarity, and transfer—all these are terms which the psychologist often applies to certain aspects of intelligent behavior. The terms are not synonymous, for they are used in different cases, yet they seem to apply to one basic characteristic of adaptiveness. This is the capacity to behave with respect to some 'element' or aspect of a situation, rather than to its full set of specific details, as shown by the fact that, although the details may be changed, so long as the essential aspect remains, the behavior is unchanged. A triangle, for example, may be represented as three dots, or three angles; it may or may not have three full sides; it may be equilateral, right, or obtuse; it may be seen or felt— yet in all these cases it remains, to the sophisticated man at any rate, a triangle. This case one usually regards as an illustration of a concept— the concept of triangularity—yet it is but a special instance of a general psychological process in which some particular aspect of a stimulus situation is singled out and reacted to.

The formation of concepts is a basic psychological capacity. In simpler form we see it when a rat, for example, responds to a 2,000-cycle tone after he has been conditioned to jump when presented with a 1,000-cycle tone. Here we call the process one of generalization, because the behavior has become conditioned not only to a 1,000-cycle tone but rather to tones in general. Indeed, it would appear that learning always takes place with reference to certain aspects of a situation and that thereby an ability is acquired to react to other situations somewhat different in detail but similar in aspect. This common property, which is responded to as 'similar,' always has a direct dependence upon the physical properties of the stimulus, yet it is finally determined by the structure and properties of the nervous system—or as some would say, in a less physiological frame of reference, phenomenologically.

Simple types of generalization take place in rats and undoubtedly in animals much lower in the phyletic scale. As in the example above, generalization occurs to the frequency of a conditioning tone. Also illustrative is the case of generalization of a brightness discrimination by rats. If trained to choose the brighter of two papers, they usually continue to do so when the brightness is changed such that the brighter of the pair is now less bright than was the one they were originally taught to avoid. Such 'transfer'—as it is often called—is present in all birds and mammals that have been studied. That no important changes in this respect are to be found in phylogenesis can therefore be concluded.

It is clear, however, that higher levels of generalization are limited to higher vertebrates. Birds have been tested for formation of the concept of triangularity by presenting them, after they have learned to discriminate a triangle (apex up) from a circle, with an inversion of the triangle. In this situation, however, they failed to discriminate and thereby showed that they had not developed a concept of *form* in their training (Bingham).

In rats, on the other hand, it appears that a concept of form can be developed, though with some difficulty (Fields). If given the same tests as the birds, they fail, but if considerable experience with triangles in several positions is given them, they will generalize to triangles in other positions and even with certain parts left out. Thus it appears that a very rudimentary capacity for the concept of form exists in the rat and can with training be developed.

From the rat to man there is considerable improvement in concept formation, although, unfortunately, the evidence available is inadequate. There are a few reports of generalization of form taking place in monkeys. In one, a monkey, after being trained to discriminate between a pair of visual stimuli, one of which was a triangle, continued to do so after inversion of the triangle (Neet). Another experiment with chimpanzees, however, did not give such clear evidence (Gellerman). That young children readily solve such problems is quite clear (Gellerman, Ray), and the capacity of human adults, although varying widely from individual to individual and depending much upon training, cannot be denied. We may conclude, therefore, that the capacity for the formation of concepts of form—a most essential basis for more complex adjustments— has undergone considerable development in mammalian phylogenesis.

Complexity of Elements.—Although there appear to be no observable phylogenetic differences in the rate or limits of learning of simple mazes, discriminations, and problem boxes, such differences do appear quite plainly in problem situations where the individual must master the *order* of acts to be performed in the solution of a problem. To illustrate: in ranning a maze, a rat or a human subject has the order of discriminations set for him; *i.e.*, he makes each choice as it comes and is not confronted with another until he has solved the preceding one. In a problem box (see Fig. 34), on the other hand, it is required that the subject depress the pedals in some definite, predetermined order. To solve the problem, therefore, the subject must *know in advance* which, of several possible orders, is the correct one. Thus the difficulty of the problem lies not so much in pushing the correct pedals as doing it in the correct *order*. This, then, is the important way in which the problem differs from those listed above.

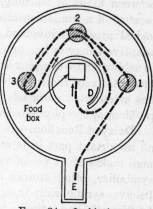

To determine the limits of learning ability so far as order is concerned, experiments have been planned and carried out in the following way (Jenkins). An animal is first taught to push pedal 1. After mastering that, pushing 1 and 2, in that order, is next required. Then pedal 3 may be added, and still later other sequences of varying degrees of complexity may be arranged. By such a series of problems of varying difficulty, a clear index of the ability of different animals in dealing with adaptations requiring the mastery of order of response can be obtained.

Fig. 34.—Jenkins's triple-plate problem box. The door *D* opens when the animal, after leaving the starting box *E*, has pushed the pedals in the correct order; whereupon food is available in the food box. (*From H. A. Fjeld. The limits of learning ability in rhesus monkeys. Genet. Psychol. Monogr.,* **15**, 403, 1934. *By permission of The Journal Press.*)

The results of testing several representative animals in the mammalian scale are to be seen in Table 3. Guinea pigs and rats are plainly very poor; some of them cannot learn to push one pedal, and the best that can

TABLE 3.—LIMITS REACHED BY VARIOUS MAMMALS TESTED ON JENKINS' TRIPLE-PLATE PROBLEM APPARATUS

Kind of animals	No. of animals	Range of steps	Median	Average
Guinea pigs (Riess)	16	0– 1	1.0	0.5
Rats (Riess)	24	0– 2	1.0	0.9
Kittens (Shuey)	62	3– 7	3.0	3.6
Rhesus monkeys (Fjeld)	17·	2–22	5.0	7.4
Cebus monkeys (Koch)	6	5–15	9.5	9.8

be obtained in others is that two pedals can be depressed in the proper order. Ascending the scale, however, we find cats definitely more proficient and the primates able to carry out extremely complex solutions. Here, then, is a psychological capacity which, unlike simple sensory-motor learning, has definitely undergone considerable development in evolution.

Moreover, it is significant that there should be such a distinction between kinds of learning, for it seems clear that it could occur only because of a fundamental difference in the nature of the psychophysiological processes involved. We see that evolutionary development of adaptive behavior has proceeded along the line of enabling the organism to achieve more complex organizations of elements rather than improving quantitatively the rate and amount of learning. To this point Lashley has given great emphasis, as we shall see later, when we deal with the problem of the physiological mechanisms of learning.

Delayed Reaction.—It is well recognized that *symbolic* processes play an important part in human mental accomplishments. That is to say, man makes great use of various stimuli in his world which stand for, or symbolize, other stimuli of his environment; in addition, he, himself, behaves symbolically in carrying out all sorts of behavior which represent to himself, and others, more concrete adjustments. Language is, of course, the example par excellence of symbolism in psychological activities. We recognize, moreover, the important part played by linguistic and other symbolic processes in the adjustments we call thought.

Symbolism is not limited, however, to stimuli which stand for others or to motor behavior representing other such behavior, for there are *central* symbolic processes which take place entirely within the nervous system. In this case, one nervous process takes the place of, or represents, another nervous process in determining behavior. A psychological equivalent of such a symbolic nervous process has frequently been referred to in the psychologist's parlance as an *idea* or *image*. For such a process, there is obviously no *direct* proof or measure, yet its existence can be inferred from the fact that animals and man sometimes respond to stimuli which are not present but which have been experienced in the past.

Consider, for example, what we speak of as *recall memory*. In this the individual shows by his behavior (*e.g.*, by language) that some representation of previous stimuli has been aroused in the brain and thus that a symbolic process governs his behavior. In *recognition memory*, on the other hand, no such process is involved, for a stimulus—not just an image of it in the brain—is necessary in order for the behavior appropriate to it to take place. Thus it is that in recall memory we recognize the operation of a *central* symbolic process, whereas in recognition memory no such process is necessary.

Such a distinction appears to provide the key to the understanding of the kind of psychological development that takes place in phylogenetic history. As we have seen above, the learning of a maze, of a simple problem box, or of conditioned reactions does not significantly improve in evolution. Significant, however, is the fact that such learning involves no symbolic process, but only a reaction to present stimuli—a recognition memory. Learning and memory of the sort involving symbolic processes, on the other hand, does undergo, as we shall now see, considerable development in evolution.

Of several kinds of learning that involve symbolic processes, the most important and most intensively investigated are the *delayed-reaction* and the *double-alternation* phenomena (Hunter). In learning to delay reaction, an animal is shown where, of several possible places, a reward is to be found and then after some period of restraint allowed to proceed to it. In this procedure one measures the greatest length of delay (restraint) which the subject can endure and still be able to 'recall' where the lure has been placed. Ability to delay in this situation has been called 'immediate' or 'recent' memory, but it appears to have as its basis some kind of symbolic process. In the double-alternation method, an animal is required to traverse a maze, in the absence of any useful cues, and to make turns in an order RRLL or LLRR. Because, in this case, sensory cues cannot be derived either from the external situation or from the animal's own movements, it is thought to involve some symbolic 'imaginal' process.

Most striking is the way in which symbolic capacity, as measured by such methods, is related to phylogenetic status (Munn, p. 154). There is some question about whether rats and dogs can delay at all in the delayed-reaction test, but if they can, the maximum delay is certainly very short, being a matter of only a few seconds. Although the cat, on the other hand, appears to do somewhat better, it is only in primates that unequivocal evidence of delay has been presented. Here delays of several minutes and even days have been obtained. The exact times vary according to the techniques employed and to individual differences in animals, but monkeys, gorillas, and chimpanzees have all been shown to be capable of delays of at least several minutes. Thus is there a clear difference in capacity for ideational or symbolic activity between primates and other mammals below them in the scale.

The same conclusion is born out by experiments with the double-alternation method (Hunter, Gellerman). Rats are usually unable to learn, although a few may do so after long and special training. At any rate, their very poorly developed capacity for this sort of problem is clearly evident. Monkeys, on the other hand, learn it with comparative ease and even go on to master more complicated alternations. Children and human adults, of course, are capable of very complex symbolic functions of this sort.

We may summarize phylogenetic differences in adaptive behavior as follows: No important relation obtains between an animal's phylogenetic status and the rate and amount of simple sensory-motor learning of which it is capable. What does undergo extensive phylogenetic development, however, is the kind of capacity encompassed by the terms concept formation and symbolization. In these, therefore, we find the most important differences in adaptive behavior between higher and lower animals. Most of the development, it may be noted, takes place in the mammalian scale between rats and man.

THE NERVOUS SYSTEM

The very brief glance that we have just given the phylogenetic development of behavior benefits us in several ways. It provides, first of all, a frame of reference for the interpretation of physiological experiments conducted with animals, particularly with respect to the application of their results to man, and we shall deal with many such experiments later. It aids, furthermore, in a better understanding of the basic varieties of psychological process in man; for in seeing how mental capacity has developed in phylogenesis we are able to sort into fundamental categories psychological performances which, when observed in man alone, are often grouped together. In addition to these uses of the knowledge of psychological development in phylogenesis is another still more pertinent. It is the possibility of observing the relation between behavioral and neural changes in phylogenetic development and thereby gaining from phylogenesis information concerning the physiological basis of behavior. Let us, therefore, turn our attention now to reviewing the important steps in the evolutionary development of the nervous system and to correlating these changes with the parallel elaboration of psychological capacities.

Invertebrates.—First let us look at the fundamental characteristics of nervous structure and function which have been laid down in invertebrate evolution. These are rooted, as we have already seen, in the differentiation of effectors, receptors, and adjustors. The adjustors, we know, make up the nervous system. This in its most primitive form is the *nerve net*, found in members of the phylum Coelenterata (*e.g.*, the jellyfish). The nerve net appears to be a syncytium of several nerve cells and, therefore, to possess no true synapses. Conduction in the nerve net, consequently, is diffuse and is not provided with the differentiation of pathways with which a synaptic nervous system is endowed.

After the nerve net came two important steps in nervous development. (1) The syncytium was dropped, and in its place arose nerve cells that could act in some measure independently of each other. Here was established the basis for the organization of the nervous system into centers and pathways. (2) The nervous system came to be gathered into one part of the organism, the part depending upon which of two organismic patterns was developed. In the echinoderms (*e.g.*, the starfish) the organismic pattern was *radial* with the nervous system accordingly disposed in a radial pattern, its center a concentric ring of nervous tissue placed at the hub of the animal with its nerves radiating out to the periphery. Evidently the radial pattern was incapable of further differentiation, for it never went beyond the rudimentary form found in echinoderms. A second type of organismic pattern, on the other hand, the *axial*, is the one that has been preserved throughout subsequent invertebrate and vertebrate evolution to man. In this we find the body and the nervous system organized along an anteroposterior axis—from the head to the tail. Examples of it will be presented below.

Accompanying the evolution of the axial form of nervous system is the development of another characteristic which becomes more and more important in later evolution—*ganglionic organization.* In worms it is not very highly developed; a chain of ganglia is arranged in pairs along the axis of the body, each pair serving a segment of the body in such a way that the nervous system takes the form of a ladder. In other animals, such as the insects, the general tendency is to bring each pair together into one ganglion located in the axis of the body and to reduce the number of ganglia, with the result that the major ganglia tend to be distributed according to the major divisions of the body; *i.e.*, head, trunk, abdomen—although smaller ganglia located according to the segmentation of the body do not entirely disappear. In vertebrates the major ganglia are still further reduced in number to one, thus forming a unified central nervous system; yet the representation of the segments of the body is still retained in greater or lesser degree.

Vertebrates.—The later stages of nervous evolution, to be found mainly, although not exclusively, in the vertebrate series, display a fourth important feature—*encephalization:* the major ganglion, which in vertebrates is the brain, comes to be located in the head end of the organism. More than that, however, in encephalization the head ganglion has taken over more and more of the integrative and controlling functions of the posterior nervous system. Still later, with the emergence of the cerebral cortex, *corticalization* of functions, in which functions are transferred from lower parts of the brain to the cortex, is the important trend in nervous evolution.

The Spinal Cord.—Turning now to more detailed aspects of vertebrate evolution, let us take up each of the major parts of the nervous system and note the changes in both structure and function which have taken place in phylogenesis (see Fig. 35). First to be considered is the spinal cord. Throughout phylogeny it remains a structure with relatively fixed capacities and functions. Its own rather independent part in behavior is as a center for reflex behavior; its relation to the brain is one of conducting impulses between the brain and the peripheral sense organs and muscles.   In so far, however, as the functions of the brain change, so

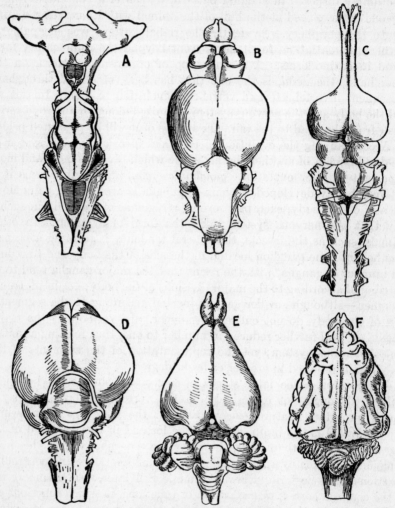

Fig. 35.—Comparative development of the brain at different levels of the vertebrate series. *A*, dogfish, no true cerebral hemispheres; *B*, salmon, no true cerebral hemispheres but a highly developed midbrain; *C*, alligator, true cerebral hemispheres, but comparatively small; *D*, pigeon, comparatively large cerebral hemispheres; *E*, rabbit, hemispheres making up a large proportion of the brain; *F*, dog, still larger development of hemispheres with the appearance of convolutions. (*After Wiedersheim. From P. H. Mitchell. A textbook of general physiology, 3d. ed., p. 153.   New York: McGraw-Hill, 1938.   By permission of the publishers.*)

does the spinal cord undergo change.   Of these changes, two are most important: the formation of the autonomic system and the changes in the termination of the spinal cord.   (1) In even the lowest fishes the spinal nerves have the structure typical of higher animals, but these must also mediate autonomic functions, and it is only in the higher fishes that sympathetic ganglia together with a distinct autonomic system are formed. (2) All connections between the spinal cord and the higher centers of the brain are, in fishes and amphibia, relayed by way of the medulla. Some are, even in man (*e.g.*, the dorsal funiculi); but it is in the reptiles that the first direct connections become established between the spinal cord and the thalamus. Moreover, only in mammals does the coordination between the brain and spinal cord entail direct tracts between the spinal cord and the cortex. This, we shall see, is related to the fact that only in mammals does the cerebral cortex take on general sensory and motor functions.

Medulla.—Quite uniform throughout all vertebrates are the general functions of the medulla. It contains the centers for respiration, cardiac activity, and gastrointestinal functions. In it also are the principal centers of the special mechanoreceptors, *viz.*, the lateral line organs, vestibular receptors, and auditory receptors. The amount of the medulla given over to the nuclei at different phylogenetic levels is proportional to their importance. The lateral line organs diminish in size and are lost in higher amphibia. There is very little change in the vestibular receptors in vertebrate evolution, and, while the auditory receptors have no independent status in fishes, appearing only in amphibia and reptiles, they become a fully developed mechanism in birds and mammals. Paralleling these various changes in sensory structure are corresponding enlargements or recessions in the size and importance of bulbar nuclei.

One of the most striking phylogenetic changes in the medulla is associated with the diminishing size and importance of the gustatory receptor system. Taste buds are distributed all over the body of many fishes and are of prime importance in the determination of their behavior. The nuclei for taste in the medulla are accordingly enormously expanded, so much so that they form large evaginations called the vagal lobes— *vagal* because they represent primarily the enlargement of the nuclei of the vagus nerve. The taste receptors are curtailed, however, in further evolution and in mammals are limited to the tongue and a small part of the internal surfaces of the mouth. With this recession of taste goes a diminution in the vagal lobes, until in man, for example, the gustatory nucleus becomes a comparatively inconspicuous center in the medulla.

Cerebellum.—The first structure of the nervous system to be specialized for the coordination of sensory and motor impulses is the cerebellum. It was apparently developed in connection with the vestibular and lateral line systems which are so important in the lower vertebrates, but even in cyclostomes, prevertebrate organisms lower than the fishes, where the cerebellum is first seen, it has connections with the frontal and spinal portions of the nervous system. Much of its later development involves the extension and increase in the number of these connections. The cerebellum achieves its greatest importance in birds, where it reaches its largest size in relation to the rest of the brain and where it is a great organ for coordinating the sensory and motor impulses involved in flying. The cerebellum, as it is seen in birds and lower forms, is known as the paleocerebellum.

In mammals, the most important changes in the nervous system are related to the formation of the cerebral cortex and the large cerebral hemispheres. Associated with this development appear new cerebellar structures, which constitute the neocerebellum. These are the cerebellar hemispheres, and they are concerned primarily with the coordination of impulses which are delivered to, and distributed from, the cerebral cortex.

Midbrain.—The principal functions of the midbrain throughout the phyletic series are audition, vision, and the conduction of impulses between the higher and lower centers of the nervous system. In fishes, some of the midbrain is concerned with the lateral line organs, but when these organs disappear in higher animals the associated midbrain centers also disappear. In inframammalian forms the colliculi are the principal sensory centers for vision and audition, but as encephalization proceeds and the cerebral hemispheres are developed, the importance of the midbrain in these sensory functions diminishes.

Thalamus.—In the lower vertebrates the thalamus constitutes almost the entire forebrain, and it is concerned principally with vision, forming relay stations between the eyes and the midbrain. It subsequently enlarges to include centers for hearing, pressure, pain, and temperature. As the cerebral cortex grows in mammalian forms, the thalamus becomes for the most part a great relay station between the cortex and lower centers, but it also probably serves very important functions as a coordinator of sensory impulses and of impulses traveling between it and the cortex. In warm-blooded animals, birds and mammals, the hypothalamus is differentiated from the main body of the thalamus and becomes an important center of integration for the autonomic system.

Corpus Striatum.—This is established as a motor center in fishes. It expands greatly in amphibia and reptiles and reaches its greatest development in birds. The cerebral cortex of the mammal takes over many of the functions of the corpus striatum, and as a result it becomes relatively less important in the later stages of phylogenesis.

The Cerebral Cortex.—In fishes there exists no cerebral cortex; only the olfactory bulbs and a primitive forebrain, made up of thalamus and corpus striatum, are present. In amphibia and reptiles, however, a primitive cortex appears in the form of a nucleus of cell bodies interposed between the olfactory bulb and the rest of the forebrain; this first cortex

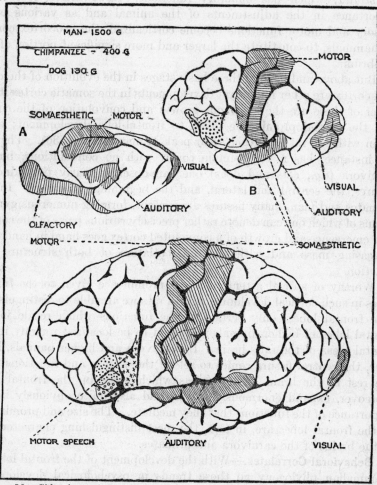

Fig. 36.—Side views of three mammalian brains drawn to scale to show their relative sizes. The scale at the top of the figures illustrates the relative weights of the three brains when weighed fresh. *A*, the brain of a large adult dog; *B*, the brain of a young adult chimpanzee; *C*, human brain somewhat below average size. The positions and sizes of the primary sensory and motor areas are indicated. (*After Campbell. From S. W. Bartelmez. Man from the point of view of his development and structure. In The nature of the world and of man, p. 466. Chicago: University of Chicago Press, 1926. By permission of the publishers.*)

is plainly concerned only with olfactory functions. Later on in birds is laid down the first cortex having nonolfactory functions, but only in mammals does it become a true cortex with a definite cortical structure as well as important functions. Such a "somatic" cortex is sometimes called *neocortex* because of its more recent phylogenetic development, and one can distinguish it even in mammals from the old cortex, or *paleocortex*, which has olfactory functions. As olfaction recedes in importance in the adjustments of the animal and as various other sensory and motor functions become corticalized, the neocortex comes, in mammals, to constitute the larger and more significant portion of the cerebrum.

But above and beyond these basic stages in the evolution of the cerebral cortex are other important developments in the somatic cortex itself. Chief of these are the enormous growth and convolution of the cortex and the special prominence given to frontal-lobe development; these begin with the rat and reach their peak in man (see Fig. 36). The rat, for instance, has a very simple cortex with no convolutions, but in carnivora (*e.g.*, cats and dogs) one can observe clearly the principal fissures, the central and lateral, and the beginnings of others. In the primates and man, many fissures are present, forming numerous gyri by means of which one can denote rather precisely various parts of the cortex. The emergence and growth of a convoluted cortex goes hand in hand with increasing mass and with the differentiation of both structure and function.

Worthy of special attention is the prominence given to the frontal lobes in such cortical development. In rats we are able to distinguish no true frontal lobes; only certain of the functions which reside in the frontal lobes of higher animals are found to be localized roughly in the frontal areas of the rat's brain. In carnivora and higher animals, however, the central fissure comes to set off these areas and functions from the rest of the brain. These areas which make up the frontal lobe, moreover, expand enormously in size and also quite obviously in the importance of the functions that they mediate. The size and prominence of the frontal lobes are, in fact, the most distinguishing characteristics of the brains of the carnivora and primates.

Behavioral Correlates.—With the development of the frontal lobes in mammalian phylogeny go those trends in psychological development which, as noted above, make the difference in behavioral capacity between higher and lower animals. Manipulative ability which displaces locomotor adjustment in higher mammals is correlated with the differentiation of special motor centers in the frontal lobes for manipulative coordination. Even more important, however, are the relations between the higher mental processes and the so-called frontal association areas of the frontal lobe. The capacity to form concepts, to organize the elements of a sequence of adjustments, to solve problems requiring central symbolic or 'recall' processes—all these mark the later stages of mammalian development, and in some cases it is rather clear that the frontal lobe is basic to the capacity, although changes in other parts of the cortex which go along with frontal-lobe development are certainly of some consequence.

Referring now to more general aspects of mental and cortical evolution, we may observe two main trends. There is, first of all, the encephalization of sensory-motor and simple adaptive functions. If we compare the effects of destruction of the forebrain in the frog, the bird, and some mammal, such as the cat, the fact that simple sensory-motor relations have become more highly encephalized in evolution, although no more highly developed, becomes obvious. The frog is handicapped hardly at all by the decerebration; the bird is slightly disturbed, as is shown by the fact that it no longer flies voluntarily, but it can still stand upright and carry out most of its behavior quite normally; the cat, on the other hand, can no longer stand, or walk, and is little more than an automaton. Thus we observe the encephalization in phylogeny of the most elementary behavioral functions.

Our information concerning sensory capacity in this respect is confined principally to vision, but here a similar situation appears to hold. Extirpation of the cortex in birds (Layman) has no great effect on visual capacity; a bird without its 'visual cortex' is quite able to carry out all normal adjustments to visual details of its environment and suffers no disability in the discrimination of patterns. This, however, is not the case for the rat, which, although it does have considerable residual capacity to deal with the brightness of objects in its environment (Lashley), is unable to discriminate differences in visual contour or to make adjustments on the basis of visual detail after removal of its 'visual' cortex. In man, encephalization has gone even further, for according to the best evidence available (Marquis), complete blindness results from removal of the visual area of the cortex. Thus, it is clear that the common visual functions are subserved entirely by subcortical centers in lower animals but are progressively taken over by the cortex in phylogenesis.

A second trend in psychoneural evolution is that, in addition to the corticalization of functions previously mediated subcortically, new psychological capacities are created by the differentiation and elaboration of the cerebral cortex. Whether or not these capacities are all of one class, *viz.*, those dependent upon the presence of central symbolic processes, we are not able at this time to state, but it appears certain that such processes are at least one of the capacities developed most prominently in phylogenesis. As previously stated, the frontal lobes play an important role in this development. Other areas of the cortex, associated with primary sensory areas, but not a part of them, also undergo some elaboration in mammalian evolution, and these undoubtedly endow the organism with psychological capacities of a higher order. Whether or not these capacities are of a "new" type or simply allow for greater complexity of adaptive behavior, we shall leave for later consideration.

Brain Weight and Intelligence.—Leaving the more specific aspects of mental and neural development in phylogeny, we may turn from the general fact that the intelligence of animals is correlated roughly with position in the phylogenetic scale to another related fact, that the ratio of brain weight to body weight increases throughout the phyletic series. Ordinarily this ratio is stated in the following form:

$$K = \frac{E^r}{P}$$

where E denotes brain weight, r an exponent which is relatively constant in different animals, and P the body weight. This ratio, extensive measurements have shown, is quite constant (K) for different members of a species and for closely related species. It does, however, increase with phylogenetic level as is shown by the following examples: birds, .04 to .05; rodents (rats, guinea pigs, rabbits, squirrels), .07; whales, .24; carnivora, .31 to .34; monkeys, .4 to .5; anthropoid apes, .7 to .8; and man, 2.8. These figures give some idea of the importance of the brain to the organism in phylogenesis. Especially noteworthy is the great difference between man and his nearest evolutionary relatives in this respect. This is comparable to the difference in intellectual capacity shown by apes and man and is compatible with man's exalted idea of himself.

General References

HERRICK, C. J., 1926. *Brains of rats and men.* Chicago: Univ. Chicago Press. Pp. 382.

LASHLEY, K. S., 1934. Nervous mechanisms in learning. In Murchison's *Handbook of general experimental psychology.* Worcester: Clark Univ. Press. Pp. 456–496.

MAIER, N. R. F., and T. C. SCHNEIRLA, 1935. *Principles of animal psychology.* New York: McGraw-Hill. Pp. xiii + 529.

MUNN, N. L., 1938. *Psychological development.* Boston: Houghton. Pp. xx + 582.

CHAPTER VII

ONTOGENETIC DEVELOPMENT

Events in the development of the evolutionary series and the individual do not interest us per se, but they do provide us with additional sources of information in our study of the physiological mechanisms of behavior. For that reason, we considered phylogenetic development in the last chapter and gained some understanding of the ways in which biological evolution is correlated with increases in psychological capacity. We shall consider in the present chapter the problems and facts of ontogenetic development as they bear upon physiological psychology. First we shall deal with the more psychological facts of development as they have been obtained in careful experimental studies of prenatal and neonatal behavior; and later we shall come to the problem of the physiological factors concerned in such behavioral growth.

BEHAVIORAL DEVELOPMENT

The question of the extent to which patterns of behavior are laid down in the innate structure of an organism—*i.e.*, are inherited—and of the extent to which they are learned has always been prominent in psychological discussion. Several years ago the behaviorists were proposing that the basic unit of behavior is the reflex and that all more complex forms of behavior are derived from reflexes though learning; 'instinctivists,' or 'purposivists,' on the other hand, contended that highly organized, so-called instinctive patterns of behavior were inherited, not learned. To settle this question and others related to it, effort was directed to two general types of experimentation: In the first, attempts were made to curtail or eliminate exercise of behavior, as well as the stimulus situations giving rise to it, until a time in ontogenetic development when such behavior had normally become full-fledged. In the second instance, recourse was made to direct observation of behavior throughout the period of embryonic growth and infancy. The results of these two lines of approach may be discussed in turn.

Maturation of Patterns of Behavior.—One of the earliest types of behavior to be studied was the pecking of chicks—a very accurate and, at the same time, rather complex type of sensory-motor coordination which can be measured readily. In the early experiments (Breed) and in several others down to the careful study of Cruze performed only recently, it has been clearly shown that in this behavior both physiological factors of maturation and the effects of exercise are at work. The essential feature of the experiments has been to keep chicks in the dark and away from any opportunity to peck for part or all of the period during which the accuracy and rate of pecking ordinarily improves for chicks in their normal environment. It was found that chicks, when given their first chance to peck, always start out with a poor score, but those which are older on their first opportunity improve much more rapidly. Thus is the importance of some maturational factor, as well as learning, demonstrated.

More complex than pecking behavior are patterns of sexual behavior. These in many animals consist of many kinds of courtship and copulatory acts knitted together in a highly organized sequence (see Chap. XX). Studies by several investigators (Stone, Beach) leave no question, however, about the constitutional (unlearned) character of sexual behavior. Although it does not appear until a relatively late date in life, such behavior is plainly not dependent upon experience; it appears, indeed, to be about as fully developed in the naïve as in the experienced animal. As we shall note in greater detail in another chapter, the appearance of the behavior, although contingent upon the appropriate environmental circumstances, is the outcome of both neural and endocrine changes in development.

Many other experiments have been carried out on the general problem of the relative importance of maturation and learning, but the present purpose is only to illustrate the procedures and the kinds of facts obtained, not to go into them in great detail. One study is particularly good as an example because of its bearing on other questions considered below. Carmichael, in a series of experiments with amblystoma in the tadpole stage of development, determined the relative importance of neural maturation and exercise in swimming behavior. One group of amblystoma was maintained throughout its early larval period in a medium containing chloretone, a drug that effectively immobilizes an animal, thus preventing exercise, but which does not interfere with the embryologic processes of neural and muscular growth; another group was allowed to grow under normal conditions. When this latter group began to swim, the chloretone was removed from the water of the first group and its swimming behavior noted. In a very few minutes, the results show, these animals were swimming as well as the control group, and even the delay of a few minutes, later experiments showed, was due largely to the time required for the chloretone to wear off. Thus was it established that the processes underlying swimming behavior in amblystoma are predominantly those of the normal course of embryonic growth in which nerve fibers are making connections with each other, the sense organs, and the muscles.

Behavioral Development in Amphibia.—We may turn our attention now to the problem of how behavior is organized and what changes it undergoes when it is studied from the time of its first appearance onward through the various stages of its development. Work on this problem has given us a host of experimental facts about many members of the phylogenetic series from fishes to man.

The classic study is by Coghill and is based upon very careful observations of the amphibian amblystoma. This animal is especially suitable for these experimental purposes because, in contrast to mammals, it is independent of the mother and is directly accessible to observation throughout its development from the gastrula stage on. It has the advantage, too, of being very much like a fish in its earlier stages of development and then, in amphibian fashion, of growing appendages for use in the quadripedal locomotion typical of higher animals.

Coghill's observations may be summarized as follows: Behavior first appears as an idiomuscular phenomenon—one in which muscles contract by stimulation applied directly to them. Then appears a true response, mediated by the receptors and nervous system. This, it should be noted, occurs first in the *head* region of the animal, a fact that is undoubtedly related to the dominance of the head over the rest of the body both in the rate of its development and in its regulation of embryonic development (see Chap. II). In further maturation, the total organism becomes involved more and more in behavior. By lateral flexion, the organism assumes the form of a C when it is stimulated. Next, the pattern of response is altered in such a way that while the head region is curved in one direction the caudal part is laterally flexed in the other, thus making an S. Through the progression of a flexor response down the body in a caudal direction, the S is so reversed that the basic pattern of the swimming movement is executed. Maturation is completed, finally, by the speeding up of these movements to the point where they become really effective in locomotion. Later of course, the amblystoma grows appendages, leaves the water, and moves upon land. In the development of locomotion, Coghill's observations show, the limbs fit into the sigmoid movement of the body, at first passively, and later actively, timing their movements with those of the body. Then, finally, from the relatively gross movements of the limbs emerge much finer adjustments of small muscle groups in which one can see the progressive involvement of the more distal parts of the limb.

The conclusion to be drawn from Coghill's experiments has been summarized in the concept of *individuation:* behavioral development proceeds from the response of large muscle groups to that of small ones, from mass movement to individual movement, or in other words in the same essential way as the histological differentiation, in embryologic growth, of specialized cells from cells of general potentiality. Fitting in with the concept of individuation are the principles of the cephalocaudal and proximodistal progression of behavioral development, and these also parallel general trends in embryologic growth. The principle of individuation has been accorded, by some, the status of a general law applying to behavioral development in all animals, and indeed, as will be related in a moment, considerable evidence of individuation in mammals has been offered, although it is by no means the only developmental principle.

Behavioral Development in Birds.—With these thoughts in mind, we may return to consider briefly the results of experimental study of avian and mammalian ontogeny. Two extensive reports of the development of chick embryos are available. In one (Kuo) a cephalocaudal development of behavior, corresponding to that observed by Coghill, was noted. That was also true in a second, somewhat more extensive study (Orr and Windle); stimulation, when first effective, brought about nodding of the head and neck flexion, and later the progressive involvement of the trunk and limbs. In this work, however, the rule that individual movements arise first as a part of mass movement and attain independent status only through individuation, was not uniformly confirmed; for even though the development of locomotor pattern appeared to emerge through individuation, local reflexes could be obtained in limbs and muscles in advance of the time when they became involved in the mass movements and locomotor behavior of the animal. Thus, in birds, the concept of individuation applies only to part of behavioral development, since there is, in addition, independent emergence in some instances of local reflexes.

Behavioral Development in Mammals.—Not nearly so easy to generalize from, or to summarize, are the studies of mammalian ontogeny, of which a great number have been amassed. For the rat, individuation has been reported (Angulo), and yet in another experiment (Windle and Baxter) local reflex movements appeared before generalized responses. In cats the emergence of specific behavior from massive response is the rule (Windle and Griffin), but there is little question that reflex behavior often appears before it has been a part of generalized behavior.

Only in the case of the human fetus, of the mammals studied, are we given confirmation of the Coghillian sequence without clear evidence of exceptions to it. Hooker, who has gathered most of the material concerning human embryonic development, is perfectly clear in stating his confidence in individuation as the principle governing development. Exception to his view, however, has been taken by Carmichael on the ground that the human material which has been available up to now is always in a dying condition and, in particular, lacks an adequate supply of oxygen in its neural tissues. This, he has shown (Jasper,

Bridgman, and Carmichael), can cause significant changes in neural activity and may produce atypical behavior. Thus some doubt is cast upon the validity of Hooker's observations.

Why many of the mammalian experiments have presented an equivocal picture is told us, at least in part, by recent experiments upon the guinea pig (Carmichael and Smith) in which special care was taken of the conditions of stimulation. By means of a series of bristles whose pressure upon the skin could be graduated, observations were made not only of the kind of behavior resulting from stimulation but also of the *threshold* of such behavior. Out of these observations came the fact that a stimulus that was ordinarily just strong enough to elicit response produced a local response characteristic of the point stimulated, but that with stronger stimulation more widespread behavior, frequently involving the whole organism, was observed. Thus it may be that because of failure to control appropriately the intensity of the stimulation undue importance has been attached in other experiments to general behavior.

Still another study (Carmichael) of behavior in the fetal guinea pig leads to a most significant generalization which applies to the guinea pig and most certainly in some degree to other animals also: There is a characteristic pattern of response associated with the stimulation of nearly every point on the surface of the body. On this point Carmichael writes (1941, pp. 15–16):

in general each stimulus point or cutaneous reflexogenous zone, when optimally stimulated, releases a pattern of behavior which is remarkably constant from the first time it appears in early fetal motile life until birth and, indeed, until adult life. For example, when a stimulus is applied to the upper lip just to the right or left of the midline on the snout of a guinea pig fetus of 50 postinsemination days, very specific behavior results. In such cases the paw on the stimulated side is almost invariably brought to the point of stimulation. If the stimulus is moved a millimeter from one side of the midline to the other, the other paw is at once brought into play. This same reaction can be demonstrated with other types of stimuli such as drops of warm or cold water, but not necessarily by drops of water of the same temperature as the fetus. Thus it is not the physical character of the stimulus but rather that it shall be above the threshold of some of the complex of skin receptors and in a specific locus, that determines the response.

In addition to noting such characteristic patterns of response to stimuli of different locus on the body surface, Carmichael goes on to state that a series of responses may be initiated by a particular stimulus and will displace each other in a sequence until the removal of the stimulus is effected. "First, it may be, it [the fetus] will attempt to remove the stimulus by curling the lip; then, if the stimulus remains, it is brushed by the forepaw on the stimulated side. If the stimulus still persists, the head is turned sharply. Finally, a general struggle is resorted to which involves movements of all four limbs and all trunk muscles." Thus are organized, in the neural maturation of fetal development, not only specific patterns of response but sequences of such patterns. In concluding, Carmichael writes: " . . . the course of fetal development is the story of the initial appearance and then the continued maintenance of a wide variety of specific mechanisms. The timing and interplay of these mechanisms make . . . the tiny body able to adapt itself in many varying and successful ways to environmental changes (p. 17)."

In reviewing, now, the results of the various studies of the ontogenetic development of behavior, we are led to the conclusion, not that any one rule governs behavioral development (although the individuation and a cephalocaudal order of the emergence of behavior are tendencies seen in greater or lesser extent in all animals) but that in the maturation of receptor-adjustor-effector cell systems rather specific, yet complex and singularly adaptive, mechanisms of behavior emerge. What physiological factors are concerned in this development will be discussed in another section below.

SENSORY DEVELOPMENT

Attempts to study the way in which sensory functions mature in ontogeny present the difficulty that there is no way to tell whether or not a sense is functioning, or if so, in what degree, except by observing reflexly elicited behavior; for neither verbal reports nor methods of conditioning or learning are possible in the fetus. The part, therefore, which is played by sensory maturation in the unfolding of behavioral mechanisms is not particularly clear, and our information on this score is rather limited. We are, nevertheless, able to arrive at a few significant conclusions as to the emergence of sensory mechanisms in ontogenetic growth.

Probably the first type of sensitivity to appear in fetal life is proprioception, as Coghill concluded from his observations of amblystoma. Carmichael is inclined to agree that this is true for mammals also, although he recognizes the experimental difficulties in avoiding cutaneous stimulation when one attempts to study proprioceptive sensitivity. For cutaneous sensitivity certainly appears early in development, and, when it does, the mechanisms for providing different degrees and kinds of behavior according to the intensity of the stimulus are already laid down. At that time, responses to cutaneous stimulation of just threshold intensity are well localized, as Carmichael has emphasized, but those accompanying stronger stimulation are more generalized.

Closely associated with the appearance of cutaneous sensitivity to pressure stimuli is the response to temperature stimuli. The fetal guinea pig, for example, may give no response to small drops of water of body temperature and yet will respond with localized reflex reactions when the temperature of the stimulus is raised or lowered from that of the body (Carmichael and Lehner). But although both tactile and thermal sensitivity are established early in fetal development, such is not the case in respect to pain. For a long time in fetal life, the prick of a sharp needle is no more effective as a stimulus than the pressure of a blunt instrument. Such a statement is true not only of the fetal development of most animals but has been observed to hold for newborn human infants as well. It appears to be true, therefore, that the sensory-motor mechanisms for pain are laid down separately from those of other kinds of cutaneous sensitivity.

In order to study visuomotor development, advantage has been taken of the fact that when black and white striations are passed in front of the eyes of most animals regular nystagmic movements of the head or eyes— oculocephalogyric reactions, as they are called—are elicited. Also useful as indices are eyewink reflexes which may be called forth by visual, tactile, or auditory stimulation. From the observations of such behavior have come the following general conclusions: Visuomotor mechanisms develop comparatively slowly; in some animals (e.g., the guinea pig), maturation is complete before birth, whereas in others (e.g., the kitten) it takes place, for the most part, after birth. The motor aspects of such development, it appears, precede the maturation of the sensory mechanisms, for it is possible to elicit eyewinks by tactile stimulation and to obtain movements from vestibular or proprioceptive stimulation before visual stimulation is effective (Carmichael). Visually determined responses, on the other hand, are dependent largely upon physiological changes occurring within the eye itself; for in experiments in which visual acuity was studied by means of the size of striations to which oculocephalogyric reactions were given, a progressive improvement in vision was found to correlate with the clearing of the optic media and with other changes in the eye (Warkentin). It is clear, therefore, that the development of basic visuomotor mechanisms is not due in any considerable measure to the influence of exercise or learning but rather to physiological processes of maturation.

NEUROMYAL FACTORS IN DEVELOPMENT

An important physiological factor in behavioral development, obviously, is the physiological gradient of metabolism extending along the head-tail axis. Such a gradient, we have already seen in an earlier chapter, is an essential feature of embryonic growth. From it we may expect that the establishment of neural structures necessary for behavior will proceed at a faster rate in the head than in the more posterior parts of the body. It is reasonable, then, that in Coghillian sequences, as well as in the order of appearance of other more specific patterns of response, the head and forelimbs should lead in behavioral development. On a similar basis we are able to understand the fact that in most cases, and particularly in the development of locomotion in amblystoma, the differentiation of behavior in the limbs proceeds in a proximal-distal direction.

A much more important problem, however, in understanding the physiological basis of behavioral growth, is that of the *organization* of relatively complex, yet quite stable, patterns of behavior. The most elementary reflexive withdrawal of a limb from a stimulus is no simple matter when viewed from the standpoint of neurophysiology, for in it are involved many different nerve fibers and very delicate adjustments of nervous activity. How much more complex, then, is the precise reflex localization of the locus of a stimulus which the prenatal guinea pig exhibits. When one realizes, moreover, as Carmichael has pointed out, that there is a more or less characteristic pattern of response for many different points of stimulation upon the body, we are confronted with the problem of understanding how, through physiological processes of maturation, organized functions of such nicety and intricacy are established. That is, indeed, the central problem of physiological psychology in all phases of the subject to which we turn.

In attacking this problem, we must realize that no distinction, other than one of convenience, can be made between the factors determining the organization of the structure and that of the behavior of an individual. Behavior must depend, first of all, upon the appropriate neural structures and upon the establishment of synaptic interconnections between neurons, or of functional relations between them. It is in the structural development of the nervous system, in particular, that we may expect to find the emergence of the organization of neurons which will determine the patterns of neural activity underlying basic forms of behavior. To the available facts concerning neuroembryological differentiation, therefore, let us turn for an answer to the problem of how patterns of behavior become organized in development.

Peripheral Influences upon Neural Differentiation.—It has been clear from the beginning of work in neuroembryology that the sense organs and effectors play an important role in determining the growth and structure of neural centers. In 1907, Harrison grafted limbs of amphibia into abnormal positions and noted that they received comparatively normal innervation and even carried out, in many instances, normal functions. These observations have been amply confirmed in recent years; and by taking advantage of the fact that in amphibia, particularly young amphibian animals, the grafting of limbs and other surgical alterations of bodily structure can be performed with considerable success, our knowledge of the importance of peripheral structures in the differentiation of the nervous system has been considerably extended (see Fig. 37).

From a series of researches by Detwiler have come several facts of importance to us. When a limb is transplanted somewhat rostrally or caudally from its normal position it tends to 'attract' nerves from the region of the spinal cord which would under normal circumstances innervate it. Significant also is the fact that if the growth of normal nerves to a peripheral structure is prevented in some way, as by mechanical blocking or surgical removal, nerves from some other part of the cord, usually the nearest possible part, will grow to innervate the struc-

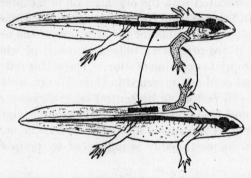

Fig. 37.—Showing transplantation of a portion of the spinal cord and of a forelimb from one amblystoma to another. (*From P. Weiss. Autonomous versus reflexogenous activity of the central nervous system. Proc. Amer. phil. Soc.,* 84, 53–64, 1941. *By permission of the American Philosophical Society.*)

ture; sometimes even nerves from the opposite side of the cord will do this (Hamburger). Such attractive influences are exerted, moreover, even by foreign structures, for when such structures as an embryonic tail, eye, or olfactory bulb are transplanted into the limb region the spinal cord grows nerves to them also (Detwiler).

This line of research, when carried further, reveals not only that nerves grow out to the periphery under the influence of peripheral structures, but that the growth, and probably also the functional differentiation, of neural centers is governed in large part by the demands of the periphery. It has been demonstrated, for example, that a hypoplasia (underdevelopment) or hyperplasia (overgrowth) of the dorsal sensory ganglia may take place, according to whether, by the excision of normal limbs or the grafting of additional limbs, there is under- or overloading at the periphery (Detwiler; Carpenter).

A similar relation holds also in the brain with respect to the influence of sense organs of the head. Removal of the nasal placode (primitive olfactory bulb), for example, greatly reduces the size and number of cells in the cerebral cortex (Burr), which, in amphibia, it will be recalled, is entirely olfactory in function. The same relation holds for the visual system. Removal of the eye causes hypoplasia of the visual centers of the midbrain associated with it, and the substitution of an abnormally large eye, obtained from another species, on the other hand, brings about increased growth in the centers of the visual system (Harrison; Twitty). Thus experiments reveal the dominant, although not exclusive, influences of the various organs of the body upon the growth of the neural centers representing those organs. We do not know, unfortunately, whether such influences go beyond the growth of these centers and include other aspects of central organization, but it seems reasonable that such growth in size may be correlated with the organization of a center.

Intracordal Influences upon Neural Structure.—Peripheral factors are not, however, solely responsible for the structure of the nervous system. Entirely within it are organizing influences, some of which have been revealed by appropriate experimentation. The motor cells of the ventral horn of the spinal cord are governed in their development not nearly so much by peripheral factors as by central ones; excision of the muscles to which they send fibers does not, as a general rule, significantly alter their development (Carpenter), although in certain cases growth of the ventral horn unquestionably is influenced by peripheral structures (Hamburger).

More important, though, are influences extending longitudinally down the spinal cord from the medulla, as the following results indicate (Detwiler). If, in the early stages of differentiation, one interchanges two different regions of the spinal cord, the transplants grow and differentiate according to the new region into which they are placed. Such is not the case, however, in the transplantation of the medulla, which tends to develop in normal fashion and to increase growth of the adjoining cord. Similarly, if the medulla is removed, a hypoplasia occurs in the cord. From these facts it has become clear that the medulla is able, within limits, to self-differentiate and, moreover, to govern in some measure the way in which the spinal cord develops. The most probable means by which such influence takes place, it is thought, is through the motor tracts extending downward into the spinal cord. We may conclude, therefore, in surveying all this evidence, that both intrinsic factors within the nervous system and the influences of peripheral structure cooperate in determining the pattern of neural structures laid down in embryonic growth.

Factors in the Organization of Motor Coordination.—Our knowledge of the way in which patterns of behavior are laid down through neural differentiation is not limited, however, to these embryological experiments of neuroanatomic nature. Considerable information of importance has come from the more direct study of physiological and behavioral relationships, through observation of the coordination of limb movements in the development of locomotion in amphibia and in mammals. Locomotor coordination is a basic instance of a well-organized pattern of behavior, the study of which is highly profitable, as the following experiments of Weiss demonstrate.

The Muscle-name Phenomena.—The budding limbs of a tadpole were transplanted to another animal in the same stage of development and were placed just a little in front of the normal limbs to which they corresponded, whether fore or hind ones. As we might expect from statements above, these supernumerary limbs attract nerves from near-by regions of the spinal cord and, in the course of time, become functional, but the question of especial interest is whether they function in a normal manner. Careful study of their patterns of movement showed that they do. Whenever the normal limb executes a movement, the supernumerary follows in exactly the same kind of coordination. This occurs, moreover, regardless of their orientation; *i.e.* the flexor and extensor muscles of the limb coordinate in normal fashion even though their position has been reversed in such a way that the limb moves in a direction opposite to that of the normal limb. In other words, the pattern of movement depends upon the muscles that make it up, rather than upon any functional significance the movement might have had. There is, moreover, no reeducation of limb coordination at any later time in the interests of a more adaptive reaction. Thus was it demonstrated that patterns of coordination are established on the basis of the *muscles* involved.

Why is motor coordination 'normal' under such circumstances? Weiss suggests that it is because in the establishment of neural functions the 'name' of the muscle is the important factor, not the adaptive functions of the muscles. For such a statement, consider the following evidence. If one interchanges the flexor and extensor muscles in a limb, while keeping their innervation intact, one thereby reverses the movement of the limb so that the flexor muscle now responds when it would have responded if it had been left in the normal position, and the same is true for the extensor muscle. One can determine, furthermore, what the movement in the normal position would have been by comparing the function of limbs in which the muscles have been interchanged with the movements of other limbs left normal in the same animal. On the basis of such observations it has been demonstrated that it is the type of muscle involved which determines, in development, the functions in which that muscle will be concerned. It appears, indeed, that each muscle 'knows its name,' for it responds wherever it is whenever a 'call' goes out in the central nervous system for its activity, no matter how incompatible with the purposes of the organism its response may be.

This we can say, then: Each muscle somehow knows its name, and it is the type of muscle, in the final analysis, which determines the pattern of behavior. This phenomenon is the first step in understanding the neuroembryologic basis of behavior. But the next problem is to uncover the processes responsible for it. How, in a word, does a muscle come to 'know its name'? Three possible answers to this question may be considered: (1) a nerve-outgrowth theory, that patterns of behavior are first formed in the differentiation of the central nervous system and then later, motor fibers are brought to their 'correct' destination in the muscles by attractive influences from the muscles themselves; (2) a resonance theory, that there is some specific functional property of neurons and of muscles which 'selects' nervous impulses from a central pool and sees to it that they get to the 'correct' muscle; and (3) a connection theory, that the muscle exercises its influence by determining the kinds of connections that its motor neurons make with other efferent tracts in the central nervous system.

The Nerve-outgrowth Theory.—There is enough evidence at hand against this theory to warrant discarding it (Weiss). For the muscle-name phenomenon to be explained on the basis of the establishment of the proper connections between nerve and muscle requires that the muscle be able to attract to itself in a highly selective manner the 'correct' nerve fibers. That such a requirement is probably not fulfilled is shown by the fact that nerves innervate indiscriminately almost any structure within their reach, even making connections with entirely foreign structures as illustrated above. Sensory nerves can, for example, readily be made to serve muscles, if their course is turned by mechanical deflection in the direction of the muscles. In cases of supernumerary limbs, moreover, it has been demonstrated that quite different sets of nerve fibers innervate the grafted limb and the normal limb. Thus, on these points, it may be argued that patterns of motor coordination are not established through the outgrowth of nerve fibers to the 'right' groups of muscle fibers. We are led, therefore, to examine the other two theories.

The Resonance Theory.—In both the resonance and connection theories, we note first, it is assumed that the organization of patterns of behavior rests upon specific nerve energies of a biochemical nature. As to what these are, we need not speculate, but we do know that a large part of embryologic development is governed by chemical organizers which induce changes in cells, and we may safely suppose that such is the case in the establishment of the muscle-name phenomenon. But there is this crucial question that distinguishes the two theories: Is the specific energy manifested in the functional relations of nerves and muscles, thereby accounting for the muscle's knowing its name? Or does the specific energy simply guide the making of connections between neurons in the central nervous system and thereafter leave all patterns of neural activity to the connections thus made? The resonance theory takes the first of these alternatives, the connection theory the second.

According to the resonance theory, a muscle has a specific functional property. It induces the nerve associated with it to take on a similar functional property and thus to be in 'resonance' with it. This specific property of the nerve fiber acts in the central nervous system to 'select' nervous impulses 'intended' for the muscle in question and to let others go by. What the nature of this resonance is, Weiss does not attempt to state, although he thinks that it cannot be any such simple matter as frequency of impulses—which is what the term resonance, as used in the parlance of physics, would imply.

The connection theory, on the other hand, does not have the weakness of postulating specific functional properties for which we have as yet no explanation. As explained by Sperry, it assumes only that the biochemical influences of muscle are extended to the differentiation of the nerve and that these govern the kind of connections made in the central nervous system. Accordingly, the specificity of the adult nervous system is one of connections but is determined in embryologic differentiation by chemical specificities.

The evidence at hand is not crucial with respect to these two theories, yet it appears to be entirely in accord with a connection theory, which is a priori the more attractive, because it does not require the postulation of a special factor of resonance. Consonant with Sperry's view, moreover, are the facts available concerning the factor of age in determining how well a muscle knows its name. When muscles are interchanged or supernumerary limbs transplanted in young amphibians, the results are as described above; *viz.,* the coordinative pattern is determined by the type of muscle. If such experiments are done in older animals, however, they are not so successful (Weiss, see Sperry); instead, we observe the more or less indiscriminate contraction of muscles. Such a result can be explained either on the view that central connections have already been established and cannot be greatly changed (connection theory), or on the hypothesis that the specific functional properties of nerves cannot be altered, or modulated, by the muscle so readily in later life as in young animals (resonance theory).

More definitely in favor of the connection theory is Sperry's study of the effects of nerve crossing in rats. The nerves to antagonistic muscles were exchanged in such a way that nerve fibers whose activity formerly caused extension of a limb now were connected with the muscles causing flexion, and vice versa. Contrary to the readjustment that one would expect if the muscles modulated specific functions of nerves and reestablished a resonance, there was a reversal of the patterns of coordi-

nation.   Thereby was it shown that in these circumstances the function
of the nerves had become so firmly fixed that it was they, rather than
the muscles, which determined the coordination pattern.   This fact
argues against the notion that a resonance between nerve and muscle is
required for their functioning together and is in favor of the view that
the connections already established by nerve fibers are the basis of the
behavioral pattern.

As the reader can see, the discussion of the physiological factors in
the ontogeny of behavior has brought us to the problem of specific energy
of nerves, a question that emerged early in the historical background of
physiological psychology and is central to many aspects of our present
study.   In only a few instances is the problem settled satisfactorily, and
there are as yet no sweeping generalizations that can be made about the
whole nervous system.   Here, however, we have seen that the problem
of specific nerve energies is one not only of the senses but also of behavioral patterns as well.   Indeed, when we confront the question again
later, it will become clear that the problem of specific nerve energies is
only one formulation of the more general question as to how mental and
behavioral processes are mediated by the nervous system; the question,
that is, of the factors through which the selection and organization of
nervous processes take place.   The facts of behavioral development
considered here suggest that specificity is first determined by the chemical processes governing embryologic differentiation but that in the adult
it is the connections which have been formed in embryonic growth that
are important.   Later we shall see how this notion is upheld in other
aspects of physiological psychology.

SENSORY FACTORS IN THE DEVELOPMENT OF BEHAVIOR

So far in the present discussion, emphasis has been put upon the
unfolding of psychophysiological mechanisms through embryonic differentiation.   Not many years ago, however, a group of theorists possessing a zeal for a less mentalistic and more behavioristic conception of
'mind' and lacking much of the knowledge of physiological development
now available to us attempted to account for the development of behavior
almost entirely in terms of learning.   Even the simplest reflexes were
thought to be derived through learning.   Holt, for example, suggested
that the grasping reflex, which is elicited by tactile stimulation of the
palm of the hand, was established through conditioning.   In spontaneous contractions of the muscles of the hand, Holt argued, the fingers
are flexed in such a way that they stimulate the palm, and thus palmar
stimulation and grasping become associated through learning.   Whether
any reflexive behavior becomes established in this way we do not know,
but we are quite sure that much of it does not.   In Carmichael's study

of the development of amblystoma which had been rendered immobile by drugs, it was clear that exercise was in no respect an important factor in the organization of the swimming pattern.

Other evidence comes from a series of experiments by Weiss in which the sensory nerves to the limbs of amblystoma were severed early in development. In every case locomotor patterns of coordination were quite normal, and it was only upon the closest scrutiny of behavior that some minor differences in coordination attributable to the deafferentiation of the limbs could be detected. The dominant role of the muscle, moreover, in determining patterns of coordination, further speaks against the theory that sensory influences establish reflex patterns. Taking into consideration also Carmichael's observations that many reflex patterns are fully developed when first elicited, we are led to conclude that basic patterns of behavior unfold through normal processes of cellular differentiation, rather than through sensory stimulation and learning.

MATURATION OF ACTIVITY IN THE CENTRAL NERVOUS SYSTEM

It is obvious to the student of infant behavior that there is considerable behavior for which there is no identifiable external stimulation and which is, therefore, thought of as spontaneous. Such behavior, several experiments have recently shown, is often of central origin; *i.e.*, it is caused by the 'spontaneous' discharge of neurons in the central nervous system. Indeed, much behavior appearing in ontogenetic development may be of this type. For such spontaneous behavior, two classes of factors are largely responsible. (1) The neurons of the central nervous system undergo cyclic changes in excitability related, presumably, to their metabolic processes; and these changes are often of such magnitude as to cause self-excitation of neurons. (2) Various chemical factors in the internal environment of the organism provide an adequate stimulus for the activation of central neurons.

Spontaneous Neural Activity.—A most striking demonstration of the spontaneous firing of neurons is to be seen in another experiment in transplantation (Weiss). A portion of the spinal cord was transplanted to a position on the fin of the tadpole (see Fig. 37). Here it soon was incorporated into the connective tissue of the fin and lived on independently of the central nervous system. Such a graft never achieved a highly differentiated structure, but it did send out fibers to muscles and became a small autonomous nervous system. The first evidence that functions had become established in it was that the muscles to which it sent fibers became active. Further study of the graft showed that its neurons were discharging of their own accord—or at least in the absence of sensory stimulation. The reason for the discharge, it appears, was to be found both in the tendency for neurons to discharge and to the facilitating influence of chemical changes in the blood on this tendency.

Development of Brain Waves.—Another aspect of spontaneous neural activity only indirectly related to behavior is found in the so-called brain waves (see Fig. 38). This name is given to electrical potentials generated in the resting brain and varying in a cyclic manner. Such waves have been found in many vertebrate and invertebrate animals and appear to be characteristic of groups of neurons gathered together in ganglia and nuclei (Adrian). In human individuals we find these waves

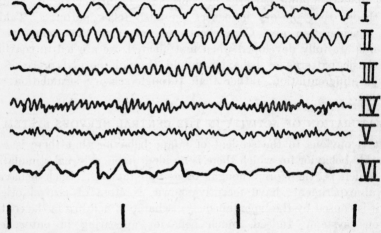

Fig. 38.—Six types of cerebral action potentials ("brain waves") recorded from the human skull. I, saw-tooth waves, seen commonly in young children and consisting of 4 to 7 cycles per second. II, Berger's alpha waves, usually between 9 and 11 cycles per second and seen in normal adults at rest (but not asleep). III, spindle waves, between 12 and 15 cycles per second and appearing in trains during sleep. IV, rapid rhythms, of 20 to 24 cycles per second and only rarely observed. V. Berger's beta waves, 25 to 35 cycles per second and seen in normal waking adults. VI, large random waves of no particular frequency, characteristic of sound sleep. (*From L. W. Crafts, T. C. Schneirla, E. E. Robinson, and R. W. Gilbert, Recent experiments in Psychology, p. 195. New York: Harper, 1938.*)

in frequencies of 1 to 20 per second, but we are able to divide them further into five main bands: 1 to 3 per second, 3½ to 6 per second, 7 to 8 per second, 8 to 12 per second, and 12 to 14 per second. Of these, the most prominent in normal wakeful adults are the frequencies of 8 to 12 per second, which are commonly referred to as the *alpha* waves. Other frequencies are characteristic of sleep and of special abnormal conditions to be reviewed later.

Rhythmic electrical activity of the brain begins before birth in the animals which have been studied. The guinea pig, for example, shows it several days before birth (Jasper *et al.*), and it is present at birth in human infants (Smith). Systematic study of the newborn infant's brain waves shows, moreover, that waves of every variety exist but are somewhat more restricted in locus than in adults, for they are found principally in the sensory-motor areas of the cortex, *i.e.*, just anterior and posterior to the central fissure.

Of special importance, however, are the changes that take place in the alpha rhythm after birth. This rhythm in the adult is, as was indicated above, between 8 and 12 cycles per second in frequency. It originates in

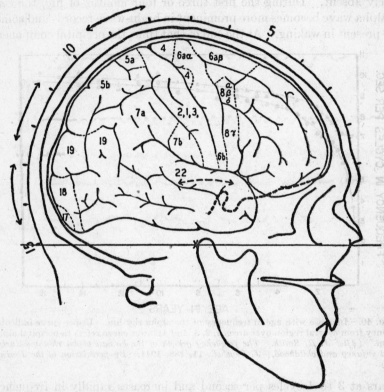

Fig. 39.—Four principal foci of alpha-wave activity in the human brain (indicated by arrows): occipital area at extreme back of brain, related area just dorsal to occipital area, primary sensory and motor areas, and the temporal area. (*From D. B. Lindsley. Foci of activity of the alpha rhythm in the human electro-encephalogram. J. exper. Psychol.*, **23**, 159–171, 1938. *By permission of the American Psychological Association.*)

four focal areas of the cortex (Lindsley; see Fig. 39): the anterior and posterior parts of the occipital lobe, which together supply the larger part of the waves; the region of the central fissure; and the temporal pole.

Contrasting with this picture of the alpha wave in the adult are two important differences in the infant (Smith; see Fig. 40). (1) Alpha waves are found only in the sensory-motor area at birth, and not in the occipital area where they later become most prominent. (2) In infancy the alpha waves are quite slow, but increase in frequency with age until an individual is twelve to sixteen years old.   Illustration of these two points is provided in Fig. 40 where the growth of the alpha wave in respect to frequency in the sensory-motor, or central, and in the occipital regions of the cortex is shown in relation to age.   From this figure we can see that at birth the central alpha rhythm has a frequency of about 7 cycles and is present only in sleep.   The occipital alpha wave, on the other hand, is entirely absent.   During the first three or four months of life, the central alpha wave becomes more prominent in brain-wave records and comes to be present in waking.   At the end of that time, the occipital component

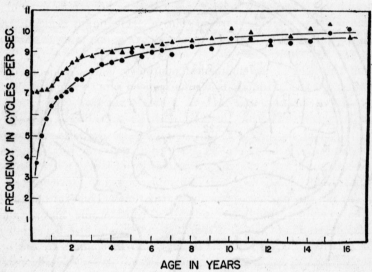

Fig. 40.—Increase with age in frequency of the alpha rhythm.   Upper curve indicates frequency from central region over areas 1, 2, 3, and 4; lower curve refers to occipital alpha rhythm.   (*After J. R. Smith.   The frequency growth of the human alpha rhythms during normal infancy and childhood.   J. Psychol.*, **11**, 188, 1941.   *By permission of the Journal Press.*)

appears at 3 to 4 cycles per second and increases rapidly in frequency until the end of the first year.   From then on until late adolescence, both components gradually increase in frequency with the occipital wave gradually catching up in frequency to the central wave.

Of the significance of these ontogenetic changes in alpha waves we cannot be certain.   Brain waves, we shall see later, are closely related to the state of waking or sleeping of an adult individual and to abnormalities of behavior, especially epileptic conditions.   In infancy, however, we can as yet, with the information available, only indicate what other changes in behavior are correlated with those in the brain waves and surmise the significance of the correlation.

The behavior of the newborn infant is of such a character as to lead us to believe that the cerebral cortex is functioning little, if at all.   A most prominent feature of infant behavior, for example, is a very strong grasping reflex. Objects thrust into the infant's hand will be gripped with comparatively great strength—so great, in fact, that in many cases the infant will support its own weight. Such a conspicuous grasping reaction, we know, is a feature of behavior *not* under the control of the cortex, as experiments involving extirpation of the cortex show (see Chap. XVI). In the first three or four months of life, there is a rapid decline in this reflex, which we may surmise is related to the maturation of cortical functions. After four months of age, moreover, we note (McGraw) the progressive improvement of behavior which is 'deliberative' and hence more under cortical control. The infant begins to reach for objects which it sees, it begins to sit and creep, and later, at about one year of age, it starts to talk.

From the field of developmental neurology comes evidence of the maturation of cortical functions at an advanced rate throughout the first few months of infancy, and then at a somewhat slower pace in later months and years. Neither the myelinization of pathways between the cortex and thalamus (Flechsig) nor the differentiation of the histological neural structure is complete at birth but goes on for many more months. Beyond such general statements of the interrelationships of neuroanatomic, behavioral, and electrophysiological development we cannot go on the basis of present information. Thus, although it is clear that cerebral functions undergo a considerable maturation in postnatal development which is reflected in the refinement and integration of behavior taking place in infancy and in changes in the brain waves (electroencephalogram), we must await further experimentation before we can go into greater detail concerning the special physiological factors operating in development.

General References

CARMICHAEL, L., 1941. The experimental embryology of mind. *Psychol. Bull.*, **38**, 1–28.

COGHILL, G. E., 1929. *Anatomy and the problem of behavior*. Cambridge. Pp. xii + 113.

MUNN, N. L., 1938. *Psychological development*. Boston: Houghton. Pp. xx + 582.

WEISS, P., 1940. Self-differentiation of the basic patterns of coordination. *Comp. Psychol. Monogr.*, **17**, No. 88, pp. 96.

CHAPTER VIII
THE CHEMICAL SENSES

One can study a machine either by watching it being built or by taking it apart after it is built. So it is with the behavior of organisms. In the last two chapters we studied the building of the human organism as it takes place in phylogeny and ontogeny, and from it we came to understand some of the physiological mechanisms of behavior. From this point on, however, we shall take the machine apart to gain further knowledge of the physiological processes involved in the human machine's behavior. Our breakdown of the organism will be done according to four main categories: (1) sensory and perceptual capacities; (2) motor and behavioral functions; (3) motivation and instincts; (4) adaptive functions. To be sure, we shall not always be able to stick rigidly to this separation of topics, for to understand one aspect of the organism's behavior we must often turn to others. We have, nevertheless, in these four divisions the major headings of an outline within which we can organize our thought.

The Chemical Receptors.—There are to be distinguished in all vertebrate organisms, including man, three classes of chemical receptors: the olfactory, the common chemical, and the gustatory receptors. These are alike in that they are more sensitive to chemical stimuli than to stimuli of any other kind. Not only that, but their chemical stimuli must, it appears, always be in solution. To be sure, olfactory stimuli are gaseous before they arrive at the receptors, but once there, they enter into solution with the mucous membranes bathing the olfactory receptors, and thus, for the receptor, itself, the olfactory stimulus is like the others—a solution.

There are, however, differences in the types of chemical stimuli to which the three classes of receptors are sensitive, although a full analysis of these differences is complex in terms of the chemistry involved. Important in accounting for them, however, is the fact that stimuli for the olfactory receptors must be capable of existing in gaseous form at ordinary temperatures and also of being soluble in the mucous fluid bathing the receptors, whereas the stimuli for taste need only be soluble in water and certain other fluids. Thus the physical properties of the stimuli are important in determining whether they reach the receptors. Once there, however, it seems quite probable that they encounter, in the two instances,

142

receptors of different chemical natures and, consequently, of different sensitivities to a given stimulus. We find, indeed, that the same stimulus applied to the two types of receptors may affect one and not the other. In addition, we may note that the smell receptors are, in general, more sensitive than the taste receptors, which, in turn, are more excitable than the common chemical receptors.

Of importance, finally, are the structural differences in the three classes of sense organs (see Fig. 5). The most primitive is the common chemical receptor; it consists simply of a neuron whose peripheral ends are frayed in a nerve ending which encircles a comparatively undifferentiated epithelial cell. The gustatory receptor, on the other hand, is made up of a neuron (the 'primary sense cell') that ends upon a highly differentiated epithelial cell (a 'secondary sense cell'), which is one of a highly organized group of epithelial cells, called the taste bud. Contrasting with this type of receptor is that of the olfactory sense. This involves no secondary sense cell but consists only of neurons whose cell bodies, having migrated to the periphery, are exposed there to stimulation and have become especially adapted for extreme sensitivity by the differentiation of hairlike filaments. Such structural differences in the three classes of chemical receptors, we may note, are representative of trends which have been observed in the differentiation of receptors in general (see p. 25).

THE NEUROSENSORY APPARATUS OF OLFACTION

Tucked away in alcoves at the roof of each of the two nasal cavities is the group of olfactory neurons and their accessory epithelial cells

Fig. 41.—On the left is sketched the human olfactory cleft opened by turning the nasal septum *S* upward; the area in black represents the olfactory epithelium (*After Parker*). On the right is a transverse section through the human left nasal cavity. 1, olfactory cleft; 2, septum; 3, 4, and 5, superior, middle, and inferior conchae. (*From C. H. Best and N. B. Taylor. The physiological basis of medical practice, p. 1711. Baltimore: Williams and Wilkins, 1940. By permission of the publishers.*)

which make up the *olfactory epithelium*. To reach it, olfactory stimuli in gaseous form must make their way through the external openings of the nose, the nostrils, and be reflected upward to the olfactory epithelium by bones (conchae) which project into the cavities (see Fig. 41). Because the olfactory epithelium is not very accessible, however, only a small part of the air which contains gases capable of stimulating the epithelium ever reaches it, since most of the air passes instead through the exit of the nasal cavities into the throat and lungs. The amount of air reaching the olfactory epithelium may, however, be increased by the act of 'sniffing,' which, accordingly, allows animals and men to increase temporarily their olfactory acuity.

The Olfactory Epithelium.—Usually about 500 sq. mm. in size, the olfactory epithelium (Fig. 42) in man can be distinguished by the sharp,

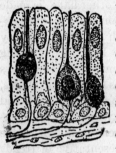

Fig. 42.—Cells of the olfactory epithelium. At bottom, basal cells; upright cylindrical cells, the sustentacular cells; oval with long hairs, the olfactory receptor cells. (*After Wieman. From G. A. Baitsell, Human biology, p. 221. New York: McGraw-Hill, 1940.*)

though irregular, boundary which it makes with the adjacent epithelium and by its typically yellowish or (in lower animals) brownish color. It is composed of three principal types of cells: (1) the pigmented *columnar* cells, between which are 'sandwiched' the olfactory cells and whose function is plainly one of support; (2) the *basal* cells, which are blocklike in form and located on the innermost surface of the epithelium, thereby providing the groundwork to which the rest of the epithelium is attached; and (3) the more numerous *olfactory* cells proper. Of these, the outer portion is of fine filaments, the middle is the cell body, and the inner part tapers off into axon fibers conducting excitation away from the epithelium. Passing upward through many perforations in the bony plate, the *cribriform plate*, just beneath which the epithelium is located, these fibers end upon neurons of the olfactory bulb, lying just above the cribriform plate.

Also to be found in the olfactory epithelium are *free nerve endings*, derived evidently from the sensory nerves innervating the skin and muscles of the face rather than from the olfactory system. These endings are believed to mediate tactile sensibility and common chemical sensitivity—a fact that must always be kept in mind in experiments with smell, for these receptors may sometimes be involved in reactions which may mistakenly be ascribed to olfactory reception.

Normally bathing the outer surface of the olfactory epithelium is mucous fluid secreted by the epithelial cells of the nasal cavities. In this fluid, it is believed, must be dissolved any gaseous materials which are to be effective in exciting the olfactory cells. For that reason, it has been argued, the amount to which gases are soluble in the mucous fluid is an important factor limiting their effectiveness as olfactory stimuli. Because, moreover, gases dissolved in the mucous fluid may thereafter have to pass into the olfactory hairs before stimulation occurs, the chemical constitution of the hairs may have a similar importance. Their composition, evidence tends to indicate, is predominantly fatty (lipoid), and it might be supposed, therefore, that olfactory stimuli must

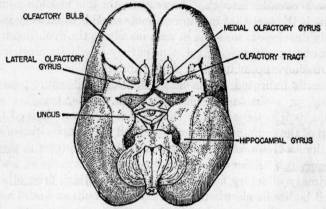

FIG. 43.—Ventral surface of embryonic human brain showing some of the olfactory centers and pathways. (*After C. J. Herrick. Introduction to neurology, p. 243. Philadelphia: Saunders, 1918. By permission of the publishers.*)

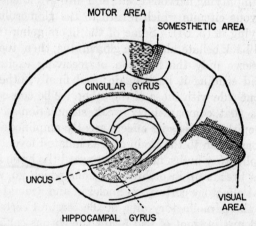

FIG. 44.—Medial view of the human brain showing some of the olfactory centers and pathways. (*After S. W. Ranson. Anatomy of the nervous system, p. 282. Philadelphia: Saunders, 1941. By permission of the publishers.*)

also be soluble in fatty materials. More in keeping with our conception of neural excitation, however, is the theory that excitation takes place at the membrane of the olfactory hairs, rather than in chemical reactions within the cell; but in this case, too, the internal constitution of the hairs is important, for it must determine the character of the polarization set up at the membrane and, consequently, the kinds of stimuli to which the hairs are sensitive.

Neural Centers and Pathways.—Of all the senses, none presents so complicated a neural system as does olfaction—despite the fact that smell is of very little use to man. In Figs. 43 and 44, only the briefest outline of the more important parts of the system is given, and this, the reader will agree, is complex enough. Accounting for this needless complexity, it appears, is the fact that in lower animals smell is often very important and highly developed; we see it in man merely as the evolutionary carry-over of a once useful system. Let us survey briefly its most important features as they appear in the typical mammal.

As already indicated, axons of the olfactory epithelium pass through the cribriform plate to the olfactory bulb. This, together with the epithelium, is like the retina in that it is a structure derived from the migration of the brain neurons, and it has all the complexities of synaptic interrelations which we find in the brain. Most important in this respect are the *glomeruli* of the olfactory bulbs, bushy networks of fibers upon which primary olfactory neurons end and from which arise other fibers, whose cell bodies lie elsewhere in the olfactory bulb and send axons into the brain.

The most important feature of the olfactory bulb is the mechanisms it possesses for amplifying nervous excitation into avalanche conduction by recurrent nervous circuits which return to the glomerulus much of the excitation leaving it (p. 64). Some of the fibers going to the brain, for instance, send back collaterals to the glomerulus; then, too, some neurons in the bulb serve only the function of receiving excitation from the glomerulus and sending it back again; and finally, others connect the glomeruli of one side with those of the other. The consequence of these connections is that comparatively weak stimulation of a few cells in the olfactory epithelium has its effects greatly amplified in the olfactory bulbs and is passed on to the brain at this inflated level.

From the olfactory bulbs, fibers pass toward the brain in the olfactory tract, but this breaks up into three divisions which go, respectively, to (1) the ventral olfactory cortex, (2) nuclei in and around the hypothalamus, and (3) the paraolfactory area of the cerebral cortex. This latter area is located just in front of and below the corpus callosum and is the continuation of the *cingular gyrus* of the cortex, located deep within the longitudinal fissure above and around the corpus callosum (Fig. 44). From the ventral olfactory cortex go fibers to the *hippocampus,* a complex structure of gray matter whose position is best indicated briefly as in the cerebrum below the cortex of the temporal lobe. From the hippocampus come fibers of the *fornix,* which can be seen running below the corpus callosum in a sagittal section of the brain and which terminates in the region of the hypothalamus. From here tracts run to the anterior group of thalamic nuclei which in turn relay impulses to the cingular gyrus. Thus we see that the ventral olfactory cortex, the hippocampus, the hypothalamus, the anterior thalamic nuclei, and the cingular gyrus of the cortex are the main olfactory centers. Even this list, however, does not exhaust all the centers and complex interconnections of the olfactory system.

PSYCHOLOGICAL PHENOMENA OF OLFACTION

Methods of Olfactory Measurement.—Chief of the difficulties encountered in studying the psychology or physiology of olfaction is that of controlling precisely the quantity and the chemical purity of the gases one uses as stimuli. Even if one masters the problem of getting the gaseous stimulus to the nose, it still is uncertain just how much gas entering the nose actually reaches the olfactory membrane, for much of it, we know, passes on through the nasal cavities without gaining access to the olfactory 'alcove.' Because of this difficulty, many of the early experiments are of little value to us, for in them it was customary to place the solid or liquid to be smelled in a chamber of some sort, and we were left in the dark as to how much of it volatilized into gaseous form, also what quantity reached the nose, and what volume penetrated the olfactory membrane.

The best of the devices used by early investigators in the study of olfaction was the *olfactometer* (Zwaardemaker, 1895), an instrument so constructed that the total area of an odorous substance exposed to a stream of air could be quantitatively regulated. It provided, however, no control of the volume of air passing over the odorous material in unit time or the amount reaching the olfactory membranes.

Much more satisfactory is an instrument recently developed by Elsberg. With it a measured concentration of gas in air can be injected into the nasal cavities under constant pressure and at a uniform rate, and consequently the quantity of stimulus reaching the nose and the olfactory membrane can be kept relatively constant in different experiments with different stimuli.

To overcome the lack of an exact method of determining the stimulus intensity in the earlier experiments, an arbitrary unit, the *olfactie*, was adapted. This was taken as the intensity of a stimulus when a certain arbitrary area of odorous material was exposed in the olfactometer. With such a unit the olfactometer, although admittedly inadequate, has provided us with much useful information concerning olfaction.

Olfactory Sensitivity.—Despite the numerous discrepancies that appear in measurements of absolute olfactory thresholds, data agree in indicating that only very small quantities of gases are necessary for olfactory sensation. The amount of odorous material ordinarily required is of the magnitude of thousandths of a milligram, but it may be as little as 0.002 millionths of a milligram.   This is, indeed, a small quantity, but only in relation to the sensitivity of other chemical receptors, for in terms of energy it is several million times that required for minimum excitation of the eye.

By using the double olfactometer, which allows separate odors or different concentrations of the same odor to be lead to the two nostrils, one can determine the separate sensitivities of the two olfactory epithelia or the slightest difference in intensity or quality of odors which can be detected.   In such tests, one finds that for most substances the differential threshold $\Delta I/I$ is about 0.30 to 0.45.   Also demonstrable by this method is the fact that the sensitivity of one side of the nose may be distinctly different from that of the other side and, indeed, that the same stimulus may be perceived as qualitatively different according to which side of the nose is stimulated.

Worthy of brief mention are the more important abnormalities of olfactory sensitivity which have been recognized and measured.   There may be total or partial *anosmia* (lack of olfactory sensitivity) in respect of all odors or of only certain kinds of odors.   Another olfactory disorder is *hyperosmia, i.e.,* extremely great sensitivity to a few or many odors.   Still another is *parosmia,* in which the qualitative experience caused by an odor is greatly distorted; this may be a permanent disorder, or it may occur only temporarily as it often does with common colds.   Such abnormalities of smell have been of interest to physiological psychology mainly as a possible opportunity to uncover basic olfactory qualities—in other words, specific nerve energies—by observing the way in which qualities are separately affected.   Unfortunately, however, we have not yet been able to discover any general rules governing such disorders nor have we obtained from them any information that points to a few elementary qualities in olfaction.

Adaptation.—As is the case in other sensory modalities, so in olfaction is it true that exposure to a stimulus for a period of time causes olfactory sensitivity to be reduced, *i.e.*, adaptation occurs.   Using the olfactometer, several investigators have systematically investigated the phenomena of adaptation.   They find, in general, that the absolute threshold increases throughout adaptation at a rate approximately proportionate to the stimulating intensity.   The effects of adaptation, however, are not necessarily confined to the particular stimulus used in adaptation, for often the threshold for other olfactory stimuli, more or less closely related to the adapting stimulus, also rises.

Olfactory Mixture.—The study of the experiences related to olfactory mixtures also fails to present any clear picture of olfactory processes. When two kinds of odorous stimuli are mixed, the resulting experience may be (1) an odor resembling one of the gases, (2) an odor whose quality shifts back and forth between those of the separate components; and (3) an entirely new odor which seems to resemble neither of them. This latter case is the most frequent of the possibilities, and our lack of understanding of the basic principles of olfaction is revealed by our inability to predict on any theoretical ground what the results of such fusion will be.

THE PHYSIOLOGICAL BASIS OF QUALITIES OF OLFACTORY EXPERIENCE

Underlying much of the attention given the senses is the hope of uncovering the basis of qualities of experience. In other words, the object of such study is to determine the nature of the differentiating properties of nervous activity, which our experience tells us must exist. Considerable success in this respect has attended the study of senses other than olfaction, but in olfaction we have little to show for our effort. It is possible, of course, that there are so many specific energies in the olfactory system that we can expect no simple answer to our problem. In order to find this answer, however, the steps to be taken are clear: we must first discover how chemical properties of olfactory stimuli are related to olfactory sensitivity and experience, and then it may be possible to find groups of stimuli which correspond to basic qualities or specific energies. This procedure has actually been followed experimentally (Henning). Let us see what has become of it.

Chemical Characteristics of Olfactory Stimuli.—Most of the substances which are odorous contain chemical elements in groups V to VII of the periodic table of elements; and in all odors the elements are of groups III to VII. Even more important, however, is the fact that most odorous materials contain carbon, *i.e.*, they are organic compounds. These, we know, make up the greater part of living material and can be very complex in chemical structure. We find it no easy matter, therefore, to classify them into related groups, yet a few important facts stand out.

Of these one of the clearest is the relation between olfactory potency of a material and its position in a homologous series. This we understand to refer, in chemistry, to a group of compounds that are similar in all respects except for the number of carbon atoms, generally represented as CH_2 groups, in a chain. In general, olfactory sensitivity increases with the length of the carbon chain, although often a limit is reached beyond which further increases in the length of the chain are attended by a decrease in sensitivity. To be noted also is the fact that members of such a series usually have the same quality, but—and this is quite important—widely separated members may have entirely different odors and be classified as of different quality. This fact does not encourage a belief in any simple olfactory qualities.

Stereoisomerism, in chemical parlance, refers to chemical compounds containing exactly the same elements, and in the same amounts, but differing in the way in which they are combined. It is important to us because it is a determinant of olfactory quality. Indeed, a chemical substance may be a very effective olfactory stimulus eliciting a definite qualitative experience, and yet its stereoisomer may not be smelled at all or may even give rise to another quality of experience. Thus both olfactory sensitivity and quality are related in a very delicate manner to chemical composition.

Attempts to carry further the analysis of the relation of chemical structure to olfactory experience have led to the distinction of *osmophores* and *osmogens*. These refer, respectively, to the parts of a chemical compound which are primarily responsible for its being odorous and to those parts which modify the effects of the osmophore. There are many kinds of osmophores and osmogens, and many sorts of chemical relationships may exist between them. The more important factors that influence either the olfactory threshold or quality of experience may be listed: (1) the position of the osmophore on the osmogen; (2) the degree to which carbon atoms in the osmogen are attached to other atoms (saturation); (3) the number of atoms in the osmogen; (4) the position of the osmogen in a homologous series; (5) the kind of atoms that may link the osmogen and osmophore to each other. These are certain specific factors which have been found important, but to put the matter generally we may state that almost any change in any feature of the osmophore, the osmogen, or their relationship to each other is likely to alter either the olfactory quality or the perceived intensity of a stimulus. Thus, we come again to the conclusion that there are about as many olfactory qualities as there are olfactory stimuli.

Groupings of Qualities.—The fervor of some investigators to find a limited group of qualities has not, however, been quenched, and undaunted, they have gone ahead classifying stimuli which they believe represent the basic qualities of experience. Two such attempts are most worthy of mention, one by Zwaardemaker and the other by Henning. Zwaardemaker's system is made up of nine categories which, together with examples, are as follows:

Odor	Example
Ethereal	Acetone, chloroform, ether
Aromatic	Camphor, turpentine, cloves, menthol, geraniol
Balsamic	Flowery perfumes, lily, vanilla
Amber-musk	Musk
Alliaceous	Garlic, onions, mercaptan, bromine, iodine
Empyreumatic	Roasted coffee, tobacco smoke, tar, benzol, cresol, naphthalene
Hircin	Cheese, sweat, urine, chestnut
Repulsive	Some orchids, some bugs, narcotic odors
Nauseous	Rotten meat, indol

For each of these nine kinds of odors, Zwaardemaker believes there is a definite chemical basis. He goes on, moreover, to postulate the existence of nine types of receptors in the olfactory epithelium, and from the blending of their activities, he thinks, arise the many olfactory qualities which we experience in everyday life.

Somewhat more attractive is Henning's classification. In it are only six basic odors: spicy, flowery, fruity, resinous, burnt, and foul. These, he believes, are related in a way represented by the so-called *olfactory prism,* and for each of them a more or less typical chemical structure is held to be responsible. As the basis for his classification, moreover, Henning has the results of experimentation with about 400 different materials. There are, he admits, several exceptions to the classification in that certain chemicals do not elicit the olfactory experiences for which it calls. 'It does seem clear, however, that in Henning's system we do have the best grouping, based upon empirical data, that it has been possible to make, and for the present it must do. That we have not yet reached the solution of the problem is nevertheless obvious.

NEURAL FUNCTIONS IN OLFACTION

Not at all startling are the results of studies on the olfactory centers of the brain. Rats, trained to discriminate various odorous materials buried in sawdust, continue their discrimination when various parts of the somatic and olfactory cortices have been removed (Swann). In the rat, therefore, there is yet no evidence of the localization of olfactory functions, even in the olfactory cortex. The recording of electrical potentials from the olfactory bulb and other centers of the rabbit shows that in them there is nervous activity attending olfactory stimulation and that it correlates with the intensity of stimulation (Hasama). There was no suggestion in the potentials, however, of any differences attending different kinds of stimulation.

In cats, the extirpation of any part of the neocortex has no effect on reactions to olfactory stimuli (Bard and Rioch). Electrical stimulation of the brain shows, however, that many of the motor reactions specifically associated with odors are represented upon the ventral surface of the brain in the olfactory centers located there (Rioch and Brenner). Salivation, chewing movements, chop licking, and sometimes 'sniffing' reactions can be elicited, and we learn thereby that the ventral olfactory areas, known by their anatomical connections to receive impulses from the olfactory sense organs, also mediate behavioral reactions related to smell.

A most careful and complete series of investigations of the central neural mechanisms of olfaction has recently been carried out by Allen. He taught dogs to raise their paws, on threat of electrical punishment, whenever the odor of cloves was presented to them. When they had this habit well in hand they were taught, further, not to respond to the odor of asafetida. Thereupon he removed various parts of the olfactory system, and other cortical areas as well, and then tested the dogs again for their retention of responses to cloves and their ability to discriminate cloves from asafetida.

Ablation of the ventral olfactory areas, the hippocampus, the fornix, or any lobe of the cortex did not interfere, he found, with the conditioned response to cloves; thus is it clear that no one center is necessary for this simple olfactory reaction. The ability to discriminate cloves from asafetida, on the other hand, could be abolished by lesions either of the ventral olfactory areas or of the frontal and prefrontal areas, *i.e.*, of the frontal lobe in front of the motor and premotor areas (p. 79). Why this happens is not completely clear, but it undoubtedly indicates, not a deficit of primary sensory capacity, but a disturbance of the higher psychological processes concerned in discrimination (see p. 555). It is evident that much more investigation is needed on this general topic before we shall be able to give a detailed analysis of the neural basis of olfactory capacities.

Worth mentioning briefly in closing this section are some results that Elsberg reports from the use of his greatly improved technique for making olfactory measurements in man. He has found that olfactory sensitivity undergoes cyclic fluctuation with the menstrual cycle in women; acuity, for instance, is much better than usual just before and during the menstrual period. Accounting for this fact, no doubt, are chemical and hormonal changes in the blood associated with menstruation, but only future research can show us the exact nature of their effect upon olfactions. Elsberg has also been able to diagnose the presence of brain tumors in some cases through the appearance of abnormalities of olfactory perception. If pushed further, research of this sort may throw considerable light on the neural mechanisms of olfaction in man, about which we still know so little.

COMMON CHEMICAL RECEPTION

That the so-called common chemical receptor is structurally different from the olfactory or gustatory receptor has been shown above. It is, moreover, more widely distributed in the body than are these other chemical receptors. The chief problem, in fact, is to distinguish it from the receptors for pressure and pain, because it is intermingled with them and resembles them. All three are typically free nerve fibers ending upon epithelial cells. That the common chemical receptor is functionally independent, however, can be easily demonstrated (Crozier). With cocaine one can anesthetize the touch and pain receptors; yet sensitivity to the application of an acid remains. Conversely, after the common chemical receptors have become adapted to stimulation by acids one can feel pressure or pain.

Common chemical receptors are widely distributed throughout the body, but especially in exposed moist surfaces such as those of the mouth or throat. They are innervated by fibers from the various cranial and spinal nerves, but they do not seem to be represented in the central nervous system by any special pathways or centers, although researches on this point have not been very adequate. Our knowledge is mainly limited, in fact, to the kinds and concentrations of substances which affect these receptors. The most effective in this respect are moderately dilute solutions of acids, alkalis, and salts, or, in general, any substances that ionize well or tend to dehydrate tissues. The threshold concentration of hydrochloric acid is, for example, about 0.01 normal;[1] for sodium hydroxide, about the same; and for alcohol, which is relatively non-ionizable, it is about 3 normal. Compared with the thresholds of taste or smell, these are very high, but this fact, we may note, reflects the relatively primitive nature of the common chemical receptors.

THE NEUROSENSORY MECHANISMS OF GUSTATION

The Gustatory-receptor Apparatus.—We see in the chemical receptors of olfaction the specialization of the neuron, but in those of taste the differentiation of the accessory epithelial cells is most evident. The most important of such accessory cells is the *taste cell* upon which the gustatory neurons end and which a stimulus must reach in order for excitation to take place. The taste cell, however, is only one type of a group of epithelial cells which support it and together with it make up the *taste bud* (Fig. 45), a flask- or bud-shaped cluster of cells embedded in the ridges or *papillae* of the tongue. In the taste bud is a pore through which solutions in the mouth enter to stimulate the taste cells.

A significant fact about the gustatory apparatus is that the original development, as well as the maintenance of the taste cells in later life, depends upon the primary gustatory neurons. Without them, the taste cell does not remain differentiated, and in embryonic development it is the neuron terminating in the cells of the taste bud that causes the taste cell to be specialized. These facts are demonstrated by sectioning the gustatory nerves (Olmsted), thus depriving the taste cell of its innervation with the result that the taste cell disappears; but after the nerves have regenerated, the differentiation of the taste cells again takes place, apparently through induction by the nerve fibers. This phenomenon

[1] A normal solution is one in which the amount in grams of a substance dissolved in a liter of water (1.06 quarts) is its molecular weight divided by the valence of ions into which the substance dissociates. This is 36.5, 40, and 46 for hydrochloric acid, sodium hydroxide, and alcohol, respectively.

has been called *sensory appropriation* (Parker). In it we see a point of significance for the problem of specific nerve energies, for it suggests

that some neurohumor (Parker) or biochemical factor 'organizes' and determines the characteristics of the taste cell in reacting to stimuli and, because taste cells are sensitive to different substances, as we shall see in a moment, it thus points to chemical factors, or organizers, as the basis of the specific energies giving rise to different qualities of taste experience.

Neural Mechanisms of Taste. Branches of three cranial nerves innervate the taste buds, the Vth, IXth, and Xth, all of which, after passing through their respective

FIG. 45.—Structure of a taste bud. (*After Ranvier. From P. H. Mitchell. A textbook of general physiology, p.* 182. *New York: McGraw-Hill,* 1938.)

cranial ganglia, enter the pons or medulla. Here they are collected in the *solitary tract* which runs a short distance caudally and makes synapses with the cells of the *solitary nucleus.* From it fibers cross to the opposite side of the brain stem and proceed toward the thalamus in the tract known as the *medial lemniscus.*

To what higher centers the gustatory fibers of the medial lemniscus ascend has not been established on anatomical grounds. Many have thought that taste and smell, since they are both chemical receptors, might have the same or closely related centers in the brain. In support of this possibility we have the fact that electrical potentials have been found to arise in some of the centers named above as part of the olfactory system when the gustatory receptors are stimulated. Little is proved by this fact taken by itself, however, and if we recall that the gustatory and olfactory receptors, despite their similar functions, are derived in quite different ways embryologically, we may expect different central mechanisms for them as well. The olfactory receptors come from the brain itself, whereas

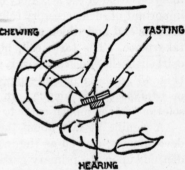

FIG. 46.—Approximate position in man of the cortical taste area relative to the areas for hearing and chewing. (*After W. S. Börnstein. Cortical representation of taste in man and monkey. I. Functional and anatomical relations of taste, olfaction, and somatic sensibility. Yale J. Biol. and Med.,* **6,** 732, 1940. *By permission of the Yale University Press.*)

the gustatory neurons are true nerves, like the cutaneous nerves, and closely associated with them, developing their receptors by inducing changes in epithelial cells. We might, accordingly, group taste with the skin senses (Chap. XII) rather than with smell.

That, in fact, is exactly what has been suggested recently by the only experimental study relevant to the question (Börnstein; Patton *et al.*). The same centers which are of significance in the cutaneous

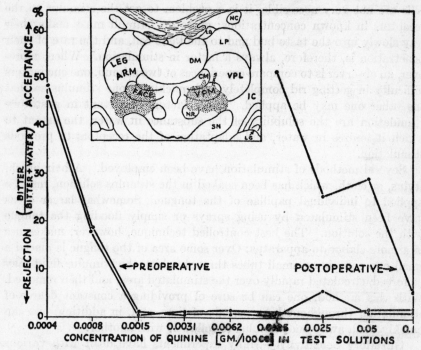

Fig. 47.—Taste discrimination of quinine before and after injury to the facial portions of the posteroventral nucleus of the thalamus. (*From H. D. Patton, M. Blum, and T. C. Ruch, 1943. Thalamic localization of the taste pathway in Macaca mulatta. J. Neurophysiol. To be published. By permission of T. C. Ruch.*)

functions of the mouth and face also are fundamentally important in taste (see Figs. 46 and 47). Monkeys, like men, do not like quinine because of its extreme bitterness, and advantage was taken of this fact in experimentation. Monkeys were presented with containers of water, which had graded concentrations of quinine in them. By determining the concentration of quinine solution which they could discriminate well enough to avoid, absolute thresholds for 'bitter' were determined. Thereupon lesions were made in the cortical area, which subserves cutaneous functions of the mouth and face, or in the arcuate nucleus of the thalamus (page 278), which sends projections to this area, and thresholds were again measured in the same manner as before. Since it was found that such lesions greatly reduce the acuity of discrimination, there can be little doubt that these cortical and subcortical centers play an important role in taste.

GUSTATORY STIMULI AND EXPERIENCE

The study of taste, like that of smell, is faced with many difficulties in obtaining great precision in gustatory measurement. Because taste cells are not very accessible, it is a problem to get the stimulus to the receptors in known concentrations; gustatory stimuli must make their way slowly into the taste bud and to the taste cell, and the rate of their penetration is, therefore, always a factor in stimulation. When, moreover, an observer is to compare experiences of two stimuli, one encounters difficulty in getting rid completely and quickly of one stimulus so that the other one may be applied. Other factors important in gustatory stimulation are the solubility of the substance in water, the extent to which it ionizes in water, and adaptation of the receptors to previous stimulation.

Several methods of stimulation have been employed. A hair brush, stylus, or cloth, which has been soaked in the stimulus solution, may be applied to individual papillae of the tongue. Somewhat larger areas have been stimulated by using sprays or simply flooding the tongue with the solution. The best controlled technique, however, makes use of a more elaborate apparatus: Over some area of the tongue is placed a small cup containing small tubes through which the stimulus fluid may be forced, circulated rapidly over the stimulated area, and then removed. With this method, one can be sure of providing a constant degree of stimulation throughout long periods of time, and, in addition, one can quickly wash away one stimulus to follow it with another.

Gustatory Sensitivity.—Many experiments have dealt with various aspects of gustatory sensitivity, but as yet few generalizations of significance have been obtained from them. Animals and man are sensitive to a wide variety of substances: mineral salts, alkalies, acids, alcohols, sugars, and many other organic compounds. Measures of minimal sensitivity have been made in a number of cases. Our knowledge of differential sensitivity, on the other hand, is limited to a few studies, based for the most part on salt solutions as stimuli.

The results of one recent investigation (Holway and Hurvich) using such solutions show that the just discriminable difference increases somewhat as the concentration of a standard solution of salt is increased up to about a $2N$ solution. With concentrations of $3N$ or higher a further increase in differential sensitivity takes place, but this is accompanied by introspective reports of 'sting' and may be presumed, therefore, to be due to the intrusion of common chemical sensitivity.

One of the important phenomena of gustatory sensitivity is the time of stimulation required for a taste experience to build up. If, for example, one applies a salt solution of $3N$ concentration it will be about 10 sec. before the sensation of salt reaches a maximum intensity. A similar situation obtains in the case of many other taste stimuli, and the factors governing it have been investigated in some detail. Two, it appears, are of primary importance: the rate of penetration of materials into the taste cell, and the rate of the consequent breakdown of taste-sensitive chemical materials in the taste cell.

Taking advantage of the fact that certain of the tissues of lower animals change color when acid substances have penetrated their cells in sufficient concentrations, investigators (*e.g.*, Crozier) have been able to study carefully the principles governing cell penetrability. They find that the degree to which a substance is ionized is one factor in the rate of penetration; but the size of the molecule of the substance, whether or not it is an organic substance, and other physiochemical aspects of its solution are also important. Although one cannot easily generalize concerning such factors, it is clear from a comparison of the penetrability of cells by various acids with the ability of these acids to excite taste sensations in man that a high degree of correlation exists; and it is accordingly demonstrated that penetrability is an important factor in the rate of growth of gustatory sensation and in maximal effectiveness of a stimulus.

There is no direct evidence that gustatory sensitivity is mediated by chemical substances within the taste cell, but such a hypothesis appears reasonable and is in accord with known facts. On this assumption Lasareff has, in fact, formulated a theory of the process of taste stimulation which runs as follows: After entering the taste cell, the gustatory stimulus reacts with a receptive substance (*cf.* visual purple, Chap. IX) which breaks down into by-products responsible for initiating nervous excitation. Such by-products are removed or reformed into the receptive substance in proportion, roughly, to the rate of their formation. The magnitude of the sensory experience (sensation level) will be governed, it is further assumed, by the rate of breakdown of the receptive substance, and this has some minimal value, which sets the absolute threshold of sensitivity. When a stimulus is first applied, moreover, the rate of breakdown will be greater than the rate of removal of the by-products, and thus the intensity of sensory experience will gradually increase, but these two rates will then approach a balance in a stationary state and subjective intensity will no longer grow. It can be assumed, as a matter of fact, that not all the breakdown products will reform the receptive substance and that the receptive substance will begin to be exhausted, leading, consequently, to gustatory adaptation.

Lasareff has presented this theory in mathematical terms, and from it many predictions of taste phenomena can be made. It accounts in particular for the way in which gustatory sensation builds up over a period of time and for the phenomena of adaptation which are so prominent in taste. Both the general structure of the theory and the mathematical equations stating it are similar to those encountered in many other physical and biologic processes, and it is therefore not a highly specific formulation applicable only to taste. So far, it has not lent itself to crucial empirical tests, and we are therefore without any direct evidence for or against it; but in all probability, it is a good model of the general events taking place in the excitation of the gustatory receptors.

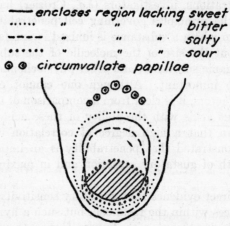

FIG. 48.—Regions of the tongue in which sweet, bitter, salty, or sour sensitivity is lacking. (*From R. S. Woodworth. Experimental psychology, p. 497. New York: Holt, 1938. By permission of the publishers.*)

Gustatory Qualities.—Foremost in the minds of many who have investigated taste is the question of how many and what kinds of qualities of such experience there are—the problem of specific nerve energies again. From time to time various answers have been offered, giving as few as two or as many as ten taste qualities. Most commonly accepted today, however, is the theory that there are four fundamental qualities of this experience, *sour, salt, sweet,* and *bitter* (Henning), each having its own particular receptors on the tongue, and each contributing its share to the complex taste experiences encountered in everyday life.

For the existence of these particular four qualities a considerable amount of evidence has been built up, and we may summarize it briefly under the following six points: (1) Qualitative differences in subjective experience fall rather definitely into four such categories. In this respect taste is much different from smell. (2) Experiences which cannot be so classified are explicable in terms of the stimulation of tactual or common chemical receptors or as the combination of these qualities. (3) Individual papillae may be found on the tongue which give rise, when stimulated, to a single quality of experience. (4) The areas of the tongue in which each quality may be aroused are not coextensive, but fall into four rather distinct zones (Fig. 48). (5) Some drugs, applied to the tongue, eliminate one qualitative experience while leaving the others relatively unaffected. (6) One can reproduce fairly accurately the taste of any substance by mixing typical sweet, bitter, salt, and sour stimuli in appropriate proportions.

The Chemical Basis of the Qualities.—Considerable effort has been expended to determine precisely what groups of chemicals are correlated with the qualities of taste experience (see Crozier, Henning). The unanimity of many investigators in finding the hydrogen ion (H^+) of acids to elicit 'sour' leaves little question about its importance in this taste quality. Even in 'salt,' however, the matter is not so simple, for more than one ion or atom is able to elicit it. In general, the inorganic salts, particularly the halides (chlorine, iodine, and bromine) of sodium, potassium, ammonium, lithium, and magnesium are most effective, and it has been suggested that the halides, in ionized form, are responsible for salt. Not in accord with this generalization, however, is the fact that the nitrates (NO_3^-) and sulfates (SO_4^-) also are capable of evoking 'salt.' Perhaps it is better to say that the negative ion (anion) is the chemical basis of 'salt,' but this statement, too, has some exceptions, and it is not known whether they can be accounted for in terms of the factors of penetrability noted above.

'Bitter' is closely allied with a family of complex chemical substances known as the alkaloids. Their basic properties appear to be due to amino groups (NH_2) or to trivalent nitrogen atoms ($N^{\equiv}$). Many substances, on the other hand, which are not alkaloids and which may be quite unrelated to them chemically, evoke 'bitter.' Some of the inorganic salts are examples. No simple chemical property, therefore, can be said, as matters now stand, to be the basis of 'bitter.' Much the same statements apply to 'sweet,' although the sugars are the class of substances most notable for their sweetness. Our failure so far to find a limited number of chemical properties correlated with sensory qualities should not, however, dismay us, for we also need to know what the receptive substances in the taste cells are. Without knowing them we cannot expect to make much progress in discovering the important properties of the stimulus, for these, it seems obvious, must be determined also by the chemical nature of the receptive substances and the types of chemical reactions in which they can participate.

The Neurosensory Basis of Taste Qualities.—A most important study of the existence and basis of gustatory qualities has recently been carried out by Pfaffmann. His study appears, indeed, to be the most decisive ever done in taste. Pfaffmann first succeeded in teasing out individual nerve fibers from the gustatory nerves of the cat; then he placed electrodes on these fibers so that he might record nervous impulses in them. When he stimulated the tongue with four different stimuli, acid, salt, quinine, and sugar, representing the four classical qualities, few if any impulses could be observed in any nerve fibers when the tongue was stimulated with sugar, but the results obtained from the other three substances were striking. *Three types of gustatory nerve fibers were unmistakably present.* One gave impulses only when acid was the stimulus; another showed impulses when either acid or salt was presented; a third responded to both acid and quinine. These three types of fibers responded to their respective stimuli regardless of the intensities of stimulation, whether weak or very intense. Thus Pfaffmann demonstrated the existence of three distinct types of fibers responsive to different kinds of stimuli.

Noteworthy, however, is the fact that all three fibers responded to acid, although one type was sensitive to acid only. This fact requires that we abandon the old conception that there is one kind of receptor and nerve fiber for each sensory quality; but it shows, nevertheless, that it is the types of nerve fibers which are activated that is the basis of the perception of quality rather than any differences in impulses within a fiber. On this crucial point as to how quality is mediated, Pfaffmann writes:

If we carry over this mechanism [from the cat] to the human, we might say that a discharge of impulses in one set of fibers will produce salt, whereas discharges in the *same* fibers combined with activity in all the remaining gustatory fibers will produce sour. In such a system, sensory quality does not depend simply on the 'all or nothing' activation of some particular fiber group alone, but on the pattern of other fibers active. (p. 255.)

We must be careful, Pfaffmann points out, not to assume that the three types of fibers found in the cat are all that exist either in the cat or man, for his stimuli were limited in number. The results, nevertheless, appear to provide a sound basis for a conception of the mechanism of gustatory quality.

General References

CROZIER, W. J., 1934. Chemoreception. Pp. 987–1036. In *A handbook of general experimental psychology.* Ed. Carl Murchison. Worcester: Clark Univ. Press.
HENNING, H., 1921. *Der Geruch.* 2d ed. Leipzig: Barth. Pp. vi + 434.
PARKER, G. H., 1922. *Smell, taste and allied senses in the vertebrates.* Philadelphia: Lippincott. Pp. 192.

CHAPTER IX

VISUAL PHYSIOLOGY

Of all the senses, vision has been the most thoroughly studied. Not only are its centers and pathways well known, but its neurons and synaptic connections have been described in accurate detail. In addition, modern physiological methods, particularly those of electrical recording, have given us much information about the physiological events taking place in the visual system. Our ability, moreover, to control various aspects of visual stimulation has permitted us to gather a vast body of strictly quantitative information concerning visual experience. Then, finally, the method of extirpation of parts of the brain, used in animals, has provided direct means, in several instances, of discovering the centers of the nervous system responsible for visual experience. To survey adequately all this material would require a volume, and, indeed, several have been written on it; but in the brief space available here we are limited to a summary of the most important aspects of vision. As a matter of convenience, the treatment has been divided into two chapters, one giving the basic physiological material and the other taking up the problems of visual experience.

THE EYE

The chief feature of the anatomy of the eye is that it is so constructed as to be able to perform the functions of a camera (see Fig. 49). Inside the eye is its photosensitive plate, the *retina,* and protecting this plate from stray light is a pigmented *choroid* coat of tissue which surrounds the eye except in front where the transparent *cornea* admits light. Such light must pass, as must the light entering a camera, through a small aperture, the *pupil,* and then through a *lens* which, by means of its curved surfaces, so bends light that it is brought to a focus on the photosensitive retina. Unlike the arrangement in a camera, however, is the fact that the light, in its course from the cornea to the retina, passes through a semifluid, but transparent, *humor.* The eye, moreover, is more adaptable than a camera, for muscular regulation of the size of the pupil and the curvature of the lens controls the amount of light admitted to the eye and the clearness of the retinal image, whether the object it reflects is near or far.

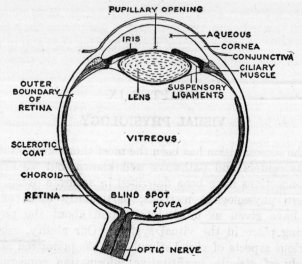

FIG. 49.—Diagram of the eye. (*From H. C. Warren and Leonard Carmichael. Elements of human psychology, p. 80. Boston: Houghton Mifflin, 1930. By permission of the publishers.*)

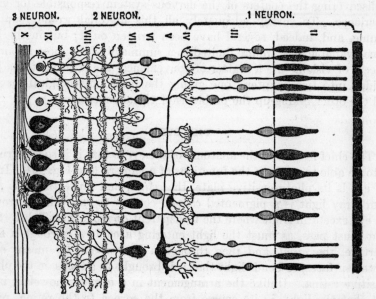

FIG. 50.—Diagram of the cellular relations in the retina. I, pigment cells lying next to the choroid coat; II, layer of the rods and cones; V, layer of horizontal cells; VI, bipolar cells; IX, large ganglion cells; X, axons of the ganglion cells uniting to make up optic nerve. (*From W. H. Howell. A textbook of physiology, p. 371. Philadelphia: Saunders, 1934. By permission of the publishers.*)

Retinal Layers.—There will be more to say later about the effect of light in the eye, but the structure of the retina may be considered first (Fig. 50). It is made up of nonsupporting cells and of neurons, but only the neurons are of importance to us. There are three main groups of these neurons, arranged in three layers. The first group is a row of primary receptive neurons, the sense cells, facing toward the exterior of the eyeball; their receptive portions have taken the highly specialized forms of *rods* and *cones* in which are contained the chemical materials responsive to light. Making synapse with such sensory neurons are the *bipolar* neurons of the second layer, and these bring impulses to neurons of the third group, the *ganglion* cells. The axons of these cells run over the inner surface of the retina and are collected at one point, the *blind spot*, somewhat medial to the center of the retina, where they leave the eyeball and proceed as the optic nerve to the visual centers of the thalamus and midbrain. Thus the visual organ is made up, essentially, of photo-receptor neurons, intervening bipolar cells, and ganglion cells, with the latter transmitting messages directly to the brain.

Lateral Neurons.—Knowledge of other details of retinal structure is also necessary for understanding visual functions. The retina, we have noted before, is an outgrowth of the brain, and careful study of its structure has shown that it fully demonstrates this kinship (Polyak). All the cells of the retina, described above, are true neurons, and their various synaptic connections appear to be as complex as many in the brain. First of all, the bipolar cells often collect from several rods and cones, and these also frequently deliver impulses to a number of bipolar cells; thus neural effects arising in the rods and cones both diverge and converge in their transmission from receptor cells to ganglion cells. There are, moreover, at least two types of 'association' cells which serve further to interconnect the activity of receptor cells: *horizontal* cells pick up from some receptor cells and deliver to others; and in the inner part of the retina *amacrine* cells spread impulses aroused by bipolar cells to several ganglion cells or, in some instances, return excitation from bipolar elements to the receptors. The functional system set up by these various interconnections, as the reader can see, permits all sorts of mutual influences between various layers and adjacent parts of the retina. In this respect the retina appears to be very much like the brain.

Rods and Cones.—Going on to other details of the retina, we may note a fact verified by many histologists, that the rods and cones constitute two distinct types of receptor cells. Their connections with bipolar and horizontal cells, however, clearly indicate that they do not form two distinct systems as has frequently been assumed (Polyak). Bipolar cells often collect from both rods and cones, and so also do horizontal cells (see Fig. 50). We may expect, therefore, that the activities of rods and cones will be intimately related in visual functions.

Fovea and Periphery.—Of considerable significance is another fact that synaptic interrelationships of the retinal cells vary according to different areas of the retina. In its center is a rod-free area, the *fovea*, in which each cone is served by one bipolar cell, and vice versa. Here, therefore, we may expect little or no interdependence of the functions of adjacent receptors. Proceeding outward from the fovea, however, we find more and more of the synaptic interrelationships described above. The number of cones, moreover, diminishes, whereas the rods become more numerous; in the extreme periphery only rods prevail, and these are associated with bipolar cells in ratios as high as 200:1. Thus in moving from the center to the periphery we find two changes: from a predominance of cones to one of rods, and from point-to-point to diffuse synaptic connections.

THE CENTRAL VISUAL SYSTEM

The Optic Nerves.—The two optic nerves, one from each eye, are made up of the axons of ganglion cells of the two retinae (see Fig. 51). Directed backward and medially, the two nerves meet in the *optic chiasma* at the base of the brain just anterior to the stalk of the pituitary body. In animals below the mammals, all fibers cross at the chiasma and end up in opposite sides of the thalamus or midbrain from the eye of their origin. In mammals, however, the fibers from the more lateral parts of the retina remain uncrossed; and since the number of uncrossed fibers in the higher mammals is about equal to that of the crossed fibers, the lateral half of the retina is represented in the same side of the brain, whereas the medial half projects to centers of the opposite side.

Subcortical Centers.—The *lateral geniculate bodies*, the *superior colliculi*, and the small *pretectal nuclei* lying just in front of the colliculi are the principal places of termination of the optic nerve fibers. Those that end in the lateral geniculate may connect with other cells ending in the other centers. But the main function of the lateral geniculate body, at least in higher mammals, is as a way station to the cerebral cortex. In the geniculate are the cell bodies of neurons whose axons leave it and proceed to the occipital (striate) areas of the cortex in the *optic radiations*. It is upon these cortical areas, we shall see, that the more complex visual functions depend.

More elementary aspects of visual experience, as well as the basic adjustments of the head, eyes, pupil, and lens, depend upon the colliculi and pretectal nuclei. Closely associated with them are the motor nuclei (IIIrd, IVth, and VIth) of the brain stem, controlling eye movements. These nuclei also include the autonomic nuclei effecting changes in the lens and pupil and the pathways to the centers of the brain and spinal cord which give rise to general behavior of the head and body.

Projection in the Visual System.—It is often said that in vision there is a one-to-one projection of the retina upon the optic cortex. By this statement is meant that in the pattern of nervous activity reaching the cortex there is a good reproduction of the stimulus pattern falling on the retina. In support of this belief is considerable anatomic and psychological evidence. Patients with a particular part of the visual cortex destroyed tend to display blindness in a corresponding part of their

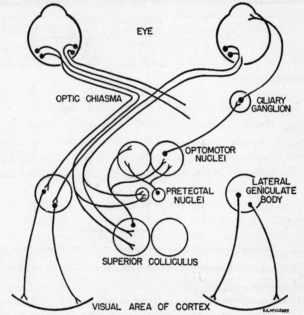

Fig. 51.—Diagram of the centers and pathways of the visual system.

visual field. If, moreover, one deliberately destroys a part of the optic cortex of an animal, cells degenerate in corresponding zones of the lateral geniculate body; a similar result follows destruction of part of the retina. By this method, in fact, accurate maps of the spatial relation of the retina, lateral geniculate body, and optic cortex have been prepared.

These facts testify to the high degree of spatial organization that exists in the visual system, but they do not close the question. When we turn to microscopic studies of synaptic connections such as have been done by Polyak for the retina and Lorente de No for the visual cortex, we see that there is a considerable amount of overlapping of the endings of visual neurons both in the retina and the cortex and, presumably, also in the lateral geniculate body. Indeed, it is fair to conclude that the degree of overlapping is much greater than the degree of acuity found in human and animal vision would suggest and that there must, consequently, be some functional mechanism in addition to the mere spatial organization of synaptic connections which accounts for visual acuity.   To explain such a mechanism for achieving point-to-point projection of impulses in spite of the apparent lack of an anatomical basis for it, Lorente de No has presented an attractive hypothesis based upon demonstrated facts which have been previously reviewed.

According to Lorente de No, the discrepancy between anatomical and physiological projection is to be admitted, the latter being pointlike.

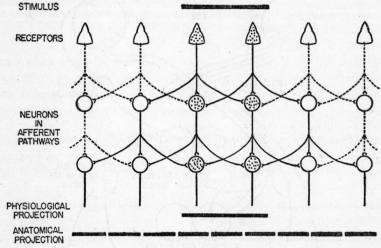

Fig. 52.—Diagram illustrating how synaptic connections at various levels of the visual system give relatively diffuse anatomical projection, and how, by means of the synaptic summation required in transmission, there can be a point-to-point physiological projection of retinal images upon the visual cortex.   (*After Lorente de No.*)

A point-to-point functional projection, however, can be explained by assuming that the neuron is a summation apparatus, requiring that two or more impulses from other neurons end upon it for it to be activated. Thus, in a situation such as is depicted in Fig. 52, the impulses arriving on the fringe of a group of neurons do not succeed in 'crossing' the synapse because there are no impulses adjacent to them with which to summate, but those in the center of the activated group mutually facilitate transmission by providing several impulses at the same instant at one synapse.   Thus, by a mechanism of summation, neuronal activity is kept in discrete pathways when it would spread considerably if anatomical connections and one impulse at each synapse were sufficient conditions for synaptical transmission.

This account, Lorente de No points out, is a much simplified version of what probably takes place.   It leaves out such important facts of the visual system as the lateral connections between neurons of the same layer—a factor that would tend still further to destroy anatomical point-to-point projection. It is, however, a simple account of a possible mechanism of physiological projection, which is useful in understanding vision and can be applied generally throughout the nervous system to other cases beside vision.

THE VISUAL STIMULUS

Although the stimulus for vision, light, can be conceived to be made up of minute corpuscles, or quanta, it is usually more useful to think of it as vibratory energy. All the various kinds of light, moreover, may be specified in terms of two variables: the amplitude of the vibration or the *intensity;* and the frequency of vibrations or its inverse, *wave length,* derived by dividing the speed of light by its frequency. Most light stimulating the eye does not, of course, consist of a single wave length but of many. The light, however, can always be specified, if we have the appropriate equipment for analysis, in terms of the intensity and wave length of the respective components, which together make up the *composition* of the light.

The Measurement of Light.—Scales which are practical for the measurement of light are based upon an arbitrary unit, the *international candle,* which is approximately equivalent to the total amount of light emitted by an ordinary candle having a flame about 1 in. in height. One is usually interested, however, not in the total intensity emitted by a light source but in the amount of light falling upon an object. That is *illumination,* and the unit of it is the *foot-candle:* the light falling upon one square foot of area placed at one foot distance from an international candle. Sometimes, however, we would rather know how much light is reflected by an object. This is *brightness,* and one of the most commonly used units of brightness is the *millilambert:* the light reflected by a perfectly diffusing and reflecting surface one foot square and illuminated by 0.93 foot-candle.

Retinal Illumination.—Much of the time it is permissible to state the comparative amount of light entering the eye in terms of the brightness of the object viewed. It must not be forgotten, however, that retinal illumination depends upon the size of the pupil through which light enters the eye, and thus one must compute this illumination from a knowledge of the brightness of the viewed object and the pupil size. Since the size of the pupil is in turn dependent upon retinal illumination, it is better to use an artificial pupil that is smaller than the real pupil ever is even at extremely intense illuminations.

The regulation of the size of the pupil, we may note, is a reflex affair. The chief center regulating it is the superior colliculus which, as described above, receives fibers from the retina. From the superior colliculus there are two pathways back to the muscles of the iris. One goes to the region of the oculomotor nucleus and thence to the iris by way of parasympathetic nerves, thus causing contraction of the pupil. The other passes down the spinal cord and out through sympathetic nerves; discharges in this pathway dilate the pupils. The former pathway is activated by high retinal illuminations, the latter by darkness.

The Retinal Image.—The eye, we have seen, functions like a camera and is so constructed that an image of external objects is formed on the retina. The retinal image, moreover, is kept in focus when objects are far or near, bright or dim, a feat that is accomplished by two mechanisms, the pupil and the lens. As in a camera, so in the eye: the narrower the aperture, the sharper the focus of the retinal image. The focus, accordingly, is best when the illumination is high and the pupil contracted as a result. To adjust the image for best focus according to the distance of the viewed object, it is necessary that the curvature of the lens be changed. This is done by reflex mechanisms controlling muscles attached to the lens, and in man the pathway seems to consist, to put it briefly, of the lateral geniculate, the visual cortex, and paths down to and out from the midbrain, although in some of the infrahuman animals the mechanism is probably entirely subcortical.

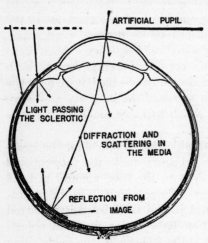

Fig. 53.—Points in the eye at which light may scatter. (*After S. H. Bartley, Vision, p. 58. New York: Van Nostrand, 1941. By permission of the publishers.*)

Even with these two devices for adjusting the focus of the retinal image, it is by no means so nearly perfect as it might be. There are at least three principal ways in which an otherwise well-focused image will be blurred by the scattering of light (Fig. 53): (1) The internal media of the eye will diffract light, even as moisture in the air distorts and makes the appearance of objects hazy. (2) The retina and internal surface of the eye are light in color and can reflect light to other parts of the eyeball. (3) Some light can penetrate into the eye through its walls. As a result, there is always a good deal of stray light in the eye which affects unfavorably the clearness of the retinal image. In some cases, the 'unilluminated' part of the retina may be about 3 per cent as bright as the bright part of the image (Bartley).

THE PHYSIOLOGY OF THE RETINA

Retinal Chemistry.—Turning now to the question of how the retina functions in vision, we may consider first the manner in which light brings about neural excitation. This, we now have much reason to believe, is through the breakdown of photosensitive substances in the rods and cones. There are, at any rate, photochemical substances in these receptors, and their reactions under different intensities of light have been studied in some detail.

At present we know of at least three such substances, rhodopsin, iodopsin, and one as yet unnamed. Iodopsin is believed to be in the cones (Chase), and the unnamed substance (Chase) seems to be an accessory material which aids in the restoration of rhodopsin. Rhodopsin, sometimes called visual purple, is the principal photochemical material of the rods, and a good deal is known about its reaction to light. It is present in comparatively great concentrations in the rods and is clearly visible as a purplish red material in retinae which have been kept in the dark for some time. It can be extracted, moreover, and studied quite conveniently in solutions outside of the retina.

Such solutions have been used to study the quantitative characteristics of the decomposition of visual purple by light (Hecht). From such a study we learn that the *rate* of its breakdown follows the course we might expect to govern the decomposition of a single chemical molecule— a course that is sometimes referred to, not entirely properly, as a *monomolecular reaction*. Its rate of decomposition is proportional to its concentration and to the intensity of light presented to it.

The Visual Cycle.—To study the decomposition products of visual purple and various aspects of their chemistry, use has been made of the fact that most chemical substances react in varying degrees to a range of wave lengths of light and so have characteristic curves of light absorption. From such spectral absorption curves, a substance often can be identified and its quantity determined rather accurately. This fact has lead to the demonstration of three definite stages in the photochemistry of visual purple. In these three stages the prominent chemical substances are *rhodopsin, retinene,* and *vitamin A,* respectively. The way in which these substances appear to be related in the normal photochemistry of the rods has been called the visual cycle, which may be described as follows (Wald):

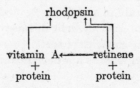

The decomposition of rhodopsin is a purely photolytic process, *i.e.*, it is dependent upon the action of light, occurring relatively rapidly, although its rate is proportional to the intensity of light. Resulting from it is retinene, a yellow-orange substance, which can be seen in the illuminated retina and which is accompanied, in all probability, by other substances whose identities are yet unknown. From retinene a further reduction takes place, apparently independent of the action of light, to vitamin A and other unidentified substances. The rate and extent of this decomposition appears to depend upon the quantities of retinene produced from rhodopsin. Thus rhodopsin breaks down into retinene, which in turn breaks down into vitamin A.

Besides decomposition, we may expect that visual purple must also be regenerated in some way; otherwise its supply in the retina would soon be exhausted and further vision would be impossible. Such regeneration takes place from both retinene and vitamin A. That from retinene, we may note, is much faster than the rebuilding of rhodopsin from vitamin *A*, apparently because of factors inherent in the process and because the latter regeneration from vitamin A must wait upon the breakdown of retinene to vitamin A. The net result is that the immediate source of new rhodopsin is retinene and regeneration from vitamin A is a relatively slow process.

The Electroretinogram.—The physiology of the retina has been studied in terms not only of its chemical processes but also of its electrical activities. These are best recorded by placing one electrode upon the cornea and another at the back of the eye. From such electrode placements one picks up the electrical changes occurring in the retina when it is stimulated by light.

These changes are as follows (Fig. 54): First, when a light is flashed on, there is a slight negative electrical change (*A* wave), but this is followed shortly by a substantial positive change (*B* wave) and then by a reduced and longer persisting positive wave (*C* wave). If now the light is turned off, there is a slight positive hump (*D* wave) and then a slow return to neutrality. These are the typical electrical effects seen in visual stimulation. They vary considerably, however, with the intensity and duration of the stimulus. With weak light the *A* wave may not be present, and with very short flashes, none but the *A* and *B* waves may be seen. Both the *latency* and the *height* of the *B* wave, on the other hand, vary with the intensity of light, and this fact has been used to measure the effectiveness of visual stimulation (Graham and Riggs).

The electroretinogram, just described, must be regarded as the composite of several different electrical effects. As yet no completely satisfactory analysis of its components has been given, although that of Granit seems most adequate and probably approximates the 'truth.' After performing experiments in which various changes in the electroretinogram were found in different species of animals, or were induced by the use of drugs or anesthetics, he proposed that the retinogram be regarded as made up of three components, called *PI*, *PII*, and *PIII*, respectively. *PI* is a slow prolonged positive wave accounting for most of the *c* deflection; *PII* is the more abrupt and short-lived positive deflection seen in the *B* wave; and *PIII* is a small negative deflection responsible for the *A* wave. The off effect (*D* wave) is to be ascribed to a combination of changes in the three components.

Even more problematic than analyzing the retinogram into components is the assignment of the origins of these components. So far we

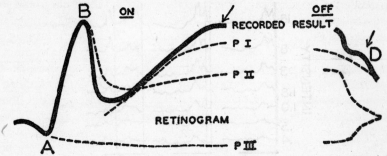

FIG. 54.—The electroretinogram and its analysis into components as suggested by Granit. (*From S. H. Bartley. Some factors in brightness discrimination. Psychol. Rev., 46, 347, 1939. By permission of the American Psychological Association.*)

have no indication of the origin of *PI*. *PII*, however, is quite certainly connected with neural activity in the second- or third-order neurons of the retina, *viz.*, the bipolar or ganglion cells. Some (*e.g.*, Bartley) are inclined to favor the bipolar cells. *PIII*, on the other hand, is believed to be due to activity in the primary sense cells, *i.e.*, in the rods and cones. To present fully the evidence for such an assignment of origins to the components would lead us into a complex subject, but the two most important reasons can be stated briefly: (1) *PIII* is the *first*, in time, to appear in the retinogram, and it would seem likely, therefore, that it indicates activities taking place relatively early in the retinal reaction, *i.e.*, in the receptors. (2) The presence of *PII* is closely associated with the appearance of nervous impulses recorded in the optic nerve, a fact relating *PII* to retinal processes farther 'downstream' than the initial excitation. *PII*, furthermore, is blocked by anesthetics and drugs that depress nervous activity while *PIII* may still be obtained. For these reasons we ascribe *PIII*, tentatively at least, to the sense cells and *PII* to neural effects farther on, probably in the bipolar cells.

THE PHYSIOLOGY OF CENTRAL VISUAL MECHANISMS

The Optic-nerve Discharge.—One can record electrical activity from the optic nerve in much the same manner as it is picked up from the retina. The form of the optic-nerve response is quite different, however, from that of the retinogram and is dependent both upon the kind of animal and the conditions of stimulation employed. In the frog one can distinguish three distinct peaks in the recorded action potential when the time of light stimulation is not too brief (Bishop). First comes a large wave and then close upon it another nearly as large; much later there is a small wave rising and falling more slowly than either of the first two. (The third wave, however, is probably not present in mammals.) This

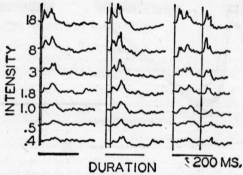

Fig. 55.—The optic-nerve discharge at different intensities and durations of light stimulation. (*From S. H. Bartley. Vision, p. 286. New York: Van Nostrand, 1941. By permission of the publishers.*)

pattern, the reader will see in a later chapter, is very much like the action potential of a cutaneous nerve. It appears to indicate three different groups of fibers of different sizes and different rates of conduction. From the largest to the smallest, they have been called *A*, *B*, and *C* fibers when considered in cutaneous nerves, and there they are associated with different sensory functions.[1] Such is probably also the case in the optic nerve.

In the rabbit no *C* waves, but only the *A* and *B* waves, are observed in the optic-nerve potential (Bartley and Bishop; see Fig. 55). In addition to these two waves, a third appears when the stimulating light is turned off and it is accordingly called an *off-response*. This is interesting, because it indicates that some ganglion-cell fibers have fired in response to

---

[1] It is not customary to designate the three waves of the frog's optic nerve potential as *A*, *B*, and *C*, respectively, nor the two waves of the mammalian potential as *A* and *B*. Since, however, the parallel has been suggested (Bishop) and since so naming them makes it much easier to refer to them, the practice has been adopted in this and the following chapter.

the *cessation of light.*   No doubt is left about that fact when the technique of recording is so refined as to give the action potential of individual ganglion cells (Hartline, Fig. 56).   We find, then, that there are three distinct types of fibers in the optic nerve: (1) The X type, which gives a burst of impulses at the beginning of stimulation and settles down to a steady rate of discharge during illumination, constitutes about 20 per cent of the total number of ganglion cells.   (2) The Y type, which fires only at the beginning of stimulation and at its end, makes up about 50 per cent of the total.   (3) (Z type), which responds only when light is turned off, constitutes the other 30 per cent.

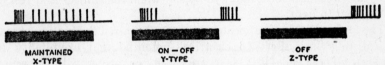

MAINTAINED   ON — OFF   OFF
X-TYPE   Y-TYPE   Z-TYPE

Fig. 56.—Diagram of the activity of three types of ganglion cells distinguished in the vertebrate eye by Hartline. (*From S. H. Bartley. Some factors in brightness discrimination, Psychol. Rev.,* **46,** 347, 1939. *By permission of the American Psychological Association.*)

Subcortical Action Potentials.—From electrodes in the external geniculate bodies or superior colliculi, records of events taking place in these subcortical stations of the visual pathways may be made (Bishop *et al.*).   One important fact which has been learned from such records is that two sets of impulses, represented by the A and B waves, tend to divide at the lateral geniculate, the A group stimulating cells going largely to the optic cortex and the B group continuing on through the geniculate without making synapse and proceeding to the superior colliculus.   Here the action potential arises mostly from B impulses although in some animals (rabbit) two elevations may be seen, one initiated by the A impulses and the other due to the B impulses.

Response of the Optic Cortex.—The optic cortex, on the other hand, though usually affected by both sets of impulses, is activated more easily and to a greater extent by the A group of fibers.   This fact suggests that only a small proportion of the ganglion cells of the retina affect the optic cortex, since the A group of fibers makes up only about 20 per cent of the total of ganglion cells.

When the retina is stimulated by light, or the optic nerve by an electric shock, electrical activity appears in the cortex, but in a complex fashion which cannot be represented by a simple diagram.   By placing the electrodes at different layers of the cortex, however, and observing the character of the changes in the cortical potential, a partial analysis of this cortical activity has been made (Bishop and O'Leary).   It appears that at least three groups of cells make successive contributions to the potential: (1) fibers of the optic radiation leading up to the cortex, (2) internuncial neurons of the cortex, and (3) corticofugal (or efferent) fibers leading back down from the visual cortex to the thalamus or superior colliculus.

A second point of interest to be made here is the relation of the optic-cortex potential to the alpha rhythm. This rhythm, it will be recalled, is the chief feature of normal 'brain waves' and in man has a rate of about 10 per second. It can be recorded, it will also be remembered, from the main sensory areas of the cortex—the somesthetic areas, the temporal auditory areas, and the optic cortex. The same is true for infrahuman animals except that the rate of fluctuation may be slower; in the rabbit it is about 5 cycles per second and in the cat 7 or 8 cycles per second. In all cases, the rhythm is most likely to appear when the subject is at rest and not exposed to light.

The alpha rhythm, it appears, is the synchronized fluctuation of many cortical cells in respect to electrical potential and excitability (see Bartley). These cells, it is clear, are closely connected with the sensory processes of the cortex. It happens, for example, that the alpha rhythm is quickly abolished if a light is turned on and left on; and we may interpret this 'blocking' to mean that activity in the optic tracts brings into play those cells which display the alpha rhythm, thereby breaking up the rhythm. Supporting this interpretation is the fact that a very short flash of light, which tends to set cells off in synchrony, or several flashes delivered at the rate of the alpha rhythm, often enhance an existing rhythm or induce one if there is none present. Also showing the close connection between visual processes and the alpha rhythm is the fact that the amplitude of the cortical response to light or an electric shock to the optic nerve depends upon the phase of the alpha rhythm in which the cortex is caught. If at the peak of the wave, the cortical response will be comparatively large, if in the trough, rather small. Putting these facts together, we may believe that the occipital alpha rhythm occurs in the same cells, or closely related ones, as those bringing visual impulses to the cortex.

THE DUPLEXITY THEORY

Our purpose in the present discussion of vision is to understand the physiological basis of the phenomena of visual experience. So far in the present chapter we have talked of the stimulus and the anatomy and physiology of the visual system; this material had to be taken first in order that we might come to terms more readily with the psychological facts. Before we turn to them, however, it is appropriate that we consider briefly one of the most prominent and basic notions of visual functions—the duplexity theory.

The anatomical basis of this theory is the distinction that is to be made between rods and cones as two types of receptor neurons in the retina.

Based on this fact, the theory—often named for von Kries, who first explicitly formulated it—goes on to postulate different visual functions for these two sets of receptors.   There is, indeed, quite a list of differences ascribed to the duplicity of retinal receptors.   The rods have one photosensitive substance, visual purple; the cones have one or several others. It is with the cones that one sees colors, the rods can only inform the brain of the intensity of stimuli.   The rods are, however, the more sensitive of the two and function at very low illuminations, whereas the cones subserve vision at much higher intensities.   Cones are most sensitive to wave lengths of 554 mμ, whereas rods are maximally excited by wave lengths of about 511 mμ.   Finally, because the cones are present in greatest numbers at the center of the retina and the rods are most numerous in the periphery, the various differences just listed apply just as well to the center and periphery of the retina as they do to rods and cones themselves.   All these statements are actual facts about human vision, rather than assumptions; for that reason it might be better to speak of the duplexity *rule* rather than of the duplexity *theory*, for the theory is so well attested that it has the status of fact.

One can make the mistake, however, and it often is made, of giving the duplexity rule the status of a general rule applying to all animals.   It probably does apply to a number of animals, but there are some in which it certainly does not take the same form as in man.   Crozier (*et al.*) has recently shown, for example, that the rods do not necessarily function at all lower intensities, nor are they necessarily any more sensitive than cones.   In comparing two different animals, one with an all-rod retina and the other possessing an all-cone retina, he found that their visual discrimination in certain very accurate tests was precisely the same at all levels of illumination.   In that respect, therefore, the rods and cones did not differ.   It may be pointed out, moreover, that no one has yet shown conclusively that cones always mediate color vision or that rods never do. We had better realize, then, that the only general rule about the rods and cones is that, when found together in the eye, they represent two different systems, but what the details of their functions are may vary in different animals.

General Reference

Bartley, S. H., 1941. *Vision.* New York: Van Nostrand. Pp. xv + 350.

CHAPTER X

VISUAL EXPERIENCE

Having covered the high lights of visual physiology, we may now turn to the psychological aspects of vision and try to see how they are explained in terms of chemical and neural events in the visual system. A considerable amount of speculation has accompanied experimentation on this topic, but that will be minimized in the present discussion in the interest of giving the facts their full due and of obtaining an empirically valid picture of the physiological mechanisms of visual experience. As a consequence of this policy, certain very interesting aspects of visual experience may be considered but briefly, because there is as yet little dependable knowledge of their physiological basis. Color vision and most of the problems of visual form perception will fall into this category; indeed, only visual brightness and the various conditions affecting it have been extensively studied from the physiological point of view. To this topic, therefore, we shall give the most attention.

First, we must understand what we mean by visual brightness. The intensity of a stimulus is measured by physical instruments and is stated in terms of the units of brightness or illumination previously discussed. When we speak of visual brightness, however, we refer to the magnitude of the visual experience or, in behavioral terms, to quantitative differences in the behavior of an organism toward a visual stimulus. Visual brightness, naturally, is related to stimulus intensity, but it also depends upon many other aspects of the stimulus, its wave length, its time of presentation, the size or shape of the stimulus, and previous conditions of illumination of the eye. In most cases, the influence of such factors on visual brightness has been quantitatively studied and the relations are known in accurate detail. The problem of physiological psychology is to find out what physiological events produce these relations.

THEORIES OF VISUAL BRIGHTNESS

The idea that the retina plays the role of a photographic plate was suggested a century ago. With the subsequent discovery of photosensitive materials in the eye and our increased knowledge concerning their reactions, we have come more and more to regard the principles of photochemistry as basic to the understanding of visual functions. The attempt, indeed, has been made to explain, in photochemical terms, most of the phenomena of visual brightness which we shall shortly consider. This *photochemical theory* of vision, most vigorously sponsored by Hecht and his associates, has been widely accepted in the last fifteen years. Recently, however, its ability to account adequately for the phenomena it proposes to explain has been questioned, and an alternative theory, the *statistical theory*, which tends to ignore photochemical processes and to emphasize instead the frequency of impulses in the retina and visual pathways, has been put forth by Crozier and his associates. We must now consider both approaches for what each may contribute to the understanding of visual processes underlying brightness vision.

The Photochemical Theory.—Although this theory, when fully developed in application to various aspects of visual intensity, entails considerable mathematics, its basic principles are simple. Three kinds of reactions are assumed to take place in the photoreceptors: a "light reaction," a "primary dark reaction," and a "secondary dark reaction." The first is a breakdown by light (photolysis) of photosensitive materials in the retinal receptors. Its rate is supposed to depend upon three factors: the intensity of the light, the amount of photochemical substance present, and certain constants such as the efficiency of the absorption of the light by the photosensitive substance which may be designated as S. These assumptions concerning the "light reaction," we may note, have been verified in the experiments, mentioned earlier, in which the rate of breakdown of visual purple by light was actually measured.

The "primary dark reaction" refers to the replacement or regeneration of S from the products of its photolysis. The reaction is independent, presumably, of the presence of light, and its rate depends upon the product of the concentrations of the substances produced in photolysis and upon certain other factors such as temperature. Hecht usually assumes, in applying his theory to psychological data, that there are two photolytic products, P and A; the rate of the regeneration of S, consequently, is regarded as proportional to the square of the amount of S which has been broken down in the "light reaction."

The "secondary dark reaction" is the process in which nervous impulses are set off in the photoreceptor, which, we remember, is a neuron. This reaction is assumed to be caused by the presence of the by-products of the "light reaction"; thus its speed and therefore the frequency of nervous impulses arising from it are proportional to the rate of production of these photolytic products.

As we shall see later, when the photochemical theory is applied to specific cases of visual phenomena, Hecht limits his consideration of the role of nervous impulses in visual experience to this reference to the "secondary dark reaction" in which they are assumed to be produced. This approach implies that these neural effects bear a one-to-one relation to the preceding photochemical events and that they do not contribute to the excitation pattern which the brain gets from the retina. Indeed, the neurons of the visual system are reduced, in the photochemical theory, to the sole function of transmitting in unaltered form the story of what the chemicals have done in the photoreceptors. In this respect the theory seems incomplete, for we have every reason to believe that the properties of the neurons, including their synaptic connections, contribute a great deal to visual experience.

The Statistical Theory.—For the weakness of the photochemical theory in failing to emphasize neural processes, the statistical theory more than compensates by disregarding photochemical processes and assuming

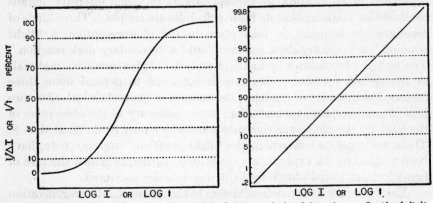

FIG. 57.—Graphs illustrating the statistical theory of visual functions. On the left it is shown that $1/\Delta I$ or $1/t$ plotted against $\log I$ or $\log t$, depending upon the visual function considered, gives a sigmoid curve or probability integral. The graph on the right shows how this curve may be adjusted to a straight line by altering the intervals on the ordinate; using the theory in this form allows one to determine quickly whether a given set of data is fitted by the statistical theory.

the behavior of neurons to be sufficient to account for the psychological phenomena of visual brightness. In presenting the statistical theory, Crozier, its chief author, does not deny the photochemical activation of nervous impulses in the photoreceptors, but merely assumes that photochemical processes are not directly reflected in visual experience. A full explanation of his theory would take us into mathematical problems, some of which are considered in a later chapter (p. 304), but its major points can be presented in nonmathematical terms. Crozier's original articles may be consulted for a more thorough account of the problem.

The essentials of the theory are to be found in three principal assumptions (see Fig. 57): (1) Visual brightness is determined by the total frequency of impulses reaching the parts of the brain where experience takes place. (2) The threshold intensity for eliciting an impulse varies from one neuron to another and from time to time in the same neuron according to the normal law of error, *i.e.*, in a random or chance way. This random variation in threshold, it happens, is in terms of log I rather than I, and thus the frequency of impulses elicited by log I will follow mathematical principles derived from the statistical theory of normal distributions. (3) There is a maximum frequency of impulses that can be produced in any particular number of neurons no matter how intense the stimulation.

Now, when the eye is stimulated with light of some given intensity, a certain fraction of the maximal frequency is used up. The difference between the number used up and the maximal can then be called the number *available* for use by any increase in intensity. The greater the number available, the easier will it be for such an increase to 'use up' a certain additional number, and the smaller, therefore, must be the size of that increase, if some particular additional number is required. Thus, in visual experience, where it may be assumed that the just discriminable difference in brightness requires a certain addition to a prevailing frequency, the more impulses that are available, the smaller must be the increment (ΔI) which is just discriminated. As a consequence of this reciprocal relationship between the available frequency and ΔI, one can state that $1/\Delta I$ measures the frequency of impulses still available after subtracting the frequency, of the total possible, used up by the standard stimulus I.

We shall see presently how this theory can be applied to the phenomena of brightness discrimination. But one important factor in such applications is the problem of how the *time* of stimulation affects brightness vision. Time, says Crozier, is essentially similar to intensity in its effects upon brightness vision, and where the occasion arises the two may be interchanged. Thus $1/t$ may take the place of $1/\Delta I$, or sometimes $1/I$, as a measure of available impulses, and log t may be used in place of log I. The reasons for this equivalence of time and intensity are to be found in the mathematical derivation of Crozier's formulas, which we do not consider here, but applications of the principle will be made below where they are appropriate.

THE ABSOLUTE THRESHOLD

One can make a distinction between absolute thresholds in which the minimal intensity required for seeing the stimulus is measured and differential thresholds in which the differences between two intensities are discriminated. This distinction is more a matter of convenience than of theoretical importance, but it will serve as a means of dividing the material to be discussed here. In any case, the data consist of measurements of the sizes of these thresholds under the controlled variation of many different conditions, the principal ones being the intensity of light, the length of its presentation, the time in the dark following light stimulation, the area of the retina stimulated, and the wave-length composition of the light.

Visibility Curves.—The absolute threshold, we noted above, is the intensity of light which can just be seen by an observer, but the physical value of this intensity varies with all the factors listed above, the first of them being wave length. The relation between intensity and wave length at the absolute threshold we call the visibility curve, an example of which is shown in Fig. 58.

Because it happens, however, that the visibility curve itself depends upon the general state of adaptation of the eye, whether to dark or to light, we have, then, not one but two visibility curves: a *scotopic* curve obtained in the dark-adapted eye and a *photopic* curve secured in high light adaptation. The two have different maxima and limits. In the scotopic curve, the wave length of greatest sensitivity is about 511 mμ, and visibility becomes zero at about 380 and 690 mμ; the same respective values for the photopic curve are 554 mμ (maximum sensitivity), 440 mμ (lower limit), and 760 mμ (upper limit). This latter curve, it should be pointed out, involves much greater intensities at threshold than does the scotopic curve, but as a matter of convenience they are drawn so that their maxima are equal.

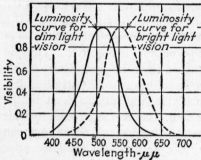

Fig. 58.—The visibility (luminosity) curves for dim-light (scotopic) and bright-light (photopic) vision. Although sensitivity in bright light is poorer than in dim light, both curves have been adjusted so that their maxima are made equal to 1 and the sensitivity (1/I) at other wave lengths is expressed as fractions of the maximum. The maximum of the dim visibility curve is generally taken as 511 mμ and that of the bright visibility curve as 554 mμ. (*After Hecht and Williams. From L. W. Crafts et al. Recent experiments in psychology, p.* 139. *New York: McGraw-Hill,* 1938.)

What, we may ask, is the physiological explanation of the visibility curve? The answer, it seems, is quite simple. The photochemical materials, which are broken down by light, and thus start impulses in the receptors, react to lights of different wave lengths at varying rates and, consequently, to produce the constant effect of threshold vision, intensities of stimulation are required for each wave length in inverse relation to the photolytic effect of that wave length. We predict, then, that the spectral absorption curves of the photosensitive substances in the receptors should parallel the visibility curves.

As a test of this explanation, the visual purple of the rods has been extracted and its sensitivity to different wave lengths determined (Fig. 59); this, it turns out (Hecht and Williams), closely parallels the scotopic visibility curve, except for a constant displacement of a few millimicrons which has been explained by applying corrections for the fact that the visual purple when so studied is under somewhat different conditions than when it is in the eye. Whether a similar explanation holds for the photopic curve we do not yet know, although a substance has been found in the cones which appears to have a curve of light absorption somewhat similar to the photopic curve (Chase). This is what we might expect, because different curves should represent different substances and these could be present in two different kinds of cells, the rods and cones.

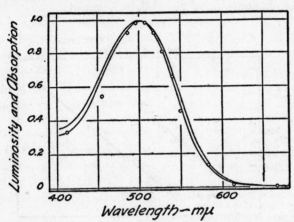

FIG. 59.—Comparison of the scotopic visibility curve (points) with the spectral absorption curve of visual purple (lines). (*From S. Hecht, S. Shlaer, and M. H. Pirenne. Energy, quanta, and vision. J. gen. Physiol.*, **25**, 831, 1942. *By permission of the publishers.*)

Time.—When a photographic plate is exposed to light, the stronger the light, the shorter the time required to darken it to some given amount. So is it with the eye. The more intense the light, the shorter the time necessary for the light to be seen by an observer. The problem has been extended, furthermore, to a careful measurement of the relation between time and intensity, in order to gain additional insight from this relation into the functioning of the eye. Figure 60 shows the results of such measurement in terms of $1/I$ and $\log t$.

Both Hecht and Crozier have applied their theories to these data, but Crozier's equations appear to be more satisfactory. As the reader can see, the curve in Fig. 60 is a sigmoid relationship between $1/I$ and $\log t$, and this is predicted accurately by the statistical theory in the following way: $1/I$ measures availability of impulses,[1] and because of the random fluctuation of excitability from moment to moment many fewer impulses will be available in a brief period than in a somewhat longer one. As one increases $\log t$, the number of available impulses for excitation will increase

[1] It will be noted that $1/I$ is equivalent to $1/\Delta I$ at absolute threshold, *i.e.*, when the standard intensity is zero. Thus $1/I$ can be used in the same way as $1/\Delta I$.

according to normal statistical principles, *i.e.*, as seen in Fig. 60; $1/I$ which measures availability will consequently increase in the same way.

Light Adaptation.—The absolute visual threshold changes as a result of length of exposure to a given intensity of light. To the change occurring with such exposure to light we give the name light adaptation. Such an increase follows a certain course in which, immediately after the onset of a light, the threshold rises very rapidly but then more and more slowly until after about 10 min. no further change in it takes place. That, briefly, is the phenomenon of visual light adaptation.

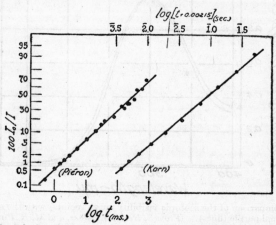

Fig. 60.—The relation between sensitivity $(1/I)$ and flash duration (log t) plotted on the probability grid. The fact that the measurements fall on a straight line indicates that they are described by a probability integral. (*From W. J. Crozier. The theory of the visual threshold. I. Time and intensity. Proc. Nat. Acad. Sci.*, **26**, 57, 1940. *By permission of the National Academy of Science.*)

Its interpretation in terms of statistical theory has not yet been made. Hecht, however, presents the following explanation. First the assumption is made that the amount of photosensitive substance (*S*) present in the photoreceptors is proportional to the threshold and thus is measured by the threshold. This is a reasonable assumption, for it seems clear that it is through the breakdown of *S* that visual excitation occurs, and Hecht has shown that the more *S* there is, the quicker will a given intensity of light break it down. Next, it may be supposed that at first *S* will break down much more quickly than it will build up, for regeneration of rhodopsin is a slow process, involving both retinene and vitamin *A*. After some time, however, an equilibrium will be reached between the amount of *S* being broken down and the amount being replaced from the products of the decomposition. As the equilibrium is being reached and the supply of *S* is being diminished, we may expect the threshold to rise, and then when equilibrium is attained, the threshold should be constant.

Thus this phenomenon has been explained in a reasonable fashion on a purely chemical basis (Hecht).

There is another form of light adaptation which is to be understood, not in terms of photochemical processes in the photoreceptors, but on the basis of neural relationships in the retina. Such light adaptation is best seen when one part of the retina is exposed to light stimulation and the threshold is determined in another part of the retina (Schouten and Ornstein). Under these circumstances it can be shown that not only does the threshold of the exposed region increase but so also does that of an *unexposed* part of the retina. This kind of adaptation, called *alpha* adaptation, takes place rapidly, *i.e.*, within a fraction of a second. It occurs more readily in regions closely adjacent to the light-adapted region than it does in parts further removed; and, other things being equal, it affects the fovea more than other regions of the retina. Thus is it demonstrated that some light adaptation must be due solely to neural effects spreading across the retina rather than to the depletion of photochemical materials.

DARK ADAPTATION

Somewhat simpler than light adaptation, at least from the point of view of photochemical processes in the receptor cells, is what has been called dark adaptation, or the increase of sensitivity that occurs when the eye is taken from the light into the dark. Such dark adaptation depends, as we shall see, upon several factors, but a good example of it may be seen in Fig. 61. Here we see that if the previous light has been relatively bright and if the threshold stimulus covers a good part of the central retina, the dark-adaptation curve consists of two distinct limbs. Each of them begins with a very rapid increase in sensitivity followed by slower and slower recovery. The second limb begins, under optimal conditions, after the first segment has reached a plateau. Complete recovery is not approached for some 30 or 45 min., and some change may indeed be observed after several hours; but the end of the first phase is usually seen within 10 min. The duplexity of the dark-adaptation curve is usually taken as indicating comparable duplexity of retinal processes, and the first limb is assigned to cone adaptation whereas the second appears to be due to processes of recovery in the rods.

Photochemical Theory.—The explanation of dark adaptation in terms of photochemistry is straightforward. At the beginning of dark adaptation, assumes Hecht, there is a certain amount of S in the rods which has been decomposed to retinene and vitamin A; and dark adaptation consists only in the replacement of S from its photolytic products. We can, moreover, test the validity of the theory by seeing what form the dark-adaptation curve takes. We assume that S should be replaced at a rate proportional to x^2 (with x equaling the amount of S broken down), because there are two by-products of S, and that log I is an adequate measure of x. These principles are all that we need to develop the equation for the dark-adaptation curve. In many cases this equation (see Hecht, 1934) has fitted the data well, but unfortunately there are many sets of data that are not adequately accounted for by it (Morgan). This being the case, it is questionable whether dark adaptation is to be explained entirely in terms of the recovery of photochemical materials.

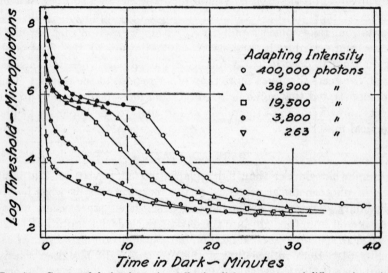

FIG. 61.—Curves of dark adaptation following light exposures of different intensities. (From S. Hecht et al. *The influence of light adaptation on subsequent dark adaptation of the eye. J. gen Physiol.*, **20**, 837, 1937. *By permission of the Rockefeller Institute of Medical Research.*)

The Statistical Theory.—Explanation of dark adaptation in terms of the statistical theory follows this line of argument: Light adaptation raises the excitability of cells and thereby decreases the availability of their impulses to a visual stimulus. Thus $1/I$ will decrease with light adaptation. In the dark, however, the cells recover, rapidly at first and more slowly later, in proportion to time in terms of log t. Since, however, the rate of their recovery will vary randomly, in terms of log t, just as their excitability, in terms of log I, varies by chance, we shall expect that the over-all recovery of excitability and thus the increment in the availability of impulses will follow statistical principles; and since $1/I$ measures the frequency available at any given moment, $1/I$, should be related to log t as it is in Fig. 62. It is gratifying that dark adaptation does follow exactly that course. Indeed, instances of dark adaptation (*cf.* Morgan) that are not fitted adequately by the equations of the photochemical theory have been fitted well by this relation deduced from the statistical theory (Crozier). This fact gives a great deal of support to the statistical theory and argues against the hypothesis that photochemical events are directly reflected in experience. Dark adaptation, being a very straightforward matter of recovery from light adaptation, seems to be simple enough to constitute a crucial test of the two theories.

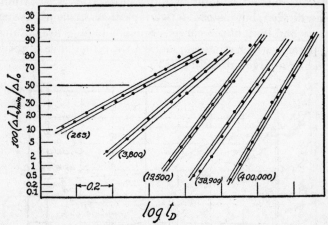

Fig. 62.—The data of Fig. 61 plotted on a probability grid and showing their conformity to the statistical theory of dark adaptation. (*From W. J. Crozier. The theory of the visual threshold. II. On the kinetics of adaptation. Proc. Nat. Acad. Sci., 26, 337, 1940. By permission of the National Academy of Science.*)

Previous Light Adaptation.—Conditions governing the form of the curve of dark adaptation bring out several facts of importance. First is the relation of the dark-adaptation curve to the duration and intensity of the light adaptation preceding it. When a constant length of light adaptation is employed but the brightness varied, the speed of subsequent dark adaptation varies according to the level of light adaptation (Hecht *et al.*). Similarly, if the brightness of light adaptation is constant but the length of application variable, the dark-adaptation curves that follow are of different velocities, as shown in Fig. 61. Both higher intensities and longer periods of light adaptation produce slower rates of dark adaptation. Explaining this fact, say Wald and Clark, are the two possible courses of the regeneration of visual purple from its decomposition products. In short exposures to light, it is retinene, for the most part, that is produced, and this quickly regenerates to rhodopsin; whereas the longer the exposure, the more retinene is broken down to vitamin A and, since the replacement of rhodopsin from vitamin A is relatively slow, dark adaptation is consequently slower after longer exposures.

Duplexity Theory.—The hypothesis that the two limbs of the dark-adaptation curve are related to cone and rod functions, respectively, is

further confirmed by the relation of the dark-adaptation curve to the size
and location of the photic stimuli used in securing thresholds during dark
adaptation.   If the threshold stimulus is small enough and is put on the
fovea, only the first segment of the curve appears, thus correlating this
earlier part of the adaptation process with the functioning of the cones.
On the other hand, if a small test spot is directed toward the periphery,
which contains an overwhelming majority of rods, little if any of the first
segment can be seen, but instead dark adaptation begins with what otherwise is the second limb of the curve.   Similar findings are obtained with
larger test patches which stimulate more of the retinal areas outside of the
fovea including a large proportion of rods.

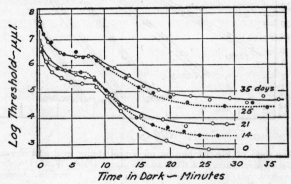

Fig. 63.—The effect of vitamin A deficiency on the curve of dark adaptation in human
subjects.   (*From S. Hecht and J. Mandelbaum.   Rod-cone dark adaptation and vitamin A.
Science,* **88,** 220, 1938.   *By permission of Science Press.*)

Similar variations in the dark-adaptation curve can be obtained by
employing threshold stimuli of different wave lengths.   If the stimulus
is in the extreme red region of the spectrum, which is covered only by the
photopic visibility curve, only the cone portion of the curve appears; but
with other stimuli—particularly the extreme violet wave lengths, to
which the rods are exclusively sensitive—the cone segment is less prominent and the rod segment much more so.   Thus the duplexity theory is
well supported by the facts of dark adaptation.

Night Blindness.—Worth considering also is the phenomenon of night
blindness.   Of this there appear to be two kinds: One seems to be a
structural defect and is true night blindness, or hemeralopia.   In it the
rod portion of the adaptation curve never appears under any conditions;
but the cone segment appears to be completely normal.   Apparently,
therefore, this type of night blindness indicates some malfunction of the
rods.   Another type of night blindness is the result of vitamin-A deficiency (see Fig. 63).   Although many experiments have been performed,
there are some problems regarding this type of night blindness which still

need explanation. It is possible, for instance, to alter the dark-adaptation curve so radically by experimental vitamin-A deficiency (Wald *et al.;* Morgan) that recovery of sensitivity never reaches a normal level. In contrast to true hemeralopia, however, the night blindness of vitamin-A deficiency involves not only the rod segment of the curve but also the cone portion. This fact indicates that vitamin A has the importance in vision which studies of visual chemistry have suggested and that vitamin A is also involved in the photochemistry of the cones of which we otherwise know so little.

Retinal Basis.—All that we have said so far points to the retina as the locus of the processes of dark adaptation. Should there be any question about that, however, we have definite experimental evidence in proof. By making use of the fact that the latency and height of the *b* wave of the retinal potential is a sign of the retinal effect produced by a stimulus, it has been possible to obtain dark-adaptation curves directly from the retina, thus ruling out the influence of the central nervous system (Riggs). The curve, shown in Fig. 64, was obtained from the eye of the frog, but it has just the same form as the curve given by human observers, including the two limbs representing cone and rod functions. There is left no doubt

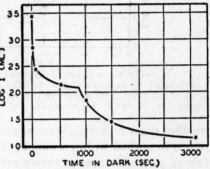

FIG. 64.—The dark-adaptation curve of the frog as obtained from the electroretinogram. (*From L. Riggs. Dark adaptation in the frog eye as determined by the electrical response of the retina. J. cell. & comp. Physiol.,* **9**, 501, 1937. *By permission of the Wistar Institute of Anatomy and Biology.*)

that retinal action is basic to adaptation and that it gives rise to the essential form of the adaptation curve. That is not to say, however, that the events expressed by the curve are not modified by central factors, for the whole visual system, both retinal and central, is necessary for the mediation of visual experience.

Metabolic Factors.—That the form of the dark-adaptation curve is not determined entirely by photochemical conditions in the retina is shown in experiments with oxygen and blood-sugar deficiency (McFarland and Forbes). In these we find that hypoglycemia, which follows the injection of insulin, or anoxia will substantially raise the threshold throughout the whole course of adaptation. The decreased sensitivity due to the former, moreover, can be offset by inducing an excess of the latter (Figs. 65 and 66). These facts are explicable if it is assumed that the threshold is dependent upon both the amount of such food materials as sugar and the supply of oxygen available for consumption. That the effect does not pertain to photochemical processes but to true neural conditions either in the retina or the brain is strongly suggested by several considerations, chief of which is the rapidity with which the impaired sensitivity can be changed when the deficient materials—

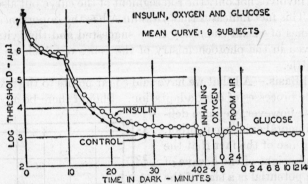

FIG. 65.—The effect of insulin hypoglycemia upon the dark-adaptation curve and its counteraction by oxygen and glucose. (*From R. A. MacFarland and W. H. Forbes. The effects of variations in the concentration of oxygen and of glucose on dark adaptation. J. gen. Physiol., 24, 86, 1940. By permission of the Rockefeller Institute for Medical Research.*)

whether sugar or oxygen—are again made available. Thresholds always return to normal within a minute or two. In view of the relatively slow rate of photochemical processes even under the best of conditions, this fact places the responsibility for anoxic and hypoglycemic effects upon

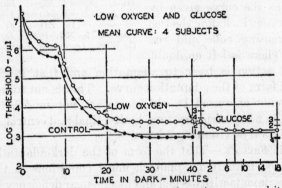

FIG. 66.—The effect of anoxia upon the dark-adaptation curve and its counteraction by glucose injection. (*From R. A. McFarland and W. H. Forbes. The effects of variations in the concentration of oxygen and of glucose on dark adaptation. J. gen. Physiol., 24, 82, 1940. By permission of the Rockefeller Institute for Medical Research.*)

nerve cells, which are more critically dependent upon such metabolic factors than is the retina.

Noteworthy in passing is the fact that such differences in metabolic conditions as obtain before and after breakfast are manifested in the dark-adaptation curve. Blood sugar is usually low before breakfast, and this is correlated with a dark-adaptation curve considerably higher than one after breakfast when the sugar resources of the body have been replenished.

AREA AND VISUAL THRESHOLD

Carrying considerable weight in the question of the photochemical versus neural basis of visual experience is the relation which we find to

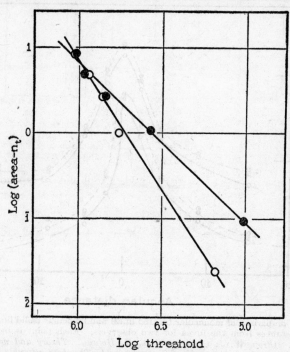

FIG. 67.—The relation between the threshold (in millilamberts) and area of the stimulus patch (in square centimeters). Open circles are for a stimulus 15° from the fovea; closed circles, 25° from the fovea. (*From G. Wald. Area and visual threshold. J. gen. Physiol.*, **21**, 282, 1938. *By permission of the Rockefeller Institute for Medical Research.*)

hold between the absolute threshold and the area of the retina stimulated (Wald). In both the fovea and the periphery, how intense a stimulus must be to be seen depends upon the area of its effect: the larger the area, the lower the threshold (Fig. 67). This fact can indicate only that receptor elements in the retina have summative effects in determining visual experience. The amount of photosensitive substance is not in this case the important condition, but rather the number of elements pressed into service by the stimulus, although these may, of course, be determined by photochemical factors.

Wald explains the relation between area and visual threshold in the following way: Within any given retinal region the elements[1] differ from one another in respect to their thresholds. If it is assumed further that a certain number of elements must be called into service for the visual threshold to be reached, there are two ways in which this number can be made up: either by increasing the intensity of the stimulus and thus activating elements that have higher thresholds, or by increasing the area and thereby securing the response of a larger number of elements with a

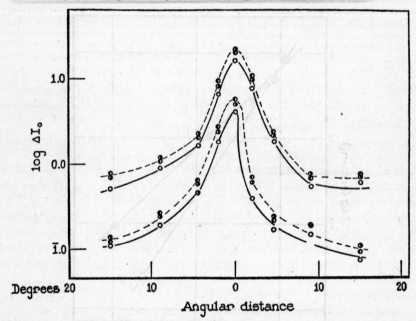

Fig. 68.—Comparison of monocular (dotted lines) and binocular (solid lines) thresholds at different distances from the fovea for two observers. Each point is based upon ten measurements. (*From W. J. Crozier and A. H. Holway. Theory and measurement of visual mechanisms. I. A visual discriminometer. II. Threshold stimulus intensity and retinal position. J. gen. Physiol., 22, 362, 1939. By permission of the Rockefeller Institute for Medical Research.*)

lower threshold. The mathematical development of this argument leads directly to the conclusion that the threshold in terms of log I should be proportional to the log area. The actual facts, as shown in Fig. 67, bear out this expectation.

Binocular Summation.—One might ask whether such an 'addition' of functioning elements in visual sensation is peripheral or central. *Both* is

---

[1] Wald has used the language of elements and thresholds here, but it is irrelevant whether one states the theory in these terms or in terms of the intensities required to produce certain frequencies of impulses. The mathematical formulation is the same. It is to be noted, therefore, that Wald's theory is in good agreement with the statistical conception of visual processes.

probably the answer. The fact that several rods and cones often send their excitations to one bipolar cell affords a retinal mechanism of 'collection.' In addition, however, there is also summation in the brain, for experiments (Crozier and Holway) show that there is a difference in visual threshold between stimulating one eye and two eyes. In Fig. 68 are shown absolute thresholds as they relate to stimulation of both eyes and to different positions upon one retina. It is clearly evident from these data that the binocular threshold is lower than the monocular threshold of the more sensitive eye, and this fact holds about equally well for all retinal positions. Such summation must occur in the nervous system rather than in the retina.

DIFFERENTIAL SENSITIVITY

We may turn now to the phenomena of visual experience which depend, not upon minimal stimulation, but upon differences in intensity. Of such phenomena there are three principal varieties: brightness discrimination, flicker discrimination, and visual acuity. These may be distinguished from each other in the following way: In brightness discrimination, the observer indicates the smallest difference (ΔI) in intensity that he can distinguish between two test patches. In flicker discrimination, the fastest rate of flicker that is still seen as flicker (critical flicker frequency) and not as a steady light is determined. In visual acuity, finally, the smallest space between two lines or the smallest object that can be discriminated is measured. Flicker discrimination, we may note, is a brightness discrimination in which time of presentation of light and dark is the limiting factor; whereas visual acuity is a brightness discrimination in which the spatial arrangement of light and dark is the crucial factor.

Brightness Discrimination.—Many workers have made accurate measurements of the discrimination of brightness at different levels of intensity, and our information on this score is quite complete. The size of the differential threshold (ΔI) varies with all the factors that have been mentioned in connection with the absolute threshold. When the more effective wave lengths of the visible spectrum are employed, the ΔI is smaller, and that is to be expected. The differential threshold, on the other hand, is smaller when peripheral test patches including the rods are used than when the stimulus is directed onto the fovea alone. Both of these relations are what we should expect from the duplexity theory.

More interesting to us here, however, is the relation between ΔI and intensity; this is summarized in the curve of Fig. 69, where log $\Delta I/I$ is plotted against log I. Of this relation we may ask, as in other cases, what its form reveals about the visual mechanism of brightness discrimination. To this question both Hecht and Crozier have applied their respective theories. For Hecht, brightness discrimination is explained as follows: The standard stimulus patch I brings about a breakdown of S in an amount determined by the balance between the "light reaction" and the "primary dark reaction." When the increment, ΔI, is added, an additional amount of S is decomposed, and this must be of a certain amount in order for ΔI to be discriminated. The size of ΔI will be determined by the amount of S left intact by I, for, as we have seen before, the amount

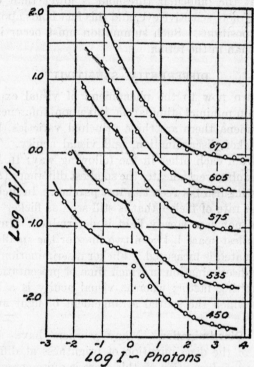

FIG. 69.—Brightness discrimination at different intensities and wave lengths of light. (*From S. Hecht et al. Intensity discrimination in the human eye. II. The relation between $\Delta I/I$ and intensity for different parts of the spectrum. J. gen. Physiol., 22, 15, 1938. By permission of the Rockefeller Institute for Medical Research.*)

of S broken down depends upon its concentration and the intensity of the stimulus. When the mathematical consequences of this reasoning are applied to the data, however, it turns out that the data are described somewhat inadequately by the theory, for a different set of equations is needed to fit the relationship under different conditions—*e.g.*, when the test patch is surrounded by a bright light and when it is not (Hecht *et al.*).

No such difficulty meets Crozier's approach to brightness discrimination. As was explained earlier, statistical theory leads one to believe that the relation between $1/\Delta I$ and log I will be a probability integral. This prediction is upheld when applied to the various curves of brightness discrimination which have been obtained under different circumstances. The data in Fig. 69, for example, are fitted very nicely by the probability integral offered by the statistical theory. Again, therefore, the statistical theory is to be preferred over the photochemical explanation of visual intensity.

FLICKER DISCRIMINATION

At any given intensity there is some rate of alternation of dark and light flashes at which an observer can no longer see the flickering but experiences a steady brightness; this is the critical flicker frequency (c.f.f.). There is probably no visual function that has been more accurately measured under so many conditions and in so many different animals as the relation between flicker frequency and intensity. It happens that many of the lower animals give reflex movements of the head, eyes, or body to flickering stimuli, and these movements can be used for measuring c.f.f. under many circumstances. Crozier and his associates have made good use of this possibility and have given us considerable data on animal subjects, as well as the best available information on human flicker discrimination. Let us begin with this and then pass over to the material obtained from animals.

The Cone Curve.—The typical curve of c.f.f. as it relates to intensity is given in Fig. 70. From it we see that c.f.f. tends to rise with intensity but forms a plateau in the middle of the curve, thereby breaking it into two limbs, the lower one of which may be assigned to the rods and the upper one to the cones.

Since c.f.f. in this curve is directly proportional to flash duration $(1/t)$ and is plotted against $\log I$, the statistical theory calls for each of the two limbs to be a probability integral. The upper cone limb is, in fact, fitted perfectly by such an integral in which the lower part of the integral is hidden by the activity of the rods; extrapolating from the cone portion gives the dotted line which completes the integral. Such extrapolation is justified because the curve has been measured in animals that have only cones in their retinas, and in that case a complete probability integral has been obtained (Crozier *et al.*).

The Rod Curve.—Assuming then that the dotted lines extending the cone limb in Fig. 70 represent the contribution of the cones, we see that the lower rod limb is actually made up of both rod and cone activities; when the contribution of the cones is subtracted from the so-called rod limb, then the true contribution of the rods is obtained in the form of the other dotted curves seen in Fig. 71. These curves are quite remarkable in that they show the c.f.f. or, in Crozier's terms, the production of neural effect, to rise with the intensity up to a certain point and then to decline

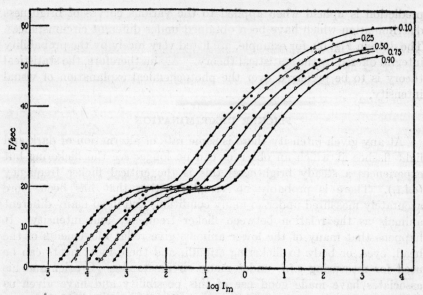

FIG. 70.—The relation between critical flicker frequency and intensity for different ratios of light-dark time. (*From W. J. Crozier and E. Wolf. Theory and measurement of visual mechanisms. V. Flash duration and critical intensity for response to flicker. J. gen. Physiol., 24, 639, 1941. By permission of the Rockefeller Institute for Medical Research.*)

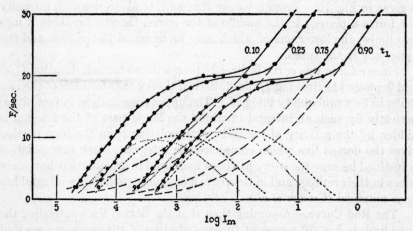

FIG. 71.—The respective contributions of the cones and the rods to flicker discrimination at low intensities. The unbroken lines and points represent actual measurements; the dashed lines are extrapolations of the cone data on the assumption that they are fitted by a probability integral; the dotted lines represent the difference between the obtained curves and the probability curve and thus represent the contribution of the rods to flicker discrimination at the given intensities. (*From W. J. Crozier and E. Wolf. Theory and measurement of visual mechanisms. V. Flash duration and critical intensity for response flicker. J. gen. Physiol., 24, 648, 1941. By permission of the Rockefeller Institute for Medical Research.*)

with further increases in intensity. This fact has been interpreted (Crozier and Wolf) to mean that cones *inhibit* the activity of the rods in proportion to the amount of their contribution. It is hard, indeed, to see what other interpretation of the effect can be made.

Related to this inhibition of the rods is an interesting fact uncovered in the study of the optic-nerve potential (Bartley and Bishop). This potential, it will be recalled, has at least two waves, the *A* wave and *B* wave which appear in succession when a light is turned on. We have no definite knowledge of the origin of these waves, but the following facts suggest that they may be related to cones and rods, respectively. (1) The *B* wave appears at lower intensities than does the *A* wave, and the threshold of the receptors giving rise to the *B* wave appears, therefore, to be lower than the threshold of the receptors responsible for the *A* wave. This fact fits well with the respective thresholds of rods and cones. (2) As the intensity is increased the size of both waves increases up to a certain point, above which the magnitude of the *B* wave falls off, while the *A* wave increases further. The significant aspect of this relation is that the *B* wave first increases and then decreases with increasing intensity and its behavior correlates, therefore, with the activity of the rods as it is deduced from the curves of c.f.f.

Light-dark Ratio.—A feature of the data in Fig. 70 that has not yet been mentioned is the way in which the flicker curve changes with the length of the light flash. The usual way of arranging a flickering light is to make the light come on 50 per cent of the time and present complete darkness for the other half of the cycle. If, however, the flash is made to last only 10 or 25 per cent or is extended to include 75 or 90 per cent of the flash cycle, the results are as seen in Fig. 70. *The longer the relative flash time, the lower the critical flicker frequency;* or put another way, the longer the relative flash time, the higher the intensity required for a given c.f.f. Crozier and Wolf interpret this fact to mean that the longer the flash, the shorter is the time between flashes for neurons to recover from the adapting effects of the flash and therefore the lower is the frequency of impulses elicited by the flash.

A different interpretation, however, for the effect of changing the light-dark ratio can be offered on the basis of physiological facts. In records of the optic-nerve potential, it will be recalled, impulses set up by a flash of light do not appear at precisely the same time but spread over a period somewhat longer than the time of the flash. Such a dispersion of impulses in transmission to the brain is not unexpected, for the reasons that all neurons of the retina probably do not respond to the light at the same instant, that synaptic latencies are also somewhat variable, and that, since nerve fibers vary in size, transmission in the optic nerve is of different speeds in different fibers. As a consequence, nerve impulses in the optic tracts will spread themselves out over a considerable interval no matter how short the flash.

Here, indeed, arises a crucial point concerning flicker fusion considered as brightness discrimination. In repeated flashes, series of waves of impulses follow each other in close succession. So long as these waves do not overlap too much, a difference in brightness between the peak of the wave and the trough, corresponding to the dark interval, can be appreciated in experience; but when these waves overlap so much as to make the difference between the peaks and the troughs below the limen, flicker is no longer seen and the light appears fused. In this manner we can account for the central discrimination of flicker. From this explanation it becomes clear that the longer the dark interval, the longer and deeper will be the troughs in the waves of impulses reaching the brain. Thus it is reasonable that flicker discrimination should improve with lengthening of the dark interval. The shortening of the flash naturally has the disadvantage that it may arouse fewer impulses in the retina and therefore lower the peaks of the waves, but this factor is probably of much less importance with the flash durations involved in flicker vision than is the length of the dark interval.

Flicker in the Retinal Potential.—Now we have assumed that visual flicker is experienced because corresponding to the flashes of the stimulus are waves of impulses which are discriminably separate when they arrive in the brain. We need not go entirely on assumptions, however, for there are some data on the matter. Study of the retinal potential (Granit and Therman) at different rates of flicker suggests that the mechanism of transmitting impulses to the brain in flicker involves two principles, the *volleying* and *synchrony* of impulses. When, for example, a frequency of about 28 cycles per second was used, responses in the retinal potential occurred only on *every second flash*. With reduction of the flash frequency, small wavelets appeared between the large responses on alternate flashes, and these grew in size with further reduction of the flicker rate until, at about 10 cycles per second, all responses became about the same size. From this fact we see that the retinal neurons are probably not capable of responding above a certain low rate (15 or 20 cycles per second) but can mediate much higher rates of flicker by sending in volleys of impulses on alternate flashes.

But for neurons to function in volleys and to respond as a group only to alternate flashes, there must be some mechanism of synchronizing their action, otherwise some cells would discharge on one flash and others on the next, and the frequency of firing would correspond to the flicker frequency. The nature of such mechanisms of synchronization is still under investigation by neurophysiologists, but one possibility is now strongly supported, that the discharge of a nervous impulse in one fiber facilitates, or lowers the threshold of, adjacent fibers (Katz and Schmidt, see Bishop). Thus, in a group of cells lying side by side, the discharge of some of them facilitates the discharge of the rest of them. Carrying this notion over to the retina, we might suppose that neurons which cannot respond to the frequency of stimulation applied to them, because their refractory periods are too long, will respond as a group on alternate cycles of the flickering stimulus, because the cells that recover first are excited and by facilitation aid those not quite recovered to discharge, thus leaving all of them in refractory period for the next flicker cycle.

The place at which such synchronization occurs in the retina is proposed to be in the bipolar cells, for from studies of the retinal potential we have reason to believe that the photoreceptors can probably respond more frequently and rapidly than the bipolar or ganglion cells (p. 171). If that suggestion is correct, it is an argument against the photochemical interpretation of flicker discrimination and in favor of the statistical theory.

Subjective Flicker.—The alternate volleying of impulses at high rates of flicker serves also to account for another aspect of visual experience not yet mentioned, the subjective rate of flicker at high intensities of light and, therefore, high rates of c.f.f. If one supposes that bursts of nervous impulses accompany every flash of a stimulus, it would then be expected that the subjective rate of flicker, when below fusion speed, will correspond to the actual rate. Such, however, is not the case, particularly at high intensities. If, for example, the intensity is such that the c.f.f. is 50 flashes per second, and an observer is presented with a flicker rate of 47 flashes per second, the rate of subjective flicker is not 47 per second but much less (Bartley). How much less is not easily measured since the observer cannot count so fast as that, but it corresponds, when he makes comparison judgments, with the subjective flicker rate of a very much lower physical flicker. That bursts of impulses entering the brain may, by virtue of alternate volleying, be much lower than the physical flash rate adequately explains this fact.

Subjective Brightness.—When dealing with the effect of flickering light upon a photographic plate it is customary to apply Talbot's law to evaluate the intensity of a steady light that is equivalent to the flickering light. According to this law the effective intensity of a flickering light is the product of the intensity of the flash and the fraction of the light-dark cycle which it takes up; thus when this fraction is one-half, a flickering light should be one-half the effectiveness of the same light presented continuously.

Now, it is possible to determine how well this law holds in visual experience, as well as the magnitude of departures from it, by having an observer adjust the intensity of a steady light so that it appears to him to be equal in brightness to that of a flickering light. From such measurements it has been found (Bartley) that Talbot's law holds only under certain conditions, chiefly at high flicker rates (see Fig. 72). As the rate is lowered, the subjective brightness of a flickering light may considerably exceed that expected from Talbot's law; indeed, under certain conditions, it may become twice as bright subjectively as the same light when steady. This degree of enhancement of brightness occurs at a flicker rate of about 10 cycles per second; above or below this rate the increase in subjective brightness is not nearly so great, and only in the region of 25 cycles per

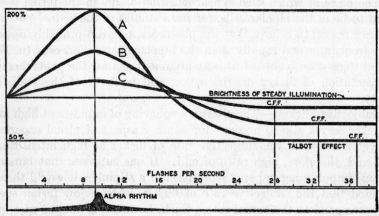

Fig. 72.—The brightness of a flickering light relative to a steady light at different flicker frequencies. Curve *A* refers to a light-dark ratio of 1:1; curve *B* to a ratio of 7:2; and curve *C* to a ratio of 8:1. Note that the brightness of a light flickering at the rate of about 10 flashes per second is substantially brighter subjectively than a steady light of the same intensity. (*From S. H. Bartley. Some factors in brightness discrimination. Psychol. Rev., 46, 344, 1939. By permission of the American Psychological Association.*)

second or above does Talbot's law hold. As shown in Fig. 72, enhancement is greatest for small light-dark ratios and least when the light flash is longer than the dark interval.

According to the photochemical theory of vision, the eye is like a photographic plate, and we therefore expect Talbot's law to apply consistently to visual experience if photochemical events of the retina are reflected, unaltered, in visual experience. Since it does not, Bartley looks to neural events for the explanation of brightness enhancement. He points out that the *flicker rate of maximum enhancement is the same as the frequency of the alpha wave* and that, since there is direct evidence of the facilitation of the cortical response by the alpha wave (p. 174), this factor may be responsible for the enhancement. Such an explanation, indeed, appears reasonable; but it should be pointed out, however, that the range of flicker rate at which the enhancement of brightness takes place is the same as that in which the rods appear to make their greatest contribution (p. 194).   This being the case, it is possible that function of the rods may somehow be related to the effect.

VISUAL ACUITY

Brightness differences, as was stated earlier, are the basis of visual acuity, *i.e.*, the ability to distinguish small objects or the separation between objects.   Visual acuity is usually measured in terms of the

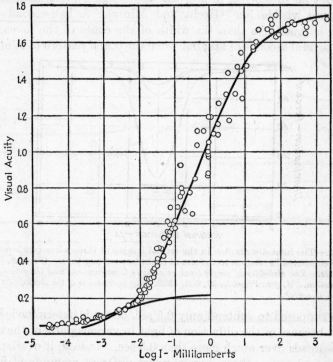

Fig. 73.—The relation of visual acuity to intensity of illumination in the human eye. (*From S. Hecht.   Vision II.   The nature of the photoreceptor process.   In A handbook of general experimental psychology.   Ed. C. Murchison, p. 774.   Worcester: Clark University Press, 1934.   By permission of the publishers.*)

reciprocal of the angle of the image on the retina of the smallest visible object or separation between objects which is just distinguishable; in this way the influence of the distance of the object from the eye is eliminated.   Like brightness discrimination and flicker discrimination, visual acuity varies with intensity of illumination; the higher the intensity, the better the visual acuity, and conversely.   The precise relation between acuity and intensity is given in Fig. 73; here rod and cone branches of the curve are again in evidence, although the contribution of the rods is not very large.

It is of interest to inquire how the best visual acuity compares with the size of photoreceptor cells, since their size would appear to place a limit on the fineness of acuity that could exist. This limit, we find, varies with the methods employed in determining it. Different investigators have used a single line or a dot of light (minimum visible method) or the separation between two lines or dots of light (minimum separable method). Depending upon the technique used, the best thresholds vary from about 30 to 0.5 sec. of arc, this latter figure being obtained with the thinnest visible line (Hecht and Mintz). A half-second of arc, however, is much less than the width of the cones of the fovea, which subtend several seconds of arc; but when the *actual* pattern of stimulation

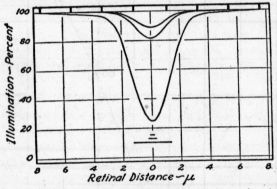

Fig. 74.—The light distribution in the retinal images of three wires (see lower part of the figure) computed in relation to the size of cones (see scale at top). (*From S. Hecht and E. U. Mintz. The visibility of single lines at various illuminations and the retinal basis of visual resolution. J. gen. Physiol., 22, 601, 1939. By permission of the Rockefeller Institute for Medical Research.*)

of a line supposed to subtend only 0.5 sec. of arc is determined, it turns out that, because of the diffaction of light in various parts of the eye this pattern spreads over much more than 0.5 sec. Indeed, it overlaps three or four foveal cones; these, however, get different amounts of light, as shown in Fig. 74. It has been calculated (Hecht and Mintz), moreover, that the difference in the intensity of stimulation of adjacent cones, when acuity is best, is precisely that difference which is just discriminable in simple brightness discrimination. Thus visual acuity reduces directly to a discrimination of different intensities in adjacent areas.

There is the further question of what the form of the curve of visual acuity may indicate about the physiological processes underlying visual acuity. The answer to this question seems rather clear, since the shape of the curve is the familiar probability integral put forth in the statistical theory as the basic form of intensity functions in vision. In this case, moreover, there is only a slight disagreement between Hecht and Crozier in the interpretation of this integral. They agree that it indicates that the properties of retinal neurons are distributed in a random or chance manner; but Hecht has supposed that it is the thresholds of cells which are so distributed. Crozier, on the other hand, holds it unreasonable that any receptors have thresholds as high as the intensities at which visual acuity is best and proposes that the randomness is in respect of the frequency of impulses produced and not of thresholds. This view seems more satisfactory than that of Hecht, especially since it also applies well to other visual functions.

RETINAL INTERACTION

In the last section it was evident that a great deal of material from both physiology and psychology can be brought to bear upon problems of brightness vision. It would be desirable to turn now to the consideration of visual objects, their shape and movement, and various spatial aspects of visual experience. Much has been done in the psychological study of such aspects of experience, but little is known, unfortunately, of their physiological basis. Thus, even though such phenomena are an important chapter in psychology as well as conspicuous aspects of everyday experience, we have little to say about them in physiological psychology, and must confine ourselves to a few suggestive facts and principles.

If the anatomic and functional mechanisms for point-to-point projection from the retina to the brain reflect the pattern of visual stimulation to the visual cortex unaltered, we would expect that the visual perception of objects would correspond exactly to the image of the objects on the retina. That, however, is not the case, as much psychological evidence indicates. The speed of seen movement may be of a quite different rate from the speed of movement of a retinal image; movement may, indeed, be seen when there is no motion of the stimulus. The size and the form of objects, too, are often not appreciated as they should be in terms of simple optical principles, and many detailed instances of these facts could be presented. Some of them can be explained by appealing to the previous experience of the individual, but certainly not all of them. We are required, therefore, to look for factors in the retina and the brain which alter the spatial pattern of nervous activity between its arousal in the photoreceptors and its arrival at the centers subserving visual experience. Such factors may be presumed to consist of the interactions of neurons representing different retinal areas, for such interactions would give rise to a lack of complete correlation between the stimulus pattern and spatial aspects of the resulting experience. In looking for such factors of interaction, however, we have no more reason, a priori, to believe that they should be of central than of retinal origin; for the retina, with its many synapses completely interconnecting various cells, must be regarded as possessing all the properties of nervous tissue.

Retinal Summation.—The relation of area to visual threshold, wherein the absolute threshold is lower if a larger area of the retina is stimulated, is one evidence that effects in different retinal areas summate. More direct proof, however, can be found in other ways. One is by the recording of optic-nerve potentials under different conditions of retinal stimulation (Adrian and Matthews). Here (in the eel's eye) the latency of the potential may be taken as an index of the amount of sensory effect; and when four points of light on the retina are compared with one point of the same total intensity they show a shorter latency and, consequently, a greater effect. That this result indicates a synaptic summation in the retina is suggested by the observation that, in the eye of Limulus (horseshoe crab), which lacks synaptic interconnections, no such summation of effects in different areas can be demonstrated (Graham).

Retinal summation has been demonstrated in the human eye by somewhat different methods (Granit). In this case the c.f.f. was used as an index of total sensory effect. Four disks were arranged as at the four corners of a square, and the c.f.f. of all four was compared with the c.f.f. of any one under the same conditions of brightness. If the disks were arranged in the periphery, it was found, the c.f.f. of the group of disks was significantly higher than that of one, a fact indicating summation. In the fovea, however, no summation—or only a slight amount—could be demonstrated. The periphery, therefore, was demonstrated to show summation more than the fovea, as one might expect from the considerably greater interconnection of cells in the periphery. Another finding, also not unexpected, was that the amount of interaction became less as the distance between the disks was increased.

Similar results can be obtained by studying the absolute threshold (Beitel). Two test patches, either one of which is below the threshold of vision when presented individually, may summate their effects, thereby becoming visible. Such summation depends, as in the case above, upon the distance between the two test patches. It extends, furthermore, over a much greater distance in the periphery—about fifteen times as far— than in the fovea. The spread of this summation, it is interesting to note, is about the same as the distance which histologists have found lateral neurons to extend in the retina (Bartley).

Worth considering, finally, is the phenomenon of temporal summation of stimuli in vision (Granit and Davis). This has been demonstrated by presenting a subliminal flash of light and determining its effect on the visibility of a flash given a brief interval later; the threshold of the second flash is then lower than that determined by the usual method of presenting single stimuli. As one might expect, the shorter the interval between the two, the lower the threshold intensity of the second flash, the limit of the summation effect being reached when the interval between the two stimuli is extended to 130 msec. Since this is a relatively long time—indeed, considerably longer than the period of latent addition in other neurons—it has been suggested (Bartley) that the summation may be mediated by recurrent nervous circuits in the retina such as have been described for the central nervous system.

Carrying their investigations further to include both spatial and temporal summation, Granit and Davis attempted to see whether such temporal addition could be obtained when the two flashes stimulate different retinal areas. It can. Two flashes, each of subliminal intensity, will add to visibility over several minutes of arc, as long as the interval between them is not larger than a few milliseconds. Such evidence of the lateral spread of subliminal effects is of considerable importance in understanding some of the more complex phenomena of vision.

Retinal Inhibition.—Not only does summation of excitation take place between different regions of the retina, but a comparable inhibition can also be demonstrated when certain appropriate conditions are observed, such as a relatively great difference in intensity between two test patches and the use of the fovea, which, it is found, is more subject to inhibition than the periphery. Several experiments agree in pointing to this conclusion.

In one (Graham and Granit), for example, change in the c.f.f. of a patch of light was used as an index of the effect of a second patch of steady light. When the flickering area was brighter than the steady patch, c.f.f. was raised; when the intensity of the flickering patch was lower than the steady one, c.f.f. was lower. Change in c.f.f. can be considered here, as elsewhere, to be directly proportional to change in neural effect. From this fact we may conclude that when there is a difference in intensity between the stimulation of two areas retinal inhibition produces an exaggeration of this difference in the neural effect, the dim patch becoming dimmer and the bright one brighter. This phenomenon, it may be pointed out, is a type of visual contrast which is well known in visual experience.

APPARENT MOVEMENT

The spatial aspect of visual perception which appears to be best understood in terms of physiological processes is apparent movement. This is movement seen by an observer when there is no real movement of the visual stimulus. Several kinds of such apparent movement have been described. We shall consider three.

Beta Movement.—If two disks of light are presented briefly and in succession to different areas of the retina, movement tends to appear in

the direction of the succession. Whether it is good movement or jerky
and incomplete depends upon three principal aspects of the stimulus situation (Korte's laws): the size and intensity of the stimuli, their distance of
separation, and the interval between their presentations. The greater
the spatial separation or the temporal interval, the greater must be the
intensity; and the impairment of optimal movement caused by changing
one of these factors can within certain limits be offset by altering either
of the others.

Delta Movement.—Sometimes in a situation that would otherwise
produce beta movement, if the second of two flashes is much brighter than
the first, movement backward from the second to the first flash is seen.

Gamma Movement.—When a disk of light comes on suddenly, its
center appears first and then expands, filling out the disk; likewise, when
the light goes off, one's experience is of a contraction of the light to its
center where it vanishes.

The explanation of these three forms of apparent movement is
explicable in terms of retinal processes by making certain assumptions
concerning retinal processes: (1) Receptors in the center of the retina
respond more quickly than those in the periphery. This assumption is
quite reasonable in view of the fact that the cones mediate much higher
rates of flicker discrimination than do the rods and that the A wave of the
optic-nerve potential, arising presumably from cones, is definitely the
first response to appear in the optic nerve, and finally that more summation is required in the peripheral rods and cones than in the fovea and
central areas. (2) It may be supposed that the more intense the stimulus,
the sooner will it activate the receptors it stimulates. Such is actually
the case in the discharge of individual nerve fibers and in the measurements either of the latency of the B wave of the retinal potential or of the
optic-nerve potential (Bartley *et al.*). (3) There is spatial interaction in
the retina such that different retinal areas can influence each other and
cause activity in intervening areas. We have already seen that such
interaction is a demonstrable fact. (4) We may employ the fact that in
any illumination of a limited area of the retina there is some amount of
stray light which, because of diffraction in the eyes, illuminates what
would otherwise be dark parts of the retina.

The first of these factors, Bartley points out, is probably the crucial
one in producing gamma movement. This expansive movement is seen
with the sudden onset of a stimulus because, when fixated with the fovea,
receptors in the center of the image respond first and are followed by those
in the periphery of the image. Then, too, the low intensity of the stray
light on the rest of the retina causes the periphery of the retina to respond
later than the part under the image and thus to aid in the 'expansion'

of the visual field.   This, in fact, plainly happens when the whole field is illuminated, rather than just a limited part of it.   Such an explanation has been given a great deal of support by experiments in which Bartley arranged images in which the center was less intense than the periphery, with the result that gamma movement was destroyed or even reversed (see Fig. 75).   Thus gamma movement is explicable in terms of the latency with which receptors are activated.

A similar description applies to beta movement except that in dealing with it the factor of retinal interaction should be introduced.   The effects of stimulation of two retinal areas must summate, we know, if the areas are not too far apart on the retina, or in time of presentation, either through the activity of lateral neurons in the retina or through the

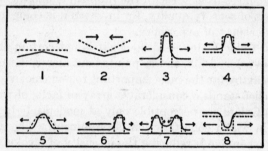

Fig. 75.—Eight cases of visual stimuli and the direction of apparent movement which they produce when the stimuli have a sudden onset (as determined in experiments by Bartley).   The bottom line in each case is merely a base line.   The dotted lines represent the distribution of light in the stimulus.   The solid line represents distribution of light on the retina; this is somewhat different from that of the stimulus outside the eye because of the optical properties of the eye.   The arrows indicate the direction in which apparent movement is seen, and the length of the lines represents roughly the relative magnitude of the apparent movement.   The cases illustrate the fact that apparent movement under the conditions indicated depends in part on the gradient of illumination in the retinal image and in part on the different behavior of the center and periphery of the retina.   (*From S. H. Bartley.   Vision, p. 159.   New York: Van Nostrand, 1941.   By permission of the publishers.*)

overlapping of synaptic endings at all levels of the visual pathways.   We are certain that the retina plays some part in this interaction, but the brain also is probably capable of it.   Consequently beta movement may be regarded as equivalent to real movement in that in both cases there are neural excitations aroused successively in the cells between the stimulated areas.

In attempting to explain apparent movement, it may be pointed out, certain psychologists have resorted to postulations of some kind of force between points in the cortex representing the flashes of light.   Such an approach is not necessary in view of our present knowledge concerning retinal interaction.   It is improbable, moreover, that the cortex is the locus of the interaction effects responsible for apparent movement, for, as will be described later, animals that lack the visual cortex show definite signs of 'seeing' apparent movement.

Delta movement, finally, can be understood in terms of the greater speed of reaction of receptors subjected to high intensities of stimulation. This different in latency of response is apparently so great that, although a light may appear after another, its greater intensity causes the cells stimulated by it to give a burst of impulses before the cells exposed to the weaker light.

COLOR VISION

We may next consider the question of the mechanism of color vision. This, of course, faces us again with the problem of specific nerve energies and of the basis of sensory quality, for in vision it is color that represents the qualitative aspect of experience.

Cones and Color Vision.—Although it is not certain that the cones always mediate color vision, as was pointed out above, it seems clear that in man they play by far the most important role in color vision. In support of this belief stands a considerable array of facts, of which two may be cited. (1) Colors are perceptible only at moderately high intensities, in the range in which cone function is prominent. There is, indeed, a definite point when one is reducing the intensity of a colored light where its color can no longer be appreciated and yet it is clearly visible as a 'white' light. (2) Color is perceived best when the more central areas of the retina are being stimulated; presenting a colored light to the periphery, on the other hand, gives only an impression of 'white.' This fact correlates with the distribution of cones and rods.

Theories of Color Vision.—The experience of color is, of course, primarily dependent upon the wave length of the visual stimulus. How, then, do the cones respond to wave length in such a way as to produce color experience? That question has occupied the minds of those who have worked with visual experience, and they have proposed two different answers to it: One is that cones differ in their sensitivity to the various wave lengths of the visual spectrum, and differences in color experience arise from differences in the extent to which different kinds of cones are stimulated. This theory we may call a specific-receptor theory. The other view is that any particular cone may respond differentially to all wave lengths, and color experience depends upon the kind of response elicited in a cone rather than the kind of cones being excited. Rarely, however, has this second theory been proposed in this pure form; more often it has been compromised in some way with the first theory.

The most prominent suggestions which employ a combination of theories have been made by Hering and by Polyak. Polyak proposes that cones give qualitatively different responses to wave length but that the bipolar cells analyze these responses through being more excitable to one type of response than to another. Thus Polyak subscribes to the second theory for the cones, but to the first theory for the bipolar cells. He was led to do that because his histological studies of the retina revealed the great extent of overlapping of cone endings upon the bipolar cells, and it appeared to him that the specific-receptor theory could not apply to the cones because the responses of different cones would not be represented in the bipolar cells. Hering, on the other hand, proposed that there are three different kinds of cones, white-black, yellow-blue, and red-green; each of which gives two different types of response—a breaking down (catabolism) and a building up (anabolism), respectively, of chemical materials.

This theory of Hering's is not favored today, because there is no good basis in physiology for different kinds of processes in the same neural cell and because, even if there were, nervous impulses are regarded as all alike and incapable of distinguishing between the kinds of stimuli which give rise to them. The same argument also applies to Polyak's view, for cones are to be regarded as true neurons giving rise to nervous impulses just as do other neurons. Everything points, therefore, to the alternative theory that the basis of color experience is not in the kind of response given by a cone but in which cones respond and to what extent they respond.

Two forms of this specific-receptor theory have been proposed: (1) The three-color theory of Young and Helmholtz calls for three different types of cones, named the 'red,' 'green,' and 'blue' cones after the experiences which they are supposed to produce. (2) The four-color theory of Ladd-Franklin postulates, in addition to the three primary colors of Young and Helmholtz, a fourth type, the 'yellow' cone. In the Young-Helmholtz theory the assumption of this fourth type of cone is considered unnecessary because 'yellow' can be produced by mixing red and green. Although there is no crucial evidence upon which to make a choice between the two theories, the Young-Helmholtz has been the most widely favored in recent times, partly because of Helmholtz's wide influence in sensory psychology and partly because most of the phenomena of color vision are as easily explained by a three-color theory as by one assuming four primary colors.

Consider, for example, the phenomena of color mixture. Any kind of color experience can be produced if we select three appropriate wave lengths and mix them in different proportions. The wave lengths selected need only be those which, taken separately, give experiences of 'red,' 'green,' and 'violet,' respectively. From this fact we are led to believe that there are three primary colors and, corresponding to them, three types of cones.   These three do not include 'yellow,' which according to some criteria is regarded as a primary color; since 'yellow' can be produced by mixtures of the other three wave lengths, it has been supposed that 'yellow' is the result of the mixture of effects from the other three types of cones.   The three-color theory, consequently, appears well supported by this fact.   There are, of course, many other phenomena of color, but none are crucial and none have quite so direct a bearing on the problem as do the data of color mixture.

The Hypothetical Color System.—Assuming the essential notions of the Young-Helmholtz theory to be true, Hecht has raised the question of the properties that the three kinds of cones should have in order to

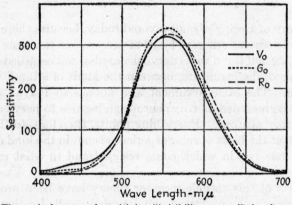

Fig. 76.—Theoretical curves of sensitivity ("visibility curves") for the postulated three types of color receptors as computed by Hecht.   (*From J. Mandelbaum and E. U. Mintz. The sensitivities of the color receptors as measured by dark adaptation.   Amer. J. Ophthalmol.,* **24,** 1242, 1941.   *By permission of the American Journal of Ophthalmology.*)

account for the various phenomena of color vision.   This question put simply is: What are the visibility curves of the three cones?   For a different distribution of sensitivity of wave length is all that is needed to distinguish the different cones.   In the absence of any direct physiological evidence on the question, he made up three curves that would meet the requirements.   These, shown in Fig. 76, are not so different as one might expect; indeed, the hypothetical curve of one cone is hardly distinguishable from that of another.   The violet 'cone' is only a little more sensitive in the violet region than the other two cones; the 'green' cone also is a trifle better than the other two in the middle ('green') region of the spectrum; and the 'red' cone, likewise, has a slight advantage over the other cones in the 'red' region of the spectrum.   The three curves, it is to be noted, are all very similar to the photopic visibility curve, as they should be, since this curve is supposed to be the composite curve of sensitivity of the cones.

By mathematical methods, which the interested reader can study by referring to Hecht's writings, it may be shown that the curves in Fig. 76 account adequately for the proportions in which the three primary wave lengths must be mixed in order to produce various color experiences. Unfortunately, however, these same three curves do not do so well in explaining certain other data of color experience and have to be modified somewhat to take care of such data. It is possible, however, that the fault lies not with the three curves but with the inaccuracies of measurement of the experience and with individual variations among subjects in the properties of their cones. Certainly much of both must be granted, for Hecht has compared the same kind of discriminations on different observers and found them significantly different, and errors of measurement are always with us even under the best of conditions.

Physiological Basis of the Hypothetical System.—The direct way of testing whether or not the theory of three primary receptors is true or not is to find some way of isolating individual receptors and to measure their responses to lights of different wave lengths, or in other words, to measure the visibility curves of individual visual receptors. Graham and Hartline have done precisely this in the eye of Limulus. They constructed microelectrodes and inserted them through the outer layers of the retina so that they could come into contact with a single receptor cell at a time. By recording the electrical activity of the cell upon response to light and adjusting the intensity of light at each of several wave lengths to the level just adequate to evoke a response from the receptor, they succeeded in obtaining the visibility curves of individual receptors. Figure 77 shows their results.

As this graph illustrates, each receptor has a visibility curve that closely resembles the gross visibility curve of the eye as measured by psychological procedures, but there are different visibility curves for different receptors. It was not possible, however, to determine just how many kinds of receptors there were because the errors of recording were of a larger magnitude in many cases than the differences between curves. The significance of the difference between the most extreme curves could, nevertheless, not be questioned, and the magnitude of the differences was of the order to be predicted by Hecht's theory. It may, therefore, be considered proved that receptors can have different visibility curves, although proof of the number of types must await more refined research procedures.

Psychological Evidence for the Hypothetical System.—Aside from the facts and methods so far described, there is still another method of getting at the problem of receptors for color. If it is assumed that there are different receptors of different sensitivity to wave length, then it should be possible to adapt one set of receptors to a greater extent than

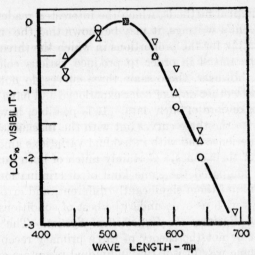

FIG. 77.—Visibility curves for three individual sense cells from the eye of Limulus as determined by their electrical responses to different wave lengths. (*From C. H. Graham and H. K. Hartline. The response of single visual cells to lights of different wave lengths. J. gen. Physiol.,* **18**, *924, 1935. By permission of the Rockefeller Institute for Medical Research.*)

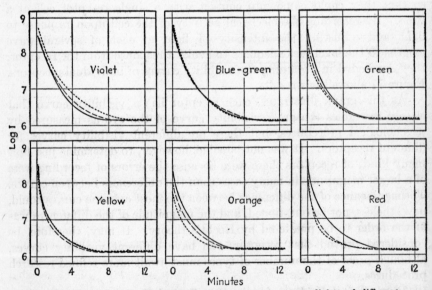

FIG. 78.—Curves of dark adaptation following exposure to lights of different wave length as indicated in each graph. The solid lines are for test paths with red light; the broken lines, green light; the dotted lines, violet light. The curves have been shifted vertically to make the final thresholds coincide. (*From J. Mandelbaum and E. U. Mintz. The sensitivities of the color receptors as measured by dark adaptation. Amer. J. Ophtalmol.,* **24**, *1247, 1941. By permission of the American Journal of Ophthalmology.*)

others by stimulating with light to a particular wave length, and this greater effect should be revealed in the sensitivity of the eye to different wave lengths in the period following such light adaptation.

Mandelbaum and Mintz have tested and confirmed this prediction (see Fig. 78). Human individuals were adapted, for example, with violet light and then tested for their sensitivity to different wave lengths in the following dark-adaptation period, with the finding that sensitivity was poorest to violet. Similarly, adaptation to red light caused a greater loss of sensitivity to red than to other wave lengths; the result was the same with other wave lengths of light adaptation. From an analysis of

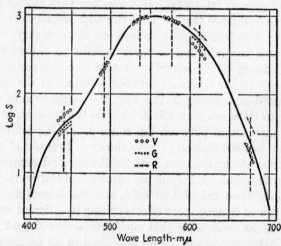

Fig. 79.—Visibility curves (in logs) for the three types of color receptors as computed from rate of dark adaptation following exposures of different wave length and tested by stimuli of different wave length. (*From J. Mandelbaum and E. U. Mintz. The sensitivities of the color receptors as measured by dark adaptation. Amer. J. Ophthalmol., 24, 1251, 1941. By permission of the American Journal of Ophthalmology.*)

the results, furthermore, it was possible to reconstruct the visibility curves of the assumed three primary receptors that would be required of them for the obtained results to have occurred. These curves, seen in Fig. 79, agree with those previously deduced by Hecht from other visual data.

Interaction of Color Receptors.—Lest it be thought that the color mechanism is a simple one, we should consider a fact recently discovered by Crozier and Wolf while studying flicker vision. It will be recalled that the relation between c.f.f. and intensity has been taken by Crozier to indicate the relative frequency of impulses being released in the neurons of the visual pathways, and further, that the lower the intensity required to produce c.f.f., the more effective is the intensity. Consulting the curves of Fig. 70 and our earlier discussions of flicker will make that point clear. In the light of this consideration, which is well supported by Crozier's experiments, the important fact is this: A light that has 'color' may require a lower intensity for c.f.f. than will 'white' light. This fact was established beyond doubt because the colored light, which in this case was 'violet,' was produced by simply slipping a violet filter in front of the 'white' light, thereby cutting out the wave lengths other than violet, which made up the 'white' light; by doing this the c.f.f. was raised a considerable amount. When interpreted according to the principles stated above, this fact means that the 'violet' light has more exciting power, in terms of the neural effect produced, than does a 'white' light of greater intensity. But how can that be, we may ask, if the experience of white is the result of the additive mixture of different wave lengths? The fact appears to lead, on the contrary, to the belief that in this case the addition of wave lengths to the violet, thereby giving 'white', did so by the *inhibition*, rather than the addition, of other nervous elements in the retina or nervous system. If the experience of white is produced even partly in this way, the mechanism of color vision will turn out to be a complex affair. Up to the present, however, the possibility of interaction between the cones producing inhibition rather than excitation has not figured in color theory. It is not at all unlikely, in view of the evidence showing both inhibitory and summative interaction in the retina; indeed, Polyak has emphasized the overlapping of the endings of cones upon the bipolar cells, and the lateral neurons of the retina also serve to interconnect effects arising in different retinal receptors. It is just as reasonable that such interaction should affect color vision as the other aspects of vision described in an earlier section.

CENTRAL VISUAL MECHANISMS

Much of our knowledge of the part played by centers of the brain in visual experience comes from experiments with animals in which the extirpation of parts of the brain has been coupled with measurements of visual capacity. In order to assess this knowledge and interpret its meaning for man, we must begin by surveying differences in the central equipment of the animals upon which it is based.

There are, indeed, such differences, particularly in the birds and higher mammals, and they follow the general principle of encephalization, explained in an earlier chapter (p. 115). The visual cortex, it will be recalled, is part of the somatic or neocortex, and this is of only slight importance in inframammalian animals. In birds and animals below them no visual functions can be demonstrated for the cortex (Layman); all forms of visuomotor capacity are perfectly intact after destruction of the cortex. In such animals the lateral geniculate body appears to act as it does in mammals, *viz.*, as a relay system, but visual integrations are evidently carried out in the superior colliculi of the midbrain. In the mammalian series, however, the cerebral cortex takes over, in varying degrees, certain of the functions of the superior colliculus. Such an encephalization of function has gone so far in chimpanzee and man that it is doubtful whether the superior colliculi participate at all in visual functions except in the primary oculomotor reflexes.

Visual Sensitivity.—There is at present very little evidence concerning the relation of absolute thresholds to the functioning of visual centers. One experiment, in which the effect of extirpation of the striate cortex in the cat (Bridgman) was studied, resulted in the absolute threshold's being slightly raised.

When considering the form of the optic-nerve potential and its relation to central visual stations, we observed that the A fibers tend to influence the visual cortex more than subcortical centers, whereas the B fibers send their impulses primarily to the midbrain. Suggested by this fact is the possibility that A fibers may represent cone activity, B fibers activity of the rods, and that consequently one might expect to find the cortex primarily concerned with cone functions and the midbrain centers of greatest importance in rod functions. Support for this suggestion comes from work in which the photopic and scotopic visibility curves were determined in the monkey before and after striate extirpation (Malmo). Normal monkeys showed both kinds of curves disposed about as they are in man, but after removal of the visual cortex, only the scotopic visibility curve remained, and measurements of wave-length visibility at high illuminations gave a scotopic, rather than a photopic, distribution of sensitivity. Thus it looks as though it is the cones which are represented in the encephalization of visual functions in the monkey.

Flicker Fusion.—The ability of the cat to discriminate visual flicker before and after removal of the visual cortex has been the subject of a careful study to discover the role of the visual cortex in this visual function (Kappauf). Flicker discrimination, it was found, is considerably impaired by the operation, particularly at high illuminations. There seems, indeed, to be a differential effect of the operation on the rod and cone sections of the flicker curve (*cf.* p. 194), the rod section being left relatively unimpaired. With prolonged training, however, the operated animals can regain their normal sensitivity at all levels of illumination; so it cannot be held that the cortex is absolutely necessary for cone functions in flicker vision. For this reason, it has been suggested that the most significant effect of striate removal is some interference with an animal's ability to give its 'attention' to visual stimuli, rather with cone functions per se.

Brightness Discrimination.—In the rat the capacity for brightness discrimination is lost with ablation of the visual areas of the cortex, but this appears to be just the habit of brightness discrimination, rather than the capacity for performing it, because the habit can be relearned in about the same number of trials as are required for normal animals (Lashley). Thus has it been demonstrated that, while the rat normally uses its visual cortex in brightness discrimination, in the absence of the cortex the superior colliculi of the midbrain will serve about as well. Essentially the same results have been found in the cat (Smith). In this case, however, thorough measurements of the differential brightness threshold disclose that some permanent impairment of discrimination follows the cortical extirpation (Mead); definite increases in the threshold follow the operation (see Fig. 80).

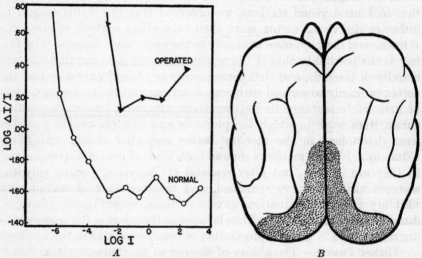

FIG. 80.—A, curves of brightness discrimination in normal cats and in cats following removal of the visual area of the cortex. B, the visual area of the cortex of the cat. (From unpublished results by L. C. Mead. By permission of the author.)

There is also a suggestion that the visual cortex plays a more important role in brightness discrimination at high intensities of illumination than at low ones (Smith). Cats trained preoperatively to discriminate brightness at both low and high general illumination of the visual field quickly regain their ability to discriminate at low illuminations following the operation, but even with prolonged training they fail to make the correct choices at high illuminations. This phenomenon corresponds to the loss of the photopic visibility curve (monkeys) and the postoperative difficulty of cats with flicker discrimination at high intensities. It may be interpreted as indicating that the functions of the cortex and midbrain represent in some measure the duplexity of retinal functions.

There is the interesting fact, demonstrable in dogs, of the effects of extirpation of the visual cortex upon brightness discrimination under different procedures of testing (Marquis). When dogs are *conditioned* to give responses to brightness, they do not lose the conditioned responses when the striate cortex is removed. When trained to discriminate brightness differences in a *free-choice* situation, however, they do suffer loss of the habit and have to relearn it, as described above. The conclusion that the visual cortex normally participates in brightness discrimination but can be replaced by the midbrain if necessary does not hold in this case, but is seen to depend upon the type of learned response which is employed in measuring the visual experience.

Pattern Vision.—Many experiments concerning the function of visual centers have been made on the ability of animals to appreciate the form or shape of visual objects. The general findings of these experiments have been that mammalian animals from rats to chimpanzee lose their pattern vision following striate extirpation and can never with any amount of training regain that capacity (Lashley, Smith). Such studies, however, have usually been conducted in daylight, *i.e.*, under conditions of high illumination, and we have seen that other visual functions are also impaired under these circumstances, although not so radically and permanently. We might expect such a finding on the hypothesis that the cortex represents the cone receptors which provide the greatest part of ability to appreciate visual details. According to the same theory we might expect, further, that some capacity for pattern discrimination, though crude, might remain in the absence of the visual cortex if the tests were conducted at low illuminations when the eye is dark adapted and the rods are functioning best. Following this general line of reasoning, Smith studied the effect of striate extirpation upon the ability of cats to discriminate such simple patterns as vertical and horizontal bars under conditions of low illumination. He found that the animals, after moderately prolonged training, could make such a discrimination and thereby demonstrated the survival of crude pattern vision after striate removal. Such vision must, presumably, be mediated by the midbrain.

Movement Discrimination.—Further evidence to this effect has come from the study of movement discrimination. Visual movement depends upon spatial aspects of the photic stimulus and in this sense is a type of pattern experience, although, to be sure, it is a primitive one. Two experiments show that movement can be discriminated by cats after the visual cortex is removed and when the tests are conducted under dark-adapted conditions. In one the animals distinguished between a stationary spot and one moving in a circle (Kennedy); in the other they discriminated stationary from moving vertical striations (Morgan). In both cases, however, the rate of movement required for discrimination was many times faster than that necessary for the normal cat and the performance of the animals was rather unstable, preventing the measurement of thresholds. Thus movement vision was radically impaired by removal of the cortex, but still unquestionably existent. The visual perception of movement, in the cat at any rate, can be carried on by subcortical visual centers.

Apparent Movement.—The facts we have been considering were gathered by teaching animals through reward and punishment to choose one of two stimuli to be discriminated. Another method of studying visual capacity is possible when the stimuli are moving striations. This takes advantage of the fact that most mammals give reflex movements of the head or eyes when presented with moving lines. Such eye and head movements, called optokinetic reactions, follow the movement of the stimulus in such a way that one particular striation is kept upon the fovea or central region of the retina until the eyes are extremely deviated; then they return quickly to a normal position and pursue the moving stimulus again. In some animals, head movements are most prominent (guinea pig), in others, eye movements.

Such optokinetic reflexes do not require the visual cortex, for they appear in all animals so far studied after the cortex has been completely removed (Smith *et al.*). If anything, the reflexes are somewhat improved in their stability by the cortical extirpation. The parts of the midbrain subserving these reactions must, consequently, preserve in their synaptic arrangements a high order of point-to-point projection, else the reflex reactions to moving patterns could not take place. Giving good support to this conclusion is the fact that when the striations are reduced in size to the point where the reactions cease and a measure of visual acuity is thereby obtained, the visual acuity of the operated cat turns out to be just as good as that of the normal cat. Thus do the subcortical centers of vision display a degree of spatial organization, so far as reflex behavior is concerned, that is as fine as that of the cortex.

Perhaps the most striking fact that comes out of the study of optokinetic reactions is that they give evidence of apparent movement taking place in the absence of the visual cortex (Smith). One can present a flickering illumination of the moving striations and thereby produce the conditions of apparent movement, *i.e.*, the successive presentation of objects on different parts of the retina. Cats respond to such stimulation with optokinetic reactions, just as they do to real movement, and their responses are not impaired by extirpation of the visual cortex. Apparent movement vision, of a sort, therefore appears to be mediated in this instance by subcortical centers. To be sure, we know nothing of the conscious experience of the animal, but the reflex behavior gives every indication that the essential neural processes for the apparent movement do not require the cortex. This fact might indicate that these processes originate either in the retina or in the subcortical visual centers. In so much as we already have reasons for thinking that the retina may produce these processes, that interpretation is preferred here.

Cortical Functions in Man.—The data and conclusions that have just been discussed are applicable only to animals below man, particularly to the rodents and carnivora. They are, nonetheless, interesting and informative. For one thing, they point out the course that encephalization has taken in visual functions and therefore suggest the way visual functions may be organized in man. It may also be said of them that they are about all the dependable information that we have, since the data on man are by no means satisfactory.

Of the numerous cases of injury to the visual cortex that have been reported as arising from war injuries, tumors, infections, or other accidental destruction, only nine are said to involve, without question, the complete destruction of the striate cortex (Marquis). As far as could be determined, these nine were completely blind. From this fact we may judge that visual functions, which are a completely subcortical affair in inframammalian animals, are so greatly encephalized in man that no function except that of controlling optic reflexes has been left to the subcortical centers. More data, however, are extremely desirable before this conclusion can be accepted without reservation. There is some hope, fortunately, of drawing useful conclusions from work with chimpanzees, since these close relatives of man appear to be affected by partial destruction of the striate area in much the same way as man (Spence and Fulton); as yet no chimpanzees with complete destruction of the visual cortex have been studied.

Most reports of visual disturbances in man due to neural injury come from cases of partial lesions of the striate area. In these, sensory defects occur in limited regions of the visual field. These are called *scotomata*, and their character depends upon the locus, size, and shape of the part of the visual cortex injured. Destruction in a specific area, however, need not be so complete as to destroy all visual functions of that area; in such a case *amblyopia* is said to exist. Such a lesion is particularly informative because it gives one an opportunity to study the ways in which certain visual capacities are lost or impaired without disturbance of others.

One may, in general, distinguish somewhat arbitrarily several kinds of visual defects resulting from cortical injuries in man: color vision, either complete or partial; distinctness of the form and size of figures; depth, distance, and direction of visual objects; brightness and differential sensitivity for white-black perception; and visual movement. Some have held that not all properties of visual experience depend upon the visual cortex, but that such aspects of experience as color and depth are 'localized' in adjacent cortical areas. All these several disturbances, nevertheless, have been found in one case or another in connection with injury to the visual cortex.

There is considerable agreement among various observers that color vision, of all the visual functions, is most easily impaired by striate injury; color vision, it is sometimes reported, may be defective without the implication of other visual functions. The localization of visual objects in space, depth perception, and the appreciation of visual patterns are closely tied up in cortical lesions; when one is disturbed, the others tend also to be. Brightness sensitivity, however, may or may not suffer impairment along with such defects. It is an interesting fact, finally, that the perception of movement is often reported as the most resistant to striate injury. Some patients, for example, observe the movement of an object without observing the object that moves; or in other instances the object may be visible when moving but be lost from perception when stationary.

Too much stock, unfortunately, should not be placed in this or any other scheme of the hierarchy of visual functions in cortical injuries. The various results available in the clinical literature are often open to question on the basis of insufficient testing of the patients, inaccurate reporting by them, or the theoretical bias of the observer entering into the selection and interpretation of the results.

It is so often reported, moreover, that patients with striate lesions show defects of visual 'attention' (Poppelreuter) that we are led to wonder whether psychological processes of a very high order do not enter into the picture and obscure it. Disturbances of visual 'attention'— whatever this may mean—are sometimes said to be the only result of small striate injuries. This observation is probably important in the interpretation of the various data on human visual scotoma. Many of the reported deficits may be no more than loss in 'attentive' capacity. One distinguished neuropsychiatrist claims, for example, that in the hundreds of cases of occipital lesion that he has observed there was no case of perfect scotoma when the patient was properly examined. The distinction to be made between 'attention' and sensory loss is subtle but undoubtedly genuine. Visual objects may be seen well enough, but they may not be able to command behavior or, in the terms of subjective experience, they may not seem 'real.' To say this is perhaps to state in another way the fact already pointed out above that a sensory capacity cannot be measured or judged independently of the type of behavior associated with it. It is as if sensory processes are tied up in the brain with certain behavioral mechanisms and not with others.

General References

BARTLEY, S. H., 1941. *Vision.* New York: Van Nostrand. Pp. xv + 350.

GRAHAM, C. H., 1934. Some neural correlations. Pp. 829–879. In *A handbook of general experimental psychology.* Ed. Carl Murchison. Worcester: Clark Univ. Press.

HECHT, SELIG, 1934. The photoreceptors. Pp. 704–828. In *A handbook of general experimental psychology.* Ed. Carl Murchison. Worcester: Clark Univ. Press.

CHAPTER XI

HEARING

Upon our ability to control precisely the physical aspects of a stimulus depends to a very large extent our progress in understanding sensory functions. Only recently have we gained that ability in acoustics, and we owe it to the great strides that have been made in electrical engineering, particularly the development of the vacuum-tube amplifier. This instrument has enabled us to record, as well as to produce, acoustic phenomena. Today, as a consequence, the field of hearing is one we can survey with satisfaction, for from the excellent research made possible by such technical developments we have come a long way in the psychophysiology of hearing.

THE AUDITORY STIMULUS

Sound waves, the stimuli for hearing, are rapidly alternating changes in the pressure of a medium which are transmitted through it. They are made possible by the elasticity of the medium, but are usually generated by the vibration of some object within it. The tuning fork, for example, which used to be the conventional source of sound, is displaced from its natural position by the force of the hammer with which it is struck, and the resulting displacement increases the pressure, or concentration of particles, in the adjacent medium, air. When the tuning fork has reached a maximum displacement, determined by the force applied to it, it will return, just as a pendulum does, to its normal position; more than that, it will overshoot with a displacement in the opposite direction, the result of which will be to decrease the pressure of air particles on the side of the original displacement. The alternation will, indeed, continue until the energy given to the fork by the first blow is exhausted. Thus will the air around it undergo a cyclic increase and decrease in the pressure of its particles.

Propagation or transmission of the sound wave, furthermore, comes about by a similar means. As pressure is increased in one part of the air, it is dissipated by increasing pressure in the region adjacent, and so on, until the wave, so transmitted, is finally extinguished.

Frequency.—The simplest form of vibratory motion is the *sine wave*, or simple harmonic motion. In such a wave the pressure increases and decreases in the same way as a bar, maintained in a horizontal axis and

219

attached to a point moving around a circle, will move if the point moves
at a constant rate around the circle.   Such harmonic motion. described
in Fig. 81, can be expressed by the following formula:

$$y = A \sin \omega t$$

where y is the displacement from the resting position that has occurred in
time t, when A is the maximum displacement (amplitude), and sin ω is
the velocity of the point moving around the circle. A, the amplitude of
vibration, may be taken as the measure of intensity of the wave, whereas
the number of oscillations which takes place in one second (and which
may be deduced from sin ω) states the frequency of the sound.

These two dimensions, *intensity and frequency*, are all that are necessary for specifying the nature of any sound wave, whether or not it is a

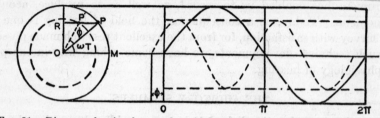

FIG. 81.—Diagram showing how a sinusoidal wave is generated by the projection of
circular motion and how two sinusoidal waves may vary in frequency, amplitude, and
phase.   If P moves around the circle in a counterclockwise direction at a constant rate of
speed, the point R on the line $RP'P$, which is parallel to OM, moves up and down in time
in the manner described by the sine wave.   (*From S. S. Stevens and H. Davis.   Hearing,
p. 5.   New York: Wiley*, 1938.   *By permission of the publisher.*)

pure sine wave.   Waves that are not sinusoidal, however, must be
analyzed into sine waves, and this can always be done, since it has long
been known that any wave, no matter how complex, can be analyzed
into some number of different sine waves, each with a particular frequency
and intensity (Fourier's theorem).   The wave which is sinusoidal without
Fourier analysis we call a *pure tone*, but others which must be analyzed
into sine waves are *complex sounds*.   Of these, there are two main classes:
(1) Some complex sounds are made up of a *fundamental* frequency and
several other frequencies, *overtones*, which are multiples of the fundamental.   Such is usually the case with sounds produced by musical
instruments.   (2) Sounds which upon analysis yield frequencies not
related to each other but rather a complex of frequencies of all sorts
constitute *noise*.

Phase.—Two sound waves may be of the same frequency and amplitude but be out of phase.   This is the case when the maximum amplitude
of one wave does not correspond in time with the maximum amplitude of
the other wave.   The two sound waves will be completely out of phase
when the peak of one corresponds in time with the trough of the other;

likewise, they will be completely in phase when their peaks occur at the same instant. In the former case, one sound wave will cancel the other to an extent dependent upon both of their amplitudes; if these are the same, the cancellation will be complete, and the resultant sound will be of zero amplitude; consequently there will be no sound. In the latter case, the resultant sound will be a simple sine wave with an amplitude which is the summation of the amplitudes of the two sounds that go to make it up.

If two sounds are of a different frequency, something else happens. They will cancel each other when they are out of phase and reinforce each other when they are in phase. The result is to give a sound whose intensity increases and decreases periodically at a rate equal to the difference in frequency of the two sounds that make it up. Periodic changes in the amplitude of a sound wave resulting from the interference of sound waves of different frequency are known as beats.

There are also other conditions under which sound waves may interfere with each other. When a simple sound wave is emitted from a source in a room, it is reflected from the wall in various places at different angles depending upon the structure of the room. As a result of such reflections, at certain points in the room the intensity of the sound will be reinforced, and at others it will be decreased. The pattern of cancellations and reinforcement arising from the reflection of sound waves in a room constitutes what are known as *standing waves*.

Intensity.—The physical intensity of sound may be expressed in one of two ways, in terms of either *pressure* or *energy*. As has already been explained, sound consists of alternations in the pressure of a medium and progresses longitudinally through it. If each of the values for the pressure at each of the various instants of the cycle of the sound wave is squared, these squared values averaged and their square root taken, the root-mean-square is obtained; it is in this form that intensity is expressed as pressure. We use this because the maximum pressure (the amplitude) can serve only as an indicator of the total pressure in the sound wave when it is strictly sinusoidal, in which case the root-mean-square pressure is equal to one-half the amplitude.

It happens that the energy which flows through a unit area of a medium in the transmission of the sound wave is proportional to the square of the pressure. Hence, the intensity of a sound may be specified in terms of either energy or pressure, the *former being the square of the latter*.

In the measurement of intensity, it is more important that we should know the ratio of the intensities of the two sounds than the absolute intensity of either of them. The logarithmic scale readily serves this purpose, and it therefore has become customary to express the intensities of two sounds in logarithms. The unit of measurement of energy ratios is the *bel*, which is defined as a ratio of 10:1 and is expressed by the logarithm of the ratio. Frequently quite useful, however, is a smaller unit than the bel, and consequently the *decibel*, which is one-tenth of a bel, becomes the most familiar expression for intensity ratios. The number of decibels is thus ten times the logarithm of the ratio of two intensities. It should be noted, however, that since the energy of a sound is proportional to the *square* of the pressure, the number of decibels expressing the ratio of two sound pressures will be twenty times the logarithm of the ratio. Thus we have

$$N = 10 \log \frac{E_1}{E_2} = 20 \log \frac{P_1}{P_2}$$

where N is the number of decibels, E represents energy, and P stands for pressure.

When sound intensities are stated in decibels (db) or ratios, it is necessary to have some intensity as a reference; otherwise our statements are meaningless. It is customary to specify the reference intensity in either one of two ways. One may select quite arbitrarily some reference intensity, as for example the intensity of sound emitted by a certain speaker when one volt is applied to it; the number of decibels which a sound is above or below this reference intensity will then be called its *intensity level*. Intensity may be expressed, on the other hand, as the number of decibels above the threshold of hearing at a given frequency; when that is the case, a sound intensity is expressed in terms of *sensation level*.

THE ANATOMY OF THE EAR

It is only with the greatest difficulty that man has been able to devise instruments for the analysis of sound; yet the human ear is a mechanism that performs such an analysis with great, if not perfect, precision. Concerned in this analysis are the intricate structures of the external, middle, and inner ear, and giving it meaning in human experience are the various auditory centers and pathways of the brain. These we shall discuss in turn.

The External Ear.—What we refer to in common parlance as the ear is only the *pinna* of the external ear as conceived in anatomy. In lower animals the pinna can be manipulated in such a way that sounds coming from one direction can be 'collected' more efficiently than those arising from another source. In man, however, little purpose is served by it. Sound waves simply travel down the *external meatus*, also a part of the external ear, and at its end strike the *tympanic membrane* which divides the external and middle ears (Fig. 83).

The Middle Ear.—Placed obliquely across the end of the external meatus, the tympanic membrane is a cone whose apex points inward. Firmly attached to it is the *malleus*, one of three ossicles (bones) in the middle ear. To the malleus is joined by tight ligaments the *incus*, a second ossicle, and this in turn articulates with the *stapes*, the third ossicle, which is attached to the oval window (see below) of the inner ear (cochlea).

Surrounding the ossicles is the air-filled cavity of the middle ear, contained in the temporal bone of the skull. Air pressure in this cavity is maintained at the same level as the outside air by means of the *Eustachian tube* connecting it with the mouth cavity. Bounded on one side by the tympanum, the middle ear is separated from the inner ear, or cochlea, by two other membranes, the *oval* and *round* windows.

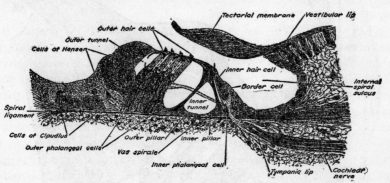

Fig. 82.—The organ of Corti in man. (*From Bailey's textbook of histology*, p. 738. Ed. P.E. Smith. Baltimore: Williams & Wilkins, 1936. By permission of the publishers.)

Associated with the ossicles are two muscles, the *stapedius* and the *tensor tympani*. The latter is attached to the malleus in such a way that, when it contracts, tension is put upon the tympanic membrane. The stapedius muscle, on the other hand, is attached to the stapes near its joint with the incus, and its contraction so dampens the movement of the bony stapes that the amplitude of vibration of the stapes is reduced (attenuated).

The Inner Ear.—The inner ear is part of a system of intercommunicating cavities in a bony labyrinth. Composing it are the cochlea, the semicircular canals, and the vestibular sacs. These latter two structures are of no importance in hearing, but will be discussed in another connection. The cochlea, however, is the primary receptor organ of hearing; it receives its name from its coiled structure. In man it has two and three-quarters turns, whereas lower animals may have more or less than that number of turns. The broader end of it is its *base*, but it becomes smaller as it coils and terminates at the *apex*.

The bony cavity of the cochlea is divided into three parts: a *vestibular canal*, a *cochlear canal*, and a *tympanic canal*. Each of these runs the length of the cochlea. Separating the first two is a thin cellular membrane, *Reissner's membrane*, and between the cochlear and tympanic canals is the *basilar membrane*. At the base of the vestibular canal is the *oval window* to which is attached the stapes of the middle ear, as has already been mentioned. At the base of the tympanic canal, on the other hand, is the *round window*, facing into the cavity of the middle ear near the opening of the Eustachian tube. All three canals are filled with fluid. Also to be noted is the fact that the vestibular and tympanic canals communicate with each other at the apex of the cochlea (helicotrema).

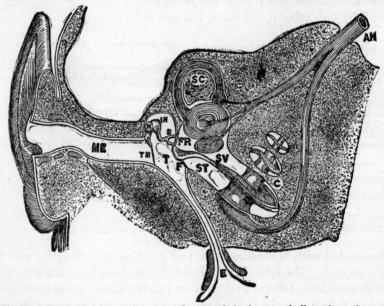

FIG. 83.—Diagram of a section through part of the human skull to show the general structure of the ear and semicircular canals. *ME*, external meatus; *TM*, tympanic membrane; *M*, malleus; *IN*, incus; *S*, stapes; *SC*, semicircular canals; *FR*, oval window; *SV*, vestibular canal; *C*, cochlea; *ST*, tympanic canal; *F*, round window; *T*, middle-ear cavity; *AN*, auditory nerve; *E*, Eustachian tube. (*After Czermak. From P. H. Mitchell. A textbook of general physiology, p. 191. New York: McGraw-Hill, 1938.*)

The Basilar Membrane.—Most important of the structures of the ear for understanding hearing is the basilar membrane. Composed of tendenous fibers, it extends from base to apex of the cochlea. Notable, however, is the fact that the width of the membrane is greatest at the apex and smallest at the base of the cochlea, a fact in contrast with the width of the cochlea itself, which is widest at its base. In the cochlear canal and situated on the basilar membrane are many cells. Of these the most important make up the *organ of Corti*, situated near the inner edge of the membrane toward the axis of the coil of the cochlea (see Fig. 83). Contributing most to the organ of Corti are the *hair cells*, arranged in rows of four from the base to the apex of the cochlea. They are divided, however, into a single inner row and three outer rows by rodlike structures making a tunnellike separation.

It is believed that the hair cells are the primary receptors for hearing. Sound waves are transmitted through the middle ear and oval window into the vestibular canal. After progressing through the fluid of this canal, they cause the basilar membrane to vibrate, and as a consequence, the hair cells are changed in shape. Beneath them arborize the ends of auditory nerve fibers, which in some manner not yet clearly understood are excited by vibration of the membrane.

AUDITORY CENTERS AND PATHWAYS

The nerve fibers that innervate the hair cells have their cell bodies in the *spiral ganglion* located in the inner wall of the cochlea between its axis and the organ of Corti. From this ganglion are collected the axons of the auditory branch of the VIIIth nerve which passes out the bottom of the cochlear coil. These axons are arranged like a twisted rope; those from the basal quarter of the cochlea form the core of the nerve, and around them twist in one direction the fibers from the apex and in the opposite direction fibers from the middle region of the cochlea. Just outside the cochlea the auditory branch is joined by the vestibular branch from the semicircular canal, utricle, and saccule. The two branches divide again, however, just before they reach the medulla; moreover, the auditory portion itself divides into *dorsal* and *ventral* branches which end in corresponding nuclei of the medulla. Here are located the cell bodies of second-order auditory neurons.

In man most of the axons of the cell bodies in the *dorsal* and *ventral* cochlear nuclei cross the mid-line and make connections with other bulbar nuclei (Fig. 84). These are the *trapezoid body*, located along the mid-line of the lower pons, and the *superior olivary nuclei*, placed more laterally at the same level. From these nuclei arise third-order neurons which run upward in the *lateral lemniscus* to the *inferior colliculi* of the midbrain and the *medial geniculate bodies* of the thalamus. Also contained in the lateral lemniscus are some fibers taking origin in the cochlear nuclei, but these probably make synapse in the inferior colliculi. Fibers from the colliculi and all lower levels end upon cell bodies of the medial geniculate bodies. Their axons project, in turn, to the *superior temporal convolution* of the cerebral cortex. In monkeys and man, it appears, the spatial arrangement of the geniculate is preserved in the cortical area representing it (Walker), much as is the case in the visual system; but in the rat projections are much more diffuse (Lashley).

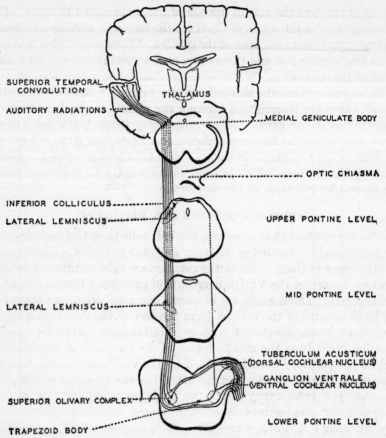

SUPERIOR TEMPORAL
CONVOLUTION

AUDITORY RADIATIONS

THALAMUS

MEDIAL GENICULATE BODY

OPTIC CHIASMA

INFERIOR COLLICULUS

LATERAL LEMNISCUS

UPPER PONTINE LEVEL

MID PONTINE LEVEL

LATERAL LEMNISCUS

TUBERCULUM ACUSTICUM
(DORSAL COCHLEAR NUCLEUS)

GANGLION VENTRALE
(VENTRAL COCHLEAR NUCLEUS)

SUPERIOR OLIVARY COMPLEX

LOWER PONTINE LEVEL

TRAPEZOID BODY

Fig. 84.—Diagram of the auditory pathways and centers of the brain. Successive transverse sections through various levels of the brain stem are shown in the lower part of the figure, but the upper part represents a vertical cross section in the region of the medial geniculate body of the thalamus. (*After Rasmussen. From S. S. Stevens and H. Davis. Hearing, p. 416. New York: Wiley, 1938. By permission of the publishers.*)

THE PHYSIOLOGY OF HEARING: THE MIDDLE EAR

Optimal conditions are required for the transmission of sound from a gaseous medium, such as air, to a solid or fluid medium. To describe these is beyond the scope of this book, but suffice it to say that the ossicles of the middle ear, together with the mechanical arrangement of the entire middle ear, satisfy these conditions about as well as any system could. Under normal circumstances, the form of a sound wave is accurately impressed upon the tympanum which causes the bones of the middle ear to vibrate back and forth, and their motion, in turn, carries the sound wave to the oval window of the cochlea and thus to the fluid of the vestibular canal.

A sound wave is not always transmitted through this chain without alteration. There are, indeed, two possible ways at least in which the sound wave may be 'distorted' in the middle ear. The first is the inability of the middle-ear bones to behave properly at very high intensities of stimulation. The stapes, particularly, can move back and forth only so far, and if the amplitude of vibration delivered to it exceeds this limit, the stapes begins to move in other directions, with the result that the vibration impressed upon the oval window does not faithfully

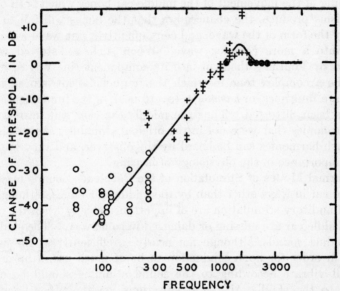

FIG. 85.—The effect of the acoustic reflex upon the transmission of sound through the middle ear to the cochlea. The measurements are in terms of the acoustic intensity required to evoke a cochlear microphonic potential of a given amount. (*After Wiggers. From S. S. Stevens and H. Davis. Hearing, p. 267. New York: Wiley, 1938. By permission of the publishers.*)

reproduce that delivered to the tympanum. A second factor engendering distortion in the middle ear is the action of the intra-aural muscles, the stapedius and the tensor tympani. These muscles contract reflexly, producing what is commonly known as the *acoustic reflex*, particularly at high intensities of low frequencies.

Attenuation.—The effect of the acoustic reflex upon sound transmission in the middle ear has been measured by taking advantage of two facts: The intra-aural muscles of the guinea pig contract more or less rhythmically when the animal is lightly anesthetized; and electrical potentials given off by the cochlea (see below) reflect quite faithfully how sound has been transmitted to the inner ear (Wiggers). As Fig. 85 shows, the principal influence of the acoustic reflex is to reduce the amplitude of sound vibrations at low frequencies. The threshold for the cochlear (microphonic) potential is raised by about 45 db at 100 cycles, and by about 15 db at 500 cycles. At 2,000 cycles and above, however, there is little or no reduction (attenuation) in the amplitude of the sound being transmitted through the middle ear.

Distortion.—The reduction of amplitude of intensity, however, is not the only change in the character of the sound wave brought about by a change in movement of the stapes or by the acoustic reflex. In the dampening of the movement of the middle-ear bones which both of these mechanisms produce, the chances are that the bones will fail to follow perfectly the form of the wave, and consequently a sine wave will be converted into a more complex wave. When such a distorted wave is analyzed by Fourier's theorem into its component sine waves, it turns out to be a complex tone in which the frequencies introduced by distortion are multiples, or *harmonics* (overtones), of the fundamental wave that has been distorted. Thus the middle ear can 'put into' a sound wave harmonics that were not in the original stimulus. As we shall see later, such harmonics can be heard by the observer, and they are therefore of importance in the physiology of hearing.

Abnormal Modes of Stimulation of the Cochlea.—Sounds may reach the inner ear in ways other than by the middle-ear bones, although such forms of auditory stimulation are of importance chiefly when the ossicles of the middle ear are missing or damaged in some way. The skull itself may conduct sounds, although not nearly so efficiently as the ossicles; indeed, in order for bone conduction to be of much use, a hard object that will vibrate according to the sound stimulus should be applied directly to the skull. Air-borne vibrations, on the other hand, may themselves affect directly the oval or round windows of the inner ear without the intervening action of the ossicles. In that case the loss in hearing, experiments show (Békésy), may be as little as 20 db, but it is more often 40 to 65 db; but even at worst, considerable hearing without ossicle-conduction through the middle ear is possible. It may be that, in normal hearing at high intensities, air-borne vibrations affecting the round window may interfere to some extent with the effects of the same sound transmitted to the oval window by the ossicles, because the middle-ear bones reverse the phase of a sound, and ossicle-conducted vibrations to the oval window are, therefore, in opposite phase from air-borne vibrations at the round window.

ACTION OF THE COCHLEA

Little is known of what happens to the sound wave once it is in the inner-ear fluid. Most of our ideas of cochlear action have been gotten from observing mechanical models of the ear (Békésy), and it is hard to tell how well we can apply them to the real ear. From the model (Fig. 86), however, we are led to believe the following: The sound wave set up in the cochlear fluid at the oval window progresses up the vestibular canal, and as it moves it causes the basilar membrane to bulge. As a result, a bulge travels down the basilar membrane. All parts of the membrane do not bulge with equal ease, however, but some parts bulge more than others and there is always one point which is maximally bulged, its position depending upon the frequency. Thus, although a considerable part of the membrane is employed by any sound, the distribution of response and the position of maximal bulging may vary according to the frequency, and we may expect, therefore, a certain degree of *localization* of response of the basilar membrane for different frequencies. For such a conception of cochlear events

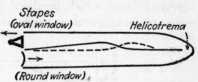

FIG. 86.—Diagram of a traveling wave set up on the basilar membrane by outward movement of the stapes against the oval window. (*After Békésy. From S. S. Stevens and H. Davis. Hearing, p. 279. New York: Wiley, 1938. By permission of the publishers.*)

we have considerable evidence from several kinds of experimentation.

Effects of Loud Sounds.—That the basilar membrane vibrates in response to sounds is shown by the damage to the organ of Corti that takes place when loud sounds stimulate the ear. After guinea pigs, for example, have been exposed to a revolver shot or to a very loud tone of brief duration, their ears have been prepared in histological sections and studied. In them one always finds that, in greater or lesser degree, parts of the organ of Corti, including its hair cells, have been dislodged from their normal position on the basilar membrane and, indeed, in some cases have been thrown completely free of it (Guild; Stevens *et al.*). Such damage must have occurred, it seems certain, because the basilar membrane had been vibrated so violently.

Studies of the position of cochlear damage resulting from stimulation with high intensities of tones over long periods of time show that the middle region of the cochlea is most often affected (Davis *et al.*)—even when very high or very low tones are used. Paralleling such degeneration in the cochlea is a loss in auditory sensitivity which most affects the middle region of tones to which the subject is sensitive. An animal, for example, which was exposed for a long time to 2,500 cycles per second showed its greatest hearing loss at 1,200 cycles (Davis *et al.*). In another experiment with dogs (Finch and Culler), prolonged exposure to 3,000 cycles per second caused a hearing loss of 40 to 50 db for frequencies of 200 to 5,000 cycles per second. The general conclusion to be drawn from experiments of this kind is that loud sounds, no matter what the frequency, stimulate a wide area of the cochlea but tend always to include its middle portion. This, we shall see, is the region of maximal sensitivity and is most concerned in tones of about 1,000 cycles.[1]

Localized Lesions.—But although a wide area of the cochlea is involved at high intensities of stimulation, there is considerable evidence that, particularly at low intensities, the area of maximal involvement varies systematically with the frequency; otherwise said, there is localization in the cochlea. One kind of evidence for this belief comes from experiments in which localized lesions in the cochlea are made. By means of a micro-needle, very small lesions may be made at various points

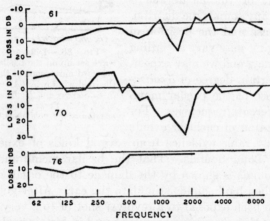

FIG. 87.—Loss of auditory sensitivity at different frequencies following localized surgical damage in the cochlea. Each graph is for a different animal (guinea pig). Number 61 has several scattered lesions, and the audiogram shows corresponding losses at different frequencies. Number 70 shows loss in the middle range without effect at either extreme. The loss of No. 76 resulted from the application of cocaine to a hole in the apical end of the cochlea. (*From S. S. Stevens et al. The localization of pitch perception on the basilar membrane. J. gen. Psychol.*, **13**, 307, 1935. *By permission of the Journal Press.*)

along the basilar membrane, and the hair cells at each point may accordingly be destroyed. Testing the hearing of an animal treated in this way usually reveals a loss of sensitivity which is related to the part of the cochlea injured (Stevens *et al.*).

In Fig. 87 are given two examples of the hearing loss in guinea pigs after different localized lesions. One shows loss limited to the region of 2,000 cycles, the other shows reduced sensitivity to low tones. In this

[1] Recent unpublished experiments with human subjects (Davis *et al.*) somewhat alter these conclusions. It appears, in general, that the region of maximum loss lies above the frequency of the exposure tone, largely in the first octave above it but also to some extent in the second octave above the exposure tone. Considerable research yet remains to be done before trustworthy conclusions can be drawn concerning the relation of damage in the cochlea or loss of auditory sensitivity to the frequency of intense tones to which the ear is exposed.

case, the deafness is not so well restricted to one band of frequencies—a fact that raises a problem with which we shall deal later. In general, however, as Fig. 96 summarizes, all results show the frequency in which there is maximal hearing loss to vary systematically with the position of the lesion; high tones are 'localized' in the basal region of the cochlea, and low tones are 'localized' in the apical end of the cochlea.

Localization of Cochlear Microphonics.—As we have already noted and will consider in more detail in a moment, when the ear is stimulated

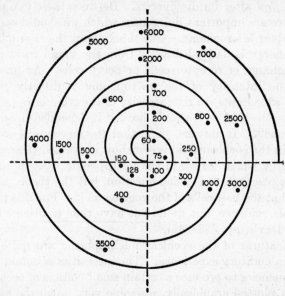

Fig. 88.—Map of frequency localization in the cochlea obtained by determining the position in the cochlea for each frequency at which the microphonic potential is maximal. (*After E. A. Culler. An experimental study of tonal localization in the cochlea of the guinea pig. Ann. Otol., Rhinol. and Laryng.*, **44**, 813, 1935.)

by sound the cochlea gives off electrical potentials, called cochlear microphonics. From these we have additional evidence of localization of effects in the cochlea according to the frequency of the stimulating tone (Culler). One can record the microphonic with electrodes placed anywhere upon the cochlea and with any frequency, but there is always some point where the microphonic is maximal. By determining this point for each frequency, one can plot, in the guinea pig, a map of the cochlea, as given in Fig. 88, which represents the place of maximal involvement of the basilar membrane for each frequency. The cochlear map obtained in this way agrees quite well with that obtained by the method of localized lesions. We are forced, therefore, to conclude that, although a considerable part of the cochlea is always involved in response to any tone, maximal involvement is localized according to frequency.

Wever has taken some exception to this statement which we shall consider in the last section of this chapter.

ELECTRICAL ACTIVITY OF THE COCHLEA AND AUDITORY NERVE

Two varieties of electrical phenomena are encountered in hearing. One is the cochlear microphonic just mentioned; the other is a true action potential of the VIIIth nerve. Both reproduce to some extent the frequency and intensity of an acoustic stimulus, a fact named the *Wever-Bray effect* after its discoverers. Between these two phenomena, however, there are important differences which we should consider.

The Cochlear Microphonic.—One thing about the microphonic seems certain: its energy is derived directly from the sound wave rather than from the discharge of receptor cells or nerve cells. As proof we have two facts: the intensity of the microphonic is directly proportional (within very wide limits) to the intensity of the stimulating sound wave; and it has *no threshold*, as it should have if it depended upon the action potentials of cells. It appears, then, that the mechanical energy of the sound wave in the cochlear fluid is somehow converted (transduced) into electrical energy which we see in the microphonic. As to how the conversion takes place, there is some question, but the theory most widely accepted is that the hair cells of the cochlea do it. For this theory there is considerable evidence, but we do not have time to discuss it here (see Stevens and Davis, pp. 333–345).

Various features of the cochlear michrophonic are quite similar to those found in auditory experience. The intensities of sound required at different frequencies to produce a certain small voltage of cochlear microphonic, when plotted graphically, resemble very much the human audibility curve (Fig. 89). The cochlear microphonic, moreover, has about the same limits of frequency (20 to 20,000 cycles) as does hearing, although technical limitations in recording have prevented actual proof of the point. Then, too, aural harmonics, which are heard in human experience and result from distortion in the aural mechanism, appear in the cochlear microphonic. The voltage of the microphonic, finally, is directly proportional to the intensity of the sound stimulus, except at very high intensities. From these facts, we may believe that the cochlear microphonic represents quite well the way the cochlea behaves in response to sound and the way, moreover, in which the nerve cells of the auditory nerve are stimulated. It has, indeed, been suggested that it is the cochlear microphonic, generated as we believe by the hair cells, that stimulates the nerve fibers associated with the hair cells (Davis), but we have no direct evidence of the validity of this supposition.

Auditory Nerve Potentials.—An action potential, as we know from our previous consideration of nerve functions, is the result of the release of energy from a cell; a stimulus serves only as a trigger for that release. The electrical activity of the VIIIth nerve is to be regarded, accordingly, as an action potential. The cochlear microphonic, however, comes of the conversion of the acoustic stimulus into electrical energy. It is in this important respect, therefore, that the cochlear microphonic differs from the action potential of the auditory nerve.

Most important of the characteristics of the VIIIth nerve action potential is the way in which its frequency is related to the frequency of the sound stimulus. Good synchrony, or 'following,' of the two frequencies holds up to 2,000 or 3,000 cycles, depending upon the intensity

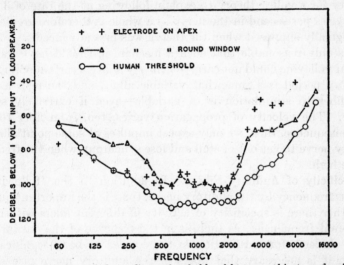

Fig. 89.—Comparison of the auditory thresholds of human subjects and guinea pigs with the intensity required at different frequencies to obtain a cochlear microphonic potential of a given magnitude. (*From S. S. Stevens et al. The localization of pitch perception on the basilar membrane. J. gen. Psychol., 13, 299, 1935. By permission of the Journal Press.*)

of the stimulus. Above these frequencies, 'following' is poorer, and above 4,000 cycles, at best, the impulses in the VIIIth nerve are so irregularly spaced that no frequency can be observed in them.

That there is 'following' above 1,000 cycles, however, is of great interest, because the refractory period of fibers of the VIIIth nerve, at its shortest, is about 1 msec. This figure obviously limits the frequency of discharge in a single nerve fiber to about 1,000 per second. In order to account for synchronization of the impulses in the nerve as a whole above 1,000, we must assume (Wever and Bray) that it comes from the staggering of impulses in different nerve fibers with the result that *volleys* of impulses keep up the frequency even though different nerve fibers may be involved in successive volleys. Such an assumption has been called the *volley theory*, and by it one can account for synchronization of impulses in the auditory nerve with frequencies of acoustic stimulation above 1,000 cycles per second.

Recent experiments, in which the frequency of impulses in individual nerve fibers was recorded by means of microelectrodes and amplifiers, show that the maximum frequency of impulses in a fiber is considerably below the value of 1,000 cycles (Galambos and Davis). Just after the onset of a sound, the frequency may reach 400 or 500 per second, but with continued stimulation it falls rapidly to a value of 200 or 300 per second and remains there, even at comparatively high intensities. The necessity for a volley theory to explain following at the rate of 3,000 or 4,000 cycles per second in the nerve as a whole is therefore greater than was originally supposed when the theory was first advanced.

It is only reasonable that such a mechanism should have its limits and that volleying could not carry synchrony above a certain point. The refractory period is a somewhat variable affair, and the response of a nerve fiber to stimulation is of variable—even if extremely short— latency. The velocity of propagation varies, too, from fiber to fiber. As a consequence, then, we may expect impulses at some point along the auditory nerve to get out of step and lose synchrony when the frequency is quite high.

Specificity of Auditory Fibers.—In addition to the 'following' of stimulus frequency by the auditory nerve, there is the important question of whether there is specificity of activity of different fibers with respect to different frequencies, as there is in the response of the basilar membrane. Indeed, for localization in the cochlea to be of significance in hearing, it is necessary that fibers of the auditory nerve also show a 'localization' or specificity of function. Galambos and Davis (1943) have approached this problem by implanting microelectrodes in the VIIIth nerve in such a way that the activity of individual fibers can be recorded.

They find that each fiber responds maximally, or has a minimal threshold, at some particular frequency, and that there is a limited range of frequencies at which any fiber will respond no matter how great the intensities. The curves of sensitivity of representative fibers which illustrate these facts are shown in Fig. 90. In each case the frequency at which the threshold is lowest probably indicates the position on the basilar membrane where the fiber ends and where the frequency most easily causes vibration. The response of the fiber to other frequencies when the intensity is raised appears, on the other hand, to represent the spread of vibration on the basilar membrane from some other region, more sensitive to the frequency, to the near-by region in which the fiber ends. From these results one may conclude that the localization of patterns of stimulation in the basilar membrane according to frequency is represented in a corresponding manner in the patterns of activity of the auditory nerve and that different stimulus frequencies initiate activity in different combinations of nerve fibers.

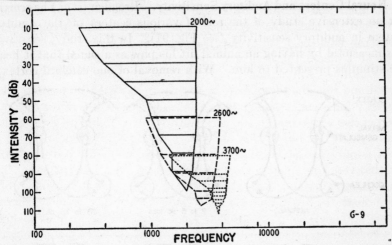

FIG. 90.—Thresholds of response at different frequencies for individual nerve fibers of the auditory nerve. Data for three different fibers are shown: a 2,000∼-fiber, a 2,600∼-fiber, and a 3,700∼-fiber. Each fiber is named by the frequency at which its threshold is lowest. (*After R. Galambos and H. Davis. The response of single auditory-nerve fibers to acoustic stimulation. J. Neurophysiol., 6, 45, 1943. By permission of the authors.*)

NEURAL FUNCTIONS IN HEARING

The anatomic and synaptic relationships of the various centers and pathways of the auditory system have already been briefly described. Let us consider now the physiological facts at hand concerning their function in hearing.

Frequency of Impulses.—Electrodes have been placed at different points in the auditory pathway to determine how well impulses synchronize with the frequency of the stimulating sound (Kemp *et al.*). The general result was that the upper limit of synchronization decreased progressively in second-order neurons, third-order neurons, and so on. Recordings from the cochlear nuclei of the medulla were not satisfactory, but those taken from the trapezoid body (p. 225) indicate that the upper limit of following is 2,500 cycles, and this can be obtained only with very intense stimuli. A similarly loud stimulus would be 'followed' in the auditory nerve up to or above 3,000 cycles. The upper limit of synchronization in third-order neurons of the inferior colliculus, however, is never more than 1,500 cycles and more often is only 1,000 cycles. Very little, if any, synchronization of impulses appears at the auditory cortex, and it is doubtful whether frequency is 'followed' in the radiations from

the geniculate to the cortex above 500 cycles. Thus with the introduction of new synapses at higher levels of the auditory system, following of the frequency of the acoustic stimulus by nervous impulses is
more and more limited to the low frequencies.

Neural Centers and Auditory Sensitivity.—Brogden (*et al.*) has carried
out an extensive study of the role of various centers of the auditory
system in auditory sensitivity (see Fig. 91). In this study, sensitivity
was measured by having an animal lift his paw as a signal that it heard
the stimulus presented to him. With removal of one cerebral cortex, a

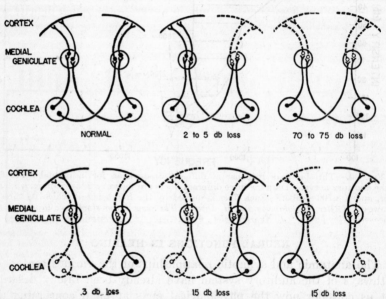

Fig. 91.—Diagram of the parts of the auditory system removed and the accompanying
effect upon auditory sensitivity. Parts shown by dashed lines are the parts extirpated
in each instance. (*After W. J. Brogden et al. Acoustic value of the several components
of the auditory system in cats. Amer. J. Physiol.*, 116, 252–261, 1936.)

very small increment in the threshold, 2 to 5 db, was evident. A similar
loss accompanied removal of one cochlea. If one cochlea were destroyed
along with one hemisphere of the cerebral cortex, a more significant loss,
15 db, followed. But causing the greatest deficit was the complete
removal of both cerebral hemispheres, for then sensitivity was changed
by about 70 to 75 db, an amount almost equivalent to complete deafness.
Such deficit, however, does not accompany the removal of the auditory
areas only; instead the loss is about 10 to 20 db; it would seem, therefore,
that the effects of complete cortical extirpation are not limited to auditory sensitivity, per se, but entail damage to other psychological capacities required for making the motor response to the auditory stimulus.
The conclusion that we reach concerning the auditory system itself is

that subcortical centers rather than the auditory cortex are of the most basic importance in determining auditory sensitivity.

We have, moreover, direct experimental evidence of the functions of the principal subcortical center, in the auditory system the medial geniculate body (Ades *et al.;* Fig. 92). By means of an instrument (the Horsley-Clarke stereotaxic instrument) which allows lesions to be made in subcortical centers with negligible damage to the cortex, small lesions were made in different parts of the medial geniculate bodies. After operation, cats subjected to this procedure showed deficits in sensitivity of as much as 20 db. What is more interesting, however, is that such deficits were associated with certain frequencies, and which frequencies were affected

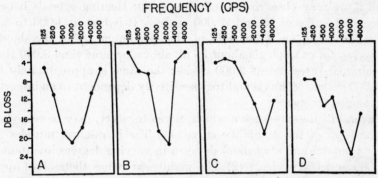

FREQUENCY (CPS)

Fig. 92.—Losses in auditory sensitivity following localized lesions in the medial geniculate body. *A, B, C,* and *D* are different subjects (cats) with somewhat different lesions in each case. (*After H. W. Ades et al. Effect of lesions in the medial geniculate bodies upon hearing in the cat. Amer. J. Physiol.,* **125,** 15–23, 1939.)

depended upon the place where a lesion had been made. Proof was obtained, therefore, of a localization of frequencies in the medial geniculate body just as there is localization of stimulation within the cochlea. It is worth emphasizing, however, that such localization is not absolute but refers only to the *maximum* of a distribution of neural effects which undoubtedly involves a large portion of the geniculate body.

Sustaining these results are recent experiments in which electrical recordings of the action potential in different parts of the medial geniculate body were made in relation to th efrequency of acoustic stimulation of the ear (Coakley). Here, too, localization is to be found— localization consisting of a point in the geniculate giving a maximal action potential for a particular frequency. This method (Licklider), as well as the method of local extirpation (Lipman; Girden), has also been applied to the auditory cortex, but with more equivocal results. Although there appears to be some localization of activity in the auditory cortex with respect to frequency, it is left for the future to know how complete it is.

PSYCHOLOGICAL PHENOMENA OF HEARING

A consideration of the psychological aspects of hearing has been left to the last because these are best understood in the light of the physiological and anatomic facts that have just been summarized. The psychophysiology of hearing has, indeed, been pushed to the point in recent years where most of auditory experience is understandable in terms of physiological processes. To that topic then, let us turn now.

Audibility.—In vision, the absolute threshold for light is a function of wave length, and this function is represented by the visibility curve. Quite similar to it is the relationship of the absolute auditory threshold to acoustic frequency; this we term the *audibility curve* or *audiogram*. From it we may observe the following facts: Hearing extends between the general limits of 20 and 20,000 cycles. It is best at 1,000 to 3,000 cycles, declining on either side of this maximum. The threshold at 125 cycles, for example, is about 35 db above, or more than 3,000 times, the minimal threshold at 2,000 cycles; the same is approximately true of 14,000 cycles. Thus is auditory sensitivity dependent to an important extent upon frequency.

Several factors are known which, taken together, may be responsible for the form of the audibility curve: (1) The intra-aural muscles (the tensor tympani and stapedius) dampen in varying degrees low tones up to 1,000 or 2,000 cycles. (2) The middle-ear bones themselves appear to have a natural period of vibration which makes for greatest efficiency in the vicinity of 1,000 cycles. (3) The length and elasticity of the basilar membrane, on the other hand, as well as the fluids of the cochlea, are probably so tuned that they respond better to frequencies of 1,000 to 3,000 cycles. All these factors taken together give the ear an over-all tuning such that the extent of stimulation of auditory nerve fibers will correspond to the audibility curve.

That the form of the audibility curve is determined in the ear, rather than in the auditory pathways, is quite clearly demonstrated by a fact already mentioned, *viz.*, that the magnitude of the cochlear microphonic is related to frequency in the same way as is the audibility curve (Stevens *et al.*). This fact can be seen in Fig. 89 where the 'threshold' of the cochlear microphonic is compared with that of hearing.

Abnormalities of the Audiogram.—Worthy of mention are some abnormalities of the audiogram which throw some light on the mechanisms of hearing. Human sensitivity to frequencies above 1,000 cycles tends, generally, to decrease with age (Bunch). Individuals of 60 years of age show a hearing loss, on the average, of 40 db at 8,192 cycles, and lesser losses at frequencies down to 1,000 cycles where sensitivity is about normal. Lesser effects are to be seen in younger individuals, but as they grow older the loss at higher frequencies becomes greater and greater, and at the same time it invades the lower frequencies more and more (Fig. 93).

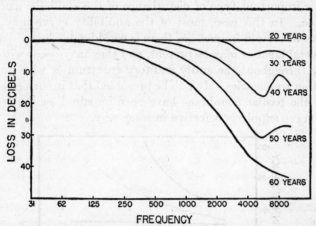

FIG. 93.—Progressive loss of sensitivity at high frequencies with increasing age. The audiogram at twenty years of age is taken as the basis of comparison. (*After C. C. Bunch. Age variations in auditory acuity. Arch. Otolaryngol.*, **9**, 625–636, 1929.)

It has been possible to study the ears of human individuals showing such high-tone deafness (Crowe *et al.*; see Fig. 94). The cause of it is a partial atrophy of the auditory nerve fibers of the basal part of the cochlea. In many cases hearing loss began abruptly at some particular

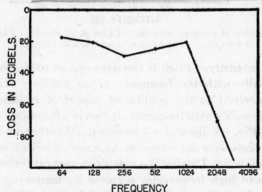

FIG. 94.—A human audiogram illustrating the abrupt high-tone type of deafness. (*After S. J. Crowe et al. Observations on the pathology of high-tone deafness. Bull. Johns Hopkins Hosp.*, **54**, 315–379, 1934.)

frequency and involved all frequencies above it. In most of these, the hearing loss was correlated quite precisely with nerve degeneration or abnormalities of the cochlea in the basal turn. Thus does the study of high-tone deafness afford evidence of localization in the cochlea. There are, however, certain results in animals concerning VIIIth nerve injury which do not fit with this picture (Neff), but we shall consider these in another connection later.

Another important type of disturbance of the audibility curve is the *tonal lacuna.* In this case, most of the audibility curve may be quite normal, but at certain frequencies there is considerable loss of sensitivity. One or several lacunae may be present, and they may occur with lowered sensitivity throughout the entire auditory spectrum or with no involvement of other frequencies. It is to be presumed that in such cases certain regions of the basilar membrane have been impaired, or that the corresponding nerve supply is defective in some way.

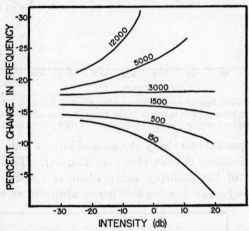

Fig. 95.—The relation of pitch to intensity. (*After S. S. Stevens. The relation of pitch to intensity. J. acous. Soc. Amer.*, **6**, 150–154, 1935.)

Pitch and Intensity.—Pitch is the name given to the experience that varies principally with the frequency of an auditory stimulus. It is commonly conceived as the qualitative aspect of auditory experience. Although pitch varies with frequency, it also is a function of the intensity of a tone, as Fig. 95 illustrates (Stevens). Whether or not, however, increasing the intensity increases or decreases pitch depends upon the frequency employed. Putting the matter in general terms, we may say that the pitch of high frequencies is raised by increasing the intensity, whereas that of low frequencies is lowered by increasing the intensity. Frequencies of the middle range, *i.e.*, frequencies to which the ear is maximally sensitive, change very little in pitch with variation of the intensity, but when they do, there is a tendency for the pitch to rise and then fall with increasing intensity.[1]

[1] Recent experiments by Galambos and Morgan (unpublished) show that the change of pitch with intensity is not so general a phenomenon as Stevens's experiments

The most general statement that can be made concerning the relation of pitch to intensity is that, as intensity is increased, the pitch of a frequency moves away from the frequency to which the ear is maximally sensitive. Accounting for this fact is the following suggestion (Stevens and Davis): Maximal sensitivity of the ear is determined by the place on the basilar membrane which vibrates most easily in response to stimulation; but this place, it is supposed, will be the first place to reach its limit of response when the intensity is raised. Further increases of intensity will then bring in parts of the membrane which are less sensitive, and consequently the distribution of excitation on the basilar membrane will be so skewed that its 'center of gravity' will move away from the place of maximal sensitivity.

Pitch and Frequency.—Of much more basic importance is the relation of pitch to frequency, and here the physiological mechanism is more definitely established than it is for the pitch-intensity relation. Three methods have been employed for studying quantitatively the relation between pitch and frequency: (1) The first is the method of the least discriminable difference in frequency, or briefly, the method of the *JND*. After determining the size of a JND throughout different parts of the auditory spectrum, the number of JND's of pitch for a given number of cycles of frequency may be plotted, as shown in Fig. 96. (2) In the method of *fractionation,* an observer is asked to set one tone so that it appears to him to be just half in pitch of that of a standard tone. The results of such judgments at different frequencies turn out to give the same curve as that obtained by the method of JND's. (3) One can ask, finally, an observer to perform a *bisection* of a tonal interval; *i.e.*, an observer is to set the frequency of a tone so that it is just midway between two other frequencies in pitch.

The remarkable thing about these three methods is that they yield the same results: a sigmoid relation between log frequency and the experience of pitch (see Fig. 96; Stevens and Volkmann). If, for example, we know the number of JND's between 500 and 1,000 cycles and know also the frequency which divides this number in two, that frequency will have a pitch which is midway between 500 and 1,000 cycles. It turns out, moreover, that zero pitch is about 20 cycles. Knowing that, we can count off JND's by the same method as was just described and find the frequency whose pitch will be just half that of another tone. All this

would lead us to believe. In most ears there is no tendency for pitch to rise with increasing intensity at high frequencies, and the change downward at low frequencies is relatively small compared with Stevens's data for his subject. There is now the very strong possibility that there is no general rule for the change of pitch with intensity but that whatever changes occur in any given ear are related to irregularities of sensitivity in that ear at different frequencies of the acoustic spectrum.

adds up to the fact that JND's are not only equal with respect to discrimination but are also subjectively equal, and equal numbers of JND's are equal as well.

Pitch and the Basilar Membrane.—Still another remarkable fact is the relation of the pitch function—as the relation of pitch to frequency has been called—to the position of the basilar membrane maximally stimulated by different frequencies (see Fig. 96). The basilar membrane,

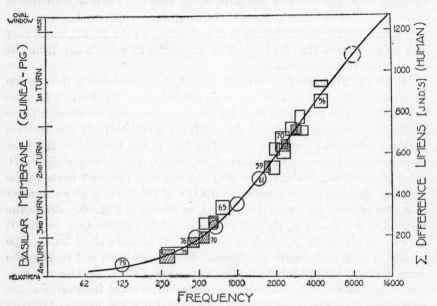

Fig. 96.—The relation between position of stimulation on the basilar membrane and pitch perception. The width of the rectangles represents the range of frequencies at which animals suffering from lesions in the cochlea showed loss of auditory sensitivity; the height of the rectangles represents the corresponding region of the basilar membrane showing damage. The centers of the circles represent the centers of the parts of the audiogram showing normal sensitivity and the centers of normal regions in the basilar membrane. The unbroken line is the integration (summation) of the JND's of frequency discrimination. (*From S. S. Stevens et al. The localization of pitch perception on the basilar membrane. J.genr.Psychol.*, **13**, 297–315, 1935. *By permission of the Journal Press.*)

the reader will recall, has been mapped by two different methods which check each other well; the part of the basilar membrane responding best at different frequencies is therefore known. When the cochlear map is compared with the pitch function, we are met with an important conclusion: Pitch is determined by the portion of the basilar membrane maximally stimulated, for equal differences in pitch correspond with equal distances along the basilar membrane. This relation has been included in Fig. 96 where distance along the basilar membrane and units of pitch are put on the same ordinate.

Loudness and Intensity.—Early in the present chapter, ways of stating intensity were pointed out, and the distinction between sensation level and intensity level was made.   To specify either of these, however, does not tell us anything about the loudness of a tone; for even as pitch is not equal to frequency, so is loudness, also a subjective attribute of tones, not directly proportional to physical intensity.   For the purpose

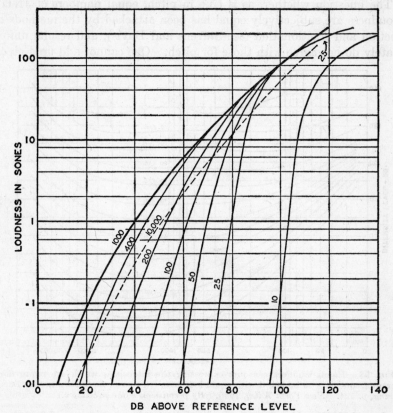

Fig. 97.—The loudness function expressing the relation between perceived loudness and intensity. (*From S. S. Stevens and H. Davis. Hearing, p. 118. New York: Wiley, 1938. By permission of the publishers.*)

of expressing the relation of loudness to intensity, an arbitrary subjective unit has been chosen: the *sone.* This is defined as the loudness of a 1,000-cycle tone at 40 db above threshold. With this as a unit, the relation of loudness to intensity, *i.e.*, the loudness function, can be determined.

Whereas the pitch function is relatively independent of intensity, the loudness function varies in marked degree with the frequency for which it is determined. A family of curves of loudness as functions of intensity at different frequencies is shown in Fig. 97. From this graph, one can see that loudness changes with frequency much more for frequencies below 300 cycles than for those above this value. The loudness, also, of different frequencies at one intensity is greatest for frequencies to which the ear is most sensitive, *i.e.*, around 1,000 cycles. It is to be noted, finally, that different frequencies tend to approach the same loudness at high intensities.

The question whether, as is true in pitch, equal numbers of JND's of loudness are subjectively equal has been attacked by the methods of bisection and fractionation (see Stevens and Davis), and results unfortunately do not agree with those for pitch. One cannot add up a given

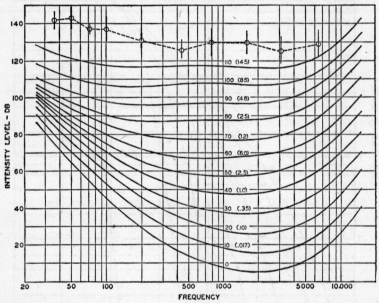

Fig. 98.—Equal loudness contours expressing the intensities which are required at different frequencies to be heard with equal loudness. (*From S. S. Stevens and H. Davis. Hearing, p. 124. New York: Wiley, 1938. By permission of the publishers.*)

number of JND's of loudness, present them to the observer, and find them equal to the same number of JND's taken at some other loudness level or at some other frequency. Thus, one cannot, at least according to the results available, establish loudness functions that are the same for the three methods of judgment, JND, fractionation, and bisection.

To explain the difference between loudness and pitch in this respect, Stevens and Volkmann suggest that it is because of the different mechanisms mediating loudness and pitch. Pitch is changed, the facts presented above would suggest, by the movement of the pattern of excitation along the basilar membrane, *i.e.*, by substituting new excitation for old. Loudness is increased, however, by spreading the pattern of excitation on the basilar membrane in such a way that new excitation is added to old. Because of the different mechanism for loudness changes, there is no simple relation of additiveness between JND's and larger units of loudness.

Worthy of mention is another approach to the problem of loudness, *viz.*, the *loudness contour*. This is the name given to the intensity values necessary at different frequencies to produce the same loudness (Fig. 98). The most interesting fact to be observed in a family of such contours is that, although the intensity required for audibility varies greatly with the frequency (Fig. 89), the intensities required for equally high loudnesses are about the same for different frequencies. In other words, frequency is less important at high than at low intensities. This fact, we find, is also characteristic of deaf persons. Indeed, the absolute threshold may be impaired by as much as 50 to 60 db, and yet at an intensity only a few decibels above this level the loudness heard is quite comparable to that in a normal ear (Steinberg and Gardner). From these facts it would appear that differences in sensitivity related to frequency are largely due to relative resistance of the basilar membrane to vibration or, in the case of deafness, to degeneration of nerve fibers, but that as the intensity is raised and these factors are overcome the ear tends to function as well in all regions as in that of maximal sensitivity.

Attributes of Auditory Sensation.—Loudness and pitch, as we have seen, are the principal psychological attributes of tones, but there are others and these may be mentioned briefly (Stevens, Boring). Some tones are found to be "big" and others "small"; thus tones have *volume*. This cannot be equated to either pitch or loudness, although it does vary with frequency and intensity. The same is true of another attribute, *density*, which is the "tightness," "hardness," or "compactness" of a tone. In both cases, the proof that we have bona fide attributes is to be found in the consistency with which observers can judge them and in the systematic way they vary with frequency and intensity without being identical with pitch and loudness. Whether these two attributes are the result of some particular characteristics of the excitation coming into the nervous system from the cochlea or are determined by the 'attitude' of the observer and by what combinations of pitch and loudness he can make consistently is not at present established. For the present, at least, their physiological basis must, therefore, go without statement.

Masking.—That one tone can mask our perception of another is a common observation. Such masking can be measured quite accurately by determining what intensity is necessary for a tone to be heard when presented in the presence of a masking tone. The results of making detailed measurements of this sort tell us, by inference, about the distribution of excitation on the basilar membrane resulting from the masking tone. (1) At first, however, we must make the assumption that a tone is masked by another because the region of the membrane which it normally stimulates is already in use by the masking tone. (2) We may then regard the rise in threshold of a tone through masking as a measure of the amount of activity occasioned by the masking sound at the position of the basilar membrane which it occupies. In this way we may plot what is known as the masking audiogram of a masking tone and derive the loudness pattern on the basilar membrane of any particular tone used for masking.

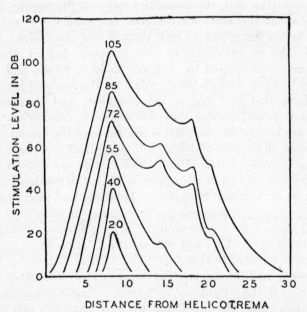

DISTANCE FROM HELICOTREMA

Fig. 99.—Patterns of stimulation on the basilar membrane at different intensities of a 1,000-cycle tone as computed from experiments on masking. (*From S. S. Stevens and H. Davis. Hearing, p. 216. New York: Wiley, 1938. By permission of the publishers.*)

Based upon these principles is the graph in Fig. 99 of the pattern of excitation of a 1,000-cycle tone at different intensities. For more details on how it is obtained the reader should consult Steinberg and Gardner. Granting the method, however, we are provided with information concerning action of the basilar membrane not available from direct physiological procedures. It is apparent, first of all, that while a particular frequency stimulated a certain place maximally there is a definite pattern spreading over a relatively large portion of the membrane. Notable also is an earlier suggestion, that at high intensities the pattern of stimulation becomes markedly skewed. Known also from experiments with masking but not shown in Fig. 99 are the following facts. Tones tend to be masked more by frequencies below them than by frequencies above them. Low tones, moreover, are, in general, better maskers than high tones. These facts indicate a conclusion, which we also have other grounds for believing, that low tones have a pattern of excitation much more widely distributed over the entire basilar membrane than do high tones.

Aural Harmonics.—In addition to a place of maximal activity, the excitation pattern of Fig. 99 also shows three other minor maxima at 2,000, 3,000, and 4,000 cycles, respectively. These peaks represent aural harmonics generated somewhere in the ear, and we can prove that fact by other methods. In recording the cochlear microphonic, for example, one obtains such secondary peaks at multiples of the stimulus frequency (Stevens and Newman). Then, too, their presence in the experience of the observer, given a 1,000-cycle tone, can be demonstrated by the fact that tones slightly different from 2,000, 3,000, and 4,000 cycles will be heard to beat (see below)—a fact to be understood in terms of the interference of the aural harmonic with the test tone. Such aural harmonics arise, we suspect, by distortion in the middle-ear bones, for we have seen that these bones do not reproduce the stimulus quite perfectly; and like distortion in the middle ear, aural harmonics appear in hearing only at higher intensities (about 50 db or above). It is possible, however, that some distortion contributing to the production of aural harmonics may also take place in the cochlea itself.

Subjective Beats.—A sound that is made up of two sine waves, differing only slightly in frequency, will appear to an observer as a single tone which is changing rhythmically in loudness. Such changes are subjective *beats*. If, for example, the two frequencies into which the sound is analyzable differ by only one cycle, the observer will hear one *beat* per second, or one change in loudness per second. If they differ by three or four cycles, three or four beats per second will be heard.

To come to an understanding of beats, we must first consider the ear as an analyzer. If it were true that one very narrow part of the basilar membrane vibrated to one frequency and a part adjacent to it, but not overlapping it, responded to a slightly different frequency, then the ear would be an analyzer comparable in precision to modern electrical instruments for the analysis of sound, and two distinct tones might be heard rather than one which is beating. Because the area of the basilar membrane stimulated by a tone is relatively wide, however, two tones different only slightly in frequency stimulate overlapping areas; and because the two tones are in phase part of the time and out of phase part of the time, the amplitude of the movement of the basilar membrane in the region affected by both tones increases and decreases rhythmically —thus beats.

Beats may be heard, too, if one frequency is led into one ear and a slightly different frequency into the other ear. Such beats are called *binaural* beats and are due, obviously, to impulses arriving at some center in the nervous system, in phase some of the time and out of phase some of the time. We are dealing, in this case, with a phenomenon of central reinforcement or summation. It is significant, however, that the binaural beats cannot be obtained when the frequencies are above 800 to 1,000 cycles. This we might expect from the fact that nerve impulses in the higher auditory pathways do not synchronize well with the acoustic stimulus above such frequencies. Binaural beats, it is also to be noted, are never of the subjective magnitude of monaural beats.

Auditory Localization.—Both the direction and distance of sounds may be judged with a high degree of accuracy by human observers. The exception to this statement may be found only in sounds that lie in the median plane of the head, where there is usually some degree of confusion. The accuracy of auditory localization in the lateral auditory fields, however, has given rise to many theories and a great deal of experimentation. It has been suspected at various times and by a number of experimenters that differences in the *intensity, phase,* or *time* of arrival of a sound at the two ears may be the basis of auditory localization.

1. *Intensity.*—If two sounds, differing only in intensity, separately stimulate each ear, it may be demonstrated that intensity differences in the two ears will determine to which side a sound is localized (Steinberg and Snow). The source of sound, which is imaginary in this case, is judged to be on the side of the greater intensity. When the possibility that this may be the mechanism of ordinary auditory localization is examined, we find that the loudness difference between the two ears is not very great for low tones, but for high frequencies (above about 5,000 cycles) the difference begins to be appreciable and may become as great as 30 db. Thus does the shadow that an object throws in the path of a sound wave vary with the frequency of the sound, and consequently, the direction of an acoustic source may be determined at rather high frequencies on the basis of binaural intensity differences.

2. *Phase.*—Similar experiments have been conducted with binaural differences in phase. In these, it has been found that the imaginary source of a sound will vary in location according to which ear is reached first by the crest of a sound wave. Phase cues cannot possibly serve, however, in auditory localization at high frequencies, because the wave length is so much shorter than the width of the head between the ears that the ear opposite to that of the sound may in some cases lead in phase and thus cause confusion in localization. Indeed, the frequency at which phase cues are no longer dependable is, by calculation from the width of the head, about 800 cycles (Stevens and Davis). Unfortunately, the

experiments on phase are not all in agreement as to the frequency at which localization breaks down, and this calculation is, therefore, as yet unconfirmed.

3. *Time.*—In the case of auditory localization of sounds of short duration it is possible that the difference in time of arrival of the sound waves at the two ears will serve as a basis of localization. Experiments show that, with a certain amount of time difference, displacement of the imaginary sound source will occur. When this difference is increased to some critical point, however, the sound appears to break up into two sources, one at each ear.

In conclusion, we may state that time, intensity, and phase may all serve as cues to auditory localization, intensity being most effective at high frequencies and phase more useful at low frequencies. These individually or combined provide a basis for the localization of unfamiliar sounds. It should be added, however, that one may quickly learn to localize familiar sounds by means of their subjective loudness and their frequency composition.

THEORIES OF HEARING

No reference has been made in this chapter to alternative theories of hearing, although in some cases theoretical assumptions have been introduced as necessary. The facts of hearing, as we know them today, do not leave very much room for theory, at least as regards general aspects of auditory mechanisms. There are, of course, as is always true in any field, many problems yet to be dealt with. Among them is the question of the function of the higher auditory centers in hearing. And there are others. Yet the basis of perception of pitch and loudness, or the fundamental attributes of hearing, appears to be rather clearly established. Lest we have been hasty in our conclusions, however, let us review the question.

Although there have been many theories to account for pitch in hearing, most of them are variants of two extremes: place theory and frequency theory. The former is represented historically by the resonance theory of Helmholtz. According to a strict resonance theory, one part of the basilar membrane should resonate to one frequency and another part to another frequency, and so on. Since the sharpness of the resonance, however, is always a relative affair, the resonance theory is also satisfied by conditions in which distribution of vibration on the basilar membrane differs according to frequency. These conditions, the evidence of the present chapter strongly indicates, exist in the ear. We are, therefore, drawn to subscribe to a somewhat liberalized resonance theory; we might better call it a 'place' theory, however, because it assumes that pitch is determined by the places stimulated on the basilar membrane.

Considerable evidence has been presented in this chapter for such a theory, and we need not go over it again. Against the theory, however, are two important points. The first is the poorness of the localization of low tones in the cochlea. Proof that low tones, particularly below 500 cycles, have different places of maximal response in the cochlea has not been satisfactory to several investigators in the field (Wever and Bray). At best, the points of maximal response are crowded together in a small region at the apical end of the cochlea. In defense of the place theory, however, we can argue that pitch discrimination is poor at low frequencies and reflects, therefore, the situation that the critics of place theory assume and that localization of low tones is about as good as it needs to be to explain discriminative ability at these frequencies.

Of more crucial weight in arguing against place theory are some of the facts of high-tone deafness. In man, as we have already seen, deafness more often occurs for high tones than for low ones and is more or less characteristic of increasing age. In most of the cases in which ears have been examined post-mortem, localized involvement of the basal turn of the cochlea has been demonstrated—a fact that supports place theory. Yet this is not always true (Crowe, *et al.*). Recent experiments (Neff), moreover, in which the VIIIth nerve of cats has been partially sectioned and its effect upon hearing determined, produce uniformly a high-tone deafness, invading the lower frequencies in varying degrees depending upon the severity of the deficit (see Fig. 100). Because it is not likely that in all cases the particular fibers serving the basal end of the cochlea were sectioned and the others left intact, these results raise serious doubts of the adequacy of the place theory.

A possible explanation is at hand, however. We know, and according to a 'liberal' place theory it is assumed, that low frequencies tend to stimulate large portions of the cochlea much more than do high frequencies. This being the case, in partial section of the VIIIth nerve one might then expect low frequencies to be the last affected with increasing severity of lesions, for so long as there are any fibers to the cochlea left at all low frequencies could stimulate them. Because high frequencies affect much smaller regions of the cochlea, however, only a small portion of the fibers of the auditory nerve needs be injured before a profound difference in the relative number available for stimulation by them will show up. Thus can we explain, on the basis of place theory, the fact that injury to the auditory nerve almost always gives high-tone deafness before involving sensitivity to lower frequencies.

Notice, however, a consequence of this explanation. Although sensitivity to low tones will be most resistant to being affected by VIIIth-

nerve damage, the *pitch of low tones should be changed by such damage.*
Let us put off the discussion of this point until we have considered the
alternative to place theory, however, *viz.*, frequency theory, for the
phenomena of changes in pitch constitute a telling point against frequency theory.

Because localization of low tones in the cochlea is not particularly
satisfactory and because the synchronization of impulses in the auditory

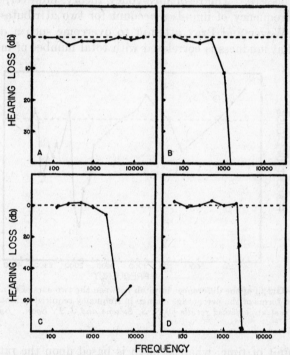

Fig. 100.—Changes in the audiograms of four cats following partial section of the
VIIIth nerve. The subject in the upper left-hand corner apparently did not suffer enough
injury to the nerve to be affected in auditory sensitivity. Note the consistency of the
loss at high tones and the relative abruptness of the drop in sensitivity. (*From unpublished
results of W. D. Neff. By permission of the author.*)

pathways is demonstrably good at low frequencies, Wever and Bray
have proposed a *resonance-volley theory* of hearing. In their opinion, the
frequency of impulses in the auditory nerve, as found both in simple
synchronization and in volleys, accounts for pitch at low frequencies.
They are willing to grant the role of 'place' in pitch perception at high
frequencies, because it is clear that synchronization of impulses cannot
mediate pitch at extremely high frequencies.

Now, to the extent to which the localization of low tones in the
cochlea can be defended, to that extent the resonance-volley theory is

unnecessary.   Aside from such a consideration, however, the resonance-volley theory runs into difficulty.   For one thing, it has become a generally accepted principle in neurophysiology (Adrian) that intensity of neural effect is determined by the number of nerve fibers giving impulses and the frequency of these impulses.   In place theory, the frequency of impulses and also the number of fibers involved as well can be the basis of loudness, because pitch 'uses up' only the 'which-fiber' aspect of auditory processes.   The resonance-volley theory, however, has the job of making frequency of impulses account for two attributes, pitch and intensity.   Wever and Bray attempt to overcome such a difficulty by assuming that loudness is correlated with total number of impulses in a

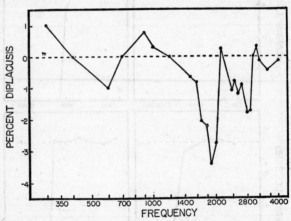

Fig. 101.—Graph of the differences in pitch between the two ears of a 'normal' subject as measured in terms of the percentage change in frequency required to match pitch in the two ears.   (*From unpublished results by S. S. Stevens and J. P. Egan.   By permission of the authors.*)

nerve per unit of time, whereas pitch is based upon the rate of arrival of volleys of impulses in the central nervous system.   The distinction is subtle, but perfectly possible.

If we accept it, however, the resonance-volley theory meets another difficulty which is not so easily disposed of—the problem of explaining *diplacusis*.   This refers to several related phenomena, but the most important one, for our purpose, is a condition met in human observers in whom there is a difference in the perceived pitch of the same frequency heard by the two ears of an observer.   Stevens and Egan have recently measured quite accurately the amount of diplacusis in several 'normal' subjects, and they find that most, if not all, persons possess it in some degree (see Figs. 101 and 102).   In one person there are usually several regions of the auditory spectrum in which it is to be found, and these vary from one individual to another.   Most crucial with respect to the question of auditory theory, however, is the fact that diplacusis can be obtained at rather low frequencies, *e.g.*, 400 cycles. This is in the frequency range where, according to the resonance-volley theory, frequency of impulses is asserted to mediate pitch perception. But how can that be, if the same frequency can have different pitches? This question the theory of Wever and Bray does not seem capable of answering.

Although we do not have as yet any direct information as to the physiological basis of diplacusis, it is clear that a place theory is capable of explaining it. It need only be supposed that there are irregularities in the response of different parts of the basilar membrane or of the thresholds and distribution of nerve fibers to them. Nerve fibers can vary

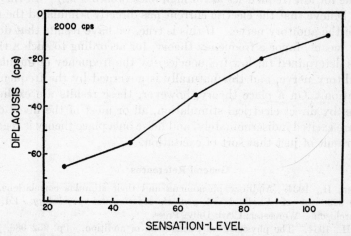

Fig. 102.—Change in diplacusis with increase in intensity. The data are for the same subject as are those in Fig. 101. Diplacusis does not always become smaller with increasing intensity, but it usually changes with the intensity. (*From unpublished results by S. S. Stevens and J. P. Egan. By permission of the authors.*)

independently of the acoustic stimulus in the place of their distribution, particularly when some of them are lacking, but the frequency of stimulation of nerve impulses must be governed by the frequency of the sound wave or not at all.

Coming back, now, to the question of how to interpret Neff's findings that partial section of the auditory nerve always produces high-tone deafness, we can now see more clearly how they are explicable in terms of a place theory, provided that the damage to the auditory nerve also causes a change in pitch. Whether that is actually the case we do not know, because such measurements were not available for his subjects (cats), but since diplacusis is a demonstrable fact, even in so-called normal ears, we can readily expect that pitch changes may have accompanied his losses in auditory sensitivity at high frequencies.

One final point which is against a frequency theory of pitch and consistent with a place theory may be brought out. One can elicit auditory experience by placing electrodes in the external meatus and applying to them an alternating electrical current (Stevens *et al.*). When done in normal persons, the pitch experience is of just about the purity of a normal pure-tone stimulus, and reasons have been advanced for believing that the electrical stimulus causes the tympanum and middle ear to vibrate in a manner like that in normal stimulation (Stevens). In some patients lacking the tympanum and middle ear, however, the electrical stimulus elicits the experience of *noise* no matter what the frequency of stimulation; indeed, the character of the noise may be just the same for low frequencies as for high ones (Jones *et al.*). In this case, we can believe that the electric current has directly stimulated the nerve fibers of the auditory nerve. If this is true, we have results that do not, by any means, favor a frequency theory, for according to such a theory pitch is determined (at low frequencies) by the frequency of impulses in the auditory nerve, and this naturally is governed by the frequency of stimulation. On a place theory, however, these results are explicable, because, by direct electrical stimulation, all or most of the fibers of the nerve are excited indiscriminately, and noise on a place theory is regarded as the result of just that sort of excitation.

General References

Banister, H., 1934. Auditory phenomena and their stimulus correlations. Pp. 880–923. In *A handbook of general experimental psychology*. Ed. Carl Murchison. Worcester: Clark Univ. Press.

Davis, H., 1934. The physiological phenomena of audition. Pp. 962–986. In *A handbook of general experimental psychology*. Ed. Carl Murchison. Worcester: Clark Univ. Press.

Hartridge, H., 1934. Theories of hearing. Pp. 924–961. In *A handbook of general experimental psychology*. Ed. Carl Murchison: Worcester: Clark Univ. Press.

Stevens, S. S., and H. Davis, 1938. *Hearing*. New York: Wiley. Pp. xv + 490.

CHAPTER XII

THE SKIN SENSES

More than a century has gone by since the first systematic observations (Weber) of cutaneous experience were made; yet we still are concerned today with the basic problem of what receptors or sensory processes mediate cutaneous experience. We are still asking whether there are specific receptors for different experiences, and, if so, what they are. Indeed, most of the research, both old and recent, centers upon these questions. Thus is the problem of specific nerve energies very much with us and basic to our discussion of cutaneous functions. There is, of course, little that is unusual about that, for the problem is not settled with finality in other senses, but in the skin senses little more than this problem has been attacked, whereas in vision and hearing we have gone on to determine with great precision the relations between the physical stimulus and experience. We shall focus our attention, consequently, upon the problem of specific nerve energies in this chapter, giving only minor emphasis to other problems.

THE SKIN

Making up the skin are three layers of cutaneous tissue (see Fig. 103): an outer layer of epithelium, the *epidermis;* an intermediate layer, the dermis or *corium;* and a deep layer of *subcutaneous adipose tissue.* The latter is not a part of the 'true' skin, but for reasons of convenience is considered along with it here. From the subcutaneous adipose tissue come both the nerve supply and the blood vessels of the two layers of the skin proper. Of these, however, only the corium is vascular, *i.e.,* has blood supply, and nerve fibers are limited to the corium and to the substratum of the epidermis, known as the *Malpighian layer.* The outer, more superficial part of the epidermis, the *corneal* layer, is devoid of both nerve fibers and blood vessels.

Blood Vessels.—Of special importance in the discussion of the skin senses is the question of blood supply and the properties of blood vessels distributed to the skin, for according to one of the leading theories of thermal sensitivity these are thought to play an essential role in thermal experience. Blood vessels are distributed in plexuses and loops to all parts of the corium and adipose layers, and no structure is more numerous than they except free nerve endings. They are capable of changes in size, because their walls are made up of circularly arranged *constricting* smooth muscle fibers and radially arranged *dilating* fibers. These fibers receive innervation from the sympathetic and parasympathetic divisions of the autonomic system, respectively. Except for very small capillaries, moreover, the small blood vessels of the skin have a sensory, as well as a motor, nerve supply; in them are numerous free nerve endings which, we may presume, can respond to the constriction or dilation of the blood vessel. In consequence of this fact, it is important to note the conditions that may cause constriction or dilation of blood vessels. Of such conditions there are four main groups: (1) hormonal or chemical conditions of the blood; (2) changes in blood pressure accompanied by the speeding

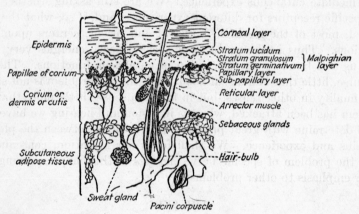

Fig. 103.—Section of the skin to show its layers and the position of the cutaneous free nerve endings and receptors. (*From J. P. Nafe. Handbook of experimental psychology, ed. by C. Murchison, p. 1044. Worcester: Clark University Press, 1934. By permission of the publishers.*)

or slowing of the heart; (3) sympathetic or parasympathetic impulses to the blood vessels; and (4) direct stimulation of the skin by thermal or mechanical means. These facts we shall later employ in the explanation of some of the phenomena of cutaneous experience.

Free Nerve Endings.—Most numerous of the receptors of the body, and particularly of the skin, are free nerve endings. They are to be found in the epidermis of the skin, where there are no other more highly differentiated receptors, in the corium and adipose layers, in the vast network of the vascular system, and in the organs of the viscera. In certain regions they are so numerous as to innervate almost every cell in the area of their distribution. They are, moreover, intimately related with the cells upon which they end, sometimes to the extent of ending within the cytoplasm of the cell. Although they vary in structure from very simple arborizations to complex plexiform networks, in the skin there is a rather clear division of types into *plain free nerve endings,* typical of the epidermal layer, and *plexuses*, not found at all in the epidermis but quite abundant in the corium and subcutaneous layers. Such a division, moreover, is correlated with degree of myelinization; the plexuses are, in general, the endings of small unmyelinated fibers, and the free nerve endings are the terminals of larger, myelinated fibers.

Encapsulated End Organs.—Found in the deeper parts of the skin, *i.e.*, in the corium and adipose layer, are complex structures called encapsulated end organs (see Fig. 104). Of these there are several varieties with as many names. When they were first discovered, it was

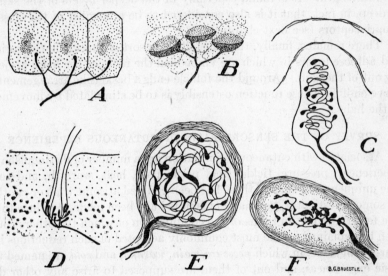

Fig. 104.—Diagrams of the principal cutaneous receptors. *A*, free nerve endings from the cornea of the eye; *B*, Merkel's cells from the snout of the pig; *C*, Meissner's tactile corpuscle; *D*, basket ending at the base of a hair follicle; *E*, Krause end bulb from the human conjunctiva; *F*, Golgi-Mazzoni corpuscle from the human skin. (*From J. F. Fulton. Physiology of the nervous system, p. 5. New York: Oxford University Press, 1938. By permission of the publishers.*)

thought that there were a few types and that each type subserved a different kind of cutaneous experience. In recent years, more and more 'types' have been described, and it has become apparent that there are, in reality, no types but only many variations of the same basic structure. Of these variations we may describe a few which have been of the greatest interest in the quest for particular end organs for different experiences.

The *Krause end bulb* is a somewhat spherical capsule of connective tissue into which a nerve fiber passes and ends in an intertwining network (Fig. 104). Resembling the Krause end bulb is the Meissner corpuscle which has a somewhat thinner capsule and a less elaborate nerve plexus within it. Both Krause end bulbs and Meissner corpuscles are distributed widely in the skin. The latter, however, are generally lacking in the hairy regions of the body, but are densest in the hairless parts particularly, *e.g.*, in the finger tips.

Other commonly known variants of the encapsulated end organs are the *Golgi-Mazzoni* (Fig. 104) and a similar organ the *Pacinian* corpuscle. Of these, the Pacinian corpuscle is more important. It consists of concentric layers of capsular tissue within which are somewhat knotty and arborized nerve fibrils. A great deal larger than other encapsulated organs, it is visible to the naked eye; sometimes it is as large as 3 or 4 mm. in length. It is found especially in the deeper layers of the skin—so deep, in fact, that it is also considered to be a member of the class of proprioceptors (see next chapter).

There remains, finally, the hair follicle, a sort of capsule in the corium and adipose layers in which are embedded the roots of the hairs projecting out of the skin. Around the follicle ends a basketlike arrangement of nerve endings whose function ostensibly is to be stimulated by movement of the hairs.

SURVEY OF THE SENSORY BASIS OF CUTANEOUS EXPERIENCE

Associated with cutaneous stimulation are a number of distinguishable experiences: pressure, tickle, itch, prick, pain, heat, warmth, and cold. The uniqueness of each of these has been claimed at some time or another by some investigator, yet many attempts have been made to reduce them to a fewer number, in terms of the combination of which the others could then be explained. The most commonly accepted of such reductions is a four-quality one, in which *pressure, pain, warmth*, and *cold* are named the basic experiences, and out of them are supposed to arise any other distinguishable experiences. That view seems quite consistent with the facts, and we shall, therefore, adhere to it here.

Cutaneous Stimuli.—The application of force to the skin, so as to deform it, is the stimulus that arouses 'pressure' experience. The pressure of a blunt object, the bending of a hair, or the pulling of a hair will do. To elicit 'pain,' on the other hand, requires a stimulus that destroys or injures cutaneous tissue. This may be mechanical, thermal, or chemical in nature. Thermal experience, finally, is aroused by raising or lowering the temperature of the skin. The skin's temperature—its *physiological zero*—is usually about 32.5 to 33.5°C., and stimuli of this temperature elicit no sensation. As the temperature is increased there is first the experience of warmth, then of heat, and above 52°C. or thereabouts pain appears. On the lower side of physiological zero there are somewhat similar stages: cold, then an experience somewhat like heat, and near 0°C. pain. So much then for the stimuli eliciting the four qualities of cutaneous experience.

Theories of Cutaneous Sensation.—Knowing the stimuli appropriate to the four qualities of experience, we may next consider the possible alternative sensory mechanisms responsible for the different experiences. There are, as usual, two extreme possibilities: that there are individual receptors for each stimulus and that the experience is determined by *which* receptors or nerve fibers are excited; or that a stimulus somehow impresses its character upon the *pattern* of excitation in nerve fibers and that the central nervous system interprets the pattern, thereby producing different experiences. Actually no one has adopted this latter view to such extremes as to deny altogether specific receptors; but some (Goldscheider, Nafe) have compromised to the extent of supposing that patterns of excitation determine, in part, the qualities of experience. Particularly has this view been applied to the problem of pain (Goldscheider). The other position, of a rigid specificity of receptors, has been widely held from the beginnings of cutaneous research (von Frey) down to the present. In the analysis of experimental data which follows we shall attempt to evaluate these general answers to the problem of specific nerve energies in respect of cutaneous experience.

The Punctate Distribution of Sensibility.—Of support to the theory of specific receptors is the punctate distribution in the skin of sensitivity to different kinds of stimulation, a fact discovered early in the history of the skin senses (1884–1885) and described as follows: Not all parts of the skin are equally sensitive to cutaneous stimuli, but, on the contrary, if a given area of the skin is explored with different kinds of stimuli, one finds certain spots sensitive to cold, others responsive to heat, and still others sensitive to pain or pressure stimuli. Because these spots are very often not coincident, it is strongly indicated that there are different receptors for pain, pressure, warmth, and cold. With that conclusion there can be little argument.

There are, however, reasons for not accepting the fact of punctate sensitivity at its face value. Instead of representing *the* spots of sensitivity for particular experiences, the spots one finds, as described above, probably represent only the regions of greatest sensitivity, and the number of spots sensitive to any intensity is probably so great that the spaces between them are of microscopic dimensions. For this belief, we may give the following evidence. Sensitive spots lack the stability that might be expected of them if they were associated with single isolated receptors; for upon one occasion one can map out the various cold, pressure, pain, and warmth spots and upon later retesting find that some of them have disappeared and others have appeared (Dallenbach). Accounting in part for such instability is receptor adaptation, for which the skin senses are noted, but more than that is involved, because it can be demonstrated that the number of spots found for any quality depends upon the intensity of stimulus employed (Heiser; Guilford and Lovewell). It has been claimed, indeed, that no region of the skin is absolutely anesthetic to pressure (Roy).

Although one may attempt to explain such facts in various ways, the most reasonable view, it appears to the author, is proposed by Jenkins: the receptors are densely packed in the skin—so densely, in fact, that more than a single receptor must be stimulated when one applies a stylus to the skin—and the *concentration* of receptors varies from region to region. For such a view Jenkins has considerable evidence in the case of thermal experience. He finds no discrete spots of sensitivity but instead 'hills and valleys' of sensitivity, *i.e.*, regions of greater and lesser sensitivity (see Fig. 105). He argues, therefore, that the phenomena of

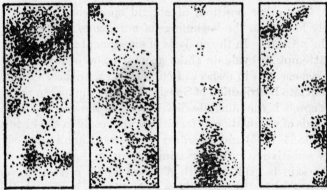

FIG. 105.—Maps of the concentrations of thermal receptors on four different regions of the skin as deduced from tests of cold sensitivity. (*After W. L. Jenkins. Studies in thermal sensitivity.* 12. *Part-whole relations in seriatim cold-mapping. J. Exp. Psychol.*, **25**, 383, 1939. *By permission of the American Psychological Association.*)

punctate distribution of sensitivity are best explained in terms of varying concentrations of receptors. And his argument is convincing, although we might also entertain the possibility that receptors vary in their threshold of sensitivity from region to region without this variation being necessarily dependent upon concentration.

However that may be, we must come back to the point that the spots of greatest concentration or sensitivity of receptors for one experience do not correspond with those for another experience, and we are therefore led to believe that there are different receptors for different experiences.

Bright and Dull Experiences.—Before going on with the question of specific receptors for cutaneous experiences, we should introduce another point. From time to time, it has been claimed by various observers that there are different kinds of pressure and pain experiences, characterized by the terms *bright* and *dull*, or *light* and *deep*. The experience of 'light touch' or 'bright pressure' is well localized by the observer and is aroused by a pointed stimulus, *e.g.*, a hair, applied to the skin surface but without necessarily deforming the skin. The same is true of 'bright pain' or 'prick' except that its stimulus is a sharp instrument, say a needle, which pierces only the superficial layers of the skin. Contrasting with these bright experiences are dull pressures and pain, both of which are poorly localized and require deformation of the skin or deep piercing of it in such a way that the deeper cutaneous layers, the corium and underlying adipose tissue, are implicated. How well this distinction will hold up will be considered in the subsequent discussion, but we should be acquainted with it at the start.

DISSOCIATION OF CUTANEOUS SENSITIVITY

Some of the best evidence that specific receptors and fibers are at the basis of the qualities of cutaneous experience is to be found in the way in which experiences are differentially affected by diseases of the nervous system or by blocking the functions of cutaneous nerves. Because such evidence throws a much clearer light upon the whole problem of cutaneous experience than do the searches for end organs in the skin we should consider it first.

Syringomyelia.—Neurologists have for some time distinguished different tracts in the spinal cord for the conduction of pain, temperature, and pressure, and there are several sorts of proof of these tracts. One of the most convincing is the way in which cutaneous experiences are affected by syringomyelia, a disease of the spinal cord which begins in the central gray matter surrounding the central canal and spreads outward. Depending upon how far the disease has progressed, one finds cutaneous experiences in various degrees of preservation or impairment. First to be lost is pain. When it has almost completely dropped out, little or no impairment of thermal and pressure sensibility may exist. Next goes temperature, and this may be considerably impaired before pressure is affected at all. Finally, in extreme involvement, pressure sensitivity goes. This order of dropping out is, of course, not inviolate, for the disease does not always progress in the same way, but it is the general rule; and the fact alone that different experiences may be independently affected is strong evidence of their representation in *different fibers* of the spinal cord.

Cocaine Anesthesia.—Further data come from the blocking of nerves by anesthesia and correlating the type and order of sensations lost with the kinds of nerve fibers known to be blocked (see Gasser). Considering one thing at a time, however, let us note first the order of disappearance of sensations. This is quite regular when cocaine is put around a cutaneous nerve and allowed to infiltrate gradually into the fibers. Cold is uniformly blocked before warmth, and pressure is always the last to go. About pain, however, there is some difference of opinion; in some instances, it seems to disappear first, *i.e.*, before cold and warmth, and in other experiments, probably somewhat better controlled (Heinbecker *et al.*), pain disappears after thermal experience but before pressure. The discrepancy, Gasser suggests, may be accounted for by assuming two kinds of pain (bright and dull?), one very susceptible to cocainization and another more resistant to it; and it is possible that, because of different methods of evoking pain in different experiments, confusion resulted.

Asphyxia.—If one places a cuff around the arm and by inflating it with air brings pressure to bear upon the blood vessels of the arm, blood is shut off from the nerves in the part of the arm distal to the cuff and they suffer, therefore, from oxygen want or asphyxia. While this is gradually taking effect, noting the order of disappearance of sensation gives the following results (Lewis *et al.*): First to go is 'light pressure,' then 'cold,' then 'dull pressure,'[1] then 'warmth,' and finally pain; the pain which is present to the last is probably of the 'dull' type, for observers report that the delay between stimulation and experience is greater than usual and that it lasts longer than in normal nerves. This order, it is to be noted, is not the same as that resulting from cocaine anesthesia; indeed, it is quite the reverse in some respects.

Fiber Types and Qualities.—With the order in which sensation disappears in these two instances we may correlate the effects of cocaine and asphyxia, respectively, upon the functions of nerve fibers. But first it is necessary to recall what was said earlier (Chap. IV) about types of nerve fibers. In cutaneous nerves, it was pointed out, one can distinguish three types of fibers, the *A, B,* and *C* fibers; these differ in respect of velocity of conduction, size of fiber, sensitivity, and degree of myelinization, and their activity may be distinguished in the electrical records taken from a whole nerve. These fiber types, we should realize, are not discrete groups but rather the three modes of a distribution of fibers, and it is to be expected that any property assigned to a given type, *e.g.*, the *B* fibers, may overlap, say, the *A* and *C* fibers.[2]

[1] The basis for making a distinction here between 'light' and 'dull' pressure is not extremely sound but is derived from Goldscheider's observation that, even when sensibility for light contact stimuli and for cold stimuli had disappeared, subjects could still tell from the pressure of the cold stylus that it was being applied. Aside from this observation, however, there is agreement among several experiments that sensitivity to light contact stimuli is lost first in the compression-cuff procedure.

[2] The letters assigned to different groups and subgroups of sensory fibers have varied among authors and with progress in research during the last few years. The scheme used here and elsewhere in the book follows convenience and simplicity rather than any authoritative usage. Gasser, for example, in his latest discussion of the classification of nerve fibers, advises that the fibers called *B* above should be considered members of the *A* group and that the category *B* be reserved solely for autonomic motor fibers. If that is done, only *A* and *C* fibers are of significance for sensory

Now cocaine blocks out these groups of fibers in a definite order; it affects the smallest first and progresses gradually to the larger fibers; C, B, and A fibers, therefore, drop out in order. Asphyxia, on the other hand, first eliminates the fastest of the A fibers, then the B fibers, later the slower of the A fibers, and finally the C fibers (Clark *et al.*). Comparing these facts with the order of disappearance of sensations under the respective conditions we have the following parallels:

Cocaine..........
$\begin{cases} \text{Quality: (dull pain?), cold, warmth, pain (bright?), pressure} \\ \text{Fiber:} \quad C \text{ fibers,} \quad B \text{ fibers,} \quad A \text{ fibers} \end{cases}$

Asphyxia.........
$\begin{cases} \text{Quality: light pressure, cold, dull pressure, warmth, pain (dull?)} \\ \text{Fiber:} \quad \text{fast } A \text{ fibers, } B \text{ fibers, slow } A \text{ fibers, } C \text{ fibers} \end{cases}$

Taken at face value, these parallels do not make a great deal of sense, because one cannot quickly assign the various qualities to one or the other of the fiber types.

If we assume, however, that each quality is to be found in a *distribution* of fibers of varying sizes and velocities, we can reach the following solution: Pressure is mediated by the A fibers; about that there can be little question. If, in addition, we suppose that the faster A fibers convey 'light' pressure and slower ones 'dull' pressure, the order in which pressure drops out with cocaine and asphyxia is fully accounted for. The facts further support the belief that pain is mediated by fibers of the A type and also by those of the C type; for pain remains in cocainization when only A fibers are left and in asphyxia when only C fibers are functioning. Supporting evidence of pain in C fibers comes, moreover, from an experiment (Clark *et al.*) in which a cat showed definite signs of pain along with demonstrable activity in the C fibers alone. Regarding cold, the conclusion is clear that it occupies a restricted position between touch A fibers and pain C fibers—or in the B group. Warmth, however, must include fibers both faster and slower than cold and overlapping the A and C distributions.

Now, when all these facts are put together, the most probable distribution of cutaneous receptors appears to be as represented diagrammatically in Fig. 106. Here C fibers are taken to be entirely 'dull' pain fibers; the B group, warmth and cold; and A fibers, pressure and pain.[1] This scheme is of maximum simplicity to be in accord with the facts. In

functions, and several subgroups of A fibers should be distinguished, which Gasser has denoted by Greek letters. To translate the scheme used here into Gasser's terms, the reader should consider the present B fibers as slow subgroups of the A fibers.

[1] In Heinbecker *et al.*, one will find the opinion that pain is mediated by B fibers, a possibility that is not entirely ruled out, but it derives, in their case, from an interpretation of their data with which we need not necessarily agree. The position taken here is based upon their *data*, as well as those of other investigators, but conforms to the view expressed by Gasser.

it the relative heights of the various curves are of no significance but are drawn as they are for the sake of convenience. No distinction between 'light' and 'dull' pressure has been made, but if it were, two distributions would replace the one for pressure.

Such fibers, it is to be remembered (Chap. IV), are largely unmyelinated, and if myelinated, only thinly so. This fact is a clue to the receptors with which they are associated. The unmyelinated fibers in the skin end, so far as we can make out, as free nerve endings in the deeper parts of the skin, *i.e.*, in the corium. Such free nerve endings tend to be of the class of interlacing plexiform networks, from which we may expect that they mediate a dull, diffuse pain (see Nafe). Corroboration of this point comes from experiments in which stimulation of *C* fibers (only)

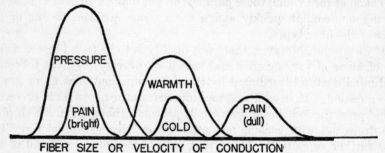

FIBER SIZE OR VELOCITY OF CONDUCTION

FIG. 106.—Schema to illustrate how different kinds of receptors are distributed along the continuum of fiber size or conduction velocity. The heights of the distributions have no significance.

was observed to cause profound autonomic changes, particularly in respiration and circulation (Clark *et al.*). Therein was shown, too, the close association of the *C* pain fibers with diffusive autonomic reactions and accordingly with the more primitive and less differentiated aspects of bodily adjustment.

'Pure' A Pain Fibers.—For the belief that fibers in the *A* group may mediate pain and pain only we also have specific evidence. The pad of a cat's paw, according to Adrian, is demarcated into two rather distinctly separate receptive areas. Pressure stimulation of one area produces large impulses conducted at a rate of about 50 m. per second; stimulation of the second area, at higher intensities, elicits much smaller impulses traveling at a slower rate of speed. Impulses in either case appear to occur in *A* fibers, but at differing speeds in the two instances. The slower impulses are also obtained when the skin is injured by cutting and crushing, and one may therefore believe that they represent pain.

PAIN

One of the most controversial of the questions that have been raised in the psychophysiology of the skin senses is whether pain is mediated by specific receptors or by the intense stimulation of other receptors. Representing the two sides of this question historically were von Frey, who argued for specific receptors for each sensory experience, and Goldscheider, who thought pain to be the result of stimulating any receptor at high intensities. Today it appears that a compromise between these views is more nearly the truth (Heinbecker and Bishop). But let us see how and why.

Pure-pain Receptors.—Considerable evidence exists in favor of von Frey's view that there are pain receptors and fibers not conveying any other experience. Most convincing, indeed, is the demonstration that only pain prevails when nerves are anesthetized with cocaine to the point where only C fibers are functioning (Clark *et al.*; *cf*. Ranson and Billingsley). Similar findings accompanied nerve blocking by asphyxia. Indeed, with the exception of some warmth fibers, more properly included in the tails of the B distribution, no other function than pain is to be claimed for this class of fibers.

Also in favor of a separation of pure-pain and pressure receptors are recent experiments in which the chronaxies of pain and pressure experience were measured (Neff and Dallenbach). The chronaxie, it should be recalled, is the time required for excitation when the stimulus is twice the intensity of the rheobase, *i.e.*, the threshold for infinite time of stimulation. Measuring the chronaxie in human observers for the pain and pressure experiences, Neff and Dallenbach found clear evidence of differences. This fact points definitely to separate receptors for them, because the chronaxie represents a time constant for excitation which is characteristic of each nerve fiber (under standard conditions). It is to be presumed that the separation thus accomplished is of more sensitive, faster conducting fibers of the A group, for these would enter into any measures of pain sensitivity before the less sensitive elements of the C class.

As receptors for pain of this type the free nerve endings to the epidermis are the best, and indeed the only, candidates. In the cornea of the eye, where there are only free nerve endings present (except at the lateral margins), there is sensitivity to pressure and to pain, and free nerve endings must in this case mediate pain. Adrian and others have shown, moreover, that the slow (A) impulses elicited in the cat's paw by painful stimulation disappear when the epidermis is removed, and since this contains only free nerve endings, pain in this case must depend upon them. Von Frey, the great exponent of specific receptors for pain, ascribed it to the free nerve endings, and there has never been reason to suppose otherwise, once specific receptors are granted. Then, too, that free nerve endings mediate pain is reasonable on the grounds that pain is a primitive sensory modality and the free nerve endings are the least differentiated of possible cutaneous receptors.

Pressure-pain Receptors?—There is no conclusive proof that receptors mediating pressure also mediate pain. As we shall see below, free nerve endings are in some instances receptors for pressure, and if it is argued that all free nerve endings must function alike because they look alike then it would appear that some receptors are concerned in both pressure and pain, but such argument is disproved by considerable evidence (see below) and it is not particularly reasonable.

Quite conclusively demonstrated, moreover, is the fact that some pressure receptors never mediate pain, even when stimulated at their maximum rate and capacity. The excitation, for example, of sensory endings associated with the hairs of the skin, which are quite sensitive to pressure, never arouses pain, for when they are stimulated by a rod vibrating at high frequencies, pain experiences never result (Adrian). Then, too, in an experiment in which the skin of a frog was stimulated intensely and at high frequency with an interrupted air jet (nerve impulses of 300 per second, the maximum rate possible in the nerve fibers, resulted), there was no indication in the frog's behavior of painful experience (Cattel and Hoagland). Proven, therefore, is the pure-pressure receptor, as well as the pure-pain receptor, and there is no evidence of other receptors that are both (see section on prick below).

Thermal-pain Receptors?—A similar conclusion applies also to the question of whether intense stimulation of thermal receptors can evoke pain, although our information concerning thermal reception is much more meager, in general, than is that about pressure. Quite familiar is the fact that upon increasing the temperature of the skin experience passes through warmth to heat and finally to pain, and parallel stages are to be found in the decrease of temperature. The critical temperatures for thermal pain are ordinarily given at 52 and 3°C. for 'hot' pain and 'cold' pain, respectively, although such values can be altered considerably by adaptation.

Now there are two views as to how thermal pain is mediated. One, held by Nafe, asserts that the same receptors that subserve temperature also convey impulses for thermal pain. These receptors, Nafe believes, are nerve endings in the blood vessels of the skin, and thermal pain, he further holds, occurs when the smooth muscles of the blood vessels are caused to go into spastic contraction by extreme temperatures. In favor of this view there is the fact that smooth muscle is caused to contract strongly at about the temperatures (52 and 3°C.) which are critical for thermal pain. This correlation, however, leaves us without any direct evidence of a causal relationship between critical temperatures for smooth-muscle contraction and pain. It may well be that such critical temperatures will stimulate all kinds of tissues—nerve as well as muscle.

For an opposed view of thermal pain—*viz.*, that it results from the thermal stimulation of pain receptors—there is some favorable evidence. First of all is the fact that free nerve endings, some of which are certainly concerned in pain, discharge at extreme temperatures. Indeed, it has been observed in the frog that excessive warmth, such as might injure tissues, causes nervous impulses in small unmyelinated *C* fibers, which according to evidence cited above mediate 'pure-pain' (Adrian). Carrying over this finding to man, we may suppose that when pain enters into thermal experience the action of pain receptors has been added to the activity of thermal receptors.

From man, moreover, comes direct support for this conclusion (Heinbecker *et al.*). A subject who exhibited marked loss of sensitivity to pain in certain areas of the skin but not in others and who had normal sensitivity to cold and warmth everywhere was stimulated with very hot rods. In areas insensitive to pricking pain the hot rods aroused heat experience but no pain, whereas in cutaneous areas of normal sensitivity to pain the hot rods brought forth pain. Thus in this case pain receptors not concerned in thermal experience were necessary for both thermal and pressure pain. Even more striking is another case (Dearborn) of a patient who was completely insensitive to pain (analgesic) and could not be made to experience pain with excessive injury to the skin; yet this individual experienced warmth and cold with no difficulty whatever. In the face of such evidence, it is strongly suggested that thermal pain is the result of the excitation of pain receptors per se and not of the intensive activity of thermal receptors.

Prick and Pain.—Taken together, the facts we have reviewed lead us to place our confidence in the theory of von Frey, that pain comes from the excitation of receptors and fibers especially differentiated for the task. There is, nevertheless, reason to believe that the experience of pain is dependent, in part at least, upon the summation of neural effects in the nervous system—the contention of Goldscheider. Experiments of Heinbecker and others have shown the following: The application of single electric shocks at mild intensities to the skin or cutaneous nerves calls forth a pressure experience. This we may expect since the threshold for pressure is less than that for pain. Next, with somewhat increased intensity applied briefly but repeatedly, the experience of prick appears. Pain that is definitely unpleasant or unbearable does not occur, however, *unless the shocks are of somewhat greater intensity and repeated for some time.* This fact Heinbecker (*et. al.;* also Nafe) takes to indicate that painful experience is the product of summation in the central nervous system. That we may grant, but it need mean only that very weak pain is not particularly unpleasant and that only when prick becomes continuous and of intense proportions is it really unpleasant or unbearable (see Stone and Jenkins; Lewis and Hess).

Localization of Pain.—It is the problem of whether pain has specific receptors and what they are which has been of the greatest concern in experimental studies relating to pain. Now it is well established that pain is mediated by its own receptors and that these are free nerve endings, but information concerning other aspects of pain reception is meager. Adaptation to painful stimulation has been demonstrated by Dallenbach and his associates, but it is highly variable, and quantitative data that have meaning are yet to be gathered. The relation between the magnitude of painful experience and intensity of stimulation is not available in quantitative form because of the many difficulties that are to be encountered in precisely controlling stimulus strength.

Most clearly established is the relatively good localization of painful stimuli. Pain 'spots' are the most numerous of any in the body—a fact that correlates with the very extensive distribution of free nerve endings. These, moreover, must have a degree of point-to-point projection in the nervous system comparable to the 'light' pressure receptors, for accuracy of pain localization is even better than that for pressure, especially with moderately intense stimuli (Kiesow). Because, however, one cannot stimulate pain receptors without also involving pressure receptors, it is doubtful whether superior localization for pain is thereby indicated; it has been suggested that the complex of pressure pain is better, in respect of localization, than either taken separately (Zigler *et al.*).

Visceral Pain.—Many of the structures of the skin are also to be found in other parts of the body. In the stomach, mesenteries, smooth muscles of the viscera, and the blood vessels of the body are sensory endings, the chief type of which is the free nerve ending or free nerve plexus, but encapsulated end organs also appear. The principal sensation that comes from the interior of the body (aside from kinesthetic impressions which are taken up later) is pain, although pressure and thermal experiences are felt. The pain of the viscera is usually a dull, persistent, unlocalized pain, and the same is true of pain arising from blood vessels (see Chap. XVII).

PRESSURE

Receptors for Pressure.—Because it appears certain that each of the four cutaneous qualities has its own receptors, it is natural to look for structurally different receptor organs to correspond with the qualities. Von Frey, the historical proponent of the specific-receptor theory, thought he found such differences; he assigned pain to the free nerve endings—correctly no doubt—pressure to the hair bulbs and Meissner corpuscles, cold to the Krause end bulb, and warmth to the Ruffini cylinder. Passing by the question of thermal receptors for the time being, let us examine the question of the receptors for pressure.

The density of pressure spots varies in different parts of the body, but it is correlated, in general, with the presence either of hair bulbs or of Meissner corpuscles (in hairless regions). Of that there is little question. It is also quite certain that in most cases the hair bulbs are organs of pressure sensitivity (Strughold). As for Meissner corpuscles, however, we are left only with a correlation of number of corpuscles with sensitivity, but without any direct evidence that the corpuscle is the organ of reception. Indeed, the number of sensitive points on the skin often seems to be entirely too large to be accounted for solely in terms of Meissner corpuscles (Goldscheider); but this fact is not crucial, for one never knows how far mechanical stimulation of the skin can spread.

We probably ought to grant that both Meissner corpuscles and hair bulbs mediate pressure, but we must also believe that free nerve endings of the epidermis do, too. It is known, in the first place, that nerve fibers which supply the hair bulbs often branch and terminate as free nerve endings in the epidermis. Such being the case, it seems reasonable that stimulation of the ending would produce the same result in experience as excitation of the fibers ending at the hair bulb, since the specificity of fibers appears well-established. Secondly, removal of the superficial epidermis, which is normally without free nerve endings, leaves pressure sensitivity intact, but when the Malpighian layer is also removed, pressure is lost and only pain is the outcome of mechanical stimulation (Watterson). Then, too, the large fast impulses, which appear in nerve fibers along with pressure stimulation, are no longer present when the epidermis is removed, and since the epidermis contains only free nerve endings their role in pressure is clearly indicated (Erlanger and Gasser). These observations, taken together, make it quite clear that, in addition to hair bulbs and other possible encapsulated end organs, the free nerve endings of the skin also mediate pressure.

On first thought, this conclusion may be disturbing, because pain, too, is aroused through free nerve endings, and it might seem that we must, therefore, abandon a specific-receptor theory. There is no really good reason, however, that receptors subserving different functions must also look different. If such were the case—and more adequate histological examination of free nerve endings might prove it to be—it would be very convenient; but there are other cases in sensory function, *e.g.*, in taste and color vision, where structural differences in receptors have not yet been discovered in relation to different functions for which there is otherwise good evidence.

There remains the question, previously raised, of the possible receptor basis for distinguishing between 'light' and 'deep' pressure. Little direct evidence is at hand with which to address this problem.   The best guess, however, is that the Pacinian corpuscle is the receptor for 'deep' pressure as contrasted with hair bulbs and epidermal nerve endings for 'light' pressure; for the Pacinian corpuscle is located deep within the sub-cutaneous adipose tissue, and its role as a pressure receptor in proprio-ceptive sensitivity appears to be well established (Chap. XIII).

Mode of Pressure Stimulation.—Quite widely accepted is the so-called gradient theory of tactile stimulation: deformation of the skin, per se, does not excite pressure receptors but rather the gradient between normal and depressed areas of the skin is critical in tactile sensation.   For this view there is the oft-quoted observation that when a finger is immersed in mercury, for example, pressure is experienced only at the surface where the pressure of the mercury leaves off sharply.   More than that, how-ever, it has been held that the perimeter of a stimulator, and thus the amount of skin subjected to a gradient of deformation, is the critical determinant of pressure experience.

Recent results of Holway and Crozier are against this view.   The JND for pressure was measured for solid disks and annular rings which had the *same area but different perimeters*.   JND's in this case were the same, and thus did they show pressure sensitivity to depend upon the area of stimulation rather than upon the pressure gradient of the perim-eter.   Holway and Crozier went on, moreover, to show that the log ΔP (the JND for pressure) was directly proportional to the log A (area of stimulation), a relationship that has been demonstrated for vision (Wald). From this fact they argue that the *statistical theory*, which Crozier has shown to apply so well to vision, also applies to pressure reception; pressure experience is dependent upon the proportion of potentially available impulses elicited by a stimulus.

THERMAL EXPERIENCE

No longer subject to reasonable question is the fact that there are different neural mechanisms for warmth and cold; the many bits of evidence that we have already seen point to different receptors for the two experiences.   In point, however, is the question of what structures are the specific receptors, and to this query there have been proposed three answers: (1) For von Frey, the Ruffini cylinder mediated warmth, the Krause end-bulb cold.   (2) Later came the notion that nerve endings in the blood vessels of the skin aroused cold when they constricted and warmth when dilated (Nafe).   (3) More recently, the work of Jenkins has led to the belief that free nerve endings of the skin are the receptors for the two experiences, although they are differentiated functionally, it is presumed, into two kinds.

The von Frey Hypothesis.—The belief that the receptors for cold are the Krause end bulbs is based mainly on the sensitivity of the cornea of the eye. From it can be elicited, without question, the experience of cold, and the only receptor organs to be found in it are, aside from free nerve endings, the Krause end bulbs. That these are the receptors for cold is strongly indicated by an experiment—a very daring one—in which the eye was injected with methylene blue so that the Krause end bulbs would be stained and therefore easily seen. The points sensitive to cold corresponded quite well with the stained end organs (Strughold and Karbe). Quite important, however, were exceptions to this conclusion; in some instances cold spots were located where no Krause end bulbs could be found, and in others Krause end bulbs did not correspond to cold spots. In line with this observation, portending ill for the von Frey theory, are experiments in which no Krause end bulbs could be found at points on the skin sensitive to cold (Dallenbach). But, on the favorable side, are several studies (*e.g.*, Bazett *et al.*) in which sensitivity to cold in various regions of the body correlated with the number of Krause end bulbs; but the mere correlation of numbers cannot stand as crucial in the face of facts, like those above, in which cold spots do not correspond specifically with Krause end bulbs.

Little evidence has been advanced for von Frey's suggestion that the Ruffini cylinder is the receptor organ for warmth. All that we have seems to be, again, a numerical correlation of density and sensitivity of warmth spots with the incidence of Ruffini organs (Bazett *et al.*); but more than that is required for proof, and little faith can be placed at present in this aspect of the von Frey theory.

The Vascular Theory.—Dissatisfied with the evidence for the von Frey theory and impressed with the parallels existing between the behavior of blood vessels and thermal experience, Nafe has proposed that thermal reception is actually a kinesthetic process initiated mechanically by the constriction and dilation of blood vessels. It happens also that Nafe has denied a specific-receptor theory of the cutaneous qualities and holds, instead, that cutaneous experience is determined in the central nervous system by the differentiation of "patterns of impulses" arriving over cutaneous nerves. In this respect we can consider his theory quite inadequate for the facts as we know them; but the vascular theory does not stand or fall with the question of specific receptors.

Several facts favor Nafe's vascular theory. The edges of the cornea are sensitive to cold and this fact, Nafe argues, correlates just as well with the vascularity of this region of the cornea as with the frequency of Krause end bulbs (or free nerve endings). Demonstrated, moreover, is the fact that vasoconstriction and vasodilation can occur in response to changes in temperature—a crucial point—and that they may do so quite independently of efferent neural discharges. He goes on, indeed, to point out that the behavior of smooth muscle (of which the blood vessels are made up in part) closely parallels changes in thermal experience. Between 12 and 45°C., it contracts or dilates, paralleling the region in which cold and warmth, respectively, are felt. Above 45°C., constriction and dilation are mixed—thus heat—and similarly below 12°C.—thus 'cold' heat. Below 3 and above 52°C., smooth muscle is spastically constricted—thus pain.

In addition to such parallelism, other points can be marshalled in support of the vascular theory. Reaction time to cold is shorter than to warmth, and cold experience sets in more abruptly than does warmth; similar statements apply to the latency and abruptness of response of smooth muscles to cold and warmth. Blood vessels are intimately related with thermal spots (if only by virtue of the fact that blood vessels supply the skin very liberally). In thermal adaptation, moreover, as the threshold for warmth increases, in terms of deviation from physiological zero, that for cold decreases, and vice versa. This behavior is a general rule, and Nafe takes it to indicate the sort of interrelation of cold and warmth receptors as would occur in the expansion or constriction of blood vessels; but it has been pointed out (Jenkins) that in certain instances the rule does not hold, and these instances would appear to be crucial.

To such arguments for the vascular theory, Nafe adds several facts of thermal experience which the theory appears to explain well. Thermal spots, it is well known, are less stable in repeated mappings than are pain or pressure spots, and accounting for this are the many factors—chemical condition of the blood, blood pressure, muscle tonus and fatigue—which are able to affect vascular size and activity. Then, too, thermal sensitivity may change without a change in skin temperature. Thus, when one hand is stimulated, the thermal threshold of the other is changed, and it can be shown that vasoconstriction or vasodilation has occurred (reflexly) in the stimulated hand (Wagoner *et al.*). Instances of chills in fever or, in some individuals, when certain 'screeching' sounds are heard, without change in skin temperature, also tend to support the notion that the constriction of blood vessels arouses cold. Nafe points, finally, to the fact that when blood is retained, by mechanical compression, in one part of the body, thereby interfering mechanically with the constriction of blood vessels, sensitivity to cold becomes poorer.

Against the vascular theory, on the other hand, are a number of important facts (Jenkins): (1) Thermal experience includes the phenomena of paradoxical cold and warmth in which an experience of cold is elicited by a warm stimulus, or conversely. This fact makes little sense in terms of vascular theory, especially in view of the fact that such paradoxical effects can be produced by radiant heat, thereby eliminating the possibility that mechanical stimulation may have caused vascular changes. (2) The independent existence of warm and cold spots is not easily understood in terms of vascular theory, unless it is assumed that some branches of blood vessels are innervated only by cold receptors and others by warmth receptors. (3) There are chemical substances which when applied to the skin raise the skin temperature while presenting the experience of cold, and this fact does not make a great deal of sense in terms of the vascular theory. (4) Radiant warm stimuli of short duration but rapidly repeated can be appreciated as discrete when only a few tenths of a second intervene; yet smooth muscles are supposed to be much more sluggish in their reaction.

So go the arguments for and against the vascular theory of thermal sensitivity. Some facts are difficult to explain without the theory; others are plainly against it. And yet there is no direct proof either way. A simple conclusion to come to, however, and one which dissolves all difficulties is that there are nerve endings functionally differentiated for cold and warmth, respectively, that they sometimes end in the vicinity of blood vessels—since these are so liberally distributed and since nerve fibers tend to follow blood vessels when laid down in embryonic growth (Chap. VII)—and can be influenced, even to the point of excitation, by quick shifts in blood flow occasioned by dilation or constriction (particularly the latter), but that the activity of thermal receptors is not necessarily related either anatomically or functionally to blood vessels.

Jenkins Concentration Theory.—Supporting the notion that free nerve endings are thermal receptors are the many data which Jenkins has collected in a most intensive series of researches. As previously stated, he finds that with sufficient intensity of stimulation thermal spots are present in relatively great abundance in many areas of the body, and that when the sensitivity of the thermal spots is measured one is led to believe, not in actual thermal spots, but in a varying *concentration* of thermally sensitive endings—thus the concentration theory. In support of this theory Jenkins has plotted very accurate maps of the 'hills and valleys' of sensitivity in the skin. The inability of either von Frey's or Nafe's theories to deal adequately with the facts of thermal sensitivity and experience is, moreover, evidence for Jenkins's view, for only free nerve endings remain as possible receptors for temperature.

We are led, as a consequence, to hold that free nerve endings are responsible for all the cutaneous qualities except instances of the pressure sensitivity mediated by the hair bulbs. Yet we should admit the cases of identity of Krause end bulbs with cold sensitivity and of Meissner corpuscles with pressure sensitivity, while denying the *sole* specificity of these encapsulated end organs. Perhaps it would be better, then, to take as our general view the position that the specificity of cutaneous nerve endings is functionally, although not structurally, evident, and that encapsulated end organs have no necessary or exclusive relation to any particular kind of cutaneous experience. Apparently their presence is largely fortuitous, except that they are more numerous where more nerve endings are found, a fact which may indicate that they are induced embryologically by free nerve endings.

Thermochemistry.—As is the case in all senses, the thermoreceptors show adaptation of sensitivity with continued thermal stimulation, and after withdrawal of stimulation recover gradually to their former normal level of sensitivity. Undoubtedly chemical processes of some kind are at the root of such phenomena of adaptation and recovery in whatever senses they are found, whether in vision, the chemical senses, pain, touch, or temperature. In vision, however, an attempt has been made (Hecht) to bring a consideration of photochemical processes into a complete theory of visual excitation. Likewise in the thermal sense a thermochemical theory of sensitivity has been proposed (Jenkins). A chemical substance in the receptor is assumed to be decomposed by the thermal stimulus, and replenishing the supply of thermosensitive substance are the breakdown products of its decomposition and other available materials in the cell. In such a scheme, the phenomena of adaptation and recovery are accounted for, at least in a general way. Two separate thermochemical systems, however, must be assumed, one in the cold receptors and another in the warmth receptors.

NEURAL ORGANIZATION OF CUTANEOUS FUNCTIONS

The Dermatomes.—One of the chief characteristics of vertebrate animals is segmentation of the body, particularly of the bony structure. In the higher vertebrates, such segmentation is limited largely to the earlier stages of embryonic development and to the structure of the spinal vertebrae. Of importance, however, is the fact that the distribution of spinal nerves to various portions of the body follows a segmental principle; each spinal nerve represents an embryological segment or *metamere* and is distributed, so far as its cutaneous components are concerned, to a limited area of the body, which we call a *dermatome*. This in the human adult is ordinarily irregular in shape and size, but the position and shape of the various dermatomes can be represented as in Fig. 107.

Despite the clear boundaries shown in this figure, considerable overlapping of the distribution of spinal nerves exists. In the experimental mapping of dermatomes in animals, it has been necessary to section the three nerves below and above that in question and then determine the area of "remaining sensibility." By such a method the dermatomes of the monkey have been determined (Sherrington), and other similar methods, adapted to the limitations encountered in studying human individuals, have been employed in mapping dermatomes in man (Foerster).

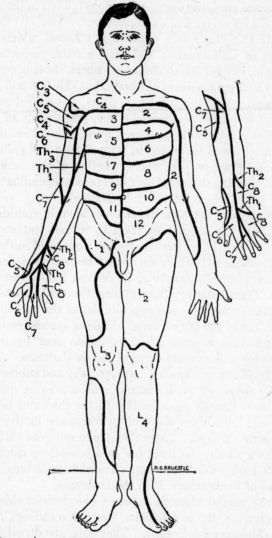

FIG. 107.—Dermatomes of the human body as determined by Foerster, in cases suffering from injury to spinal nerves, by the method of "remaining sensibility." (*From J. F. Fulton. Physiology of the nervous system, p. 37. New York: Oxford University Press, 1938. By permission of the publishers.*)

Cutaneous Fibers of the Dorsal Roots.—Cutaneous nerve fibers innervating the skin have their cell bodies in the dorsal ganglia, and their axons terminate in the spinal cord. Such dorsal root fibers vary in size from about 1 to 20 μ, the larger ones being myelinated, and the smaller being thinly myelinated or without myelin. Such differences in fibers correspond to those already described for the cutaneous nerves. As they approach the spinal cord, the dorsal-root axons fan out in the rostrocaudal axis and enter the spinal cord at the *dorsolateral sulcus*. At the same time they divide into two *filaments*, a *medial* and a *lateral*, which cross to the dorsal columns of white matter and gray matter, respectively. Both filaments contain, in addition to cutaneous fibers, those of proprioceptive function from the deeper parts of the body, but this fact will be discussed in the next chapter. Of the cutaneous fibers, the medial group is composed largely of the large myelinated fibers, presumably of the *A* type, whereas the lateral division is composed principally of small myelinated and unmyelinated fibers concerned in temperature and pain, and therefore of the *B* and *C* types. All fibers, whether of the medial or lateral filaments, upon entering the spinal cord divide into ascending and descending branches each of which has several collaterals.

Spinal Pathways of the Skin Senses.—Known in considerable detail are the relations of the dorsal root fibers to various tracts and nuclei of the spinal cord. Yet the matter is a complex one, and in the brief space allowed for its consideration here we cannot be entirely accurate. What is to be said now, therefore, is true, *in general*, but not in every detail (see Fig. 108). Immediately after entering the cord, most of the fibers of the lateral filament cross to the opposite side of the cord and terminate in the gray matter of the dorsal horn. Making synapse with these endings are second-order neurons which assemble near by in the *lateral spinothalamic tract* and conduct upward to the thalamus. In this tract there are two divisions, one located more laterally and subserving thermal experience, the other situated ventrad and conveying pain impulses. The thermal fibers usually pass directly to the thalamus before making further synapses; pain fibers more often terminate in the gray matter during their course upward. There they make synapses with other fibers in the tract; as a result, the tract for pain is really a chain of neurons rather than one long continuous tract. Their ultimate termination, however, like those of temperature, is in the thalamus.

Fibers of the medial filament appear to be derived chiefly from the receptors for pressure, the hair follicles, free nerve endings, and encapsulated endings (Meissner corpuscles). They enter the dorsal fiber columns and cross to the opposite side some distance up the cord from their point of entrance. Some continue in the dorsal columns to the *gracile* and *cuneate nuclei* of the medulla, but others leave the dorsal columns at some point and proceed to the ventral part of the cord where they assemble in the *ventral spinothalamic tract* and run upward to end in the thalamus.

Cutaneous Functions of the Hindbrain.—The pathways mentioned so far serve only the trunk and limbs. Joining these pathways in the pons and medulla are impulses from the face and head.   They arrive to some extent over the glossopharyngeal and vagus nerves, but principally over the *trigeminal* nerve fibers.   These enter the pons and end upon three main sensory nuclei, the *spinal nucleus*, the *chief sensory nucleus*, and the

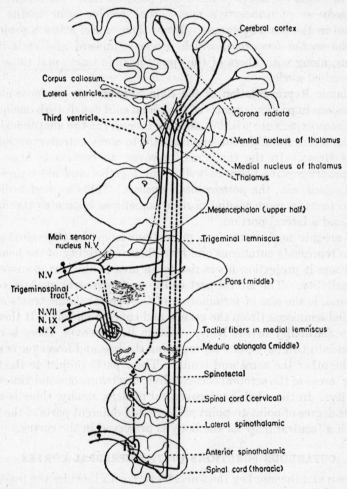

Fig. 108.—Diagram illustrating the chief centers and pathways of the cutaneous sensory system.   (*From A. Kuntz.   A textbook of neuroanatomy, p. 227.   Philadelphia: Lea and Febiger, 1942.   By permission of the publishers.*)

mesencephalic nucleus.   The latter happens to subserve proprioceptive functions and need not concern us here.   In the spinal nucleus are represented the smaller fibers concerned mainly with pain and temperature; upon the chief sensory nucleus end the larger myelinated fibers of the *A* type serving hair bulbs and other pressure receptors of the head and face. Projection fibers from these two nuclei ascend in separate tracts to the thalamus.

Besides the inflow of cutaneous impulses from the trigeminal nerve, there are in the medulla the gracile and cuneate nuclei, previously mentioned, in which the fibers of the dorsal columns end. Although important chiefly as proprioceptive nuclei, they receive some tactile fibers contained in the dorsal columns. From these nuclei arises a projection tract, the *medial lemniscus*, which proceeds upward and ends in the thalamus, along with fibers of the spinothalamic tracts and those from the trigeminal nuclei.

Thalamic Representation of the Skin Senses.—As we have already noted, lesions in particular parts of the spinal cord can disturb one quality of cutaneous experience without another because, as the anatomical facts show, the fibers for different qualities are to some extent grouped into different tracts. In the thalamus, however, all cutaneous fibers, and indeed proprioceptive fibers as well, come together and are represented in one nucleus, *viz.*, the *posteroventral nucleus*.[1] This we find is divided into two parts, a more medial portion sometimes known as the *arcuate nucleus* and a lateral portion.

The arcuate nucleus receives projections from the trigeminal nuclei and thus represents cutaneous and kinesthetic sensibility of the head and face. From it projection fibers rise to an area of the cortex subserving such sensibility. The lateral part of the posteroventral nucleus, on the other hand, is the site of termination of the spinothalamic tracts and of the medial lemniscus (from the gracile and cuneate nuclei). It therefore mediates sensibility of the body. Within it, moreover, there is differentiation into two parts, one representing the legs and lower parts of the body, the other the arms and trunk. These parts project to the 'arm' and 'leg' areas of the cerebral cortex subserving cutaneous and kinesthetic sensitivity. In the whole posteroventral nucleus, finally, there is a considerable degree of point-to-point projection of different parts of the body, and such a 'central map' of the body is preserved in the cortex.

CUTANEOUS FUNCTIONS OF THE CEREBRAL CORTEX

In man and the monkey the somesthetic cortex includes the precentral gyrus (motor area) and a large part of the parietal lobe. Only the pre- and postcentral gyri, however, receive projections from the posteroventral thalamic nucleus, and the postcentral area is the most important projection area. In both, however, there exists a topographical organization

[1] It may be recalled that the ventral nucleus of the thalamus is made up of two main divisions, a lateroventral nucleus which is concerned mostly with cerebello-cortical projections, and the posteroventral nucleus of cutaneous and proprioceptive functions.

such that the most dorsal part of the areas represents the legs and lower body; the more lateral part, the arms and trunk; and the most lateral parts, the face and head. This plan follows closely that of the motor areas (Chap. XVI). The posterior part of the parietal lobe, on the other hand, is more an 'association' center than a primary sensory area. It receives projections from the *lateral nucleus*, an 'association' nucleus having synaptic connections with the primary somesthetic nucleus of the thalamus, the posteroventral nucleus. In line with the associative anatomical character of the posterior parietal lobe are several facts, to be mentioned below, which indicate its role in 'associative' somesthetic functions.

Studies of the role of cortical somesthetic areas in cutaneous experience have been carried out by means of four general methods: (1) sensitization of cortical areas by the application of strychnine, sometimes called the method of strychninization; (2) the recording of electrical potentials from different parts of the cortex during peripheral cutaneous stimulation of various kinds; (3) behavioral tests of the effect of ablation of different parts and amounts of cortical tissue in man and animals; and (4) electrical stimulation of the intact cortex in man under local anesthesia. The information that we have acquired concerning cortical functions in cutaneous experience and perception is best discussed under these four headings.

Electrical Stimulation.—This method has been employed by several medical clinicians who have had the opportunity of recording the introspective reports of patients whose brains were exposed in such a way as to be electrically stimulable (Foerster; Penfield and Boldrey). The precentral and postcentral regions, the results show, are spatially organized with respect to different parts of the body in the manner described above. Most capable of arousing cutaneous experience is stimulation of the central lips of these two areas. Experience may be obtained, however, from the posterior part of the lobe (areas 5 and 7 in Fig. 109), but the intensity of the stimulus must be higher. But wherever the electrical stimulus is applied, the most common experiences are of numbness, tingling, or movement. Very rarely are sensations of pain, warmth, or cold reported. The spatial organization of the somesthetic area is with respect to the parts of the body, not with respect to quality of experience. We find, consequently, no explanation in these data of the cortical basis of cutaneous quality.

Strychninization.—The subjects used in experiments with strychnine have been monkeys (Dusser de Barenne). Applying strychnine to their cortex is like presenting a peripheral cutaneous stimulus so far as their behavior is concerned. They scratch and bite at some part of the body as though it were itching or tickled. It happens, however, that, even though strychnine is put on only a small area of the cortex, it 'fires' a comparatively large area, and consequently the topographical organization of the cortex cannot be studied adequately by this method. Yet such 'irradiation' of the effects of strychnine does bring out an interesting point. The somesthetic cortex is divided into *three areas*, the boundaries of which are never crossed in strychnine irradiation: these are called the *arm, leg,* and *face* areas. They are, we have already seen, anatomically distinct in the projection system of the skin senses, for they represent the cuneate, gracile, and trigeminal nuclei, respectively. In respect of irradiation within one of these areas, we may note, there is no difference between the precentral and postcentral gyri.

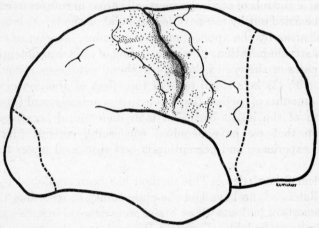

Fig. 109.—Distribution of points on the cerebral cortex at which electrical stimulation evokes cutaneous sensations in human subjects under local anesthesia. (*After Penfield and Boldrey.*)

Another point of significance has been demonstrated in this work: strychninization of the cortex causes neural activity in the corresponding part of the thalamic nuclei. Such a result tends to indicate that more than a simple projection of impulses from the thalamus to the cortex takes place in this sensory system and that in addition there are interacting connections of a sort to allow impulses in the cortex to affect the sensory nucleus. Since this nucleus has associative connections with other thalamic nuclei—*e.g.*, the lateral nucleus—a route is provided via the thalamus by means of which activity in one area of the cortex can affect other cortical areas.

Electrical Recording.—From the study of the position of neural impulses in the cortex when peripheral cutaneous areas are stimulated has come very precise information concerning the spatial organization of the somesthetic cortex (Marshall *et al.*). It has been possible, in fact, to map the point-for-point relations between the cortex and the skin with this method. From such a map it is clear that the cortex is arranged in terms of the dermatomal distribution of nerve fibers (see Fig. 107), not with respect to gross areas of the body. There is, however, a precise point-to-point representation of cutaneous areas in the somesthetic cortex.

Experiments of this kind show further that when 'pressure' stimulation of the skin is employed electrical responses appear in the *contralateral* cortex alone, and principally in the postcentral area. Only when stronger stimuli are used, such as are capable of arousing pain, are responses observed in both hemispheres. Whether or not this fact indicates anything about the projection of pain is not clear; it may mean that pressure representation is not only predominantly contralateral but also to some extent ipsilateral.

Cortical Extirpation.—When the entire cortex of an animal is removed on one side (hemidecortication), there follows a comparatively complete anesthesia of the *contralateral* skin surfaces (Walker and Fulton). Loss in cutaneous sensibility is greater in man and chimpanzee than in lower animals. After some time, sensitivity to pain reappears, although its localization remains poor. The sensation of cutaneous pressure also returns, but this, like pain, is poorly localized. Unfortunately no acceptable data regarding thermal experience are available. Well established, however, is the fact that such decortication abolishes, in addition to the ability to localize cutaneous stimuli accurately, all vestiges of deep (kinesthetic) sensibility. We are led, therefore, to believe that kinesthetic sensitivity is entirely dependent upon the contralateral cortex. Cutaneous sensibility, on the other hand, although present in highest degree only when the contralateral cortex is intact, must be subserved in part by other structures. To be suspected is the other hemisphere, to which, it is known, go some ipsilateral fibers of the cutaneous pathways. The thalamus, however, is capable of mediating some cutaneous sensitivity, if behavioral responses of an animal are any sign, for after bilateral extirpation of most of the cortex, one can still elicit responses to pinprick and heavy pressure.

Indicating the role of particular cortical areas in cutaneous functions are the experiments of Ruch with chimpanzees; these point to the pre- and postcentral gyri as the areas of primary sensibility for pressure but to the posterior parietal area as important in the higher 'associative' processes in somesthetic perception. Extirpation of the postcentral area, Ruch found, has no effect upon the discrimination of roughness, so long as the precentral areas are left intact. Removal of the posterior parietal area, however, causes some deficit; but a much greater impairment can be obtained by completely removing the parietal lobe. Most indicative of the role of the posterior lobule in perception, however, is the effect of its removal upon capacity to discriminate the form of objects by touch (stereognosis).   This is completely lost following removal of the posterior area.   Some, but not all, stereognostic capacity is recovered in time, however, for the animal can later distinguish between a cone and a pyramid, but not between a pyramid and a wedge, a discrimination it can make normally.

From the study of rats comes some evidence of the dependence of *learning* to discriminate the roughness of materials upon the cerebral cortex (Smith).   Rats that had previously acquired a discrimination habit based upon the different roughnesses of sandpapers lost in greater or lesser degree their memory of discrimination after removal of a particular area which had been mapped (see Fig. 110).   Since they were able to relearn

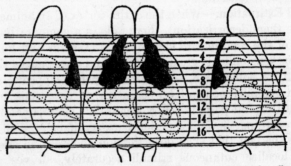

Fig. 110.—Area bilaterally common to the lesions of four rats which suffered postoperative amnesia of ability to make a tactile discrimination of roughness of sandpaper. . (*From D. E. Smith.   Cerebral localization in somaesthetic discrimination in the rat.   J. comp. Psychol.*, **28**, 173, 1939.   *By permission of Williams and Wilkins, publishers.*)

the discrimination, it is not clear whether the operation interfered with basic sensory functions or with higher order processes concerned in learning and memory (see Chap. XXIV).

Worth pointing out in closing this chapter is the research that yet remains to be done concerning neural functions in cutaneous sensitivity and perception.   Little or nothing is known of either thalamic or cortical functions in thermal experience.   The sort of work Ruch has done with chimpanzees could be carried much further in them and in other animals; for operative techniques and methods of testing discriminative capacity in animals are readily available.

General References

JENKINS, W. L., and L. J. STONE, 1941.   Recent research in cutaneous sensitivity: II.   Touch and the neural basis of the skin senses.   *Psychol. Bull.*, 38, 69–91.

NAFE, J. P., 1934.   The pressure, pain and temperature senses.   Pp. 1037–1087. In *A handbook of general experimental psychology.*   Ed. Carl Murchison. Worcester: Clark Univ. Press.

STONE, L. J., and W. L. JENKINS, 1940.   Recent research in cutaneous sensitivity: I.   Pain and temperature.   *Psychol. Bull.*, 37, 285–311.

CHAPTER XIII

PROPRIOCEPTION

The sense organs that remain for discussion are the kinesthetic receptors of the muscles, tendons, and joints and the vestibular receptors of the nonauditory labyrinth. Taken together, these receptors constitute the proprioceptors and are located within the organism away from the direct influences of external stimuli. They differ from the exteroceptors in several ways which can be indicated briefly: (1) They are stimulated by the action of the body itself, whereas the exteroceptors are activated by stimulus conditions in the organism's environment. (2) In contrast to the intermittent and occasional action of the exteroceptive stimuli, proprioceptive stimulation is always with the organism, guiding its every movement. (3) The functioning of exteroceptor systems is usually present in vivid detail in the 'conscious' experience of the organism; but seldom is one clearly aware of the proprioceptive activity going on within him. (4) Closely related to this fact is the lack of prominence of qualities of experience in proprioception; 'pressure' and 'pain' are its sole attributes, and these are much more poorly localized and less vivid than comparable qualities in cutaneous experience. (5) With respect finally to the adjustment of the organism, proprioceptive stimuli are a 'ground' upon which exteroceptive influences are a 'figure'; indeed, the reflexive and postural behavior with which proprioception is closely related constitutes the fundamental frame of reference in which are differentiated the specific adjustments controlled exteroceptively.

The proprioceptors are almost exclusively mechanoreceptors, and it is therefore of interest to compare them with other mechanoreceptors. These include the auditory, vestibular, kinesthetic, and cutaneous receptors. Special features of the auditory receptors make them quite distinct from other such receptors; the vestibular mechanism, too, is structurally different from the other members of this class. Somewhat more difficult to distinguish, however, are the cutaneous and kinesthetic receptor mechanisms. The blood vessels of the body are liberally supplied with nerve endings, and these are in both the skin and deeper parts of the body; but excepting the possibility that vascular nerve endings are thermal receptors, we usually consider them among the kinesthetic endings. The Pacinian corpuscle, moreover, is found in the subcutaneous adipose tissue in a position to participate in cutaneous excitation, but it is also distributed in deeper parts of the body. Such an interrelation of cutaneous and kinesthetic pressure fibers is further evidenced in the intermingling of both types of fibers in the dorsal columns of the spinal cord (p. 276). The principal kinesthetic receptors, the pressure organs of the muscles, tendons, and joints, are, however, easily identified, and it is these which will be our main concern in the following sections.

NEUROSENSORY MECHANISMS OF KINESTHESIS

The Kinesthetic Receptors.—Besides free nerve endings in blood vessels, three main types of kinesthetic end organs may be distinguished: the *muscle spindle*, the *Golgi tendon organ*, and the *Pacinian corpuscle*. The muscle spindle, a somewhat complicated structure found in the equatorial region of muscles, consists of muscle fibers innervated by sensory nerve endings which are enveloped in a tissue fluid and a capsule of connective tissue (Fig. 111). Within the muscle spindle are nerve endings of two types which have been given names suggesting their respective structural appearances: *annulospiral* and *flower-spray* endings. The annulospiral endings, which are terminals of large myelinated *A* type fibers, are arranged spirally around the muscle fibers of the muscle spindle; clearly different from them are the flower-spray endings, which are associated with somewhat smaller myelinated fibers and end in spraylike arborizations upon the muscle fibers. Both the annulospiral and flower-spray endings are so arranged that they are stimulated when the muscle stretches, rather than when it contracts, and they are, therefore, called *stretch afferents*.

The Golgi tendon organs are specialized structures that surround a few muscle fibers near their distal ends in the vicinity of the juncture of muscle fibers with the tendons which attach muscles to bones. Innervating the Golgi organs are afferent nerve endings, called *tendon endings*, which are stimulated by either an increase or decrease of tension at the tendon-muscle juncture. There seems, in fact, to be no distribution, in the excitation of tendon endings, between muscle contraction and muscle stretching, but since the stretch afferents of the muscle spindles register stretch, it is plain that the tendon endings are the principal organs for recording muscle *contraction*.

The Pacinian corpuscles are structurally similar to other encapsulated end organs encountered in the skin, particularly to the Krause end bulb, but they are generally much larger than cutaneous encapsulated organs. They consist of a capsule, made up of several layers of fibrous tissue, and nerve endings ramify within them. They are distributed widely in the body, being found commonly in the sheaths of tendons and muscles, in the linings of various organs of the body, and (as mentioned before) in the subcutaneous tissue. They are organs of deep-pressure sensitivity and are activated by deformation of the tissue in which they are located. They are associated, as are the other kinesthetic receptors, with the large

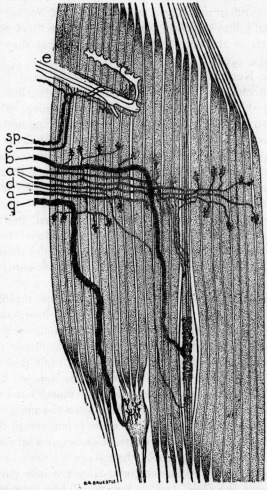

Fig. 111.—Diagram of the sensory and motor innervation of muscle. *a*, motor fibers ending on various muscle fibers; *b*, annulospiral ending terminating in the muscle spindle; *d*, flower-spray ending also terminating in the muscle spindle; *g*, sensory fiber serving a Golgi tendon organ; *sp*, a sympathetic plexus serving the blood vessel, *e* and accompanied by a sensory pain fiber *c*. (*After Denny-Brown. From J. F. Fulton. Physiology of the nervous system, p. 8. New York: Oxford University Press, 1938. By permission of the publishers.*)

myelinated fibers, although, as we shall see in a moment, there are systematic differences in respect of fiber size and conduction velocity among the various kinesthetic receptors.

Free nerve endings are also kinesthetic receptors, but they seem to be restricted, so far as muscles are concerned, to the blood vessels serving the muscles and to the sheaths covering muscles and tendons; they probably do not end directly upon muscle fibers. Adequate information concerning the number and places of termination of free nerve endings in the tendons and joints is lacking, but from what we know of pain arising from these parts of the body, we may presume that they are supplied with free nerve endings.

Kinesthetic Nerve Fibers.—The study of different fiber types in kinesthesis has rendered information comparable to that already presented for the skin senses; in many respects it is more satisfactory for kinesthesis than for cutaneous functions. Amplifying and recording of nervous impulses in kinesthetic nerves have led to the delineation of four types of fibers (Matthews). These have been designated by the letters A_1, A_2, B, and C, but the reader should not presume that these types parallel those of the skin senses. The *A-B-C kinesthetic* fibers do not, in fact, include any pain fibers comparable to the cutaneous C fibers; altogether they are much thicker, more myelinated, and show faster conduction than the average cutaneous fibers. Indeed, they parallel in these respects the cutaneous A fibers. Let us consider them in turn.

The A_1 and A_2 fibers are associated with the flower-spray endings and annulospiral endings, respectively. They are very similar in their properties, except that the A_2 fibers conduct more rapidly and have larger diameters than the A_1 fibers. Because they innervate the muscle spindle, they are called stretch afferents. When the muscles which they serve are in their normal state, *i.e.*, nearly but not entirely relaxed, they discharge impulses at a rather slow rate (5 to 15 impulses per second); but their rate of discharge quickly increases the moment the muscle is stretched (by the contraction of an antagonistic muscle) and may reach as high a level as 500 impulses per second. When the muscle fibers upon which they end contract, however, they cease firing, except that A_2 fibers sometimes discharge a little if the contraction is quite intense.

B fibers have a higher threshold than A_1 or A_2 fibers, conduct more slowly, and have smaller diameters; and they are believed, upon good evidence, to serve the Golgi tendon organs. Their rate of response is increased *either by active contraction or passive stretch* of the muscles, and the number of impulses per second which they produce is proportional to the *logarithm* of the tension exerted by the muscle. They are therefore *tension recorders*, in contrast to the A fibers which register *stretch*.

C fibers are associated with Pacinian corpuscles, for responses in them *disappear* when the muscle sheaths containing Pacinian corpuscles are dissected away. These fibers behave quite similarly to the A fibers of the cutaneous group in respect of impulse size, conduction rate, and so on.

Not included in the *A-B-C* scheme for kinesthetic fibers are deep-pain fibers, which we know must exist both from subjective experience and from the free endings of nerve fibers in the vicinity of muscles. Such fibers are undoubtedly present in the nerves which have been studied (above), but it happens that the impulses from the *A-B-C* fibers are so prominent that pain fibers do not show up in the recordings. It can be assumed that in kinesthetic fibers, as well as those of the skin senses, small, and for the most part unmyelinated, fibers mediate pain; but as stated above, it is probable that most of them are distributed to blood vessels and to the sheaths of muscles and tendons rather than directly to muscle fibers.

Neural Centers and Pathways.—Because the kinesthetic cutaneous pathways are closely interrelated and in some instances identical, we have already reviewed the general scheme of the kinesthetic system while considering the skin senses. Here it is necessary only to bring out the relations between the kinesthetic and cutaneous systems and to emphasize those facts which are peculiar to kinesthesis (see Fig. 112).

Kinesthetic nerve fibers, together with those from the skin, approach the spinal cord by way of the dorsal ganglia and dorsal roots. As we noted before, the dorsal roots divide in the immediate vicinity of the cord into two filaments, the medial and lateral. Except for the unmyelinated fibers for pain which come from blood vessels, muscles, tendons, and joints, the kinesthetic fibers enter the cord by way of the medial filament and pass directly into the dorsal columns. There they divide into a short descending and a long ascending branch. This latter, unlike cutaneous nerve fibers, ordinarily does not make synapse until it reaches the gracile and cuneate nuclei of the medulla.

Some of the fibers of the medial filament, instead of entering the dorsal columns, terminate in the gray matter of the cord. Of these there are several kinds. A few pass directly to the ventral horn of the gray matter and there terminate upon the ventral horn cells; thus is made the simplest sort of reflex mechanism in which only a sensory and a motor neuron is concerned. Others end upon internuncial cells in the dorsal horns of gray matter, and the internuncial neurons end in turn upon ventral horn cells, thereby making the more common type of reflex mechanism which consists of sensory, internuncial, and motor neurons. Still other kinesthetic fibers of the dorsal root terminate upon cells in the gray matter whose axonal branches ascend in the spinothalamic or spinocerebellar tracts. These latter, it is to be noted, are important elements in the integration of kinesthetic and vestibular impulses in the motor functions of the cerebellum.

Returning now to the fibers of the dorsal column, we may observe, as before, that these end upon the cells of the gracile and cuneate nuclei.

From their second-order neurons, axons ascend in the *medial lemniscus* to the lateral division of the posteroventral nucleus where they join the cutaneous fibers which have ascended from the spinal cord in the spino-thalamic tracts. As previously noted, this thalamic nucleus is so

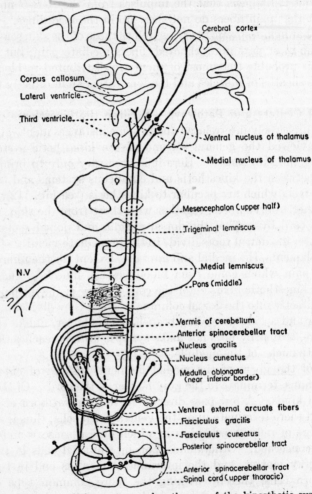

Fig. 112.—Diagram of the centers and pathways of the kinesthetic system. (*From A. Kuntz. A textbook of neuroanatomy, p. 225. Philadelphia: Lea and Febiger, 1942. By permission of the publishers.*)

organized spatially that there is present within it a 'map' of the body (Walker); the gracile tracts of the dorsal columns (see Fig. 29) and the cuneate tracts, as well as the centers of the medulla and thalamus to which they project, represent the lower (leg) and upper (arm) parts of the body, respectively.

The head and face are innervated, not by spinal nerves, but by the trigeminal cranial nerve. Of its fibers, those going to the mesencephalic nucleus (p. 277) are most important in kinesthesis. This nucleus, it may be observed, differs from all other sensory nuclei in that it contains cell bodies of first-order neurons, whereas these are otherwise found in spinal or cranial ganglia outside of the central nervous system. From the mesencephalic nucleus of the trigeminal nerve, fibers ascend to the arcuate nucleus (medial part of the posteroventral nucleus) of the thalamus. Thence projections lead to the somesthetic cortex as described below.

THE NEURAL BASIS OF KINESTHETIC DISCRIMINATION

Kinesthesis is an important sensory modality, and an adequate knowledge of its neural mechanisms should contribute a great deal to understanding other psychoneural functions. Indeed, certain behavioristic psychologists have held that kinesthetic functions, together with implicit muscular responses giving rise to them, constitute the fundamental basis of higher 'thought' processes. However that may be, kinesthesis is unquestionably important as a factor in organizing patterns of behavior, as we shall see in the chapters that follow.

Subcortical Functions.—The effect of lesions in the kinesthetic pathways leading to the thalamus is a straightforward matter. Kinesthetic fibers entering the cord do not cross but ascend in the dorsal tracts of the same side; lesions in the spinal cord therefore interfere with sensitivity of the same side of the body. Crossing of the kinesthetic pathways occurs above the cuneate and gracile nuclei of the medulla, and there it appears to be complete; for, as we observed in the last chapter, destruction of the thalamocortical pathways or their cortical areas of termination destroys sensitivity on the opposite side of the body (Walker and Fulton). Because parts of the cortex other than the primary projection areas are concerned in kinesthetic functions, the role of the cortex in kinesthesis is somewhat more complex than is that of lower centers.

Cortical Functions: Monkeys.—Although research on this problem has recently begun in the rat (Stellar *et al.*), the information at hand is limited to a few studies of monkeys, chimpanzee, and man. In these animals we may distinguish for the purposes of experimental analysis three main areas: the precentral (motor) area, the postcentral area, and the posterior parietal lobe. The first two of these, it will be recalled, receive primary projections from the posteroventral nucleus of the thalamus, but the last is associated with kinesthesis by way of the lateral nucleus which receives 'association' fibers from the posteroventral nucleus.

Tests of kinesthetic sensibility in monkeys before and after removal of these areas has given us the following results (Ruch): When the precentral *or* postcentral area is extirpated, no significant impairment of ability to discriminate in weights is observed. Indeed, when large, though incomplete, lesions of these two areas are made together, there is no disturbance of discriminatory capacity. (One cannot remove both of these areas completely without causing profound paralysis which itself interferes with the motor ability required for discrimination.) When, however, unilateral extirpation of the postcentral areas is combined with that of the posterior parietal lobe, in other words, with parietal lobectomy, considerable impairment is sustained. Discriminative performance improves somewhat with additional training but never again becomes entirely normal. From this fact we may conclude that (1) there is no focal area in the parietal lobes for kinesthetic sensibility, but that both the primary and 'associational' areas are important, and (2) that some discriminative capacity depends upon centers other than those of the cortex opposite the side used. Whether such centers are subcortical or are contained in the cortex of the other side could not be determined in this experiment, because the effects of bilateral extirpation were not studied.

Chimpanzee.—The same sort of experiments have been carried out with the chimpanzee (Ruch), which stands higher in the phylogenetic scale than the monkey. Here it appears that kinesthetic functions are somewhat more 'corticalized', *i.e.*, are dependent more upon the (contralateral) cortex than in monkeys, for the results of extirpations are more severe. Removal of the postcentral area alone, for example, causes deficit in discrimination although it is slight and temporary. Ablation of the posterior parietal lobule (alone), however, causes much more severe effects, and these are improved only after rest and retraining, but eventually the animal regains almost normal discriminative capacity. Then, with parietal lobectomy profound impairment follows, and after many months of rest and retraining it is not effaced. From such results we may conclude that in the chimpanzee the posterior parietal lobe is more important than the primary projection area but that both together are required for optimal sensitivity.

Man.—Seldom is it possible to make quantitative measurements of the effect of brain lesions in man, but in the case of kinesthetic (weight) discrimination we have measurements quite comparable to those just described for the monkey and chimpanzee (Ruch *et al.*). Two patients were studied in which surgical lesions had been made and were therefore known with some precision. One had a lesion in the anterior (postcentral) part of the parietal lobe and the other in the posterior parietal area. Both, it is to be noted, showed pronounced and lasting deficit of ability to discriminate weights. In this result we find good agreement with the findings in the monkey and chimpanzee.

How to account for remaining sensibility even after complete removal of the primary and 'association' kinesthetic areas is still to be determined by appropriate experiments. It is possible that other parts of the cortex are implicated, for we know that the interrelationships of thalamic nuclei projecting to the cortex are quite complex and other 'association' areas beside the posterior parietal area may mediate residual functions. Thalamic mediation, on the other hand, is not improbable either, for some

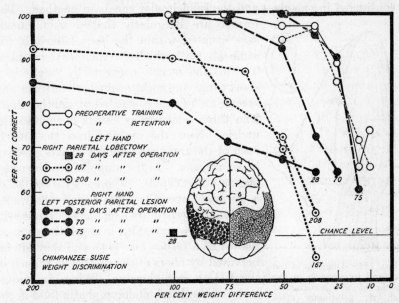

Fig. 113.—Performance of a chimpanzee on the discrimination of lifted weights following removal of the postcentral gyrus and the posterior parietal lobule. Note that there is recovery following the postcentral removal but no improvement after complete parietal lobectomy. (*After T. C. Ruch. From J. F. Fulton. Physiology of the nervous system, p. 390. New York: Oxford University Press, 1938. By permission of the publishers.*)

sensation certainly depends upon the thalamus, as we shall see when we come to consider the topic of feeling (Chap. XVII).

THE LABYRINTHINE MECHANISMS

The receptors of the nonauditory labyrinth, unlike most others that have been discussed, do not give rise to experiences which are 'conscious' except by bringing about behavioral effects which are 'experienced.' This characteristic they share in some measure with their fellow proprioceptors, the kinesthetic receptors. For this reason and from other neuroanatomical facts, it is clear that they have no important connections with mechanisms of sensory integration in the cortex, but, through their connections with the brainstem, cerebellum, and indirectly with motor centers of the cerebral cortex, they do have important influences upon the character of behavioral responses. This being the case, we need only consider here the structure and mode of function of the nonauditory labyrinth and its central connections, for the reflexive and behavioral phenomena of vestibular origin are considered in later chapters.

The Receptor Mechanism.—The nonauditory labyrinth consists of three principal parts: the saccule, utricle, and semicircular canals, all of which are filled with endolymphatic fluid. The saccule and utricle may be considered in one class and the semicircular canals in another. The former are irregularly shaped membranous sacs situated within the bony labyrinth, the same labyrinth which also encloses the cochlea. To this the saccule connects by means of a short canal, the cochlear duct; the utricle and saccule are in turn connected by another duct. The three semicircular canals open into the utricle. Near the opening into the utricle each of the three semicircular canals enlarges in an *ampulla*. In the ampulla are the sense organs of the canals. These organs consist of a group of specialized epithelial cells whose chief characteristic are long hairs. These cells and hairs are embedded in a gelatinous mass known as a *crista* (Fig. 114), and they are innervated by fibers of the vestibular branch of the VIIIth cranial nerve. When, by movement of the head, endolymphatic fluid in the canals is caused to move or to change in pressure, the crista is bent and with it the hairs that are embedded in it; therefrom arises the excitation which stimulates the VIIIth nerve fibers and which is conducted to the brain stem.

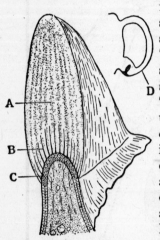

Fig. 114.—Diagram of the crista and its position in the ampulla of the semicircular canal. *A*, gelatinous mass (cupula); *B*, hair tuft; *C*, hair cell; *D*, diagram of crista's position in ampulla of canal. (*After Schaffer. From E. G. Boring et al. Introduction to psychology,* p. 622. *New York: Wiley,* 1939. *By permission of the publishers.*)

In the utricle and saccule the sense organs are the *maculae*. These are groups of hair cells located on the membranous wall of the sacs, and they are innervated by VIIIth-nerve fibers in a manner similar to that of the cristae. They are stimulated when pressure in the utricular or saccular sacs is changed by movement of the head. Between the maculae and the cristae, however, there is this important difference: The cristae of the ampullae are deflected only during *change* of position of the head, indeed, only when the change is one of *acceleration* or *deceleration, i.e.,* only when movement is increasing or decreasing in speed (Fig. 115). The macular receptors are stimulated, on the other hand, according to the resting position of the head. They are static or *positional* receptors, therefore, whereas the cristae receptors function in accelerating or decelerating *movement*. To be noted, also, is the fact that the semicircular canals are arranged in such different positions that no matter what the direction of head movement one or another of the ampullae will be affected.

The Vestibular Neural Apparatus.—Fibers from the maculae and ampullae make up the vestibular branch of the VIIIth nerve. This joins the auditory branch, already discussed, just outside the bony labyrinth

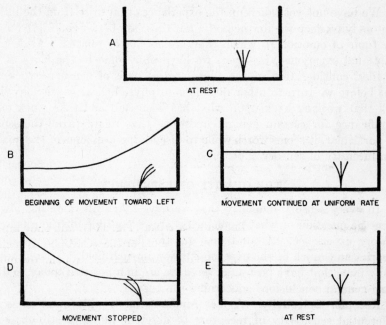

A

AT REST

B

BEGINNING OF MOVEMENT TOWARD LEFT

C

MOVEMENT CONTINUED AT UNIFORM RATE

D

MOVEMENT STOPPED

E

AT REST

Fig. 115.—Illustration of the way changes in the fluid in the semicircular canals can cause stimulation of the hairs. (*After E. G. Boring et al. Introduction to psychology, p. 623. New York: Wiley*, 1939.)

and runs with it to the medulla. Just before reaching the medulla, however, the two parts divide again into vestibular and auditory branches and terminate on their respective nuclei in the medulla. The vestibular nuclei are located somewhat caudally from those of hearing and are, in general, just beneath the cerebellum. Their arrangement, however, is rather complex, and it is probably better that we do not attempt to describe them here; suffice it to say that their chief connections are with the cerebellum (see Chap. XV), although some fibers are delivered to the colliculi of the midbrain, to the oculomotor nuclei of the IIIrd, IVth, and VIth cranial nerves in the midbrain, and to certain subcortical centers concerned in the control of posture (see Chap. XV).

CHAPTER XIV
SURVEY OF THE SENSES

We have not yet taken up the experiences that arise from the interoceptors lying deep within the body, but these are better considered under the topic of emotion to which they are so closely related. Aside from emotional experience, however, we have now come to the close of our detailed consideration of the physiological basis of sensory experience. But before we turn to other questions in physiological psychology, it is well that we look back upon what has been said and take stock of its significance for certain general questions that relate to all the senses. In particular, it seems worth while to discuss the problems of the quality and intensity of sensory experience.

THE QUALITY OF EXPERIENCE

In every sensory modality that we have taken up there has always been the question of what mechanisms are responsible for the quality of sensory experience. Around that question have centered many of the theories and much of the experimentation in each field. Thanks to the many facts that have been uncovered we are in a position today to draw some general conclusions concerning the answer.

Receptor Selectivity.—A fact fundamental to this question is the differential sensitivity of receptors to different kinds of stimuli; some receptors are most sensitive to one type of stimulus and other receptors to other kinds. Accounting in part for such selective properties of receptors are the location of the receptors and the nature of the accessory structures related to them. For purely mechanical reasons, light cannot get into the ear; for similar reasons sound does not get to the receptors of the eye in anything like the intensities at which it reaches the internal ear. The olfactory receptors likewise are protected from most kinds of stimuli except those in gaseous form; and so it is with other receptors. Every set of receptors is surrounded by accessory structures which serve the purpose of permitting only particular kinds of stimuli to reach the receptors.

In addition, however, chemical and structural features of the receptors themselves determine in part receptor selectivity. The hair cells of the cochlea and nonauditory labyrinth are especially suited in structural

294

design to be excited by mechanical stimuli; similarly, in the visual cells are chemical materials that endow them with photosensitive properties.

Yet neither accessory structures nor the obvious features of the receptors themselves always account for the selectivity. In the skin senses, for example, it seems quite clear that free nerve endings which are quite indistinguishable from each other may in one case mediate pressure, in another temperature, and in another pain. Whatever is responsible for such differences is not visible to the eye by existing techniques of study but appears to lie in some other 'functional' characteristic of the receptors. Possibly these are in the nature of different chemical constitutions of the nerves and of the polarized equilibrium (p. 20) set up at their membranes. Of that, however, we so far have no knowledge.

Even if such differences in chemical constitution are postulated, they will not account for the phenomena of sensory quality; for although most receptors are more easily stimulated by one kind of stimulus than another, they usually can be excited by other forms of stimulation, provided these are intense enough. Receptor selectivity, in other words, is a relative rather than an absolute matter. The eye, for example, can be activated by pressure on the eyeball; the thermal receptors sometimes respond to pressure; heat and cold are believed to activate 'pain' receptors which normally respond only to noxious stimuli; and all the senses, it should not be forgotten, are electrically excitable. Such sensitivity to other stimuli than the most adequate is, indeed, of utility to the organism; in cutaneous experience, for example, the fact that excessive thermal stimulation activates pain receptors warns the organism of danger.

Physiological Theories of Quality.—The important question about the differential sensitivity of receptors, however, is: How does it operate in determining sensory quality? If it were true that sensory quality depended upon receptors being of different types and therefore upon which receptors are activated by a stimulus, receptor selectivity would serve the very important purpose of seeing to it that a receptor practically always is excited by one kind of stimulus. Which receptor is stimulated could then be a rather reliable means of informing the central nervous system of the kind of stimulus with which it had been stimulated. If, on the other hand, the kind of stimulus were to impress its character on the message from the receptor, no matter which receptor was excited, it is hard to see what purpose receptor selectivity would serve.

But which of these alternative possibilities is realized in the mechanisms of sensory quality is the crucial question. The first is the one suggested by Johannes Müller more than a century ago in his doctrine of specific nerve energies. He held that each receptor, or the sensory fibers associated with it, possesses a characteristic quality or specific nerve energy of its own and that no matter how it is stimulated it always presents this particular quality to the brain. Upholding this view of the mechanism of sensory quality have been many workers in the various sensory modalities; Helmholtz was probably the most prominent. His theories of pitch and of color vision were based explicitly on the notion that each fiber had its own quality and in explaining pitch or color vision it was necessary only to learn the means by which the receptors reacted selectively to different kinds of stimuli, since the specific quality of fibers would take care of sensory quality after the selection had been performed. In the ear this means of selection was the resonance of different parts of the basilar membrane to different sound frequencies; in the eye it was the selective sensitivity of different receptors. Parallel theories, based upon the same basic assumption of specific nerve energies, were proposed by von Frey in the cutaneous senses and by Henning for taste, as we have already seen. All such theories which rest upon the doctrine of specific nerve energies we may call specific-fiber theories.

Opposed to them are various theories in which it is supposed that the qualitative character of a stimulus is somehow impressed upon responses of receptors and their sensory fibers independently of any particular property of the receptors or fibers themselves. These theories we may call nonspecific-fiber theories. In hearing, for example, the belief proposed by Wever and Bray that pitch may depend upon the frequency of impulses in the auditory fibers rather than upon which fibers are excited is a nonspecific-fiber theory. Hering's view that a single color receptor may mediate two kinds of color experience, depending upon the kind of stimulus presented to it, falls into the same category. And in the cutaneous experience, the theory of Goldscheider that pain results from intense activity in pressure receptors and Nafe's theory that the pattern of impulses in cutaneous nerve fibers determines the quality of experience, whether pressure, pain, or temperature, are also nonspecific-fiber theories.

Peripheral Basis of Quality.—Now, we may inquire: What is the standing of these two classes of theories in the light of the experimental facts of today? We can answer this question without much hesitation. Specific-fiber theories have uniformly been upheld wherever they have been put to the test, and nonspecific-fiber theories have either been disproved or have not been favored by the facts. As the reader will remember, whenever the question was raised in previous chapters, the available knowledge, in all cases except in olfaction where nothing is very certain, pointed definitely to a specific-fiber theory. The evidence for the place (specific-fiber) theory of hearing, coming as it does from many sources and from accurate data, appeared almost overwhelming. Similarly the data of color vision are usually taken as supporting a three-color theory and with good reason. A similar conclusion was also reached in cutaneous and gustatory experience.

Most crucial to the question, however, have been the results of experiments in which single nerve fibers were studied or in which groups of fibers in a sensory nerve were sorted out by means of the analysis of the action potentials or of differential blocking. Galambos's results with records of the individual activities of nerve fibers in the auditory nerve demonstrated that each fiber has some frequency to which it responds maximally and a limited range of frequencies within which it will respond at all. Similar records of optic fibers showed each fiber to have its own visibility curve and the curves of fibers to differ from each other. Pfaffmann's study of gustatory nerve fibers brought out three groups of fibers related to acid, bitter, and salt, respectively. In kinesthetic nerves, Matthews separated the activity of nerve fibers according to the type of receptor activated; and in the cutaneous senses, finally, definite evidence was presented of the participation of different nerve fibers in the responses to pressure, pain, cold, and warmth, respectively. Some of this evidence, to be sure, is not entirely crucial, for the activity of different fibers has not, in every instance cited, been correlated with sensory quality. All the material taken together, however, points strongly in the direction of specific-fiber theories of quality for all senses; it shows, at the very least, that the selective activation of different receptors, which is the prerequisite of such a theory, does exist.

The following point, however, should be emphasized. Although the qualities of experience may depend upon which receptors are activated, it is very probable that different combinations of specific receptors are, in normal circumstances, concerned in the production of any given sensory quality. Look, for example, at Pfaffmann's findings regarding specific gustatory receptors. Of the three types which he found, all three were responsive to acid, although one of them could be excited by nothing else, and each of the others reacted to a particular chemical stimulus, bitter or salt, in addition to acid. This situation, Pfaffmann pointed out, must mean that the quality of gustatory experience depends upon which combination of specific fibers is activated by stimulation. Such a consideration certainly applies to color vision and to auditory pitch. In both senses, the specific fibers react to a distribution of frequencies which overlaps the distribution of other specific fibers. In the skin senses, on the other hand, it appears that a group of fibers of one specific energy may be activated without the involvement of others of a different specific energy; yet even here mixtures or combinations often occur. The experiences of burning heat and cold, for example, have been explained in terms of the combined action of warmth and cold receptors. Thus, although we can hold to the belief that sensory quality rests upon which fibers are excited, the general rule is that in the normal experience of an individual sensory quality is made up from the combination of many fibers of different specific energies.

Central Basis of Quality.—Suppose, then, that we assume sensory quality to depend upon which receptors and sensory fibers are excited by a stimulus. Do we then have the question of the nature of specific nerve energies solved? It would seem not, for we have so far only established the existence of specific nerve energies. To answer this question we want to know what it is about any particular receptor's activity which, when it has reached the central nervous system, determines the quality. It may be, on the one hand, that with which central neuron the sensory neuron connects constitutes the specific nerve energy, or, on the other hand, that the energy consists of the kind of impulses a particular fiber delivers to the central stations. These two alternatives, it will be realized are the same two that were considered at the level of the receptor.

Evidence concerning these alternative modes of mediation of quality in the central nervous system is not so clear as was the argument for specific-fiber theory at the level of the receptors. In vision we have the observations of neurohistologists (Le Gros Clark) that there are three sets of visual fibers ending in, respectively, different layers of the lateral geniculate body, and it has been suggested, on the assumption of a three-receptor theory of vision, that these three groups of endings represent three types of color receptors (cones) in the retina. If this suggestion is given any credence, it means that a specific-fiber theory works as well in the central nervous system as at the periphery and that it is the connections of the specific fibers which are important. There is, however, no direct evidence in support of this suggestion. Aside from it, we have in vision only the clinical reports of patients with lesions of the visual cortex; these indicate that color vision is very easily disturbed by damage to the cortex and is in some measure independent of other visual defects, but they throw little light on the problem.

Hearing is unique among the senses in that pitch, the quality of auditory experience, is related in the sense organ to a spatial arrangement of the receptors. Hearing, then, is a convenient sense in which to test the question of the specific-fiber theory of quality for the central nervous system, for if such a spatial arrangement is preserved in the central nervous system and determines pitch there is crucial evidence for the place theory. What we know of the central auditory system does, indeed, point in this direction. Spatial arrangements according to the frequency of stimulus have been found in both the medial geniculate body and the auditory cortex. Several different methods have attested that. Unfortunately, however, such a spatial arrangement is not so good as we would like it to be to convince us that it can mediate pitch, but it is possible that the methods of study need further perfection. Then, too, no experiments have yet been done in which pitch perception has been directly correlated with this spatial arrangement. The expectation is that when they are done they will yield such a correlation.

In somesthesis, there is, in the spinal cord, a rather good separation of pathways for at least some of the sensory qualities. Yet in the thalamus the various pathways come together and, so far as we can tell, are completely interwoven with one another. The same is true of the somesthetic cortex; indeed, all types of somesthetic experience may be aroused by electrical stimulation of a considerable part of the cortex, although the postcentral area is of primary importance. What is perfectly clear, moreover, is that different somesthetic experiences are *not* separated in different cortical areas. It is interesting that in electrical stimulation pressure experiences are much more common than those of warmth, cold, or pain. Accounting for this fact may be either our failure to find proper frequencies and intensities for stimulation or, on the other hand, the possibility that these less frequently aroused experiences depend upon *layers* of the cortex situated somewhat more deeply than those for pressure.

In considering the cortical mechanisms of sensory experience, we must, of course, realize that to believe in specific fibers for different experiences we need not expect to find different cortical areas for different qualities. Such is certainly not the case with peripheral sense organs (*e.g.*, cutaneous receptors). What is basically required is that fibers of one 'kind' make synaptical connections with other fibers of the same 'kind'; *i.e.*, the separation of fibers of different quality need only be in microscopic dimensions rather than in the macroscopic terms of different areas.

Because, however, fibers of different qualities (in the cutaneous senses, for example) are different in respect of excitability, impulse size, length of refractory period, and velocity of conduction, the possibility cannot be excluded that such factors may enter into the selection of pathways in the nervous system. Not to be ruled out, moreover, is the possibility that nervous impulses in fibers of different specific energies are qualitatively different from each other. We have, of course, no evidence at all for this possibility, but since the vast majority of studies of nerve activity have been done by means of electrical recording, which indicates only the electrical aspects of impulses, we have not yet put the possibility to a fair test. Then, too, from work on synaptic transmission at neuromuscular junctures of the autonomic system there has come an overwhelming body of evidence indicating the transmission to be chemical and, moreover, to involve different kinds of chemicals having different effects on the effectors. The researches in this field suggest that similar mechanisms may obtain in the central nervous system. If that were the case, we could expect chemical differences in synaptic transmission to be the basis of central specific energies. Unfortunately, experiments on this question are still inconclusive; therefore, as matters stand today, we are inclined to put the greatest emphasis upon the kind of connections made in the nervous system.

Obviously important in this connection is the question of the physiological nature of sensory experience. Suppose we could trace to the cerebral cortex separate pathways for different qualities; would this be an advantage? Leaving aside all problems as to the nature of the 'conscious' aspects of experience (Chap. XXVI), we can answer this question by pointing out that qualities are different because they eventuate in different behavior, *i.e.*, they are discriminated. In order to account fully for the qualitative aspects of experience, therefore, we should like to trace neural effects beyond sensory areas of the brain to motor neurons whose activity is observed in different kinds of behavior. This we are unable to do at present, and a very important part of the problem of sensory experience remains entirely unsolved. There is, moreover, no guarantee that it will be solved in terms of synaptic connections, even though our present thinking runs along that line.

THE INTENSITY OF EXPERIENCE

Turning now to the intensitive aspects of experience, we must first note with emphasis that there is no simple one-to-one relation between attributes of a stimulus and the attributes of the experience which it arouses. The pitch of a tone, we have seen, is dependent upon the physical intensity of the stimulus, apparently because intensity governs to some extent *which* fibers of the cochlea are stimulated. The intensity of a thermal stimulus may change the quality of experience because other receptors for pain may be stimulated in addition to those for temperature. In each of these cases, of course, the dependence of quality upon intensity is a matter of the peripheral receptors brought into play, but there is no reason to suppose that similar factors may not also operate in the excitation of nerve fibers in the synapses of the central nervous system. The point of importance, however, is that, because of the positions of receptors and their comparative excitable properties with respect to different stimuli, quality and the intensity of experience are both dependent upon the kind and intensity of stimuli.

Despite the fact that the attributes of experience are not related in any one-to-one fashion with the properties of stimuli, the major determinant of the magnitude of experience is the intensity of the stimulus. For our discussion here, therefore, the most important question to be considered is the nature of the physiological mechanisms subserving experienced intensity.

The Frequency Principle.—When this question is raised, about the first fact to come to mind is the all-or-none law governing the nervous impulses. If it were not for this fact, we might easily suppose that the intensity of stimulation governed the size of the nervous impulse and that the magnitude of experience was changed accordingly. Since the size of the nervous impulse is a property, not of the intensity of the stimulus, but of the size of the fiber and of its metabolic condition, we must look to other factors for a neural basis of the intensity of experience.

Of the other characteristics of nervous function which might be suggested, two appear plausible, the number of fibers being set off by a stimulus and the frequency of impulses in these fibers (Adrian). There is no doubt but that the receptors or nerve endings in the area of application of a stimulus differ from each other in respect of their thresholds. This fact has been demonstrated in bundles of nerve fibers, and it can be assumed to apply elsewhere. It has, indeed, been shown in certain instances that the variation in threshold of different nerve fibers follows the principle of randomness or chance (see Bishop), *i.e.*, it is described by the normal probability curve which applies to the distribution of many other measurements in life such as intelligence, height, or the proportion of heads that turn up when a number of coins are flipped. Such variability will naturally determine the number of receptors of nerve fibers activated by a given stimulus intensity; the greater the intensity, the more fibers will be fired.

It is also easy to see how the greater the intensity of a continuing stimulus, the more will be the frequency of impulses obtained from any particular fiber. After a nervous impulse is elicited, a fiber becomes completely refractory for a brief moment and then passes through a period in which its excitability progressively increases or, otherwise said, the intensity required to excite it becomes less and less, gradually approaching the normal threshold intensity. Now, when the stimulus intensity is great, the fiber will be excited at an earlier stage in its refractory period than if the intensity is weak, and the number of impulses elicited in any given period of time will be greater. Thus the intensity of the stimulus will be reflected in the frequency of impulses it sets off.

These two factors, number of fibers and frequency of impulses, have been accepted as the neural basis of the intensity of experience. Different investigators, however, have tended to place more emphasis upon one than upon the other. In Hecht's treatment of visual functions, for example, one sees the factor of number of fibers given the greater importance; visual acuity is explained entirely on the basis of more and more fibers brought in by a stimulus of increasing intensity. It has been objected, however, that this factor can operate only at rather low intensities, for variation in thresholds from fiber to fiber is thought not to be very large compared with the range of intensities normally involved in experience. If that is true, then the number of fibers is important only at low intensities, and above them frequency of impulses is the only variably determining experienced intensity. Crozier may be cited as one who holds this view and puts it to use, as we shall see, in formulating his theory of the physiological basis of intensity discrimination.

There need be no controversy about the matter, however, for if there is some overlapping of the endings of neurons at various levels of the sensory pathways—and that seems to be a safe assumption in view of the amount of overlapping demonstrable in so highly organized a sensory system as the visual system—then it matters little in the end whether we emphasize the number of fibers stimulated or the frequency of impulses, for it is what happens in all the fibers put together that counts. Each fiber that responds at each moment contributes an impulse to the other impulses being elicited at that moment and thereby contributes to the total frequency of impulses elicited by the stimulus. Thus the whole question comes down to the number of impulses per unit time, or the frequency of impulses, being elicited in the group of receptors or fibers subjected to stimulation, and we may think of the intensity of experience as being the result of the frequency of impulses produced by a stimulus.

Weber's Fraction.—Although frequency of impulses may be taken as the principal factor in perceived intensity, to give its complete mechanism we must show how stimulus intensity, frequency of impulses, and perceived intensity are causally linked to each other. The first steps in that direction were made many years ago in the work of Weber and Fechner. In the absence of information concerning neural processes, these early students of sensory processes attempted simply to formulate in quantitative terms the relation between the intensity of stimuli and the magnitude of experience. Only in recent years have the intervening physiological processes been fitted into the picture.

Weber attacked the problem by studying the increment in stimulus intensity necessary to produce a just noticeable difference in the perceived intensity. From experiments in the various senses, he concluded that the magnitude of the difference in intensity which can be detected (JND) is proportional to the intensity of the standard intensity, a change in which is discriminated. Put in mathematical form, his conclusion was that

$$\frac{\Delta I}{I} = C \tag{1}$$

This equation has subsequently become known as Weber's law or the

Weber fraction. Throughout the range of intensities that Weber studied the law seemed to hold, but for reasons which will become clear below it has since been shown not to apply at all intensities.

The Weber-Fechner Law.—Weber's equation, the reader will note, says nothing at all about the intensity of experience (sensation), but speaks only of discriminative ability. How sensation is related to stimulus intensity was taken up by Fechner (1860), who introduced this important assumption: *all JND's* (or ΔI's) *no matter at what intensity level represent equal magnitudes of sensation;* and putting this assumption into Weber's formula, he wrote

$$dS = c \frac{dI}{I} \tag{2}$$

where c is a constant of proportionality which it is customary to introduce into such equations and S represents the magnitude of sensation, dS being any small change in it that accomplishes change in intensity. Equation (2) is a differential equation and tells us only how sensation (S) changes with intensity (I), and if we want to know the total amount of S associated with any total I we must perform the mathematical operation of integration. Doing that and making other minor rearrangements in the results, we obtain

$$S = k \log I + C \quad \text{or} \quad S = k \log \frac{I}{I_0} \tag{3}$$[1]

which states that sensation intensity is directly proportional to the logarithm of I divided by the threshold intensity (I_0).

The correctness of this formula depends upon two assumptions: (1) that Weber's law holds and (2) that JND's represent units of sensation which are equal and additive. Concerning this latter assumption we have recently obtained proof that it is true in at least one case—curiously enough that of pitch, which we ordinarily do not consider an intensitive attribute. As we have previously noted, the way to determine whether sensation units are equal is to add them and see whether equal numbers of them are equal. This Stevens (*et al.*) has done in studies of the bisection and fractionation of tones (see p. 241); he finds, it will be recalled, that when the pitch of a tone is halved, the number of JND's is halved, and when a pitch halfway between that of two other tones is determined, it turns out to represent a number of JND's which is half the number between the two tones. Thus Fechner's assumption of the equality of sensation units passes the test in the case of pitch. For some reason, it does not hold in the case of loudness; and other sensory modalities have not, unfortunately, been studied on this point.

[1] It will be observed that the right-hand equation is obtained by setting S in the left-hand equation equal to zero and solving for C, which becomes $- \log I_0$ or $\log 1/I_0$.

Fechner's other assumption, *viz.*, that the Weber law is true, has been tested in many sensory modalities and found wanting. When the Weber fraction $\Delta I / I$ is determined for the full range of intensities in a modality, from very low to very high ones, it always comes out that it is a constant for only a part of the range, the middle intensities. At lower intensities it is not constant, but is very large when I is smallest, and diminishes gradually with increasing intensity until it is relatively constant in the middle range. In some experiments, moreover, it begins to increase again with further increases in intensity; in others it does not. Accounting for the different results in this case, it has been suggested, is the failure of some experimenters to extend the measurements to high enough intensities. In any case, the Weber fraction is not a constant; much laborious experimentation amply proves that.

The Statistical Theory.—If we had to leave the matter there, we would not have made much progress toward understanding the mechanisms of intensitive experience. But, fortunately, we can make some positive statements of significance concerning stimulus intensity and experience. Weber and Fechner, we may note, made only psychophysical statements; *i.e.*, they regarded only the relation between stimulus and experience in their theorizing. Recently, however, Crozier has taken the question of intensity discrimination to the psychophysiological plane by introducing the consideration of nervous impulses, and the principles governing them, into the equation between stimulus and sensation. In doing this, he has made clear, at least in part, what was wrong with the Weber-Fechner approach, and he has developed equations based upon physiological theory which are more applicable to the facts, fitting them so well in the case of vision that the theory upon which the equations are based becomes very credible. Some aspects of this theory have already been considered (p. 178), and these will be covered again in presenting a more complete outline of the theory.

Basic to Crozier's treatment of the relation between stimulus intensity and sensation is the idea that a JND, whether it is the absolute or differential threshold, is the result of the addition or subtraction of some particular frequency[1] of impulses to the frequency already being produced by the standard intensity, I; the prediction or explanation of the relation between the JND (ΔI_t) and I rests upon the neural mechanisms for producing or withdrawing this particular frequency of impulses. With certain modifications designed to clarify the theory, it may be set forth as follows.

---

[1] Crozier avoids the use of the term *frequency of impulses* and speaks rather in terms of neural effect, because it is probable that discrimination depends not merely upon frequency of impulses but also upon the spatial pattern or distribution of the frequency. For the present purposes, however, the term will be satisfactory.

There is some maximum frequency of impulses that can be elicited no matter how large the intensity. If all the neurons to be excited have been resting before the addition of ΔI, *i.e.*, if I is zero, then that maximum corresponds to the number of stimulable neurons, for one impulse can be gotten from each neuron. If, however, I is not zero but some definite amount, the neurons that it sets off will be set into refractory periods and will not be available for stimulation by ΔI. Which particular neurons are thus made unavailable to ΔI will vary from moment to moment according to the recovery of neurons from their refractory periods; but the total number of impulses available to ΔI at any given moment will nevertheless be cut down by I, and the difference between the maximum and those used up by I will be the number of impulses available to ΔI. Putting this statement into the form of an equation, we have

$$A = M - U \tag{4}$$

where A is the number of impulses (per unit time) available after the number U (per unit time), used up by the intensity I, is subtracted from the maximum, M.

Now, as stated above, the JND represents some given number of impulses, per unit time, being added to, or subtracted from, that elicited by I, and this number is the same for all JND's whether at the absolute threshold or high in the scale of intensity. The size of ΔI_t (differential threshold), furthermore, required to elicit these impulses will be a measure of the number left available by I. If the number available (A) is large, it is relatively easy to secure the number required for the JND, and thus ΔI_t is smaller. Assuming this relationship to hold rigidly, the size of ΔI_t will be inversely proportional to A, *i.e.*, $1/\Delta I_t = A$, and we can substitute $1/\Delta I_t$ for A in Eq. (4). Not only that but we can see that M can be measured by the reciprocal of the absolute threshold ($1/\Delta I_0$), for when I is zero, U becomes zero and $A = M$, and under that condition $1/\Delta I_t$ is the same as the reciprocal of the threshold intensity. Thus Eq. (4) becomes

$$\frac{1}{\Delta I_t} = \frac{1}{\Delta I_0} - U \tag{5}$$

The problem that now remains is to evaluate U, the number of impulses per unit time (frequency) used up by I. To this problem we can apply the same considerations as go into the Weber-Fechner equations except that in this case they have a more rational basis. We could assume that impulses would be used up in direct proportion to increases in intensity, *i.e.*, that dU, an increment in impulses, would equal dI, an increment in the intensity of the stimulus, if it were not for two factors: (1) Neurons become adapted, or accommodated, according to the intensity with which they are stimulated, and consequently, although increasing intensity augments the number of impulses obtained, their thresholds are increased according to the intensity employed. Taking this accommodation into account we may write: $dU = dI/I$, thereby stating that the increase in intensity required to augment impulses by a given amount is proportional to the intensity I. This equation, we may note, is essentially the same as Fechner's first equation, for the quantity dU is equivalent to dS (see above). Since the quantity dI/I is exactly the same as $d \log I$, as can be attested by examining any list of differentials, this equation can be written $dU = d \log I$. (2) The second factor to be considered is the variability of thresholds of impulses from one neuron to another and from moment to moment. The distribution of thresholds, as has previously been stated, is at random or according to chance. We must, therefore, introduce the equation for this variability into the equation above; thus

$$dU = ke^{\frac{-(\log I)^2}{2\sigma^2}} d \log I \qquad (6)$$

states how the thresholds of neurons vary in terms of $\log I$ at any given moment and consequently how increasing $\log I$ will increase the frequency of impulses. If, however, the total number of impulses per unit time is desired—and it is—this equation must be integrated, thereby adding the frequencies obtained from each group of neurons having a particular threshold. The resulting integral, called a probability integral, is the value of U and may be substituted in Eq. (5) above. When that is done we obtain[1]

$$\frac{1}{\Delta I_t} = \frac{1}{\Delta I_0} - \int_{-\infty}^{\log I} ke^{-\frac{(\log I)^2}{2\sigma^2}} d \log I \qquad (7)$$

which is the final equation for describing the relation between ΔI_t and $\log I$. Though complex in form, its meaning is simple; as shown in Fig. 57, it means that the curve of $1/\Delta I_t$ plotted against $\log I$ will be an S-shaped curve, sometimes called the normal ogive, which depicts all cases in which variation is by chance (see p. 178).

This statistical theory of intensive discrimination has been put to the test in vision, and there it works very well. Crozier has stated that the same theory should apply to intensive discrimination in all the

---

[1] This equation can be rearranged, by multiplying with ΔI_0, to give

$$\frac{\Delta I_0}{\Delta I_t} = 1 - \int_{\infty}^{\log I} ke^{\frac{-(\log I)^2}{2\sigma^2}} d \log I$$

in which ΔI_0, being a constant, is absorbed into the constant k. It is in this form that Crozier customarily plots the data of visual-intensity discrimination.

senses, provided there are not extraneous factors entering into the excitation of the receptors. In hearing, for example, it is very difficult to know exactly what intensity of stimulus actually excites the receptor cells even though one measures accurately the intensity of the sound put into the ear; the reason is that mechanical factors in the ear alter the amount of stimulus getting to the receptors. If these could be measured and taken into account, we should expect the theory to fit hearing too. The task of applying the theory to other senses, however, remains to be done. As we have seen in the earlier chapter on vision, the same theory when applied to other types of visual functions besides intensitive discrimination fits the actual facts very well, and we are therefore given considerable confidence in its validity.

More than that, the two fundamental assumptions concerning nervous functions entailed by the theory have been confirmed in actual fact. The idea that increase in the number of impulses is proportional to $\log I$ has been shown to be true in actual recordings of nervous impulses. Measurement of impulses in kinesthetic nerves as a function of the pressure exerted in muscles is proportional to $\log I$ (Matthews); and a similar statement is roughly true of impulses in the auditory nerve (see Stevens and Davis). Crozier's second assumption that the excitability of neurons varies randomly from moment to moment has been demonstrated in the fibers of peripheral nerves (see Bishop). The use of these assumptions in the construction of a theory of intensitive discrimination rests, therefore, upon demonstrable facts.

It is worth noting, finally, in connection with the statistical theory of intensitive discrimination, how it is related to the classic Weber-Fechner law. If one goes back through the derivation of the statistical theory, it will be seen that both Weber's and Fechner's formulas appear in the derivation. According to Crozier, $dI/I = dU$ for the individual nerve fiber and if dU is constant, as in the case of a just noticeable increment in sensation, then this formula is the equivalent of Weber's law. If dU is not a constant but is allowed to vary and dI/I is transformed into its equivalent $d \log I$, then $dU = d \log I$, which when integrated becomes Fechner's formula. Thus the considerations of Weber and Fechner enter into the statistical theory.

There are, however, two important differences between the Weber-Fechner law and the statistical theory: (1) The JND does not measure impulses in terms of $\log I$ but rather the impulses left available for use by ΔI_t; (2) the threshold of impulses varies at random in terms of $\log I$. It is these two factors which prevent the Weber-Fechner law from applying to the actual measurement of sensation, although it does enter into the formula (law) which according to the statistical theory, should be applied to sensation.

CHAPTER XV

REFLEXES AND POSTURE

With our survey of sensory processes completed, let us turn now to the behavioral side of psychological activities. We shall begin in this chapter with the more automatic or reflexive types of behavior and proceed in the next chapter to the more highly evolved, manipulative aspects of behavior. This order of considering behavior will take us, in general, from the lower, spinal levels of behavioral organization up through subcortical brain mechanisms and finally to cortical functions in behavior, although such a schedule cannot be followed strictly. In a later chapter we may turn to certain disorders of behavior which are of interest to the psychologist because of their natural occurrence in human beings and of the light they throw on normal mechanisms of behavior.

NEUROMUSCULAR RELATIONS

Muscles, it will be recalled, are of three types: smooth, cardiac, and striated. It is their contraction which we ordinarily conceive to make up behavior; yet we must remember that many of the glands, both duct and endocrine, also receive motor innervation and must be considered behavioral effectors. All glands, and the smooth and cardiac muscles, receive innervation from the *autonomic* system and are concerned in the internal adjustments of the body. The striated (skeletal) muscles are the effectors of the *somatic* nervous system and mediate adjustments of the organism to its environment. We are, consequently, able to distinguish between autonomic behavior and somatic behavior as two types of behavior dealing with the internal and external environments, respectively. In the present chapter we shall deal largely with the somatic behavior of striated muscles.

A muscle is a group of muscle fibers gathered together in a bundle covered by connective tissue sheaths and joined to bones by tendons of connective tissue. In some instances muscles are attached to each other. There are many muscles in the body, but there is no need to detail their names and positions here. Most important to note, however, is the distinction between flexor and extensor muscles in the limbs. The contraction of flexors lifts limbs from the ground, whereas contraction of extensors has the opposite effect, thereby providing support for an animal. Other necessary distinctions among types of muscles will be made as they are needed.

The Motor Unit.—The cell bodies of motor neurons serving striated muscles are situated in the ventral horns of the spinal cord or, in the case of cranial musculature, in motor nuclei within the brain stem. From these centers in the nervous system, motor axons proceed to the various muscles of the body; just before reaching them, the axons so divide into fibrils that the number of axon fibrils reaching muscle fibers is greater than the number of neurons from which they are derived. Each axon fibril ends upon a muscle fiber, and each muscle fiber, it appears, usually receives only one fibril (Wiersma). Thus is it that one motor neuron has under its more or less exclusive control a number of muscle fibers. A functional *motor unit*, consequently, is made up of one neuron and several muscle fibers. The several muscle fibers of a motor unit may be distributed somewhat within a muscle and be separated from each other by other muscle fibers, but they are nevertheless a unit by virtue of their common innervation by one motor neuron.

The size of a motor unit varies from place to place in the body. In some muscles the *innervation ratio, i.e.,* the ratio of motor neurons to the muscle fibers innervated by them, is as high as 1:150, whereas in others the ratio may be as low as 1:3. Such differences in innervation ratio are of considerable functional significance; for it is in the large muscles of the body which are involved in gross bodily movements that the innervation ratio is highest, whereas in the small muscles concerned in fine manipulative adjustments, those of the human eye, for example, the ratio is very low. Thus is the innervation ratio closely related to the crudeness or fineness of the behavior that muscles perform. When we come later to consider the representation of motor functions of the cerebral cortex, we shall see even better the significance of this fact.

Properties of Muscle Fibers.—We should turn for a moment to the way in which muscle fibers function. The nervous impulse arriving at the neuromuscular juncture is the stimulus for muscle activity. Whether the electrical aspect of the nervous impulse directly stimulates the muscle fiber or whether there is some intervening chemical mediator is a question not yet satisfactorily settled for striated muscles (see Feng). That a chemical mediator is involved in transmission at neuromuscular junctures of smooth muscles is strongly indicated by a considerable body of evidence (Cannon and Rosenbleuth).

However that may be, the muscle fiber, when stimulated, has many of the same properties as nerve fibers (see Young). The stimulus causes a local process to take place at the cite of stimulation and then builds up to a size sufficient for propagation (*cf.* p. 49) giving a spike potential which, like that of nerves, is all or none in nature. In its wake come negative and positive after-potentials which complete the parallelism between nerve and muscle in respect to electrical activity. It has been supposed, consequently, that muscle fibers possess polarized membranes whose equilibrium is disturbed by stimulation, and, as in nerves, the after-potentials appear to represent chemical readjustments following the depolarization.

How the action potential of muscle fibers is related to their contraction is a point in dispute (see Wiersma). Between these two events there is no perfectly consistent relation, although contraction tends to follow the spike potential rather than coincide with it, and we may think, therefore, of the contraction as resulting from chemical changes within the fiber having some common origin in the conditions leading to the action potential. That this is not necessarily the cause of the contraction seems to be proved by the fact that contraction can take place in the absence of an action potential.

Red and White Muscle Fibers.—Also worthy of mention in these introductory paragraphs is the fact that in many muscles of the body, particularly the extensors, there are two kinds of muscle fibers, red and white. Red fibers owe their color to the presence of muscle hemoglobin and are characterized, in addition, by the presence of large amounts of stored fat granules, both of which characteristics one would expect, and correctly, to indicate ability for long sustained activity. White muscle fibers, on the other hand, lack such supplies of materials for prolonged energy expenditure and, therefore, function only for brief periods of time.

Related to these two kinds of muscles are several facts of interest. In soaring birds one finds a predominance of red fibers in the flying (pectoral) muscles ('dark meat'), whereas in birds that seldom fly, e.g., the chicken, the muscles of flight are largely white ('white meat'). Corresponding to this difference is the fact that white fibers contract much more quickly, reach their highest tension in contraction more rapidly, and relax to a normal resting state much more rapidly than do red fibers. We may note, finally, that flexor muscles tend to be made up of white fibers, but extensor muscles predominate in red fibers; this is related to the use of flexor muscles in quick, temporary adjustments and to the function of extensors in supporting animals in long sustained postures or activity.

The point, briefly, is that effectors are of two kinds, *phasic* and *postural;* the phasic are for quickly executed, temporary adjustments, the postural for sustained, more permanent behavior. In reflexive behavior itself, as we shall see, a similar distinction can be made.

SPINAL REFLEXES

In the interest of a systematic presentation of the facts of reflex behavior, we may classify spinal reflexes into two kinds, *segmental* and *intersegmental* reflexes. In the first class are included those reflexes which depend upon only one segment of the spinal cord; in them nervous impulses entering the spinal cord from sensory stimulation pass out the motor axons at the same level. Intersegmental reflexes, on the other hand, are those which involve several segments of the spinal cord with respect either to the afferent impulses which initiate them or the motor impulses producing them. Sometimes a third term, *suprasegmental* reflexes, is employed to denote automatic adjustments involving the brain as well as the spinal cord. These we shall consider in a subsequent section.

The Nature of the Reflex.—The segmental reflex, although it is the simplest behavior brought about by sensory stimulation exhibited by an intact animal, is nevertheless a highly organized affair. As a pattern of response, it is made up of many neuromuscular units adjusted to each other in a relatively precise, although somewhat variable, manner. The organization of the neural activities in segmental reflexes takes place, not with respect to particular groups of muscular fibers or any other 'mechanistic' factors, but in terms of a pattern of movement. It has, indeed, been said, "The simplest spinal reflex 'thinks', so to say, in movements, not in muscles" (Fulton, p. 55).[1] Contained in this comment is the implication that reflex behavior is organized with respect to functional utility, and if more complex modes of behavior can ever be said to be 'purposive,' so also can the reflex.

Governing the pattern and form of a reflex reaction are several properties of central neural activities, some of which have already been touched upon in an earlier chapter (IV). Of these, one is *reciprocal innervation* (inhibition). Through it the contraction of one muscle, a flexor for example, is accompanied by relaxation of its antagonist, the extensor; this comes, we have reason to believe (p. 67), from the fact that within the nervous system certain neurons are common to the pathways of antagonistic responses but must be 'commanded' into either one or the other, leaving one relaxed while delivering excitation to the other. The reflex is organized, secondly, through the *recruitment* of internuncial neurons into the service of a reflex. In this way the response builds up gradually and smoothly. Then, too, *after-discharge*, accomplished we believe by the activity of internuncial neurons, causes a response to disappear slowly and smoothly.

To be mentioned finally is the fact that, in the normal animal, the neural activity which leads to the segmental reflex spreads to other segmental levels and causes responses in the body which are consistent with the simple reflex reaction; on the other hand, any given segment is always under the influence of many other parts of the nervous system,

[1] J. F. FULTON, 1938. The physiology of the nervous system.

and thus facilitative and inhibitory factors are brought to bear upon segmental activities, modifying them in intensity or form. Indeed, one can say that even in the most elementary reflex response of a normal organism events taking place in the whole organism, in the nervous system and internal environment, are implicated. This is not to say, of course, that all parts of the organism are *equally* involved, but they do have their influences. One can look at the stimulus to the reflex as being a 'figure' on the 'ground' of other existing stimuli and the reflexive behavior as bearing a similar relation to other coexisting adjustments. The general principles by which this relation takes place are understood rather well and have been reviewed in a previous chapter on the physiology of nerve cells and particularly of synaptic relations. The precise manner in which they work in any given instance, however, is not always easy to state.

Before turning to the detailed phenomena of the reflex, a point of methodology should be brought out. In order to observe spinal reflexes in the simplest form and freed in the greatest possible degree from extraneous influences, it has been necessary to observe certain precautions in experimentation. For one thing, it is usually necessary to section nerves to muscles other than those involved in the behavior under study. For another, care must be taken to maintain the general posture of the animal as constant as possible by placing him in a comfortable rack that gives him ample support. Finally, since the influence of higher centers upon reflex behavior is considerable, it is best to study spinal preparations, *i.e.*, animals in which the connection between the brain and spinal cord has been severed.

Segmental Reflexes.—In addition to recognizing the difference between segmental and intersegmental reflexes, we must also distinguish two types of segmental reflexes, the *flexion* and *extension* reflexes. The first, it will be recalled, is a response of limbs in which part or all of the limb bends in the direction of the body and away from the ground. In one sense, this reflex is one of the most primitive of the phasic adaptive reactions, for it readily occurs in response to any painful stimulus. The motor units involved in it may be activated in varying numbers and combinations depending upon a variety of factors; *e.g.*, the motor units of the ankle alone, of the hip or the knee, or all these taken together, may constitute the reaction. Generally speaking, the number of units which may be brought into play in any particular response depends partly upon the type and number of sensory elements whose stimulation calls forth the reflex. Stimuli which activate pain fibers command the largest flexion responses, whereas those which stimulate pressure receptors produce less effect, because pressure stimulation, as we shall see, is more likely to produce the antagonistic extension reflexes. Also of importance is the influence of higher centers of the brain; when these are eliminated, more vigorous flexion reflexes involving a larger number of flexor units are obtained than when part or all of the brain is allowed to send its impulses to the reflex center. Apparently motor impulses from the brain tend to 'inhibit' the flexion response, probably by means of the type of mechanism described for reciprocal inhibition (p. 67).

There are several types of *extension reflexes*. One, the *stretch reflex*, or *myotatic reflex*, as it is sometimes called, is an increased tension (contraction) in extensor muscles. These muscles support the animal's body against the pull of gravity and for this reason are sometimes referred to as the antigravity muscles. Innervating them are the annulospiral and flower-spray endings which, it will be recalled (p. 286), are stretch receptors responding whenever the muscle is stretched. It is their stimulation by the stretch of the extensor muscle, as for example when the opposing flexor muscles contract, that calls forth the myotatic reflex.

This reflex may consist of two stages, the *phasic* and *postural*. The first is a quick increase of tension in the extensor muscle immediately after it has been stretched; the second is a more permanent and longer lasting response, for it occurs when the muscle is undergoing no movement and serves to maintain a constant *tonus* or slight tension in the muscle when the limb is not otherwise being used. The myotatic reflex, whether phasic or postural, is generally restricted to the muscle in which stretching (the stimulus) occurs, although it may sometimes include other extensor muscles of the same limb which are related functionally to the muscle stretched. As we shall see in several connections later, this reflex is a basic reaction in many aspects of behavior.

Here we may refer again to the difference between red and white muscles. Wherever myotatic reflexes are obtained, one always finds these two kinds of muscles. Other muscles besides those participating in stretch reactions ordinarily have only white fibers. This fact is related to the special role of red muscle fibers in *tonus* and in the postural stretch reactions sustained for considerable periods of time.

The so-called *extensor thrust* is another type of extension reflex. It is the reaction of a limb in such a way as to straighten it to support the body against gravity, or to thrust the body into the air. The stimulus for the extensor thrust is any sudden pressure on the pads of the foot or a quick separation of the toe and foot pad (in dogs and cats particularly). This reaction, one can see, is a basic one in normal walking and particularly in the gallop. Closely related to it is the *crossed-extension* reaction in which the leg on the opposite side to that stimulated is extended. This does not take place so quickly in response to the stimulus as does the extensor thrust and is slower in reaching its maximal tension as well as in relaxing.

Intersegmental Reflexes.—Reflex responses which involve, to an important degree, more than one segment of the spinal cord are called intersegmental reflexes. Of these we may distinguish two main classes, *somatic* and *autonomic* intersegmental reactions. Here we shall deal principally with the somatic reactions, for the functions of the autonomic system are considered elsewhere (Chaps. V and XVII). In employing the rubric intersegmental reflex, we do not refer to any essentially new type of response, except for the case of the scratch reflex to be described in a moment; but the reference is rather to an integration and organization of the so-called segmental reactions which occur when several stimuli operate simultaneously or in quick succession at different segmental levels of the spinal cord. Thus the term *intersegmental reflex* does not, in general, indicate responses fundamentally different from segmental reflexes, but rather a different level of neural organization.

Cooperative Reflexes.—Intersegmental organization may be said to involve neural activity of two types, cooperative and competitive. Of these the first refers to integrations in which different sensory patterns of stimulation mutually reinforce their respective effects or lead, at least, to the organization of their different effects into a pattern. In competitive integrations, on the other hand, different stimuli tend to bring about reactions that are physically incompatible or cannot take place at the same time.

An example of the cooperative reflex is the *scratch reflex*. It consists of the rhythmic alternation of flexor and extensor responses, in which reciprocal inhibition suppresses first the extensor and then the flexor muscles in the different phases of the reflex. Evoking the scratch reflex is the 'bright' pressure stimulation of two points on the skin, either simultaneously or successively. Thus a very specific pattern of stimulation, precisely the kind of stimulus presented by a crawling flea, is required for the scratch reflex to be brought out.

The Final Common Path.—A moment must be taken at this point, before going on to the topic of competitive reflexes, to introduce the concept of the final common path. This is the term applied to that pathway of nerve fibers which is the *only one* leading from some point in the nervous system to the muscles concerned in a given behavior. The motor horn cells and their axons, obviously, always constitute a final common path; but also included frequently are other pathways leading to them. Thus if a response is crucially determined, as it sometimes is, at the level of the cerebral cortex, the final common pathway may extend from the cortex downward and out through the motor nerves. Contrasting with the final common path are the pathways of internuncial neurons, of which there may be an incalculable number leading to any given point in the nervous system. Also to be pointed out is the fact that, although there may be a great many possible patterns of behavior executed by muscles to which a final common path leads, only one of these patterns of activity can be in operation at any one time, because the final common path is the sole pathway to the behavior and it can do only one thing at a time. Now we ordinarily think of final common paths as beginning in the motor pathways from the brain or spinal cord, but this is only the simplest case. In the phenomenon of reciprocal inhibition, which was reviewed earlier, internuncial neurons may take on the properties of a final common path because they are sometimes required in several different competing responses but can function in only one of them at a time, depending upon what neural impulses 'command' them.

Competitive Reflexes.—Now, competitive (antagonistic) intersegmental reflexes are cases of the competition of two or more sensory stimuli for the final common path. In such competition one of three things may happen: (1) one stimulus may consistently dominate the final common path and consequently evoke one of the two reflexes while inhibiting the second; (2) the reverse may happen; or (3) the final common path may be dominated first by one stimulus and then by the other in such a way that the competing reflexes alternate.

Several factors govern which of these possibilities actually takes place; three of them are most important: (1) the nature of the reflexes concerned; (2) the intensity of the stimuli that set up competing excitations; and (3) the duration of the action of one of the reflexes. Illustrating the first point is the fact that the flexion reflex usually predominates over the scratch reflex, a fact in line with the primitive utility of the flexion reflex in avoiding noxious stimuli. Flexion reflexes also tend to win over extension reactions; *e.g.*, an animal or a human being wounded in the foot will fall to the ground because the painful stimulus elicits flexion reactions and inhibits the extensor reactions needed for support. As an example of the role of intensity of stimuli, one can cite the fact that a natural prepotency of the flexor response over the scratch reflex can be overcome by using a relatively more intense stimulus for the scratch reflex and a weaker noxious stimulus for the flexion reflex. Or, finally, if the scratch reflex has been in operation for some time, even though the stimulus for it would under normal circumstances be strong enough to command its response, another reflex can displace it much more easily.

This last point brings us to another important aspect of competitive intersegmental integrations, *successive induction*. In this phenomenon we see that antagonistic reflexes may actually support each other and become allies when they occur in certain temporal patterns. As was just noted, if one stimulus has had a final common path for some short interval of time, it is easier for a second antagonistic reflex to take over, provided the stimulus for it is present, and this sequence is precisely what happens in walking and locomotion. Concerning this phenomenon of successive induction, Fulton has said (p. 128):

Successive induction no doubt plays an important role in all rhythmic movements of the nervous system, especially walking and galloping. Thus when a leg is lifted from the ground, a flexion reflex is in operation. When it is replaced on the ground the positive supporting reactions [see below] and stretch reflexes combine to bring out an extensor contraction whose appearance is facilitated by the fact that the flexor reflex had dominated the final common path immediately before.

Fig. 116.—The reflex figure. *A*, resting position after decerebration. *B*, *C*, and *D*, positions taken following stimulation of the part of the body indicated by the arrow. (*After Sherrington. From C. H. Best and N. B. Taylor. The physiological basis of medical practice, p. 1317. Baltimore: Williams and Wilkins, 1940. By permission of the publishers.*)

Related to successive induction is the interaction of forelimb and hind-limb reflexes which occurs in walking. Such interaction, and, indeed, the movement pattern of walking, can be induced in spinal preparations of animals that normally have quadripedal progression. Here are interrelated the flexion and extension reflexes of all four limbs. A flexion reflex in one hind limb (Fig. 116) is accompanied by the extension of the contralateral hind limb. Also, the flexion reflex of the hind limb is accompanied by the tension of the homolateral forelimb. The *reflex figure* thus elaborated is necessary for the maintenance of balance and locomotion.

SUPRASEGMENTAL NEURAL MECHANISMS OF REFLEXIVE BEHAVIOR

It was only by eliminating the influence of higher centers upon spinal functions that the study of reflexive behavior which depends upon the spinal cord has made important progress. Likewise our knowledge of the contribution of various parts of the brain to basic forms of behavior mediated by the brain has come through eliminating surgically various parts of the brain leaving those to be studied. The material to be presented a little later has been gathered by such methods. First, however, in order to deal with it properly, attention must be turned in this section to anatomical relations of the various centers and pathways of the brain important in this connection. Here, as elsewhere in this chapter, the treatment will be restricted to somatic mechanisms and those of an autonomic character will be left to other topics to which they are more relevant.

The Motor System.—Of importance in this connection are three principal motor systems of the brain: (1) the proprioceptive-cerebellar, (2) the pyramidal, and (3) the extrapyramidal systems. The proprioceptive-cerebellar system consists of (a) afferent fibers and nuclei of the kinesthetic and vestibular pathways, particularly those of the medulla; (b) the cerebellum, which receives fibers either directly or indirectly from the proprioceptors and is therefore concerned in the mediation of reactions arising from vestibular or kinesthetic stimulation; and (c) projection fibers leaving the cerebellum and ending on nuclei of the other two systems (pyramidal and extrapyramidal). The cerebellum is an organ of complex structure, the details of which it is of little use to present here. Sufficient for the present purposes is the fact that the cerebellum receives fibers from the kinesthetic and vestibular pathways, as indicated above, and contributes to the motor functions of the rest of the brain, chiefly through connections with the extrapyramidal system which will be detailed in a moment.

In order to consider the pyramidal and extrapyramidal systems, we must first go over some general anatomical facts about the brain. In higher mammalian animals, the cerebral cortex is divided, the reader will recall (Chap. V), into anterior and posterior portions by the central fissure; corresponding roughly to this division is a separation of motor and sensory functions of the cortex. The frontal lobe, the part anterior to the central fissure, is divided on both structural and functional grounds into four regions: the motor area (precentral gyrus), occupying the dorsal and lateral aspects of the lobe immediately adjacent to the central fissure; the premotor area (intermediate precentral gyrus), lying immediately in front of the motor area; the frontal 'association' area; and the prefrontal area in the extreme anterior pole. Of these four areas, we shall here attend only to the first two, the motor and premotor areas.

The Pyramidal System.—The motor area, in addition to being known as the precentral gyrus, is also frequently called the *pyramidal area*, because of the giant pyramidally shaped neurons that characterize it. Within this area there are also cells that contribute to the extrapyramidal system (see below), but the pyramidal cells and the functions in which they are concerned are of greatest importance. These send very long fibers down through the brain stem into the spinal cord where they terminate upon the ventral horn cells. Such fibers make up the *pyramidal tracts.* Nearly all of them cross from one side to the other at the level of the pons and medulla, and consequently, so far as the motor area of the cortex is concerned, one side of the brain 'controls' the movements of the opposite side of the body. Going 'straight through' and making only a few connections with other centers of the brain, these fibers constitute a final common pathway to the motor cells of the medulla and spinal cord. This pyramidal system, made up of the motor area and pyramidal tracts, is, as we shall see, of relatively little importance in reflexive adjustments, except as an interfering influence, but takes on great significance in 'volitional' or 'skilled' movements.

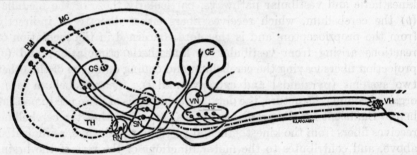

Fig. 117.—Diagram of the principal motor centers and pathways. The dot-dash line represents the pyramidal pathway; the unbroken lines, the extrapyramidal pathways. *MC*, motor area of cortex; *PM*, premotor area; *CS*, corpus striatum; *TH*, thalamus; *RN*, red nucleus; *SN*, substantia nigra; *CE*, cerebellum; *VN*, vestibular nuclei; *RF*, reticular formation; and *VH*, ventral horn cells. (*After Cobb.*)

The Extrapyramidal System.—Contrasting with the relative simplicity of the pyramidal system are the complex relations of the centers and pathways making up the extrapyramidal system (Fig. 117). At the level of the cortex it consists of motor fibers derived from the so-called sensory areas of the parietal lobe, from the frontal 'association' areas, from the premotor area, and to some extent from the motor (pyramidal) area too. Of all these the most important focal extrapyramidal area of the cortex is the *premotor area.*

Below the cortex, the extrapyramidal system splits into two main divisions: one which includes the corpus striatum, the substantia nigra, and red nucleus of the midbrain region and is called accordingly the *cortico-strio-nigral* system; and another which consists of the cortex, the nuclei of the pons, the cerebellum, and the connections between them and is known as the *cortico-ponto-cerebellar* system. The most important subcortical nuclei of these two systems are the corpus striatum, the red nucleus, and the cerebellum.

SUPRASEGMENTAL REFLEXIVE BEHAVIOR

The behaviors that we shall now consider are not exclusively mediated by the nuclei of the brain, for the conduction paths of the spinal cord are required for their expression and, indeed, the reflex mechanisms of the spinal cord also enter into them. The contribution of the spinal cord, however, has already been considered apart from influences of the brain; now we shall see how more complex organizations of reflexive behavior are accomplished through the additional reflexive mechanisms residing in the

FIG. 118.—Extensor rigidity in the decerebrate cat. *A*, decerebrate with intact labyrinths; *B*, decerebrate and labyrinthectomized. (*After Pollack and Davis. From C. H. Best and N. B. Taylor. The physiological basis of medical practice, p. 1338. Baltimore: Williams and Wilkins, 1940. By permission of the publishers.*)

brain. The behavior mediated by such suprasegmental mechanisms has frequently been referred to as *postural* behavior or postural reflexes, because it tends to involve the body as a whole, whereas reflex effects of the spinal cord are more likely to be restricted to more discrete movements of limbs.

Decerebrate Rigidity.—First of the behavioral phenomena to be considered are the mechanisms for maintaining muscular tonus throughout the body, and these are best seen in what is known as decerebrate rigidity (see Fig. 118). A decerebrate animal is technically one in which the cerebral hemispheres have been cut away from the rest of the nervous system. In decerebration we should expect the thalamus and lower centers to be intact, but the cerebral cortex, the white matter beneath it, and the corpus striatum to be eliminated. In practice, however, operations for decerebration often include some or all of the thalamus and even some of the midbrain, and it is necessary therefore to denote at which level the decerebration has been performed. For this purpose the following terms prove serviceable: the *bulbar* animal has its brain stem sectioned between the medulla and the midbrain; the *midbrain* animal has the section between the midbrain and thalamus, or roughly so; and the *thalamic* animal, or sometimes the *high* decerebrate, has the section between the thalamus, or most of it, and the cerebral hemispheres. The *decorticate* preparation, on the other hand, lacks only the cerebral cortex, and the *decerebellate* only the cerebellum.

In any type of decerebrate preparation, a posture is assumed which is characterized chiefly by a contraction of all the *extensor* or antigravity muscles of the limbs and to some extent other muscles of the body normally associated with extensor behavior (Sherrington). We accordingly call such decerebrate posture *extensor rigidity* or decerebrate rigidity. Revealed in it, apparently, is a mechanism of adjustment basic to much of normal behavior, and it therefore merits our interest. As the result of appropriate experiments, the mechanisms underlying it have been revealed with considerable clarity.

First there is the fact that decerebrate rigidity is the result of the *elimination of extrapyramidal functions*. This is shown by the following phenomena (Fig. 119): (1) If one performs a midbrain decerebration *on only one side*, the rigidity develops on that side, and since the pyramidal system is a *crossed* system, it is immediately ruled out as the basis of the disturbance. (2) The intensity of the rigidity increases in proportion to the amount of the extrapyramidal system that is removed. High decerebration, which takes out only the striate and cortical portions of the system, produces only slight effects, but with lower decerebrations the symptoms are more prominent and persistent. Particularly when the *red nucleus* is eliminated is the rigidity severe. One may conclude, therefore, that this is of special importance in *inhibiting* rigidity. Extirpation of the red nucleus alone, however, does not produce the rigidity; we must therefore be observing the additive effect of removal of parts of the extrapyramidal system. (3) In connection with the fact that the cerebellum contributes to the extrapyramidal system, it has been shown that, once extensor rigidity is produced, removal of the cerebellum enhances it. Thus has it been demonstrated that the extrapyramidal system is responsible for inhibition of the rigidity and that the rigidity appears in proportion to the amount of it removed.

The conclusion that follows from these facts is that in decerebration some center responsible for the rigid extensor tonus must be released from inhibition normally exercised by the extrapyramidal pathways. The locus of this center has been determined by performing appropriate experiments. Although decerebrate rigidity is quite severe in the bulbar animal, it is not present in the spinal animal free from the influences of the medulla. The center, then, must be in the medulla. Following that clue, successive sections at different levels in the medulla have been carried out with the result that so long as the *vestibular* nuclei are intact extensor rigidity remains, but when these are included in decerebration it disappears. The vestibular nuclei, therefore, are the source of the rigidity.

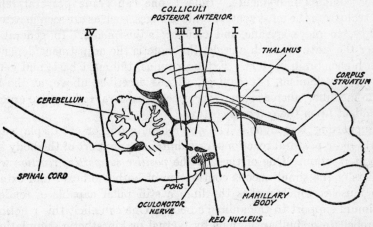

FIG. 119.—Levels of section of the brain in experiments with decerebration. I, thalamic animal in which righting and tonic labyrinthine and neck reflexes are retained; II, midbrain animal with some decerebrate rigidity; III, low midbrain animal in which red nucleus is eliminated, great decerebrate rigidity; IV, low bulbar animal in which vestibular nuclei are sectioned, decerebrate rigidity abolished as well as labyrinthine reflexes. Section lower down at the second or third cervical segment of the spinal cord abolishes tonic neck reflexes also. (*After Magnus. From C. H. Best and N. B. Taylor. Physiological basis of medical practice, p. 1351. Baltimore: Williams and Wilkins, 1940. By permission of the publishers.*)

Inhibition of Extensor Tonus.—Carrying this conclusion over to the normal organism, we may suppose that vestibular influences tend to maintain postural tonus at a high level but that impulses from the higher extrapyramidal centers regulate this tonus by inhibition. Confirming this supposition is the fact that electrical stimulation of the cerebellum or of the base of the midbrain, thereby activating extrapyramidal fibers (among others), will inhibit such extensor tonus. So also will stimulation of the pyramidal pathways, although these are clearly not the most important mechanisms of inhibition of tonus.

Also of importance, however, are the kinesthetic mechanisms, which have not been mentioned before. If, for example, one electrically stimulates limb muscles, the proprioceptive stimuli arising from muscle contraction will inhibit the extensor tonus of the opposing limb. Then, too, if a sensory nerve is stimulated in the decerebrate preparation, the reflex figure, previously mentioned, will displace extensor tonus; activation of the dorsal kinesthetic columns will do the same thing. Kinesthetic factors as well as extrapyramidal influences, therefore, control tonus of vestibular origin.

The Postural Reflexes.—Extensor tonus is only one of the most general aspects of posture. Several other phenomena of posture form a class of reflexes known as the postural reflexes. Some of them are little more than changes in tonus in certain parts of the body, but others are rather complex movements. Indeed, one can grade postural reflexes on a scale from the most general tonic changes, such as are seen in extensor rigidity, to more specific and complex adjustments. In general, the higher the status in such a scale, the more is the adjustment dependent upon higher brain centers. Extensor tonus, the most basic and general postural mechanism, is organized, as was described above, at the level of the medulla, whereas some very specific postural reflexes are crucially dependent upon the cerebral cortex.

Supporting Reactions.—The decerebellate dog or cat displays quite clearly basic postural reactions for maintaining support of the body in an upright position. One of these is the *positive supporting reaction* which consists of the simultaneous contraction of both the flexor and extensor limb muscles which makes the limb a stiff pillar capable of rendering maximum support to the animal's body. One can elicit this reaction in decerebellate or bulbar animals by tactual or kinesthetic stimulation of the pads or toes of the foot. Just the opposite sort of reaction, called the *negative supporting reaction,* consisting of the relaxation of all the muscles of the limb, is obtained when the digits of a limb are passively flexed. These two types of supporting reactions figure in walking or quadripedal progression: when the weight of the body is shifted from one foot to the other, one limb becomes stiff in the positive supporting reaction, while the other, because it is flexed by the pressure of the ground against it, is reflexly inhibited and relaxed.

Shifting Reactions.—Closely related to the supporting reactions is the so-called shifting reaction. An example of it is as follows: If an experimenter passively flexes the left hind limb of a dog and at the same time causes the animal's body to veer toward the left, a strong extensor tonus develops in the flexed limb, its 'purpose' being, presumably, to support the body under the new conditions. Responses of this sort can be observed in the various limbs when an animal's body is pushed from side to side or forward or backward. In each case, the response is due, we know, to kinesthetic impulses from the limb muscles *stretched* or extended in the veering of the body. Although the shifting reaction depends essentially upon the medulla, it is more perfectly organized in the midbrain animal.

Tonic Neck Reflexes.—There are a group of reflex adjustments, involving the muscles of the body more or less as a whole, which have been called the tonic or attitudinal reflexes because they are of the type seen in an animal when it is putting itself in readiness for some complex response. These reflexes are dependent principally upon kinesthetic impulses from the neck (tonic neck reflexes) or excitations from the vestibular receptors (tonic labyrinthine reflexes). The separate influences of these two kinds of stimulation have been studied by extirpating the labyrinth, thus freeing the animal from labyrinthine stimulation, or, on the other hand, by severing the kinesthetic pathways.

The tonic neck reflexes may be summarized as follows: (1) When the head of an animal is rotated to the right, one observes an immediate increase in the extensor tonus of the side toward which the jaw is turned and a relaxation of the limb toward which the top of the head is rotated. (2) When the head is turned toward one shoulder, extensor tonus is increased in the limbs of that side and decreased in the limbs of the opposite side. (3) When the head is bent upward, extensor tonus increases in the forelimbs and decreases in the hind limbs—a posture observed in a normal animal when it is looking upward. (4) Tonus is redistributed in precisely the opposite way when the head is bent downward. All these reactions, we may observe, are of basic importance in the preliminary 'attitudinal' adjustments of an organism.

Thus, when a cat standing on all fours hears a noise ahead and to its right, its head turns and the extremities on the right side automatically exhibit increased extensor posture, which would tend to support the weight of the body in case the animal takes off with its left fore-limb. If the noise is made by a mouse, the cat has only to decide whether to dash at it or not—the postural adjustments for the act are made automatically (Fulton, p. 177).

Tonic Labyrinthine Reflexes.—Since the kinesthetic influences from the neck come in through the dorsal spinal roots, one can study labyrinthine attitudinal adjustments, free of kinesthetic influences, by sectioning the dorsal roots. The reactions observed then depend only upon changes of the head in space, as they stimulate the receptors in the labyrinth. The important conclusion reached from the study of animals prepared in this way is that changes of extensor tonus depend upon the position of the head. When the head is pointed 45 deg. above the horizontal plane, tonus is maximal; when it is in a downward position at 45 deg., tonus is so inhibited that it is minimal. With the head in intermediate positions, extensor tonus is between minimal and maximal values. This adjustment of posture is what we would expect to go along with positions of the head, for it corresponds to the preparatory adjustments required in arising from a supine to a standing position. Such reflexes, it has been shown, are *positional* responses dependent upon the utricle and saccule, not upon the semicircular canals. It may be pointed out in passing that such labyrinthine reflexes cause contractions in neck muscles which, through kinesthetic stimulation, may, in turn, bring about tonic neck reflexes. Thus can the labyrinth affect tonic reflexes both directly and indirectly, through the kinesthetic stimulation resulting from the labyrinthine reaction.

Righting Reactions.—The righting reflexes are another class of automatic adjustments which help the organism to regain its normal posture when this has been lost. Five main classes of such reflexes have been distinguished according to differences in their form and in the sensory conditions arousing them. All except the last to be mentioned depend upon centers below the cerebrum, but the last of the list, the optic righting reactions, are cortically mediated. (1) In the *labyrinthine righting reflex* the head is brought back to the normal position, whenever turned away from it, irrespective of whether the body or any part of it is in the normal position. It depends, as the name implies, upon the nonauditory labyrinth. (2) In the so-called *body righting reflex acting upon the head*, there is a strong tendency for an animal to rotate its head into the horizontal position, when the animal is laid upon its side. Giving rise to this reflex is the asymmetrical stimulation of the tactual and kinesthetic receptors which is the result of the animal's lying upon its side. (3) The two reflexes just mentioned serve to bring an animal's head into normal position horizontal to the ground. When such reflexes have been operative and yet the body is still left in an abnormal position, asymmetrical tension results in the muscles of the neck. Therefrom arises kinesthetic stimulation which initiates a chain of postural responses in which the trunk of the body is first rotated back into the horizontal position, then the abdominal region, and finally the hindquarters. Such a righting reaction has been called the *neck righting reflex acting upon the body*. (4) A *body righting reflex acting upon the body* occurs when an animal is placed in a lateral position and force is applied to the head or shoulders. Then the whole body tends to right with the hindquarters initiating the reaction. All these four types of reactions can be obtained in the absence of the cerebral hemispheres but depend upon the thalamus and midbrain remaining intact. (5) A fifth righting reflex, the *optic righting reaction*, however, depends upon the integrity of the visual areas of the cortex. By means of it animals right themselves on the basis of visual fixation of objects in the environment; animals tend to right their heads first, then, successively, the more caudal parts of the body.

The question of the brain mechanisms subserving these righting reactions deserves more than the brief comments given it above. It is quite certain that the various righting reactions, except for the optic, depend upon the region of the brain stem where the midbrain and thalamus join. Because the red nucleus is in this area and is otherwise important in posture (see above), it was thought for some time that this nucleus was responsible for the righting reactions; but it has recently been shown (see Fulton) that destruction of the red nucleus alone does not abolish righting reflexes, although it does cause a slight increase in extensor tonus. The vicinity of the red nucleus, however, where lie the numerous nuclei and fibers making up the *reticular formation* (Fig. 117) is implicated; it is believed now that these nuclei mediate the non-visual righting reflexes.

Placing and Hopping Reactions.—Remaining for consideration are two types of postural reflexes, the placing and hopping reactions, both dependent for their existence upon the integrity of certain areas of the cerebral cortex. Both, briefly, are adjustments of the limbs in such a way as to bring about better support for the body.

Placing reactions may arise from either visual or somesthetic stimuli. In the visual reaction, an animal, which is being held in the air with its legs hanging free, will attempt to place its legs on any solid object near by in the field of vision, so long as the eyes are not blindfolded and the visual cortex remains intact (Smith). There are, on the other hand, several kinds of somesthetic reactions. When an animal is held with the edge of a table in contact with the back of its feet, the legs will be placed upon the table. So also will they when its chin or vibrissae touch the table. When, on the other hand, an animal is standing on the edge of a table and then is suddenly pushed forward in such a way that its forelimbs hang over the edge, they will be lifted backward in a manner designed to regain for the animal its previous position. Whenever, finally, the leg of an animal is passively lifted, and then released, it will at once be lowered back to the table for the 'purpose' of being used again to support the body.

The hopping reaction consists of a flexion, lateral movement of the leg, and then an extension, all in quick succession, much as a person behaves when he has been shoved off balance. It can best be obtained in an animal (*e.g.*, monkey) which is made to stand on one leg and then, by a push, is caused to veer forward, backward, or sideways; thereupon the animal makes a series of hops which serve the purpose of getting the limb squarely beneath him again to support him. Such hopping reactions have been studied in the rat, cat, and monkey.

Both the hopping and placing reactions depend upon particular areas of the cortex (Brooks). In the rat, in whose cortex functions are, as a rule, poorly circumscribed, the reactions are abolished when a rather large, but definite, dorsal area is extirpated on both sides (see Fig. 120).   In the cat they are localized somewhat more precisely in areas analogous to the motor areas of higher animals.   In monkeys they are restricted to the pre- and postcentral areas.   The motor functions of the precentral area are integral to their existence; although, on the other hand, removal of the postcentral somesthetic areas also leads to their disappearance. The visual placing reactions, however, are an exception to 'this statement; they depend upon the visual area of the cortex.

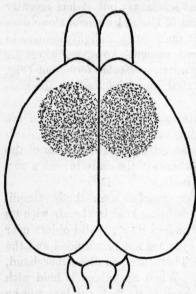

Fig. 120.—Approximate size and position of the hopping and placing areas of the cerebral cortex of the rat.   (*After Brooks.*)

OCULOMOTOR REFLEXES

The discussion above has progressed from reflexes mediated by the spinal cord through those of the brain stem, ending with reflexive behavior at the cortical level. In following this outline, we passed by the various optic reflexes which are dependent largely upon centers of the midbrain, but it was better that they be reserved for separate consideration here, for they present a topic somewhat aside from the main class of postural reflexes.

Oculomotor Neural Mechanisms. The lateral geniculate body and the superior colliculus, as has already been described (p. 164), are the chief subcortical centers in vision.   Some fibers, however, run through the geniculate and end in the pretectal region of the thalamus immediately in front of the superior colliculi.   From the pretectal and collicular centers, fibers descend to the nuclei of the three nerves concerned in oculomotor functions, the IIIrd, IVth, and VIth.   Of these, the IIIrd is the most important, for it controls four of the six external muscles of the eyeball. Within it, moreover, we may distinguish a division, called the Edinger-Westphal nucleus, which controls autonomic reflexes of the eye (see Fig. 121).   Naturally, the three optic motor nuclei are closely associated with each other, and upon them end fibers from several other parts of the brain: the cerebral cortex, the pretectal and tectal regions, and, quite important, the vestibular nuclei of the medulla.

Labyrinthine Optic Reflexes.—The eyes give two types of reflex movements in response to vestibular stimulation: (1) *Positional* reflexes consist of compensatory movements of the eyes and occur when, because of a change in the position of the head, the receptors of the utricle and saccule are stimulated. Such reflexes are more important in fishes than they are

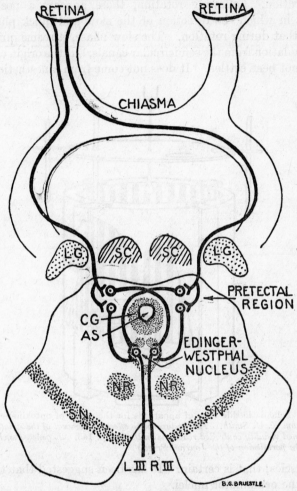

Fig. 121.—The centers and pathways concerned in reflex responses of the pupil to light and in motor adjustments of the eyes. *LG*, lateral geniculate body; *SC*, superior colliculus; *CG*, central gray matter; *AS*, aqueduct of Sylvius; *NR*, red nucleus; *SN*, substantia nigra; *LIII* and *RIII*, left and right third nerves. (*From J. F. Fulton. Physiology of the nervous system, p. 199. New York: Oxford University Press, 1938. By permission of the publishers.*)

in higher animals, for in the latter visual fixation of objects usually overrules any positional reflexes. (2) Such a statement is not true, however, for the second class of labyrinthine reactions, the *acceleratory* reflexes, which depend upon accelerated (or decelerated) rotation of the head in such a way that the semicircular canals are stimulated. Such reflexes are sometimes spoken of as *vestibular nystagmus*. In them one can observe two phases, a slow movement of the eye in the opposite direction from rotation (acceleration) and a quick returning phase in the same direction as the rotation. Following rotation, there appears a postrotational nystagmus in which the direction of the slow and quick phases is the reverse of that during rotation. The slow phase, it seems quite clear, is due to stimulation from the semicircular canals, but the origin of the quick phase has not been settled. It does not come from kinesthetic stimuli of

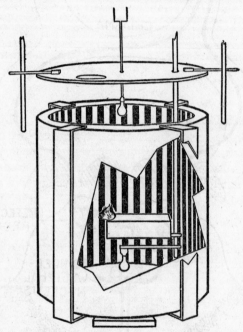

Fig. 122.—Schematic side view of apparatus for the study of optokinetic reactions in animals. (*From K. U. Smith. The postoperative effects of removal of the striate cortex upon certain unlearned visually controlled reactions in the cat, p. 145. J. genet. Psychol., 50, 137–156, 1937. By permission of the Journal Press.*)

the eye muscles; that is certain. It has been suggested that the mechanism is in the oculomotor nuclei.

Optokinetic Reactions.—When black and white stripes are rotated in the visual field (Fig. 122), most animals present nystagmic movements of the eyes, head, or both. Such optokinetic reactions, like those of vestibular origin, consist of a slow and a fast phase, the former being a movement in 'pursuit' of the striations and corresponding in speed to their movement. K. U. Smith has studied them in some detail and finds that they remain unaffected by extirpation of the visual cortex, provided the number of striations is sufficiently great. The reflexes, therefore, depend upon subcortical centers, but which subcortical centers are involved has not been determined.   It is to be supposed that connections between the superior colliculus and the optomotor nuclei subserve them.

Accessory Visual Reflexes.—In addition to oculomotor reactions involving the movement of the eyes, there are three other important visual reflexes.   (1) The *accommodative* reaction, or change in the shape of the lens, regulates the focus of the visual image on the retina, as we have already noted.   (2) Assisting in such focusing and regulating the amount of light entering the eye is the *pupillary* reflex in which the radial or annular fibers of the iris contract or expand, changing the size of the pupil accordingly.   (3) There is, finally, the *palpebral* reaction, or eyewink reflex, in which the eyelid is suddenly closed over the eye whenever a sudden intense light or sound is presented or when the cornea is stimulated tactually.   In the latter case the reaction is called the corneal reflex.

With the exception of the pupillary reaction, the precise neural mechanisms for these reactions are not known.   They all involve autonomic outflow, and in this the Edinger-Westphal nucleus is concerned.   The superior colliculus is probably concerned in the palpebral reactions, if not in the accommodative reflexes.   Such is not the case, however, with pupillary constriction, which involves only sensory fibers to the pretectal nuclei, interconnections to the Edinger-Westphal nucleus, and parasympathetic outflow from it.   Pupillary dilation, we know, is a sympathetic phenomenon and takes place by impulses going out via the superior cervical ganglion.   It is probable that centers in addition to the oculomotor are concerned in it, for pupillary dilation is a common thing in emotion and in other conditions of generally increased sympathetic discharge, which originate, probably, in the hypothalamus or cerebral cortex.

General Reference

FULTON, J. F., 1938.   *The physiology of the nervous system.*   New York: Oxford.
   Pp. xv + 674.

CHAPTER XVI

CEREBRAL MOTOR FUNCTIONS

The last chapter was concerned with relatively fixed automatic reactions and their physiological basis. Here we may turn to the more variable aspects of behavior which involve the coordination of reflex actions into patterns of movement. Such behavior includes the locomotor, manipulative, skilled, and voluntary adjustments normally observed in the intact animal or human being: the rat running a maze, the monkey pulling the latch of the puzzle box, the carpenter turning the screw, the secretary typing the manuscript, and so on. Also worth considering are certain abnormalities of behavior which occur relatively commonly in human individuals and whose physiological basis is understood, at least in part. Two of the most important of these are epilepsy and catatonia.

Although special varieties of abnormal behavior can be considered separately and their physiological determinants in each case discussed, it is not easy, unfortunately, to take particular forms of normal patterns of behavior and give their physiological basis, for they are highly variable and are adapted to the circumstances in which they occur. The best way of dealing with them, therefore, is to turn to various centers and pathways of the nervous system and to see how these play their respective roles in organizing patterns of behavior. We shall consider in turn, accordingly, the contributions to normal behavior of the cerebellum, the pyramidal system, the extrapyramidal system, and the kinesthetic system. Here, as is so often the case in physiological psychology, the principal methods of study are those of the surgical extirpation of parts and of electrical stimulation, and one observes the changes in behavior which follow upon the use of these methods.

THE CEREBELLUM

Removal of the Entire Cerebellum.—Luciani made the classical observations of the effects upon behavior of removal of the cerebellum. These effects, according to his description, fell into three main classes and are sometimes called, accordingly, the Luciani triad.

1. In the period immediately following operation the chief symptoms are those of *functional exaltation*. They are very similar to the phenomena of extensor rigidity which follow decerebration. From time to

330

time the animal goes into a seizure, called *opisthotonus*, in which the head is retracted and all the extensor muscles of the body are strongly contracted. Such spasms of extensor rigidity are undoubtedly related to the fact that the cerebellum is part of the extrapyramidal system sending fibers to the red nucleus (p. 320) and contributing to the suppression of extensor rigidity, which, in the absence of sufficient extrapyramidal influences, results from incoming vestibular impulses.

2. During the times when the decerebellate animal is free from the opisthotonic seizure, it displays a set of symptoms called *phenomena of deficiency*. These consist of *asthenia*, which is a general weakness of muscles used in voluntary movement; *hypotonia*, which is a deficiency of the postural tonus required for normal movement; *astasia* or *intention tremor*, which is tremor manifested in voluntary but not postural adjustments; and various disturbances of the accuracy of movements, which taken together are labeled *dysmetria* and may consist of overshooting (hypermetria) or undershooting (hypometria) of the position that the movement is designed to attain.

3. With the passage of time these various effects of removing the cerebellum wear off and there is a general *compensation* of the motor difficulties produced by the operation. Both the seizures of opisthotonus and the phenomena of deficiency become less severe, and the animal comes gradually to move about again with some proficiency and to execute voluntary movements without as many indications of astasia, hypotonia, or dysmetria. Such compensation may take a considerable amount of time; indeed, it seems to go on for several years after operation (Rademaker).

Localization in the Cerebellum.—The facts just described apply to the removal of the entire cerebellum. This organ is of complex structure, however, and the question has arisen whether different functions might not be localized in different parts of the cerebellum. Luciani did not think so, but in recent years experiments done with great care have tended to indicate a considerable degree of functional localization in the main anatomical divisions of the cerebellum (see Fulton). These main divisions consist of the four lobes of the cerebellar cortex and of the subcortical nuclei lying deep inside the cerebellum.

1. The *ventral* (flocculonodular) lobe (Fig. 123) is plainly concerned with labyrinthine postural reactions. When it is extirpated by itself, disturbances of equilibration develop. Labyrinthine righting reflexes disappear, and the gait and balance of an animal is disturbed in the same way as when the labyrinths have been destroyed. Indeed, the additional removal of the labyrinths causes no new symptoms, and we must conclude, therefore, that the ventral lobe is the primary center for mediating the labyrinthine postural reactions.

2. The *posterior* lobe consists of the pyramis and uvula, which lie, respectively, in dorsal and ventral positions. On functional grounds the uvula belongs with the ventral lobe, for its destruction produces transient disturbances of equilibration and enhances the effects of removal of the ventral lobe. The pyramis, on the other hand, seems to have little to do with labyrinthine mechanisms, for its removal results in none of the expected symptoms. It does have something to do with the coordination of visual perceptions with behavior, however, for a monkey lacking it displays a marked inability to "arrest forward locomotion in time to prevent crashing headlong into a clearly visible obstruction" (Fulton, p. 524). Why this disturbance appears is not clear, but it has been

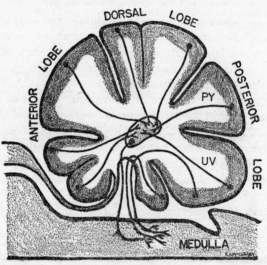

Fig. 123.—Schematic longitudinal section of the cerebellum showing its division into four main lobes. The two lower lobules make up the ventral lobe. (*After Fulton.*)

suggested that the pyramis in some way integrates proprioceptive and visual impulses related to movement (Fulton). Interesting in this connection is the fact that electrical stimulation of the pyramis produces movement of the eyes.

3. The *anterior lobe* of the cerebellum is without doubt the part that is most intimately concerned with the extrapyramidal system. Surgical removal of the anterior lobe results in many of the symptoms of decerebrate extensor rigidity, most prominent of which are, in this case, increase of extensor tone, of the stretch reflexes, and of the supporting reactions. As has been indicated before, moreover, removal of this part of the cerebellum enhances the effects of decerebration. Then, too electrical stimulation of the anterior lobe will inhibit extensor posture resulting from decerebration, and herein is positive evidence for the inhibition of extensor

tone by extrapyramidal mechanisms. From the anatomical data, finally, we learn that the anterior lobe sends fibers into the brain stem to join the extrapyramidal system at the level of the red nucleus. Thus is the anterior lobe clearly concerned in the control of postural tone.

4. The *dorsal lobe* of the cerebellum is known as the *neocerebellum* because, in phylogenetic development, it has developed last and is most important in higher mammals. It is closely related, moreover, both anatomically and functionally to the cerebral cortex. From the nuclei of the pons, which are way stations of motor fibers from the cortex, come the majority of afferent fibers serving it, and it also sends projections to the cortex. Their influence is shown by the fact that upon electrical stimulation of the neocerebellum the excitability of the motor area of the cortex is markedly altered; so also are spontaneous electrical fluctuations of the motor area. As for behavior, removal of the neocerebellum causes animals to show considerable awkwardness of movement and some hypotonia, but these do not last for long after operation. The general conclusion to be reached about the neocerebellum is that it exercises a modifying influence upon the functions of cortical centers for behavior. That it probably does not participate directly in movement, however, seems to be indicated by the fact that electrical stimulation of it never produces movements.

5. Deep within the cerebellum are several subcortical nuclei which are related in various ways to the lobes of the cerebellar cortex just described. These nuclei fall into two groups, called neocerebellar and paleocerebellar nuclei, because of their recent and remote origins, respectively, in phylogenetic development. The functions of the paleocerebellar nuclei are complex and not well known. Better understood is the role of one of the major nuclei, the *dentate* nucleus, which is largely neocerebellar in origin and cooperates with the dorsal (neocerebellar) lobe in modifying motor functions of the cerebral cortex. Its extirpation along with that of the dorsal lobe gives a very definite syndrome of motor disorder, known as *astasia*. This denotes a tremor which appears only in volitional movements, not in automatic postural adjustments, and is accordingly referred to as intention tremor. The dentate nucleus and dorsal lobe appear, therefore, to supply mechanisms for smoothing out behavior originating in the cerebral cortex. Supporting this conclusion is the fact that extirpation of the motor and premotor areas of the cortex abolishes the astasia that is created by removal of the dorsal lobe and dentate nucleus.

Cerebellar Lesions in Man.—Although the experimental study of animals supplies the more reliable and basic facts concerning cerebellar functions in behavior, some information of importance comes directly from instances in which human patients suffering from cerebellar lesions have been observed. The most important of such lesions in man and the chimpanzee are those involving the neocerebellum, since this lobe has become very highly developed in the primates and the other parts of the cerebellum, particularly those concerned with vestibular function, have become considerably less important. The neocerebellar syndrome which follows neocerebellar lesion is recognized to consist of four types of behavioral disorders: dysmetria, decomposition of movement, disturbances of rate of movement, and disturbances of the force of movement. All concern *volitional* movement. The nature of these several aspects of the neocerebellar syndrome can be considered briefly by quoting from Fulton and Holmes, who have observed the syndrome in both chimpanzees and man.

Dysmetria in man has been described as follows (Fulton, p. 535):

Excessive range of movement is perhaps the most easily recognized sign of cerebellar disorder. Thus when attempting to touch the nose with his finger a patient with a cerebellar lesion is likely to strike his cheek violently; a monkey raises his foot higher than is necessary from the ground in walking and an affected extremity is passively raised from a position of rest and when released it drops back violently on to the body of the subject.

On the decomposition of movement, Holmes has said (p. 1234):

If asked to bring his finger from above his head to the tip of his nose the patient may depress the arm at the shoulder before beginning to flex his elbow; and in placing his heel on the opposite knee he may complete the flexion of the hip before bending the knee, with the result that the heel is raised too high and then lowered to the knee. Sometimes this decomposition of movement seems to be a purposive device to control its irregularities; on attempting to feed himself the patient often fixes the elbow firmly to his side and then brings the spoon to his mouth by simply flexing his forearm. Others, in trying to touch an object, extend their arm or leg rigidly and then swing the limb from the shoulder or hip towards it.

The nature of disturbances of rate of movement can be seen in the following quotation from Fulton (p. 535):

In the chimpanzee, after a small lesion of the neocerebellum, the extremities on the same side lag behind the normal extremities in the execution of such rhythmic acts as are involved in walking and climbing. When obliged to feed with his affected extremities, movements designed to obtain a given morsel are initiated after an abnormal latency and are carried out with a deliberateness wholly foreign to the normal movement patterns of a hungry chimpanzee.

A similar disturbance in the rate of movement has been described in man (Holmes).

Of disturbances of force, Fulton has this to say (p. 536):

In addition to errors of range, direction and rate, there is likely to be marked disturbance in the force of volitional movement. . . . [It] is particularly conspicuous following neocerebellar lesions in chimpanzees. In the first days after such a lesion climbing movements are not only slow, but prehension [grasping] is impaired and the fingers frequently slip from the rungs of the cage because the grasp is not sufficiently forceful.

THE PYRAMIDAL (MOTOR) CORTEX

That the precentral gyrus of the cerebral cortex (otherwise known as the precentral area, motor area, or pyramidal area) possesses motor functions was first established by the experiments of Fritsch and Hitzig (1870), who found electrical stimulation of this gyrus to cause discrete

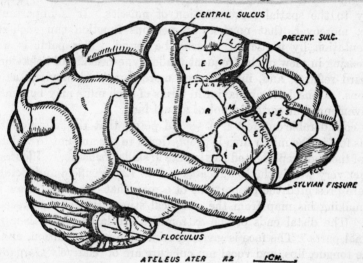

Fig. 124.—Side view of the right hemisphere of the spider monkey showing the tail, leg, arm, and face representation in the motor area. (From *J. F. Fulton and J. G. Dusser de Barenne. The representation of the tail in the motor cortex of primates, with special reference to spider monkeys, p.* 408. *J. cell. & comp. Physiol.,* **2,** 399–426, 1933. *By permission of the Wistar Institute of Anatomy and Biology.*)

movements of the limbs and various other parts of the body. In recent years the role of this gyrus in behavior has gone forward by the use of the methods of electrical stimulation and of experimental extirpation.

Electrical Stimulation.—The first fact of importance about the motor area is the orderly representation of movements of different parts of the body which can be found in it when different points in the area are electrically stimulated (Fig. 124). The most central and dorsal portions of the area control tail movements (in animals possessing tails). Moving the stimulus laterally one finds a locus for movements of the hind limbs, then, in order, movements of the trunk, forelimbs, neck, jaw, and facial muscles. On the extreme lateral aspect of the motor area, in the vicinity of the temporal lobe, is an area in which stimulation produces vocalization. The general arrangement of this localization is quite similar to that of somesthetic functions which are also found in this area and in the postcentral area.

Two further features of localization in the motor area are worth emphasizing. The first is that *movements, not muscles, are represented.* In this respect the same statement holds for the motor cortex as for reflex centers of the spinal cord (see p. 311). Movements that are distinctly different to an observer and are obviously of different compositions often involve essentially the same muscles, yet which of these movements is elicited depends upon which point is stimulated. Localization of function in the motor area refers, therefore, to patterns of movement and not strictly to the spatial representation of muscles. It is important to realize, moreover, that nowhere in nervous function can such strict representation by particular muscles be found. This point is worth emphasizing in view of the frequent tendency, especially of behaviorists, to regard reflexes, and, indeed, even more complex behaviors, as unit reactions. Considering behavior in terms of such units may be a matter of convenience but certainly not of actual fact.

Of considerable interest is a second point, that the relative size of various foci in the motor area is proportional to the amount to which the parts of the body represented participate in skilled behavior. Illustrating this fact very well is the *homunculus* of Fig. 125 (Penfield and Boldrey). In it are presented the proportions of a man that one would draw if he were making his map from the electrical stimulation of the precentral gyrus. The distal ends of the extremities are larger than their more proximal parts. The face is given considerable representation, and loci for the tongue, lips, and vocal musculature are of relatively Gargantuan proportions.

Such a proportional representation, it is interesting to note, corresponds with the innervation ratios of motor units, mentioned in a previous section, but even more striking is the relation between the homunculus and the use of the parts in skilled or voluntary movement. The parts of the body capable of the finest and most skilled movements are given the greatest representation. From these facts one can hardly escape the conclusion that the motor area must be very closely related to manipulative behavior.

Of importance, further, is the fact that the excitable properties of the motor area probably depend upon a particular group of cells, the giant pyramidal cells of Betz, after which the area has been named. Supporting this conclusion is the following evidence (see Fulton, p. 441): In infant monkeys, and probably also in human infants, the pyramidal cells are poorly differentiated, and corresponding to that fact is the conspicuous courseness of their behavior. They lack all the finer movements which after several months gradually appear as the maturation of the pyramidal cortex progresses. In infant monkeys, moreover, it is very difficult to secure motor responses by stimulating the precentral gyrus, even if the electrical stimulus is very intense. Other evidence to the same effect comes from experiments making use of the technique of thermocoagulation (Dusser de Barenne). By applying a heated metal surface to the

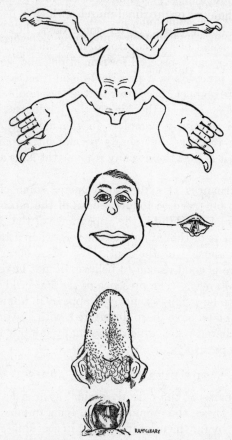

Fig. 125.—A homunculus showing the relative extent and position of the representation of various parts of the body in the motor area of man. (*Based on the observations of Penfield and Boldrey*, 1937. *After Fulton.*)

cortex it is possible to destroy it to varying depths depending upon the temperature and length of application. So long as the cortical layer containing the pyramidal cells is intact, it has been found, the excitable properties of the motor area are preserved; but when this layer is destroyed, with it also go behavioral responses to electrical stimulation.

Extirpation.—The primary result of extirpation of the motor area, as could be expected from the preceding facts, is a disturbance of skilled movements and manipulations. After motor-area ablation, the monkey or chimpanzee is deprived, at least temporarily, of his ability to carry out voluntary reactions in any acceptably good manner, and he is consequently reduced to making awkward, more or less postural, responses to situations that formerly called out quite specific adjustments. Such disturbances are much more pronounced in the fingers and distal extremities than in the shoulder or proximal muscles which is just what we might expect from the homunculus. After some days, however, the animal begins to regain some of the control of movement which he has lost. Thereafter, recovery may proceed for some time, and, so far as the limbs are concerned, it proceeds in a proximal-distal direction; *i.e.*, control of the fingers tends to reappear last, after that of the shoulder and arm. The amount of recovery is less, the higher the phylogenetic status of the animal; although relatively complete in the monkey, the chimpanzee never quite fully recovers, but shows permanent impairment of finger dexterity. Why it is that there is any recovery at all is a vexing problem (see p. 537).

Besides disturbances of skilled movement, some changes of reflex behavior are also observed to follow lesions of the motor cortex. Most prominent change of this kind is the appearance of the Babinski reflex, a pattern that consists of the fanning of the toes when a tactile stimulus is applied to the undersole of the foot. We often observe it in human infants who, there is good reason to believe, do not have maturely functioning pyramidal areas. The presence of the Babinski reflex is, in fact, ordinarily taken to be a sign, whenever it appears in human patients, that the pyramidal tracts have been interfered with. Apparently it is a subcortically mediated reflex which is normally inhibited by the activity of the pyramidal pathways.

THE EXTRAPYRAMIDAL AREAS

The various parts of the extrapyramidal system have already been enumerated. Of these, the premotor area, lying immediately in front of the motor area, is by far the most important in coordinated behavior. As part of the extrapyramidal system, the premotor area is concerned in many of the postural aspects of behavior, and it is in this capacity that it makes an important contribution to voluntary and skilled behavior, for the reason that behind every skilled movement is a requisite postural adjustment.

Electrical Stimulation.—Although the precentral gyrus is the focal area for the electrical excitation of behavior, the premotor also is responsive to an electric stimulus. The stimulus must in this case, however, be much more intense than in direct stimulation of the motor area, and the reactions that are obtained are much more complex than those elicited from the motor areas. Both of these facts turn out to be explicable in terms of neural excitation in the extrapyramidal areas spreading to the motor area, for when the motor areas are extirpated such responses can no longer be obtained.

Extirpation.—More about the functions of the motor area can be learned from the behavioral results of removing premotor areas than from electrical stimulation. For a few days following the operation, monkeys or chimpanzees exhibit a pronounced weakness (hypotonia) in the limbs of the side opposite the lesion. Such hypotonia is accompanied by peculiar postures of the limbs and a reluctance of the animal to use its limbs. Although essentially postural in nature, this disturbance interferes markedly with all skilled movements of the animal. Even after the hypotonia and peculiar posture pass away, as they will do within a few days, disturbances of skilled movement still persist; it appears, therefore, that the premotor areas are more directly concerned in motor coordination than in merely exerting influences on posture.

The disturbances of skilled movement which tend to last indefinitely after removal of the premotor areas are best seen in an animal's attempts to make such specific adjustments as those required in solving a problem box (Jacobsen). The composition of movement, especially when precise manipulatory movements are demanded, is deficient, and the animal requires a great deal of practice to relearn with satisfactory proficiency manipulatory movements that it has acquired preoperatively. In such a pattern of behavior as grooming, for example, the impairment is also observed; attempts to remove fleas from the body are executed awkwardly, and it is especially difficult for the animal to coordinate the action of the thumb and index finger, as grooming behavior demands. In man, too, it has been reported that injury to the premotor areas produces similar impairment; a prominent difficulty here is in approximating the thumb and index finger and in making such adjustments as buttoning a shirt or fingering a musical instrument (Kennard *et al.*).

KINESTHESIS

Still remaining to be discussed is the contribution of kinesthetic impulses in the execution of coordinated behavior; this is by no means unimportant. In studying it, use has been made of animal subjects in which the kinesthetic fibers have been sectioned in the dorsal roots. The behavioral defects resulting from this operation are given the general name *ataxia*. This, however, has been subdivided into *reflex* and *voluntary* ataxia, depending upon the nature of the deficit.

Reflex Ataxia.—Changes in reflex behavior resulting from the elimination of kinesthesis may be ascribed to a lack of the *inhibiting* effects of kinesthetic impulses which normally smooth out a reflex response. This conclusion has been reached by studying the crossed-extension reflex (see p. 313) in the normal cat and in one deprived of kinesthetic excitations from the limb concerned (Fulton and Liddell). The behavior of a deafferented cat differs from the normal in three principal ways: (1) The reflex response in the deafferented subject is more abruptly produced and is more readily obtained; in other words, 'resistance' to the reflex is reduced. (2) The same stimulus elicits a higher total tension in the deafferented subject than in the normal—another evidence of reduced 'resistance' or, one might say, of a release from inhibition. (3) The response, in the absence of kinesthetic stimuli, falls off much more abruptly than is normally the case. From these facts it is to be concluded that the kinesthetic receptors supply an inhibiting mechanism that resists the reflex, throughout its entire course, thereby smoothing out the response and making it, in effect, better coordinated. As we saw earlier, the stretch receptors and the reflex effects that they control constitute such an inhibiting mechanism.

Voluntary Ataxia.—Kinesthesis performs this inhibitory function not only in segmental or spinal reflex behavior but also in movements issuing from the pyramidal cortex. The disturbances of voluntary behavior which accompany kinesthetic deafferentation are, indeed, quite severe. When an animal tries to use its limb for feeding or in any other manipulation, the limb behaves as though 'it does not know where it is going,' for it usually shoots quite wide of the mark. Such disturbances of coordination, moreover, affect different parts of the limb in precisely the way that one might predict from a knowledge of the homunculus. Impairment is slight at the hip, more marked in distal joints, and so great in the digits that these are virtually useless. Nothing is wrong, though, in the pyramidal pathways, for electrical stimulation of the motor area will elicit the normal movements (Mott and Sherrington). What the motor cortex lacks, apparently, is adequate information concerning events taking place in the muscles.

LATERAL DOMINANCE

Speech and vocal behavior are properly considered a part of the voluntary and skilled behavior of an individual; yet speech is so closely allied with symbolic functions and higher psychological processes that its discussion is best left to the place where these other topics are also taken up. One question, however, which is most emphasized in regard to speech and yet related to the general topic of motor coordination is that of *lateral dominance*. With this term one refers to the fact that in the execution of voluntary movement animals and human beings seem to prefer the use of members of one side of the body and thus of one side of the brain.

There is a great deal of evidence for this belief (Downey). Rats, when they are required to secure an object with only one paw, most often use the right one (Tsai and Maurer). Human individuals usually write, throw balls, and carry objects with their right hands; as a rule, too, they are more dexterous and in various ways show greater skill with their right hands and limbs than with their left ones. In some individuals the picture is the same except that they are primarily left dominant; *i.e.*, the use of the left hand and limb is preferred in voluntary movement. Other individuals turn out to be ambidexterous and use both sides of the body with about equal facility. Then, in many subjects, one encounters no consistency of dominance from one type of behavior to another, although in any one the dominance may be clear. Some, for example, prefer the right hand in writing and the left in throwing a ball, or they may show right dominance in respect of the arm and hand, but left dominance in the use of legs or eyes. In specific habits, however, and even in the general family of habits, there can be little question but that individuals tend to show a right or left dominance (usually right), even though the incidence of disagreement between dominances of several psychomotor functions is an important matter in considering the physiological basis of dominance.

Since the pyramidal areas of the brain are clearly of great importance in voluntary movement and since their pathways are almost entirely crossed, it is to be presumed that behavioral dominance in any given case represents cerebral dominance on the opposite side. Since people in general are right-handed, a dominance of the left cerebral hemisphere in controlling manipulative and skilled behaviors is indicated.

Attempts to deal with the causes and nature of cerebral dominance have brought forth many speculations and a few facts. According to some (see Downey), lateral dominance is displayed in the greater growth of one side of the body than of the other, and measurements tend to confirm this belief. Lateral dominance has even been traced back to a genetic basis (Newman). With respect to the brain itself, however, it has been suggested that the dominant hemisphere receives a better blood supply than the other and that, as a result, it functions somewhat better and takes over the control of affairs in both hemispheres (Orton). This suggestion has not yet been established as fact, however.

If speculation is avoided in favor of factual evidence, we find that, although we have some interesting information, we do not yet possess a clear solution of the problem. Rats, it has been shown (Peterson), change dominance, so far as handedness goes, if a particular rather small area of the cerebral cortex is destroyed; but the shift in preference may be the result simply of impairing slightly the motor functions of one side, thus making the other limb preferable. In monkeys, at any rate, destruction of one motor area representing the limb customarily used in manipulation causes the animal to shift readily to the use of the other limb (Lashley). Thus will paralysis cause the dominance to change, as we might expect, but through what mechanism is not clear (*cf.* p. 478).

One thing, however, seems definite: cerebral dominance is not established through the interconnections of the corpus callosum. The mass of fibers connecting the two hemispheres, *i.e.*, the corpus callosum, looks like one possible mechanism for having one hemisphere 'tell' the other one what to do, and the corpus callosum was formerly thought to be important in this way in so regulating activity in the two hemispheres that one hemisphere could be dominant. That has now been contradicted by good experimental evidence, and in man. Smith and his associates have given patients an exhaustive series of tests of lateral dominance before and after surgical section of the corpus callosum and are unable to find any differences of significance accompanying the operation. Thus the locus of interaction between the two sides of the brain, assuming that to be required for the establishment of lateral dominance, must be located at some subcortical level.

MOTOR DISORDERS

Now to be considered briefly are some of the more common disturbances of motor coordination which occur in organic diseases of the nervous system.

Anterior poliomyelitis, commonly known as infantile paralysis, is a disease in which the ventral horns of the spinal cord are invaded by a virus (Fig. 126). The consequence is inflammation and sometimes death of the ventral horn cells; sometimes the disease is so mild as to result only in a temporary functional abnormality of motor functions, or it may be so acute that most of the cells die, and, since they are irreplaceable, complete paralysis results. When this happens, the muscles are weakened through lack of exercise and grow smaller in size (atrophy).

Tabes dorsalis is a disease in which syphilis affects the nervous system, particularly the dorsal sensory roots of the spinal cord. We have seen above how removal of kinesthetic impulses by sectioning the dorsal roots modifies both reflex and voluntary movements, causing *ataxia;* in tabes dorsalis quite the same syndrome appears. The most often observed results of tabes in the human patient are difficulties of walking; a patient cannot keep his balance or gauge his step on the basis of kinesthetic stimuli and must, therefore, 'watch his step' closely in order that he may guide his walking through visuomotor coordination. Often there are other symptoms of tabes dorsalis, for the disease may invade the spinal cord and even affect motor neurons directly, but its most characteristic symptom is the *locomotor ataxia* just described.

In *syringomyelia* the cerebrospinal fluid and the membranes encasing it are infected by certain bacteria. The infection, as a result, begins by affecting the nervous tissue in the immediate region of the central canal of the spinal cord and of the ventricles of the cerebrum. The symptoms of spinal involvement are most uniform. First there is a loss of pain and thermal sensibility because the pathways of both cross the cord in the vicinity of the central canal. As the disease progresses and invades more and more of the spinal cord tissue, it tends to lead eventually to the destruction of ventral horn cells and, consequently, behavior disturbances quite similar to those of anterior poliomyelitis make their appearance.

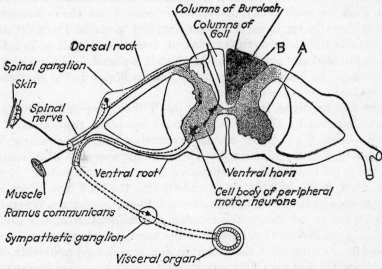

Fig. 126.—Diagram showing the parts of the spinal cord most commonly affected in (*A*) acute anterior poliomyelitis (infantile spinal paralysis) and in (*B*) tabes dorsalis (spinal syphilis). (*From L. W. Crafts et al. Recent experiments in psychology, p. 173. New York: McGraw-Hill, 1938.*)

Apoplexy, commonly known as a stroke, refers to the bursting of blood vessels in the brain; blood is diffused into nervous tissue, a clot is formed, and circulation tends thenceforth to be cut off, all of which leads to the death of the nerve cells. In an apoplectic attack, a patient usually loses consciousness quickly and falls into a coma; sometimes convulsions intervene and the attack looks something like an epileptic attack. After the attack, if it is not fatal, the patient may suffer from any one of a variety of disorders of sensation, perception, memory, or motor facility, depending upon where the hemorrhage occurred and how severe were its effects. Motor disorders appear when the locus of the stroke is in the motor or premotor areas, and the symptoms in postural and volitional behavior are as one might expect from our earlier review of the functions of these areas.

CATATONIC BEHAVIOR

Plastic Behavior.—Because they fit best into the present chapter, two important types of reflex reactions were passed by in the chapter on reflex behavior. These are the so-called *lengthening* and *shortening* reactions of the decerebrate animal and may be described as follows (Sherrington): When, for example, an experimenter attempts forcibly to *extend* the leg of a decerebrate cat, he at first meets a great deal of resistance; the leg 'does not want to move.' Once the resistance is overcome, however, by applying sufficient force, it melts away and the leg can be placed in any position desired. There it will stay until it is again forcibly extended when it will again show the same behavior. If, on the other hand, the experimenter forcibly *flexes* the leg, he finds that the limb first 'gives' and then develops considerable resistance to further flexion, even though, just as in extension, it will hold any new position in which it is placed. The response to extension is the lengthening reaction, that to flexion is the shortening reaction.

The two reactions, it seems clear (see Fulton), are dependent upon reflexes initiated by the *tendon* and *stretch* receptors, respectively. In flexing a limb, the extensor muscle is stretched and, consequently, the stretch receptors are stimulated. These, we have seen (p. 313), initiate the stretch reflexes in which the extensor muscles are contracted. Explicable, then, is the fact that in forcible flexion the limb first 'gives' but later, as soon as the stretch reflexes come into play, resistance is encountered. Thus is the shortening reaction a manifestation of the stretch reflex. In extending a limb, on the other hand, its extensor muscles are allowed to contract and the Golgi tendon recorders, presumably, are thereby excited; but then their activity results in an inhibition (reciprocal) of the stretch reflexes. Thus, in the lengthening reaction the initial resistance is due to the operation of stretch reflexes and the compliance that follows comes from their inhibition (*cf.* p. 313). The interplay of these two mechanisms gives to the limb the property of resisting any change of position, but, if the resistance is overcome, of taking up the new position and holding it. The limb, consequently, is like some plastic clay which can be molded into whatever form is desired.

Such plasticity of behavior, it should be repeated, is encountered in decerebrate preparations; like other phenomena of extensor tonus seen in decerebration, it probably represents the release of spinal and bulbar mechanisms from higher extrapyramidal and pyramidal influences. Such plasticity is found, however, not only in animal preparations but also in the behavior of human beings. Some patients presenting it give evidence of tumorous conditions causing a functional decerebration; but this is not true for all. It appears, indeed, in quite intact individuals, principally, however, in the psychosis known as *schizophrenia* and in the after-phases of the *epileptic fit*. When the plastic shortening and lengthening reactions and general plasticity appear in schizophrenia, the state is known as *cerea flexibilitas,* and the kind of schizophrenia is known as the *catatonic* type. For convenience, we may refer to the behavior as *catatonic* behavior, even though the patient suffering from catatonic schizophrenia may present many other symptoms besides plasticity.

Forced Grasping.—Closely related to catatonic behavior, if not a part of it, is the phenomenon of forced grasping. It is a strong flexion of the fingers in which an object that tactually stimulates the palm of the hand is strongly grasped, sometimes so powerfully that the weight of the body may be supported for a considerable length of time. Present in most infants at birth, it grows less pronounced with age and tends to disappear after 5 or 6 months (see Richter); this fact can be correlated with the maturation of the cerebral cortex, particularly of the pyramidal motor areas, during this period (*cf.* p. 141). In older individuals who, in contrast, practice voluntary grasping, the behavior does not appear except in connection with catatonic behavior or in injuries to the motor and premotor cortices.

The studies of the effects of experimental ablations in monkeys show that the grasp reflex, like other phenomena of extensor tonus and catatonic behavior, is the result of the release of lower centers from the control of higher ones (Richter and Hines). Such studies indicate clearly the primary importance of the premotor areas—the primary cortical center, the reader will recall, of the extrapyramidal system. After bilateral removal of the premotor area, grasping appears in force, but goes away in the course of a few weeks. To ensure predictable and permanent forced grasping, the motor areas must also be removed on both sides, thus imposing upon the animal a volitional paralysis as well as postural disturbances. Why both the motor and premotor areas must be ablated for permanent grasping has been the subject of some discussion (Richter and Hines; Fulton); but all that is yet certain is the fact of its existence under these circumstances.

The Role of the Internal Environment in Catatonic Behavior.—As we have seen, the typical phenomena of plasticity and the closely related grasping reflex depend upon decerebration in general and, more especially, upon the primary motor centers of the cortex. From this, however, we cannot conclude that the catatonic patient has a *lesion* in these centers; for in many cases no evidence of gross injury to the brain is to be seen. To be suspected is some functional disturbance of these centers and also, possibly, of such subcortical centers as the corpus striatum, which aid the cortical areas. Experimental results confirm this suspicion (Richter *et al.*).

Catatonic behavior can be induced in monkeys by any one of a long list of chemical agents; some of them are bulbocapnine, carbon dioxide, ether, luminal, morphine, and cocaine. The agent that has been used most frequently, it happens, is bulbocapnine. When this drug is given, the animals present a typical catatonic picture. For the purpose of getting a definite and quantitative measure of the presence and depth of this catatonia, the grasping reflex has been used. One observes the length of time that an animal will support his weight by grasping and hanging from a horizontal pole. In normal monkeys, of course, there is no hanging at all, but after the administration of bulbocapnine an animal will hang for several seconds or, sometimes, minutes. The effect, moreover, is much more pronounced in young than in adult monkeys—a fact that falls in line with the presence of the grasp reflex in infant individuals and with their less mature cortices.

Richter points out that all the chemical agents that evoke catatonia are known to produce depression of the excitability of the cortex when given in doses comparable to those inducing catatonia. He suggests, therefore, that their effect is to stimulate the cortical areas normally concerned in the inhibition of the catatonic behavior in much the same way as the extirpation of these areas. When, on the other hand, he used agents known to increase neural excitability, he did not observe any catatonia. The matter is not so simple, however, as it might appear. In other experiments (Richter *et al.*) it was found that agents which ordinarily produced catatonia, cocaine, for example, will abolish it if given in addition to bulbocapnine, the drug by which the catatonia was produced. This fact should not be too disturbing, however, if we realize that the chemical reactions of various agents in the body are always a complex affair, being quite different one from another. The really significant point, moreover, is that the catatonia can be produced by changing the chemical environment of the nervous system and thereby depressing its excitability.

Even more to the point in understanding catatonia in man are experiments in which catatonic patients have been brought out of their condition by altering the internal environment (Solomon *et al.*). The agent used in this case was carbon dioxide, and with it the catatonic patients were aroused to a normal state, in which the behavioral symptoms disappeared and thought and verbal expression were remarkably lucid, but only for a brief period. Within a few minutes they lapsed back into their former state. This we might expect, however, for carbon dioxide itself can produce catatonia in animals. In order to account for the period of lucidity, it may be supposed that carbon dioxide acts, as it will briefly, to dilate blood vessels of the cerebrum and bring to it a greater supply of oxygenated blood (p. 100) or that the decreasing pH of the blood, which the breathing of carbon dioxide brings about, temporarily increases the excitability of the cortex, as we know it will do (p. 55). Here again the remarkable fact is that a psychotic condition ordinarily considered to be functional in nature can be relieved completely, if only for a short time, by chemical changes in the internal environment. Suggested by this fact is the view that catatonia is a disease in which, by some manner or means, the cerebral cortex, perhaps a rather restricted part of it (motor and premotor areas?), is functioning at a very low level of excitability.

EPILEPTIC BEHAVIOR

Convulsions are patterns of behavior frequently observed in animals and human beings. They may be limited to only a part of the body, such as the face or arm (focal convulsions), or they may take in the whole musculature of the body (general convulsions). In any case, they consist of violent contractions of muscles. Sometimes the contractions alternate rhythmically with relaxations, so that quite violent movements are observed; in this case, the convulsions are called *clonic*. Sometimes the contraction goes on without interruption, and one position of the parts concerned is held with relative constancy, but with extreme exertion and 'locking' of muscles; such convulsions are *tonic*. In any particular convulsive episode, either or both types may be observed; sometimes one appears first and passes gradually into the other, or the two may alternate with each other several times. After the convulsions subside, there is usually a subnormal period of waxy flexibility, similar to that described for catatonia.

Epileptic Phenomena.—Now, convulsions may be produced in many ways; some of them will be considered below. Convulsions are found in man and in animals, but their presence in human individuals is taken as the manifestation of epilepsy. Although regarded by the layman as a disease, epilepsy is a name assigned to several kinds of disturbances that may have quite different causes; convulsions, moreover, may or may not characterize it. Besides convulsions, other psychological disorders, called epileptic, may be grouped roughly into two main classes; (1) sensory disturbances and (2) disorders of conscious processes. Both go along with convulsions in the full-fledged epileptic fit. A 'typical' attack begins (in man, for example) with hallucinations in some sensory field, or perhaps several in succession; these are often the warning of an attack and are called *aura*. Thereafter consciousness and upright posture are lost, and it is after this that the convulsions occur. All these events do not always take place, however, and when they do, the order is not necessarily as just stated. In some instances, an attack may be only a short period of faintness or dizziness; in others it may consist of a dreamy state, mental confusion, or temporary loss of memory; in others it may be a short lapse of consciousness with or without slight twitching of muscles (usually facial muscles). How these are combined depends, as we shall see, upon what parts of the cerebral cortex are involved, in what order, and to what extent.

Epileptic phenomena have many causes, some of which are known, whereas some are not. In the latter case, the only known physiological correlate that can be tied up with it is cerebral *dysrhythmia*, referring to the abnormality of the individual's brain waves. Whereas normal adult individuals show rather regular and smooth alpha rhythms of 10 per second (p. 138), many epileptic individuals possess brain waves of markedly different frequency and regularity. In them the waves are too slow, too fast, or both in alternation. The rhythms change particularly before and during an attack.

Although cerebral dysrhythmia is present sometimes in cases of lesions of the cerebral cortex accompanied by epileptic symptoms, it is not a sign of specific injury to the cortex but of some general functional defect in the cortex. We cannot believe, of course, in functional disorders apart from some fundamental abnormality of the constitution of the nerve cells, but whatever that abnormality, it is not seen in either the gross or histological structure of the cells. That dysrhythmia is evidence of a different constitution of the nerve cells is supported by the fact that it is inherited; members of the same family tend to have it. The presence of dysrhythmia is not, of itself, any sign of epilepsy, however, for more than 5 per cent of the population show it, and yet only a small proportion of these show actual epilepsies. Those with dysrhythmia but not overt epilepsy are probably only more susceptible to epilepsy from definite organic causes, such as cerebral lesion; so at least it is believed (Cobb).

Origin of Epileptic Phenomena.—The causes of epilepsy are not clearly understood. Some of the factors known to produce it are: abnormalities of the chemistry of the blood; lack of oxygen in some part of the central nervous system, brought about in any one of a number of ways; diseases of the nervous system in which nerve cells are irritated; tumors or other mechanical conditions in the brain that similarly irritate nerve cells; and, finally, in some cases excessive sensory stimulation. Whatever the cause, however, one general conclusion that can safely be reached concerning the nature of epilepsy is that it is a relatively primitive and disorganized response of nerve cells.

Weiss, for example, has shown that epileptic discharges are characteristic of nerve cells which in embryonic development have not been sufficiently differentiated and organized in their functions. In experiments already mentioned (p. 131) he transplanted a part of the spinal cord of the young salamander to the tissue of the fin. The transplants usually received a blood supply from blood vessels in their new locality and therefore many of them managed to survive, but some of their cells, nevertheless, died, and the previous structural relation of the cells became disorganized. Those which survived soon sent out fibers to surrounding muscles, and the behavior of these muscles could be watched for indications of the functions of the transplanted nervous system. Eventually, true reflex activity could be elicited from it because it also sent sensory fibers to surrounding skin and sense organs; but before this happened it passed through a state in which epileptic activity was often in evidence. Weiss writes:

[This] is characterized by intermittent or almost incessant twitching of the limb muscles. The twitches usually appear in spells, starting with irregular fibrillations and gradually building up to violent convulsions. A single fit may last for several minutes. . . . The seizures appear no matter whether the animal is at rest or in motion, but are usually more intense following a period of host activity (Weiss, p. 351).

From these observations one may venture the hypothesis that epileptic activity is characteristic of nervous tissue that is in a relatively primitive stage of differentation. Confirming this hypothesis are three other additional points: (1) Convulsions in infants are commonly observed, although they usually disappear as the infants grow older; we know that the infant cortex is not so well organized structurally or functionally as that of the adult. (2) In epileptic patients, furthermore, convulsions tend to occur as the individual is going to sleep; indeed, many normal individuals show slight jerks and twitches of a convulsive character as they doze. With this fact is correlated the change in the organization of cerebral functions which takes place between waking and sleep; the brain wave, for example, loses its alpha rhythms and produces random waves that are more similar to the dysrhythmic brain waves of epilepsy than are the waking brain-wave patterns (see p. 138). (3) Finally there is the fact that in a great many instances of epilepsy the cause may be assigned to a tumor, local disturbances of circulation, or other conditions tending to interfere with the normal organized functions of some part of the cortex.

Organic Epilepsy.—As stated before, epileptic episodes do not always include convulsive behavior but may be limited to mental confusion, loss of consciousness, or sensory disturbances. All these, as well as convulsions, may take place in sequence, however, and according to some observers the order of the sequence is dependent upon that area of the cortex in which the epileptic disturbance begins (Cobb). If, for example, there is a lesion in the occipital lobe, the attack is said to begin with visual hallucinations of flashes of light or scintillating figures; then the epileptic neural excitation seems to spread to the parietal areas, giving somesthetic hallucinations of tickle, numbness, and the like; it finally reaches the motor areas (4 and 6), where it is expressed in convulsive behavior. If a lesion is in the frontal lobes, in front of the motor areas, consciousness, it appears, is disturbed first, and later, when the neural discharge has spread to areas 4 and 6, convulsions intervene. In general, however, 'consciousness' is not localized in any area, but its loss in epilepsy seems to depend upon how much of the cortex is concerned in the attack.

Electrical Stimulation.—In 'spontaneous' convulsions arising either from organic lesions or cerebral dysrhythmia, it is probable that the excitability of cells, which is always fluctuating (*cf.* brain waves), becomes so great that they fire of their own accord; presumably then, the firing is kept up and may spread, by recruitment, to adjacent cortical areas through the recurrent-circuit mechanisms of after-discharge. Spontaneous firing is, of course, dependent upon the chemical environment of the cells as well as upon their own constitution, and other factors outside the cells are therefore involved, as we shall see below. It is probably also true, on the other hand, that in the case of actual stimulation by some organic condition, such as a tumor, nerve cells may actually be excited by stimulation. Epileptic discharges, at any rate, can be induced by sufficiently strong stimulation.

The best example of this fact is to be found in electrically induced convulsions (see Fulton). To secure them, one applies an alternating current directly to the cerebral cortex or, with a somewhat higher intensity, to the outside of the skull. With a weak stimulus and electrodes on the motor cortex, the convulsion is limited to a small part of the body, depending upon the part of the motor cortex stimulated. If the stimulus is somewhat stronger, the convulsion begins with one part of the body but spreads progressively to take in the whole musculature of the body in a general convulsion. With quite strong stimulation, it does not matter where the electrodes are placed on the motor cortex; neural activity develops in the whole cortex and expresses itself in a generalized convulsion. The convulsions may last only a few seconds or several minutes, depending upon a variety of conditions attending them. They may show either tonic or clonic phases or mixtures of these interrupted by brief periods of rest. Following the convulsion there is usually a period of greatly reduced excitability in which the animal is quiet, flexible, and relatively unresponsive to most stimuli.

It is worth mentioning in passing that epileptic disorders can sometimes be elicited in man and various animals by sensory stimulation. The type of stimulus that evokes them is usually peculiar to the individual or to a particular strain of animals. There is, for example, a strain of goats which when startled or scared become rigid and fall upon their sides in what is apparently a tonic convulsion (Lush). Certain strains of mice present a pattern of disorganized running followed by convulsion and coma when stimulated with tobacco smoke or with a loud sound. The animals that respond to smoke are not necessarily those reacting to sounds. In rats the same type of epileptic behavior occurs in response to loud sounds (Maier; Morgan *et al.*). Several cases of epileptic reactions to sounds have also been reported in human beings (Critchley). What may be the neural basis of the disorders in the various cases is a question that has not been answered.

Chemical Causes of Epileptic Attacks.—It was explained in an earlier chapter (p. 54) that an increase of the pH of the environment of nerve cells increased their excitability and might, particularly if the change is rapid, set them into oscillations of excitability in which nervous impulses appear spontaneously. It was also stated that depriving nerve cells of oxygen makes them hyperexcitable for a brief period and then depresses their excitability. Both of these facts accord well with observations of the relation between changes in the internal environment and epileptic manifestations.

Patients are sometimes encountered, for example, in whom holding of the breath (hypoventilation) only briefly will induce a convulsion, and it may be supposed in this case that depriving the brain of oxygen has so increased its excitability that any tendency to convulsiveness is brought out. Hyperventilation, *i.e.*, increasing the rate of breathing, may, on the other hand, also produce an epileptic attack in some cases. This fact is explicable in the following way: Hyperventilation does not significantly increase the amount of oxygen in the blood because the red corpuscles which carry the blood's oxygen are already near their saturation points. What hyperventilation does do, however, is to raise the rate at which carbon dioxide leaves the blood and is exhaled; removing carbon dioxide from the blood raises its pH and therefore tends to raise the excitability of the brain. Thus it appears that either decreasing the oxygen or increasing the pH, which are the consequences respectively of hypo- and hyperventilation, is a factor favoring epileptic attacks.

The role of pH in producing convulsive attacks is also seen in other ways. Many drugs which when injected produce convulsions also increase the pH of the blood, and although it cannot be claimed that all convulsive drugs produce their effects through raising the pH, some of them certainly do. Some convulsive drugs, on the other hand, actually decrease the pH and this, too, appears to be a factor in producing convulsion. Their manner of action, it seems, is through raising the pH of the nerve cells themselves. Although the reason for the rise in cellular pH accompanying a decrease in blood pH is not clear, the fact itself has been demonstrated. In an experiment in which an animal was injected with a convulsive drug and the pH of its blood and brain cells separately recorded (see Fig. 127), it was shown that the pH of the brain cells gradually rose, and when it had reached a certain point a convulsive discharge from the brain was observed (Dusser de Barenne *et al.*). Subsequently the pH of the cortex went down to about the same level as that of the blood; with that the convulsive discharge ceased and general excitability was, in fact, depressed just as one might expect from the fact that low pH causes a depression of the excitability of nerve cells.

Although pH and oxygen play a role in producing convulsive behavior, in some instances neither of them is of primary importance but instead the convulsions are produced by the irritating effects of the products of metabolism of nerve cells subjected to oxygen deprivation. In one series of experiments with animals, for example, the blood was shut off from the head for a few seconds by occluding the carotid arteries (Pollack *et al.*).

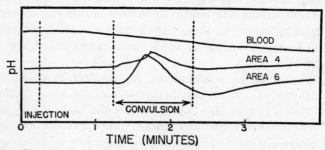

TIME (MINUTES)

Fig. 127.—Changes in pH of blood, area 4 and area 6 of the cortex following injection of a convulsive drug and accompanying the occurrence of a convulsion. (*After Dusser de Barenne et al.*, 1938.)

This procedure, of course, produced a cerebral anoxemia and might of itself be expected to produce convulsions. It was only after the blood was let back into the brain, however, that convulsions occurred. The experimenters could show that convulsions resulted primarily from materials that had been deposited in the brain during the period of anoxemia, for when they washed out the brain with physiological salt solution during the anoxemia, restoring the cerebral blood supply did not produce convulsions. They concluded, therefore, that the acid metabolites of brain activity in the absence of oxygen were the irritating factors leading to convulsion.

Somewhat similar to this result is the tendency to convulsiveness that shows up in vitamin B_1 deficiency. Animals severely deprived of this vitamin can be set into convulsions by almost any rather strong stimulus. Rats that have convulsions when stimulated with loud sounds, for example, are made to have them much more easily and more often when deprived of vitamin B_1 (Patton *et al.*). On the other hand, feeding vitamin B_1 to rats considerably reduces their susceptibility to having seizures induced by sound (Patton *et al.*; Fig. 128). This vitamin, it is known from studies of its chemical effects on the body, is necessary for the disposal of such products of the sugar metabolism of the brain as lactic and pyruvic acid. In the absence of the vitamin, these accumulate in the nerve cells and, it appears, make them hyperexcitable.

Coma.—Sometimes a period of hyperexcitability follows a convulsive seizure, but the more usual sequel to the seizure is a period in which the individual is left unconscious, immobile, and relatively unresponsive to stimulation. In this condition, a man or animal is much like the catatonic individual; he may show an augmentation of stretch reflexes and offer little resistance to being molded into various positions. This phase of the epileptic attack appears to represent a depression of excitability of the principal motor systems of the cerebral cortex and basal ganglia, much as the removal of these systems causes permanent catatonic behavior. In

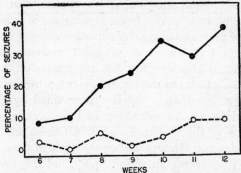

Fig. 128.—Effect of vitamin B₁ deficiency upon the incidence of audiogenic seizures in rats. Unbroken line, vitamin-deficient animals; dashed line, control animals. (*After Patton et al.*, 1941.)

this instance, the immediate cause of the plasticity and unresponsiveness is a lowering of the pH in these systems—at least that is the explanation offered us by animal experiments. Whenever nerve cells are caused to discharge continuously, rapidly, and for a relatively long time, the pH of the nerve cells drops rapidly, apparently as the result of the accumulation of acid metabolites in the cell (Gasser; Dusser de Barenne *et al.*). Lowering of pH under ordinary conditions depresses nerve excitability (see p. 55). Thus, once the nerve cells participating in the convulsion stop discharging, they can be expected to be inexcitable for a time until their pH returns to a more normal level. Support for this belief comes from the experiment cited above in which pH of the brain was recorded during an epileptic attack; when the convulsive neural discharge had been in force for a while the pH began to drop, and when it got very low the discharge stopped and the cortex became markedly depressed in excitability.

General References

Cobb, S., 1942. *Foundations of neuropsychiatry.* Baltimore: Williams & Wilkins. Pp. xi + 231.

Fulton, J. F., 1938. *The physiology of the nervous system.* New York: Oxford. Pp. xv + 674.

CHAPTER XVII

EMOTION

Under the heading of emotional behavior are included a great many kinds of behavior, both somatic and autonomic in character. Some common instances of somatic emotional behavior in man are smiling and laughing, crying, screaming, running (in fright), startle responses to sudden loud sounds, and various facial expressions of emotion. In addition to these there are cases of general somatic behavior consisting only of great tension and restlessness or of great activity and excitement. Autonomic emotional behavior, too, has many aspects: the pallor of fear, in which blood tends to leave the head; fainting, which is a more extreme case of circulatory disturbance and is accompanied by gross changes in bodily posture; increases or decreases in heartbeat; changes in blood pressure; secretion of the various glands. All these are aspects of emotional behavior in man. In animals we see some of these same reactions and others as well: snarling, purring, yelping, tail wagging, the baring of fangs, hissing, and certain patterns of facial and bodily reaction which go along with them. Obviously the topic of emotional behavior takes in a great gamut of reactions.

But that is not all. Before we go very far in studying emotion we meet with pleasantness, unpleasantness, hedonic tone, and other aspects of emotional experience. Individuals feel 'afraid,' 'mad,' 'pleasure,' and the like. In these instances, there is often no readily observable behavior, other than the verbal report of a subject concerning his 'conscious' experience. For that reason one finds it very difficult to work with such aspects of emotion in a sound scientific manner. They represent, presumably, much more subtle aspects of the subject's behavior than are recorded by any methods of measuring nonverbal behavior. It has been generally assumed, indeed, that pleasantness and unpleasantness stand for tendencies within the organism to approach or avoid, respectively, the conditions giving rise to them, whether these conditions are inside or outside the organism. In this way, we can understand in behavioral terms, or at least in terms of neural processes tending to lead to behavior, what is meant by the mentalistic concepts of pleasantness and unpleasantness. Many think of emotional experience in this way, but, lest the question be treated with prejudice, and in the interest of keeping the definition of terms clear, it is better to let *emotional behavior* refer to behavior that can be observed or recorded directly and to use the term *emotional experience* where a subject's report or 'consciousness' of his feeling is meant.

THE NEUROSENSORY BASIS OF EMOTIONAL EXPERIENCE

Interoceptors.—Besides the various receptors of the eyes, skin, muscles, and labyrinths, there are a great number of receptors in the viscera, blood vessels, and organs of the body which make up the class of *interoceptors*. Some of these are encapsulated end organs similar to those found in the skin and muscles. Pacinian corpuscles, or organs very much like them, are found liberally distributed in the mesenteries (the tissues that support the various visceral organs), in the pancreatic gland, in the genital organs, and in many blood vessels. From these organs, therefore, continually arises a great deal of excitation leading to 'pressure' experience. Also in the smooth muscles of the esophagus and bladder there are receptor organs that have the appearance of stretch receptors.

Of more importance, however, are free nerve endings which are distributed to every conceivable part of the organism: the esophagus, stomach, intestine (though not so liberally), the linings of the heart, lungs, and other organs of the viscera, the mesenteries, kidney, bladder, genital organs, lungs, and the blood vessels. Of this list, the last item is to be emphasized; the arteries, veins, and even the arterioles and venules are richly supplied with sensory free nerve endings, and probably only the capillaries are without such innervation. What they subserve—whether 'pressure,' 'pain,' or 'thermal' experience—is not known, although it is quite possible that they are concerned in all three types of experience. The important point, however, is that the nervous system is always being bombarded with sensory impulses arising from within the body.

The James-Lange Theory of Emotion.—The James-Lange and Cannon-Bard theories of emotion are well known to most students of elementary psychology. Both of these theories were framed in reference to an introspective psychology of consciousness. They therefore seek to explain emotional experience, rather than behavior, although it happens that both found it necessary to bring behavior into their discussion, and Cannon and Bard have experimented extensively with patterns of emotional behavior. Both theories are concerned more with the way emotional experience arises in a situation in which there is a definite emotional object presented to the individual, as when a cat is faced with a dog, than with the general problem of feeling.

The details of the James-Lange theory may be stated briefly as follows (see Fig. 129): An emotion-arousing object in the environment initiates perceptual processes in the brain which lead immediately to emotional behavior. This consists not only of overt and observable acts but also of changes in the smooth musculature of the blood vessels and viscera and of the secretion of glands. From such changes come sensory impulses that proceed to the brain and there are appreciated as emotional experience. The kind of emotional experience depends upon the type of bodily reaction brought about by the stimulus object. Thus does the James-Lange theory hold that emotional experience rests upon the sensory impulses from receptors, particularly the interoceptors, which are evoked in emotional behavior.

Thalamic Theories of Emotion.—Opposed to the James-Lange view of the origin of emotional experience are several other theories which, taken together, may be called the *thalamic* theory of emotional experience. Its first leading exponent was Head, a clinical neurologist. From his study of patients showing various disturbances of feeling and of emotional

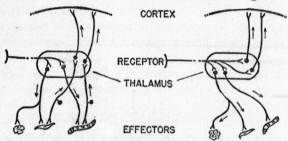

FIG. 129.—Diagram illustrating the difference between the James-Lange (left) and the Cannon-Bard (right) theories of emotion. The former states that emotional experience in the cortex arises from autonomic reactions to the emotional stimulus; the latter holds that both emotional experience and autonomic effects arise from the stimulus.

expression, as a result of nervous injuries, Head came to believe that the thalamus contained a center in which the character of emotional experience was determined. The perception of the experience, however, was carried out at the level of the cortex.

A more modern version of the thalamic theory is offered by Cannon and Bard. They propose that nervous impulses initiated by a stimulus object go to an integrative center in the thalamus, which they have reason to believe is located in the hypothalamus. From here impulses proceed directly to the cerebral cortex and there determine the nature of emotional experience. Concurrently, according to the Cannon-Bard theory, motor impulses leave the hypothalamic center and eventuate in patterns of somatic and autonomic behavior. Thus in this theory it is claimed that emotional experience and behavior arise separately from an 'emotional' center, whereas in the James-Lange theory emotional experience is made to depend upon the behavior.

Calkin's Theory.—Not as well known but nevertheless of importance in physiological psychology are two other theories of emotional experience. One, offered by Calkins, proposed that 'pleasantness' and 'unpleasantness' depend upon the condition of nerve cells in the frontal lobes. If these are fatigued, the theory runs, unpleasantness is the result; if at rest, pleasantness is experienced. Thus, for Calkins, the frontal lobe and its 'health' are the determinants of emotional experience. As we shall see later, her emphasis upon frontal-lobe functions was not misplaced, although in other respects the theory has little value.

Meyer's Theory.—A second additional theory was proposed by Meyer. It is worth mentioning because it contains what has turned out in recent experiments to be an element of truth. It begins with the assumption that neural activity set up by sensory stimulation diffuses widely in the nervous system. Next it assumes that neural activities coming from different sources are different in kind. As a consequence, different kinds of activity will diffuse and meet with each other. When they meet they may 'agree' or 'disagree'; if they agree, then pleasantness is the result; if they disagree, unpleasantness is experienced. Thus the kind of emotional experience depends upon the conflict or harmony of excitations in the nervous system. In this respect, Meyer's theory anticipates the modern finding that neurosis and anxiety tend to arise from 'conflict.'

THE SENSORY BASIS OF FEELING

Each of the theories of feeling which have been summarized emphasize one particular point about the basis of emotional experience. The James-Lange theory puts its weight on sensory excitations from the internal receptors of the body; Meyer's theory points to conflict; the notions of Head and of the Cannon-Bard theory emphasize a thalamic integration of emotional experience; Calkins, finally, thought the frontal lobe to be important. As we turn now from speculation to experimental fact, we find that each of these theories was partly correct in that it named some factor of importance in feeling.

Pain and Emotional Experience.—The relation of pain to 'unpleasantness' and feeling is perfectly obvious. Pleasure and pain are often used in hedonistic terminology as synonyms for pleasantness and unpleasantness, respectively. How painful stimuli are directly appreciated in experience we do not know, for the neural processes that make up this experience are not understood. One fact about painful stimulation, however, is quite clear; its effect upon experience is amplified through behavior which it evokes and which in turn excites other pain receptors in the interior of the body. The first effect of a painful stimulus, especially if applied to the limbs, is usually to cause a specific and reflexive withdrawal response which often serves to eliminate the stimulus. Along with this response, particularly if the painful stimulus continues for some time, there are sometimes certain other specific modes of somatic behavior, such as crying, a general heightening of skeletal muscular tonus, and many diffuse autonomic responses. In this latter category are changes in the activity of glands, in smooth muscles, in respiration, in blood pressure, and in the sizes of blood vessels. From these effects impulses are evoked in the various interoceptors, particularly pain receptors, serving the organs involved, and thus the behavior elicited by the original painful stimulus also adds some more painful stimulation.

Somesthesis and Feeling.—Although the sensory mechanisms of pain play a prominent role in feeling, these are not the only peripheral sensory mechanisms concerned. Touch (pressure), warmth, cold, and tickle have affective consequences. Warmth and tickle possess a pleasant character; pressure and cold are frequently 'unpleasant.' Sexual sensations are also a case in point. In them excitation appears to arise from tactual receptors in the erotic regions, and the effect is usually judged to be 'pleasant.'

One conception of the role of pressure and pain in the production of emotional experience has been offered by Nafe in what he calls the *quantitative theory of feeling.* He holds that the distinction of 'pleasantness' and 'unpleasantness' in experience is related to brightness and dullness, respectively, of somesthetic sensations. 'Pleasantness,' he supposes, consists of bright sensations, similar to those producing the 'thrill'; whereas 'unpleasantness' is derived from dull and heavy sensations. It may be said in favor of this theory that observers who report on the nature of unpleasant and pleasant experiences derived from sensory stimulation often confirm this general conception. A well-localized 'bright' stimulus is judged as pleasant, a more poorly localized diffuse stimulus is reported as unpleasant. There are, however, relatively few facts to show that this theory is an adequate and complete one to be applied to the understanding of emotional experience.

Feeling and the Vasculature.—Many students of emotional experience have wondered whether the difference between 'pleasantness' and 'unpleasantness' might not lie in sensory excitations arising from the two general types of autonomic activity, parasympathetic and sympathetic responses, respectively. Experiments designed to answer this question have in no case been crucial, but they tend to favor the notion.

In favor of parasympathetic activity's being the basis of pleasantness there is first the fact that warmth stimulation, unless it becomes so excessive as to produce pain, is generally 'pleasant.' It is known, of course, that warmth produces dilation of blood vessels, and aside from the question of whether this effect is the basis of thermal experience, it is possible that it may stimulate receptors which produce 'pleasantness.' There is the fact, furthermore, that various functions connected with eating are parasympathetically governed, and these are usually associated with pleasure; the secretion of saliva in the anticipation of food, and the secretion of gastric juices in hunger, for example, are parasympathetic activities. The generative and evacuative functions are also pleasant, and the sacral parasympathetics govern them; in sexual behavior, the vasodilation and certain muscular responses leading up to the orgasm are of parasympathetic origin.

Besides these verbal arguments for the parasympathetic basis of 'pleasure,' there are several experiments designed specifically to test the point. The measure of parasympathetic function most often used in them has been the volume of blood present in some particular area of the body, for example, in the hand or finger. If the notion is correct, one would expect increased blood volume to accompany pleasantness, and most experiments have found this to be the case (see Landis). Several well-executed studies, however, have not found it to be true, and that is reason for doubting the hypothesis. A possible explanation of such negative results lies in the fact that parasympathetic functions are relatively well differentiated from each other, and measurement of volume in one part of the body, particularly in the periphery, may give evidence only of local conditions or even register changes which are the reverse of those in the body as a whole.

The question of whether different autonomic responses are related to the type of emotional experience can also be investigated by determining whether the dominance of sympathetic activities is correlated with 'unpleasantness.' Particularly useful for this purpose is the fact that by the injection of adrenalin one can mimic the general effects of neural discharge in the sympathetic system. In studying the subjectives states of human observers given adrenalin, it has been found that they experience "cold emotion." This is a general "stirring up" of the individual such as occurs in unpleasant emotion, but without any external reference toward a stimulus to which emotional reactions can be directed. In many such subjects 'true' emotional experience is reported, but its nature is variously described by different observers. Some seem to feel fear, others describe joy; and there must be some hesitation in concluding that the sympathetic effects of adrenalin are 'unpleasant.'

Headache.—Only in the case of the unpleasant experience which we know as headache has there been a clear answer to the question of the sensory basis of affective experience. Headache, of course, is not exactly in the same class with anxiety, fear, or pleasure, but it certainly is closely related to them. Different kinds of headaches are often distinguished. The migraine headache is severe, throbbing, poorly localized, and rather persistent; it tends to be associated with epilepsy, but that is by no means the general rule. The hypertensive headache is associated with heightened blood pressure. Headache also can be correlated with acidosis (low pH) of the blood, but acidosis and hypertension are very closely related, one condition often leading to the other.

Extensive studies recently carried out upon human patients suffering from headache demonstrate a relatively simple fact (see Graham and Wolff): headache is directly correlated with the distension of cerebral blood vessels. Experimental diminution of the quantity of blood going to the cerebrum, either by mechanical pressure on the arteries serving the brain or by the use of drugs which contract arteries, will bring relief from the headache. Drugs (e.g., histamine) that cause distension of the cerebral blood vessels, on the other hand, produce headaches. Fitting in well with these facts are the effects of hypertension and of acidosis upon headaches. The high blood pressure of hypertension forces the cerebral vasculature to distend; so also does acidosis cause vasodilation both by direct stimulation of the muscles of the vessels and through reflex channels involving the brain. In vasodilation, therefore, is found the basis of one particular type of unpleasantness.

That this is essentially a matter of sensory excitation of interoceptors is a conclusion made plausible by the following facts: The blood vessels of the cerebrum are known from anatomical studies to be served by sensory endings, especially by free nerve endings. Muscle pain and ache are rather certainly the result of the stimulation of free nerve endings in blood vessels, for it is believed that there are no sensory free nerve endings in muscle tissue itself but only in the blood vessels associated with the tissue. The subject experiencing the headache refers the unpleasantness to the parts of the head in which blood vessels are dilated, and the experience, therefore, appears to have a sensory basis. We may conclude, then, that sensory stimulation occurring in changes in the sizes of blood vessels may be the basis of unpleasantness, and until there is better evidence to the contrary, we may believe that this may be a general principle governing feeling in other parts of the body as well.

The Utility of Unpleasantness.—In another section below, it will be shown that emotional behavior of certain kinds is of value to the organism in meeting emergencies in the environment with which its repertoire of specific responses is incapable of dealing. Pain and unpleasantness may, likewise, be regarded as conditions which serve emergency functions when other kinds of stimulation fail to rouse the organism to danger. In this connection a fact mentioned in an earlier chapter (p. 265) is significant: many of the pain fibers, viz., those of the C type, are the slowest conducting fibers among sensory nerves. These impulses travel at about 1 m. per second, whereas those of temperature and pressure travel much faster, sometimes as high as 100 m. per second. From this fact we can gather that it is only after these latter types of impulses have arrived in

he nervous system and have begun to take their effects that the pain
mpulses enter and through their widespread effects ensure the adjustment to the situation if the faster touch and temperature impulses have
not succeeded. It may also be recalled that painful stimuli rather characteristically become effective through the summation of impulses in the
central nervous system. Such summation probably involves the recruitment of some internuncial fibers and takes time, but after it has built up,
the consequences are widespread autonomic and somatic responses which
back up the more specific responses which may have occurred to the other
types of stimulation.

THE NEURAL BASIS OF FEELING

In the history of the problem of emotion a great deal of attention has
been given to the thalamus. The eminent clinical neurologist, Henry
Head, studied many human patients with thalamic lesions and noted the
prevalence of disturbances of emotional experience in them. He supported, as a consequence, what may be called a thalamic theory of feeling.
Cannon and Bard, on the other hand, though attempting to draw conclusions concerning the emotional experience, studied the somatic and
visceral expressions of emotion in animals and found them to be 'located'
in the hypothalamus. Thus they too came to a thalamic theory of
emotional experience.

Peripheral Nerves and the Spinal Cord.—A survey of the recent evidence, however, leads us to believe that the thalamus is only one of
several places in the nervous system where feeling and emotion are
integrated (see Lashley). One important fact in this connection is that
disturbances of feeling may result from lesions at points in the nervous
system other than the thalamus. There are, indeed, many instances of
hyperalgesia (hypersensitivity to pain) in conditions affecting peripheral
nerves. The painfulness of a pain, for example, may be quite excessive
during the regeneration of a cutaneous nerve which has previously been
cut—an effect associated with the greater irritability of a growing nerve
fiber. Hyperalgesia may likewise occur in neuritis and other conditions
in which peripheral nerves are hyperexcitable and have more powerful
effects at their synaptic terminals in the spinal cord. Then, too, there
are many instances of a similar accentuation of 'unpleasantness' accompanying lesions in the spinal cord, particularly in spinal afferent pathways.

The Thalamus.—One can expect the thalamus to be important in
feeling, if for no other reason than that it is the main way station for all
afferent pathways to the cerebral cortex. There is, in fact, no good
reason to suppose that the thalamus is any more important in emotional
experience than its status as a relay station would suggest, the theories of
Head, Cannon, and Bard to the contrary nothwithstanding, for the

symptoms to be observed in cases of thalamic lesion are quite similar to those obtained in lesions of peripheral nerves or the spinal cord.

One can arrive at this conclusion by drawing upon the recorded observations of Head: (1) When one side of the body is affected by a thalamic lesion, various sorts of stimuli, such as pricking, scratching, heat, or pressure may be very disagreeable or painful to a patient when applied to the affected side but not when presented to the normal side. (2) Similarly, it sometimes happens that stimuli which are unpleasant on the normal side may have no effect on the side of the thalamic lesion, even though the patient may clearly recognize the character of the stimuli (*e.g.*, pricking, heat, etc.). (3) Hyperalgesias often present on the affected side consist, not in a lowering of the absolute threshold to pain, but in a heightening of the emotional effects attached to the stimuli. These observations indicate that in the thalamus, as elsewhere in the afferent somesthetic paths, nervous injury may cause disturbances of affect, but they do not provide any evidence for specific integrating centers of emotional experience in the thalamus.

It is to be noted, and with emphasis, that emotional experience, so far as both the spinal cord and thalamus are concerned, is related exclusively to somesthetic functions. There is, according to one authority (Lashley), no case on record of a patient suffering only from a thalamic lesion who shows any disturbances of feeling in sensory modalities other than somesthesis. Excessive unpleasantness of other affective disturbances associated with other kinds of stimulation, *e.g.*, those of olfaction, are associated with lesions in the sensory pathways or nuclei of that modality, not in the thalamus. Olfaction, of course, is crucial, because its relay centers lie chiefly outside the thalamus, and it happens that many clinical symptoms of emotional disturbance are related to olfaction. Here, however, wherever the area of injury can be determined it turns out to be in the primary olfactory centers rather than in the thalamus. It is to be concluded, therefore, that the thalamus does not contain special integrating centers of feeling, as thalamic theories would suggest, but is important mainly insofar as it contains the principal centers of most of the sensory systems.

Conclusion.—The present status of the psychophysiology of emotional experience is not so clear as might be desired, but all the facts that we have point to the belief that emotional experience is to be regarded as arising from peripheral stimulation. One cannot be dogmatic about that conclusion, but it is the best that can be drawn from the available data.

It is interesting to note, in connection with this view, how important are the somesthetic receptors and pathways, particularly those of the interoceptive variety, in the continuous feeling tone of an organism. Transient olfactory, gustatory, visual, and auditory stimuli introduced into the organism by the external environment may have their temporary effects in emotional experience, but the organism never escapes from the impulses arising in its muscles, blood vessels, and, to a great extent, its skin. Somesthetic impulses, therefore, form a battery of excitation continuously impinging upon the central nervous system. In this way they form a sensory background upon which other sensory effects are produced by external stimuli. The analogy to posture is easy to draw. Whereas specific reflex or skilled movements are evoked in a behavioral matrix of postural tonus and responses and are to some extent determined by this matrix, so also must the effects of external stimuli fit into and be determined in part by the preexisting and ever-present effects of somesthetic stimulation.

THE AUTONOMIC ELEMENTS IN EMOTIONAL BEHAVIOR

Theories of Emotional Behavior.—The Cannon-Bard theory of emotion attempts to deal with both of its aspects, the experiencing of emotion and the behavioral expression of it. The first has already been taken up. The theory has two main points to make concerning emotional behavior: it may consist of special patterns of behavior falling into the three main categories of pleasure, fear, and rage; and, particularly in the patterns of autonomic responses which it entails, emotion serves the purpose of mobilizing the resources of the organism to meet a situation that might endanger it. This latter point is often made by referring to the emergency functions of emotion. These are mechanisms in which the organism returns to more primitive adjustments in order to ensure its success in coping with situations for which it has no specific and intelligent somatic response.

The notion of emotion's being a primitive adjustment has been put forth in many treatments of emotion, among them Ruckmick's so-called phylogenetic theory of emotion. The organism low in the phylogenetic series, says Ruckmick, is one in which there is little differentiation of structure or function, and behavioral activity in such an organism is relatively unspecific and diffuse. In evolution, structural differentiation and specialization lead to the development of highly specific sensory and behavioral mechanisms; but certain characteristics of the primitive organism are always preserved in both the structure and functions of the highly evolved animal. These can be called upon whenever the more highly differentiated and specific mechanisms fail; they constitute the mechanisms of emotion. Emotional behavior, therefore, is relatively undifferentiated behavior involving much of the nervous system and particularly those parts which are oldest and most basic in phylognesis. Wholly consistent with this view is the fact that autonomic responses figure prominently in emotion, for these are concerned with the most primitive and essential job of looking after the internal environment of the animal and, indeed, those functions upon which life itself depends.

Experimental studies on the behavioral expression of emotion have dealt mostly with rage and fear. These are emotions which, it will be conceded, are perceived in experience as unpleasant. It is significant, therefore, that the autonomic components of these emotions are prominently sympathetic. Changes occurring in the alimentary tract in such emotions, for example, are perfectly in line with the generalization that these emotions involve a diffuse sympathetic discharge. Salivation is inhibited, as the person who has once been stage struck will attest. Gastric motility, the secretion of gastric juices, and peristaltic movements of the intestine are also inhibited, and these effects have the net result of slowing down or stopping digestion. Evacuation of the colon and bladder will ordinarily be inhibited with constipation resulting. It sometimes happens, however, especially when sympathetic effects have a rapid onset, that compensatory parasympathetic discharges occur transiently, and then, as if by overflow from the sympathetic to the parasympathetic system, evacuation of the colon and the bladder may result. Such effects are often taken as a measure of emotionality in animals.

Like alimentary activities, circulation changes in rage and fear in a manner predictable from a knowledge of the effects of sympathetic discharge. Sympathetic fibers to the heart, it will be recalled, cause the heartbeat to be accelerated. The vasoconstrictor functions of the sympathetic system also come into play and cause a redistribution of the blood from the viscera and skin to the musculature and brain. Acceleration of the heart and vasoconstriction, taken together, raise the blood pressure. The net result of these activities is that in rage or fear the body drops its constructive processes of digestion and food storage and mobilizes its resources for the expenditure of energy.

Cerebral Blood Supply.—Quite often in the emotional reactions of man one can observe changes in the distribution of blood to the head. The extremes of such changes are, on the one hand, the blushing of shame or embarrassment, or the flush of rage, and, on the other hand, the pallor of fear. These changes are to be attributed to circulatory reactions of dilation or constriction of the blood vessels leading to the face. In some instances these circulatory effects are so pronounced as to lead to fainting. This is, for the most part, the result of such extreme vasodilation in the body that blood leaves the head, thereby depriving it of oxygen and leading to the loss of consciousness. It can come about directly or by way of a compensatory reaction to sympathetic discharge. If, for example, the blood pressure rises very abruptly and stimulates in an excessive amount the pressure receptors located in the carotid sinus (p. 100), reflexes are brought into play in which the parasympathetic system discharges and produces general expansion of blood vessels, inhibition of the heart sometimes so extreme as to bring the heart to a standstill, and consequently greatly reduce blood pressure.

Chemical Effects.—The sympathetic reactions of emotion express themselves in still another way, by changing the chemical and endocrine balance of the blood. One of the most prominent instances of this action is to be found in the release of adrenalin from the medulla of the adrenal glands. Adrenalin, as already pointed out, mimics the action of the sympathetic system and when circulated in the blood stream produces the same general effects as do sympathetic impulses. It causes acceleration of the heart, for example, in addition to and independently of the direct sympathetic outflow to the heart. It also causes glycogen stored in the liver to be converted into sugar and released into the blood stream, thereby raising the blood-sugar level to meet the requirements of great energy expenditure by the brain and muscles. Adrenalin also stimulates the thyroid gland to greater efforts and in this way increases general oxidation in the body. Thus in the secretion of adrenalin in emotion very important changes in the internal environment of the individual take place.

Quite recently the importance of the adrenal and thyroid glands in emotional behavior has been demonstrated in a striking way (Hall; Yeakel and Rhoades). Through extensive experimental observations it was shown that there is a very close relationship between the glandular make-up of an organism, its genetic constitution, and emotional expression. First, certain standard tests were developed through which emotional and fearless rats could be distinguished from each other; these tests employed defecation and urination in controlled situations as measures of emotionality and determined the readiness with which animals gave their emotional responses to strange situations. The two kinds of animals were then kept apart, and by controlled breeding strains of fearless and emotional rats were obtained. Anatomical analyses of the glandular constitutions of these rats were then made, and it was shown that the emotional rats had much larger adrenal, thyroid, and pituitary glands than did the fearless rats. Thus was emotionality correlated with constitution and, indeed, by inference, with an internal environment that must be considerably different from that of the less emotional animal.

General Sympathetic Effects.—There are still other sympathetic effects appearing in emotion which have not been mentioned; they may be indicated briefly. The sweat glands of the skin, which are under sympathetic control, are caused to secrete their fluid, thus preparing the way for the disposal of the large amounts of heat which may be liberated in emotional activity. The muscles at the bases of the hair follicles contract, and thus the hairs are erected and "goose pimples" form.

Profound changes in respiration also take place, but these are not stereo-typed; gasps, catching of the breath, panting, and labored breathing are variant components of emotional respiration. One change connected with respiration which regularly occurs under sympathetic influences is dilation of the bronchioles of the lungs; in this way the rate of exchange of oxygen and carbon dioxide in the lungs is stepped up to a considerable degree. Another physiological effect, finally, is the release of red cor-puscles from the spleen where they are ordinarily stored, and with an increase of their number in the blood the oxygen-carrying capacity of the blood is raised accordingly.

SOMATIC PATTERNS OF EMOTIONAL BEHAVIOR

Having covered the autonomic aspects of emotional expression we may turn now to the behavior that involves the somatic musculature. The first question to be considered under this topic is whether or not there are different innate patterns of emotional response. Later the problem of the neural mechanisms subserving somatic emotional expression can be treated.

Emotional Patterns in Infants.—It probably goes without saying that in man the expression of emotion has been entangled in the influences of learning and social acculturation to such an extent that one cannot expect to determine whether or not there are innate patterns of expression by observing adult human beings. The matter has, therefore, been referred to observations of infants in whom such influences have had little chance to work.

One of the first and most notable researches along this line was con-ducted by Watson and Morgan. Infants, ranging in age from birth to a few months, were presented with a number of stimuli which in older children are usually accompanied by emotional behavior. The many different responses observed by these men nevertheless seemed to fall into three basic patterns, which they called fear, rage, and love. The typical emotional reactions that comprised the *fear response* were catching of the breath, random clutching of the hands, and the appearance of the grasp reflex, blinking of the eyelids, puckering of the lips, and later crying. These seemed to appear whenever the infant lost his support or was stimulated with a loud noise. The *rage response* consisted of screaming vocalization, stiffening of the body, slashing and striking movements, holding of the breath, and flushing of the face. It attended restraint of the infant's movements. The *love response* typically included smiling, gurgling, cooing, and extension of the arms and could be elicited by tickling, stroking, rocking, and related types of somesthetic stimulation.

Watson and Morgan, it has been claimed, allowed their own biases to enter into their judgments of the infants' behavior, for subsequent investigators have failed to concur in these conclusions. They find instead that almost any type of stimulation, if not too intense, leads to random mass movement in infants and not to any particular pattern of emotional expression. Their results indicate, moreover, that the infant's emotional behavior can only be classified with any degree of accuracy when the nature of the stimulating conditions is known. This means, of course, that we are more likely to judge emotional expression, not in terms of its components, but through a knowledge of what they are supposed to be.

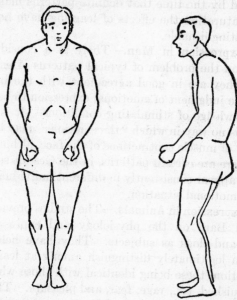

Fig. 130.—The startle pattern. (*From W. A. Hunt and C. Landis. The overt behavior pattern in startle. J. exper. Psychol., 19, 312, 1936. By permission of the American Psychological Association.*)

The Startle Pattern.—There is one pattern of behavior that appears unquestionably and with remarkable consistency in infants (see Fig. 130). This is the "startle pattern" and consists of closing of the eyes, head movement, raising and bringing forward of the shoulders, abduction of the upper arms, bending of the elbows, pronation of the lower arms, clenching of the fists, forward movement of the trunk, contraction of the abdomen, and bending at the knees. This pattern appears at about four months of age and continues without significant modification into adulthood. It is believed that this pattern is the basic emotional response of the human infant and that it includes most of the significant components that are later grouped through learning into socialized emotional patterns. Such a belief is, of course, in accordance with negative findings in respect of other emotional patterns.

There is, however, some difficulty in believing that the startle pattern is the only dependable emotional pattern and that there are no more specific patterns of emotion in man that the various investigators, besides Watson and Morgan, have found. Lower animals certainly possess rather definite modes of emotional response, as we shall see below, and we do not expect them to be entirely dropped in man. Perhaps the obscuring factor is that physiological maturation of the mechanisms of behavior is relatively slow, as certain other studies in walking, for example, indicate; and by the time that definite patterns make their appearance through maturation the effects of learning have been sufficient to make them indistinguishable.

Emotional Expression in Man.—There is a considerable body of studies bearing on the problem of typical patterns of emotional expression in man. They are in good agreement with the infant studies in that they find the judgment of emotional expression to be largely contingent upon a knowledge of stimulating conditions. It is certainly quite clear that there is no way in which "the emotions" may be analyzed into components, say of muscle contractions of the face, although it is claimed by some that there are certain patterns, in the Gestalt sense of the word "pattern," that appear consistently in different individuals in association with the same emotional situation.

Emotional Expression in Animals.—The studies previously mentioned of Cannon and Bard on the physiology and expression of emotion employed cats and dogs as subjects. They have held that in these animals one can legitimately distinguish among at least three definite patterns of emotion, these being identical with those which Watson and Morgan distinguished, *viz.*, rage, fear, and pleasure. The motor expressions of *rage* in the dog are described by Cannon and Bard as follows: lashing of the tail, arching of the trunk, thrusting and jerking of the limbs, protrusion of the claws and clawing movements, snarling, movements of the head from side to side, attempts to bite, and very rapid panting respiration. A somewhat similar description also applies to the cat. The *fear* reaction as seen in the cat consists of dashing off in a furtive or precipitate manner, mewing plaintively, trembling, and taking to cover behind any available object. The *pleasure* reaction in dogs and cats is familiar to the layman; its most evident sign in dogs is tail wagging, and in cats purring, but other reactions such as those to petting and stroking are also a part of the syndrome.

The negative results of many studies on infant behavior with respect to basic patterns of emotion have led to some skepticism of the validity of Cannon and Bard's observations. It has been argued that the so-called rage responses of the Cannon-Bard animals can be interpreted as fear reactions and that there is, in animals, as had been held for human beings, only a general pattern of excitement. The position that Cannon and Bard, and Watson and Morgan, have taken is, however, much more in accord with common-sense observations, and even though emotional patterns may not be rigidly stereotyped and may overlap a great deal in their composition, it seems reasonable to accept the Cannon-Bard classification in its general form. It should be recognized, nevertheless, that most instances of emotion are probably mixtures of the extreme patterns and that the multiple aspects of most situations are not such as to bring out any simple, constant, or stereotyped pattern. It is to be expected, furthermore, that in both man and animals the various influences of the environment impressed on the organism's repertoire of behavior will liberally modify what might otherwise have been relatively simple prototypes of emotional reaction.

THE CENTRAL MECHANISMS OF EMOTION

Cannon and Bard have also performed the best known and most informative experiments dealing with the nervous centers and pathways involved in emotion. Their observations on cats and dogs, together with certain other data gathered from human patients with neurological lesions, make up the bulk of the available material. Cannon and Bard, in attempting to select some particular type of emotional reaction for observation, decided upon the rage response, because this seemed to be a fundamental pattern readily elicitable and identifiable in animal subjects. Only a few data are available on the fear and pleasure reactions in animals. The human material indicates, in addition, certain important facts about the mechanisms of laughing and crying.

The Spinal Cord and Medulla.—Considering these various topics in turn, we may give our attention first to the animal experiments and particularly to the problem of localizing, if possible, general mechanisms of emotion in the central nervous system. Different studies by many investigators have shown that in the absence of higher centers of the nervous system the autonomic aspects of emotion, particularly the sympathetic, can be readily produced. The stimuli by which they are obtained are of course greatly restricted because the autonomic outflow is shut off from the higher sensory mechanisms. Painful stimulation is, however, quite capable of producing the typical autonomic effects. These are probably mediated in such cases by local spinal mechanisms or, since the medulla is also intact, by various bulbar sympathetic centers. Such centers for vasoconstriction, the reflex secretion of adrenalin, and respiration can be excited without the intervening influence of higher mechanisms. Thus the fundamental sympathetic reactions of emotion are to be found at the spinal and bulbar levels.

The Medulla and Hindbrain.—The medulla, in addition, is capable of mediating somatic behavioral reactions which make up the typical rage pattern of the intact animal. The repertoire of such reactions is somewhat larger when the midbrain is also intact. These reactions are, however, quite unintegrated and appear as isolated bits of behavior attached to nearly any slightly disturbing stimulus. Spitting, growling, tail waving, pawing, together with sympathetic activity and other signs of rage behavior may be observed in such animals, but never do they exhibit the normal ,pattern and sequence of responses. It appears, therefore, that the basis of the somatic patterns of rage behavior is to be found in the midbrain and hindbrain but that higher centers are required for the organization of the components of the patterns.

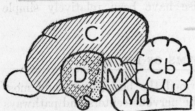

Fig. 131.—Schematic longitudinal section of the cat's brain showing the different parts removed or left intact in studies of the neural basis of emotion. *C*, cerebral cortex; *D*, diencephalon; *M*, mesencephalon; *Md*, medulla; *Cb*, cerebellum. Cross-hatching from right downward to the left indicates portion of the brain which can be extirpated without interfering with the expression of rage. (*From W. B. Cannon. The mechanism of emotional disturbance of bodily function. New Engl. J. Med.*, **198**, 877–884, 1928. *By permission of the publishers.*)

The Hypothalamus.—Such organization can be said with assurance to take place in the hypothalamus. A series of careful experiments by Cannon and Bard demonstrated this fact. The brains of dogs and cats were sectioned at various levels such as to exclude the cortex, or the cerebral hemispheres, or, in addition, all the thalamus except the hypothalamus (see Fig. 131). After all such operations, the expression of rage, as described earlier, appeared as an organized pattern of behavior. When, however, the brain section was made more posteriorly so that the hypothalamus was also excluded, the rage pattern dropped apart, so to speak, into isolated bits of behavior as already indicated.

It must be noted, further, that the decerebrate preparation, with only the hypothalamic portion of the forebrain intact, does actually lack certain of the behavioral components of normal rage behavior. In particular, there is a marked rigidity of the antigravity muscles, such as is seen in decerebrate preparations (see Chap. XV), and, in general, the somatic postural manifestations of emotion are lacking. This result is what we should expect on the basis of our knowledge of the importance of the cortical and striatal mechanisms of posture. It is not strictly true, therefore, that the whole of the rage pattern is integrated at the level of the hypothalamus.

The Cerebral Cortex.—Very remarkable changes in reactivity to emotional stimuli take place when the cortex alone is removed. In the decorticate animal appear phenomena similar to those of hyperalgesia and feeling which were previously stated to be related to cortical and thalamic injury. The decorticate animal shows great sensitivity to emotional stimuli, and displays the rage response, usually including vigorous activity of the limbs, at the slightest provocation. The cortex and striatum, therefore, seem to contribute considerably to both the felt and the expressive components of emotion; some inhibitory function of the cerebral cortex is also indicated.

Another feature of emotional expression, seen in the absence of the cortex, is that emotional behavior lacks 'direction.' Although rage behavior in decorticate animals is well coordinated, the animal seems to lack an appreciation of what it is that disturbs him. When, for example, the experimenter produces rage by pinching the decorticate dog's tail, he can rest assured that he is safe from attack, for the dog's snapping and biting will be addressed to a region in front of him rather than to the region of noxious stimulation. The reason for this fact is not hard to understand. The perceptive processes dependent upon the cortex and serving to direct behavior have been abolished in decortication. It is also probably true, as work in the field of cutaneous localization has shown (see p. 281), that good localization of the point of cutaneous stimulation depends upon normal cortical functions, and in their absence, cutaneous stimulation, and particularly painful stimulation, is very diffusely localized.

Still another difference between the decorticate and the normal animal in respect to emotional behavior is that the normal animal, when once excited, continues in an emotional state for some time, whereas the decorticate dog gets over his rage very quickly. In other words, the after-discharge which is characteristic of normal emotion is minimized in the absence of the cortex. Thus an experimenter may pinch a decorticate dog's tail, thereby eliciting rage behavior, and then place his finger in the dog's mouth without danger of being bitten, which is not nearly so likely in intact animals. We may conclude from this fact that the cortex contributes something to the maintenance of emotion, once it is elicited, just as it tends to inhibit or suppress emotional reaction and to contribute resistance to the elicitation of emotional behavior.

Cortical Functions in Man.—With reference to the inhibitory effect of the cerebral cortex upon subcortical mechanisms of emotional expression, two sets of observations on human patients may be cited. The first is related to the differential action of anesthesias in suppressing the activity of the cortex before that of lower centers. When, for example, an anesthesia such as ether is administered to man (or animals), nearly always a period of somatic excitement and restlessness intervenes before deep narcosis and immobility are attained. In human individuals during the period of excitement, very striking emotional behavior may be observed. There may be weeping, groaning, laughing, or signs of rage. Comparable manifestations are sometimes seen in animals also. In such a stage of anesthesia, surgical operations may be performed without memory or consciousness of it on the part of the patient. Such facts indicate that in the release of the thalamus from cortical control emotional phenomena are readily elicited or appear spontaneously and that such expressions are not necessarily dependent upon conscious emotional experience.

Similar conclusions are secured from instances of permanent cortical lesion in human patients. Here, it has been observed, any interruption of motor pathways which interferes with the voluntary control of facial expression has no effect upon emotional expressions. Muscles that are otherwise paralyzed readily participate in emotional expression when the appropriate stimulating situations are present. It occasionally happens, furthermore, that patients with cortical injury are given to spells of uncontrollable laughing or crying. These may come on spontaneously or be set off by some stimulus ordinarily inadequate in normal individuals; it is of interest that very frequently the type of emotional expression in such cases may be at variance with the affective experience. Thus laughing may accompany extreme sorrow, or crying sometimes occurs when pleasantness is experienced. These facts lead to the conclusion that there is a great deal of interaction between the cortex and subcortical centers in the expression of emotion by the normal individual.

Fear.—Little information, unfortunately, is available concerning the neural mechanisms of fear or of pleasantness. Bard has described what he considers to be fear behavior in decorticate cats in response to sounds of high frequency, but the behavior as he depicts it resembles so closely epileptic patterns recently discovered in rats that the significance of the behavior is to be questioned (*cf.* Maier; Morgan and Gould). Bard believes that fear behavior is also basically integrated at the subcortical level, probably in the hypothalamus.

Pleasure.—Observations of pleasure responses seem to be restricted to the purring responses of cats and the tail wagging of dogs, and there is some question as to whether purring is a good sign of pleasure, since it sometimes occurs when cats otherwise appear angry. Scanty and rather poorly controlled observations in decorticate dogs seem to indicate that tail wagging in response to petting or any other stimulus does not occur in the absence of the cerebral cortex. The facts, such as they are, do not point, therefore, to any subcortical mechanisms for the somatic expression of pleasure.

Conclusion.—A brief summary of the material bearing upon the neural mechanisms of emotional expression is in order. The Cannon-

Bard theory of emotion holds that patterns of emotion are integrated in the hypothalamus and that emotion is therefore to be considered 'localized' in this region of the diencephalon. The arguments for the notion rest upon the fact that certain particular patterns, more or less arbitrarily selected and restricted to rage, seem to depend upon the hypothalamus for their integrity. The facts presented above indicate, however, that various aspects of rage behavior, or of emotional response in general, are integrated at different levels of the nervous system. Fundamental sympathetic responses depend only on the spinal cord and medulla. Certain items of somatic behavior are mediated by the medulla and midbrain. These are more perfectly integrated in the hypothalamus, but certain additional components of emotional behavior are mediated by the thalamus and striatum. The most complete expressions, involving first the restraint of emotion and later its maintenance, including localizing behavior with respect to the emotional stimulus, depend upon the intact cerebral cortex. Thus in emotion, as we have seen elsewhere in sensory and motor systems, different sorts of integrations are performed at different levels of the nervous system, and no one nucleus or region can be said to constitute the neural center of the emotional behavior.

BRAIN WAVES AND EMOTION

Attempts have recently been made to study neural processes in emotion as they are reflected in brain waves (Hoagland *et al.*). Subjects were selected who were known to be emotional about certain questions and topics. They were then presented with these questions while their brain waves were being recorded, and at another time they were given questions which did not provoke emotional responses so that their brain waves could be compared for the two conditions, emotional and nonemotional. The brain waves were recorded from the scalp in the region of the occiput and also from a position in the pharynx near the hypothalamus.

The brain waves that one obtains in the nonemotional situations are made up largely of waves between 8 and 12 cycles per second, *i.e.*, of alpha waves. When the emotional topics were presented, however, many delta waves appeared, these being waves below 8 cycles per second. Put in other words, the delta index, which is a measure of the proportion of the brain waves that are slower than alpha waves, is increased in emotional situations. With this increase could sometimes be correlated an acceleration of the heartbeat, but in general the delta index was a better measure of emotion than the heartbeat. Since we do not understand the nature of the physiological changes governing the brain waves, it is not possible to interpret the significance of this change, but it does offer one more correlate of emotion, one that perhaps can be put to good use in experiments with emotion.

General References

BARD, P., 1934.　The neurohumoral basis of emotional reactions.　Pp. 264–311. In *A Handbook of General Experimental Psychology*.　Ed. Carl Murchison. Worcester: Clark Univ. Press.

RUCKMICK, C. A., 1936.　*The psychology of feeling and emotion*.　New York: McGraw-Hill.　Pp. 529.

CHAPTER XVIII

SLEEP AND ACTIVITY

In the chapters that have gone before, we have dealt mainly with particular kinds of behavior—spinal reflexes, postural reactions, manipulative behavior, and so on. In this chapter, however, we shall consider behavior at large and aside from any particular pattern of reaction. Our subject is simply *activity*. An animal may run, walk, climb, manipulate objects, or do any one of many other things, and we do not care which; they may all be taken together as activity. By looking at behavior from such a general point of view we can see some points of importance in understanding behavior which are not dealt with when we dissect behavior into its component patterns. Then, too, the study of activity provides an introduction to the topic of motivated behavior to which we shall come in the chapters that follow.

PHYSIOLOGICAL CHARACTERISTICS OF SLEEP

Any discussion of general activity must, of course, include the topic of sleep, for sleep is a very conspicuous case of activity being reduced to its minimum. To be sure, sleep appears to be more than a state of comparative inactivity because it is marked, in addition, by lack of consciousness. That difference, however, need not concern us at present, and we can take sleep as it appears, consider it as a special kind of behavior, and see where it leads us. Let us begin by considering its various behavioral and physiological characteristics and then turn later to more basic questions of its nature and cause.

Somatic Activity.—The general level of somatic muscular activity is probably the best index of sleep. Indeed, it is about the only one we can use in observing animals, although in some animals closing of the eyes or the assumption of particular postures may be more or less satisfactory. In man, of course, his verbal report can be used.

Employing general activity as our index and applying it to all animals, we find, first of all, that there are marked individual differences from one species to another and at different age levels with respect to the length and frequency of periods of sleep. Many animals, including man, sleep during one long period in a day; these are spoken of as *monophasic* animals. Many, on the other hand, display alternate periods of rest and muscular activity during a day, and such animals are said to be *poly-*

phasic. Rats, rabbits and, in general, all the rodents, are polyphasic; canaries, snakes, and man are monophasic. Several animals are intermediate between these, for they observe one long period of rest daily but also take short naps in between. Even in polyphasic animals—the rat, for example—there may be diurnal (monophasic) variations in activity level superimposed upon polyphasic cycles. The human infant, it is interesting to note, is a polyphasic creature, but as it grows older it gradually changes to monophasic sleep habits.

One author (Szymanski) suggests that a relation exists between the periodicity of sleep, *i.e.*, whether an animal is polyphasic or monophasic, and the sensory mechanisms that predominate in the control of an animal's behavior. Animals in which vision plays a very important role seem to be monophasic with their periods of sleep taking place at night. Other animals, including the human infant, in which tactile and nonvisual senses are more prominent in governing behavior, are polyphasic. Although not without its exceptions, this generalization appears to be fairly sound. From it, one can gather that polyphasic activity would be the normal case in the absence of a diurnal light-dark cycle, but that this cycle, imposed upon the organism from outside, manages to alter the habits of sleeping and activity to conform to it. The importance of the diurnal cycle in controlling highly complex instinctual activities will also be evident when, at a later point, we consider the problem of migratory activity.

One other fact about muscular activity in sleep has been much emphasized in recent years. It is that the reduction in activity which takes place in sleep is only a relative affair. Carefully recorded measurements of movement during human sleep reveal that a certain amount of muscular activity is normal to sleep and that this activity alternates regularly with periods of rest. In one study (Johnson *et al.*), for example, it was found that the average period of uninterrupted rest was about 11 min., but that in particular individuals it might be as low as 7 or as high as 25 min.

Autonomic Activity.—In the hope of finding clues to the nature of sleep, many investigations of autonomic conditions in sleep have been carried out. Not all of them are in perfect agreement, but the following list of results (see Kleitman) can be accepted with considerable assurance: (1) Heart rate is significantly reduced, in some cases as much as 20 to 30 beats per minute, but it corresponds, in general, to the rate that obtains under similar conditions of muscular relaxation or after prolonged periods without sleep. (2) Blood pressure also tends to go down in sleep; in one group of subjects it was reduced 24 mm. Diminishing gradually after the onset of sleep, it reaches a minimum in about the fourth hour of sleep, thereafter rising somewhat, and comes up abruptly upon waking. (3) The volume of the brain increases, due, it seems probable, to an increase in the amount of blood in the arterioles. (4) Respiration is somewhat slower and its depth is greater, but the chief change in it is its greater regularity. (5) Gastric contractions and alimentary activity go on as usual, if not with somewhat greater vigor.

In general, all autonomic functions are about as one would expect to be the case when the organism is not engaged in activity and is no longer

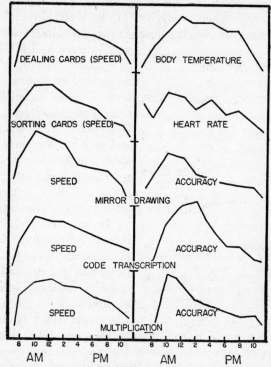

Fig. 132.—The relation of the diurnal cycle to body temperature and to various measures of motor and mental performance. (*After N. Kleitman.* Sleep and wakefulness, *p.* 217. *Chicago: University of Chicago Press,* 1939. *By permission of the publishers.*)

subject to calls upon it by the stimuli of the outside world. The general picture is one of the dominance of parasympathetic activities—those which subserve restorative and conservative functions.

Body Temperature.—Falling into this picture but worth special mention is the relation of body temperature to motility. The ability to keep the temperature of the body relatively constant and independent of environmental temperature has been developed only in the later stages of phylogenesis, and especially in birds and mammals. Even in them, however, minor variations in body temperature can be observed, and these appear to be closely related to the sleep habits of an animal. In birds, for example, which are usually monophasic, going to bed at dark and getting up at dawn, the body temperature rises in the daytime and falls at night. There is no doubt, moreover, that the diurnal temperature rhythm is related to their sleep habits, for when the light-and-dark conditions are experimentally reversed, the temperature rhythm, as well as the sleeping rhythm, is also reversed.

The same diurnal temperature rhythm is present in man, as is shown by a number of studies; and this rhythm is, in this case also, a close correlate of the individual's activity. Indeed, the rise and fall of body temperature during the waking hours is paralleled in a truly remarkable way by a rise and fall in the speed and accuracy with which various motor and mental tasks can be performed. The higher the temperature, the better the performance (Fig. 132). So it is also with sleep and activity; the body temperature tends, on the average, to reach a maximum in the afternoon or early evening and a minimum in the early hours of the morning.

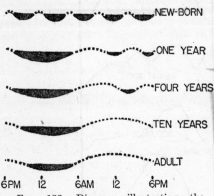

Fig. 133.—Diagram illustrating the cycles of sleep and the change from polyphasic to monophasic sleep from birth to adulthood. (*After N. Kleitman. Sleep and wakefulness, p. 515. Chicago: University of Chicago Press, 1939. By permission of the publishers.*)

In order to establish the meaning of the rhythm, Kleitman and his associates have studied the cycle in human infants, and others have considered the role of muscle tonus in producing it (Fig. 133). From the observations of infants it was learned that the cycle is not present in appreciable degree at birth but is developed only after about the first 12 months—a fact that correlates with the infant's acquisition of diurnal (monophasic) sleep habits. In an experiment with birds (Burckard *et al.*), in which a large part of their musculature was paralyzed by sectioning nerves, the diurnal variation was almost completely abolished, and this result appears to point definitely to muscle tonus as its cause. Muscle tonus, we must realize, however, comes from cerebral activity, and as Kleitman has pointed out, a vicious circle is thereby set up: a high 'activity' level of the brain increases muscle tonus which through the production of heat increases the 'activity' level of the brain; and the reverse, of course, is true in sleep.

Reflex Excitability.—From the remarks above we know that in sleep muscular activity is lowered, the parasympathetic system dominates autonomic functions, and the body temperature is lower. To these characteristics of sleep we may add another, the heightening of sensory thresholds for eliciting reflexes, although this characteristic does not apply equally well to all the senses. Whereas the proprioceptive mechanisms are considerably depressed, the cutaneous reflexes are more

FIG. 134.—Diagram of the way in which the depth of sleep varies throughout a night of sleep. (*From N. Kleitman. Sleep and wakefulness, p. 146. Chicago: University of Chicago Press*, 1939. *By permission of the publishers.*)

nearly normal. The knee jerk, for example, which is a reflex obtained by striking the knee tendon, gradually disappears as a man goes to sleep; and when it can still be elicited in the lighter stages of sleep it is of less

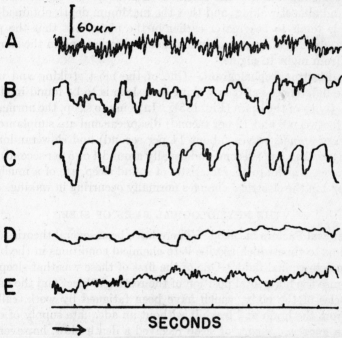

SECONDS

FIG. 135.—Change in the brain waves of a person going to sleep. *A,* alpha rhythm of wakefulness; *B,* alpha and delta waves of light sleep; *C,* delta rhythm of deep sleep early in the night; *D,* "null" rhythm which later replaces the delta rhythm; *E,* alpha rhythm on awakening. (*After N. Kleitman. Sleep and wakefulness, p. 46. Chicago: University of Chicago Press*, 1939. *By permission of the publishers.*)

than normal extent. Cutaneous stimulation, on the other hand, seems to bring out rather normal responses; brushing of the face produces a grimace, or tickling stimuli may elicit scratching movements. Of particular interest, moreover, is the fact that the Babinski reaction, which is notable for the fact that it appears in infants but not in the waking adult unless there is neural injury, may make its appearance in sleep. The Babinski reflex, it may be recalled, is a symptom of defective functioning of the pyramidal pathways from the precentral gyrus of the cortex.

The 'Depth' of Sleep.—Many attempts have been made to measure the depth of sleep by presenting various sensory stimuli and finding the intensity required to awaken an individual. Great variability of 'threshold' is always obtained no matter what method is used, although statistically it turns out that the depth of sleep tends to be greater in the early period of sleep than later on in the night. After considering the various facts which have been gotten together on this topic, Kleitman comes to the conclusion that the depth of sleep in any given individual on a particular night is a cyclic function (Fig. 134) varying between great depth and almost waking, and that the maximum depth obtained in any one cycle tends to be greater earlier in the night, but that the pattern varies a great deal from one individual to another and in the same individual from night to night.

The Electroencephalogram.—One of the most striking and unquestionable differences between waking and sleep is to be found in the electrical activity of the brain (Fig. 135). In going to sleep, the normal *alpha* waves (between 8 and 12 per second) disappear and are supplanted by a mixture of *spindle* waves (about 14 per second) and slow random *delta* waves (less than 8 per second and usually around 4 or 5 per second). The *delta* waves, which are characteristic of sound sleep, are of a much larger voltage than the electrical changes normally occurring in waking.

THE PHYSIOLOGICAL BASIS OF SLEEP

Chemical Factors in Sleep.—There have been several theories of sleep from time to time which ascribe it to chemical conditions in the blood or in the cerebrospinal fluid. One of the first of these was that sleep comes on because the horizontal position of the resting subject and the demands of muscles of the body, which have been fatigued by work, call blood away from the brain and leave it without an adequate supply of oxygen. Such an *anoxemic* theory of sleep received a death blow, however, when it was shown in several studies that the brain of a sleeping subject receives not less, but more, blood than usual.

It has also been argued that the waste products of metabolism affect the brain so as to bring on sleep. Most suspected of such products is carbon dioxide. This shows a significant increase in sleep, both in the amount that is expired in air and in that which is excreted; but the trouble with believing carbon dioxide to be a *cause* of sleep is that the increase in it occurs after the onset of sleep rather than before, and in animals and human beings forcibly kept awake for long periods of time, no changes in the carbon dioxide tension of the blood have been observed.

One can find many other suggestions for a chemical basis of sleep, but none so far have proved attractive (see Kleitman). One further possibility worth mentioning, however, is Pieron's so-called *hypnotoxin* theory, according to which it is supposed that there is some particular, though unidentified, substance produced in the blood and cerebrospinal fluid which leads to sleep. Supporting such a belief are the early experiments of Pieron in which cerebrospinal fluid was removed from a greatly fatigued animal and injected into the cerebral ventricles of a normal animal. Thereupon, Pieron observed, the normal animal became drowsy and fell asleep, and he thought, therefore, that the fluid of the tired animal must have contained a hypnotoxin. Because Pieron's experiment left something to be desired in the way of adequate experimental controls, it has been repeated by Schnedorf and Ivy. From their well-controlled study have come the following revision of Pieron's conclusions: the injection of 'fatigued' cerebrospinal fluid into a rested dog's cerebral ventricles does, in some instances, produce sleep. It is not certain, however, that this effect is due to a hypnotoxin, for there is an accompanying increase in cerebrospinal-fluid pressure and in body temperature, and these factors, of themselves, often produce sleep. That a hypnotoxin does exist in not, however, ruled out; the evidence for it is simply equivocal.

One of the strongest arguments against any simple theory that sleep is produced by chemical conditions in the internal environment of the nervous system comes from studies of Siamese twins. These have certain parts of the body in common and have, in the cases studied (Kleitman, p. 483), interconnecting circulatory systems. In each of the three such instances available it has been reported that one member of the pair may be very much awake, nursing for example, while the other one is fast asleep. Then, too, in an experiment with two dogs (Neri *et al.*) in which a cross circulation had been established, inducing sleep in one animal by thrusting a needle into the hypothalamic region of the brain (see below) had no effect upon the other animal. Thus the available evidence does not support a hypnotoxin theory of sleep, although it is not impossible that such a substance might play some secondary role in facilitating sleep.

The Action of Hypnotic Drugs.—The question of the neural mechanism of sleep has also been approached by inducing sleep with drugs (hypnotics) and then studying the parts of the nervous system that they affect and the type of changes in the electroencephalogram that they produce. Unfortunately the site of action of hypnotic drugs tells us little about the mechanisms of sleep. There is, in the first place, some disagreement as to just where, whether in the cortex or in the thalamus and striatum, a given drug has its greatest effect. However that may be, it is quite certain that sleep can be induced by depressing the activity of either the cortex or subcortical centers.

Somewhat more illuminating is the character of the brain wave in hypnotically induced sleep and in normal sleep. Results from several studies (Derbyshire *et al.;* Adrian; Gibbs) have shown, in general, that the barbiturates (dial, veronal, luminal, etc.) produce rather 'genuine' sleep; for under their influence the brain waves change in the manner described above for normal sleep. Ether, on the other hand, causes changes in the brain wave but of a different type from that of normal sleep. Now, if we are to believe the contention of some, notably Pick, who have determined the place of action of hypnotics, we should be led to believe that sleep represents the depression of the thalamus and striatum, for it is on these centers that the barbiturates are alleged to act. Unfortunately, however, this conclusion is contradicted by other researches which are equally reliable (Koppanyi *et al.*).

Cortical Factors in Sleep.—In his famous experiments on conditioned reflexes, Pavlov noted some interesting facts about sleep. He found that if an animal were required to wait a considerable period of time for the reinforcement of the unconditioned stimulus, after the conditioned stimulus, he frequently went to sleep during the period of delay. Pavlov, as we shall see in a later chapter, explained all the phenomena of conditioning in terms of "excitation" and "inhibition." Under appropriate conditions, these two kinds of nervous activity could "irradiate" across the cortex, and since sleep made its appearance under conditions calling for "inhibition," Pavlov took sleep to be the result of the *irradiation of inhibition.* From this notion, he went on to generalize about all sleep as a cortical phenomena in which inhibition of neural activity spread across the cortex.

Pavlov was probably wrong in believing the sleep he observed to have anything to do with conditioning and conditioned inhibition, for Kleitman has observed dogs going to sleep in the stock when they have not had any experience with conditioning procedures. Boredom is all that is necessary. This fact Kleitman interprets as indicating, in accordance with his theory of sleep (below), that lowering of cortical activity is favorable to sleep. In this respect, perhaps, Pavlov was right in ascribing importance to cortical "inhibition." Because such sleep is usually quite brief, Kleitman likens it more to animal hypnosis than to true sleep.

Also worth mentioning is the idea of another prominent researcher in the field of sleep. Johnson proposes that there is a cortical sleep center whose activity controls neural processes in other parts of the cortex and by shutting them off brings on sleep. The only trouble with this theory, as with any cortical theory of sleep, is that animals which have been completely decorticated (Kleitman and Camille) sleep, and there can be little doubt about it. Indeed, the sleep of decorticated dogs meets most of the criteria, taken up above, of normal sleep. Their eyes close, their breathing becomes regular, they may even keep a diurnal cycle, their threshold of reflex excitability is markedly raised, and they assume sleeping posture. Similar observations are available on monkeys (Karplus and Kreidl).

The Role of the Thalamus in Sleep.—For many years now, records have been gathered of human patients with brain lesions and with abnormal tendencies to sleep (somnolence). In a large proportion of these cases, lesions have been found in the lower part of the thalamus, in the general region of the hypothalamus and the anterior part of the floor of the midbrain. In not every instance has this been true, for in some patients with somnolence the lesions have been restricted to the thalamus and cerebral cortex. The general purport of the evidence, however, has been to point to a "sleep center," as we might call it, in the hypothalamic-mesencephalic region. Recently the matter has been put to experimental test by Ranson and his associates, who have made lesions in various subcortical centers of monkeys and then observed their behavior. The rather uniform result of their work has been that whenever the destruction was in the suspected area their subjects were made sleepy, and in many cases distinctly abnormal somnolence was produced. The precise localization of the center has not been established, and it is probable that it is not a neatly circumscribed area but extends, rather, over a considerable part of the hypothalamus and mesencephalon, perhaps even into the thalamus proper. If, however, we were to point to any given nucleus as the focus of the area, it would be the mammillary bodies, for lesions in them (Ranson) are most likely to cause hypersomnia.

The Phylogenetic Theory of Sleep.—Whatever the size and locus of the center, it is quite clear that instead of calling it a sleep center we should name it the *wakefulness center*, for the reader will note that *destroying* it causes sleep, and its activity must, consequently, be responsible for wakefulness. Kleitman has emphasized that point and made it the basis for the development of a theory of sleep, which is the most attractive one presented to date and without doubt comes very close to being the truth. Its principal features may be outlined as follows:

The normal vegetative functions of an organism go on all the time in sleep or waking, but for the higher integrative processes of the brain which are concerned in adjustment with the external world the activity of the *wakefulness center* is necessary. This center is kept in action mainly by the host of nervous impulses that are continually coming into it from the sense organs, the most important of which are the proprioceptive impulses from the muscles. The muscles, however, become fatigued through activity and tend to relax or to get the organism to take a position in which they can be relaxed. When this happens, the impulses that keep up the activity of the wakefulness center are greatly reduced. But the wakefulness center through its fibers to the thalamus and cortex exercises a facilitating influence upon the activity level—we might look at the center as a priming mechanism—and when its activity is reduced, so also is that of the cortex and its responses to incoming stimuli. Thus sleep is brought on.

During sleep there is always the chance that sensory impulses, either those of kinesthesis from which the organism can never completely escape or fortuitous stimuli from outside the organism, will pour into the wakefulness center and rearouse it to activity. Then, too, during sleep, both the center and the cortex are rested and their excitability improves, and eventually these stimuli lead to wakening. The cortex, finally, can send influences to the wakefulness center and keep it going when otherwise it might be inclined to stop or lower its activity; or the cortex can keep up tonus in the body musculature so that sensory impulses from it keep exciting the wakefulness center. In this way, Kleitman believes, the polyphasic sleep habits of lower animals and of the human infant are converted either partly or entirely into monophasic rhythms (see Fig. 133). A wakefulness of choice, as he puts it, is thrust upon the wakefulness center by the adjustments of the cortex to the light-dark cycle of the world. Otherwise, whenever the muscles become tired, say in an hour or two of wakefulness, the organism would take a relaxed posture, thereby reducing the barrage of impulses keeping the wakefulness center active, and sleep would follow for a brief period; this cycle would be repeated several times daily.

There is much that can be said for the phylogenetic theory of (monophasic) sleep. It seems to contradict no established fact and conforms to, or explains, many others. It fits in quite nicely, for example, with the fact that muscular relaxation and generally reduced stimulation is a primary factor in getting to sleep. By the assumption that the wakefulness center is a 'priming' device for cortical activity and without it the cortex is largely nonfunctional, it explains why conscious processes and similar functions are largely blotted out in sleep. There is anatomical evidence, too, for this assumption; the hypothalamic regions and particularly the mammillary bodies have comparatively massive projections to the thalamus and cortex which could serve this 'priming' function. Similarly, there are fibers downward from the cortex by which the cortex might influence the wakefulness center. And they suggest a mechanism for establishing the monophasic cycle. Indeed, in experiments of Camille and Kleitman it was found that decorticate dogs lapse back to the polyphasic sleep habits of infancy—a fact that fits in nicely with the assumptions of the phylogenetic theory. Then, too, if the cortex is inactive and its pyramidal area is at a greatly lowered level of activity, the appearance of the positive Babinski reflex is explained. Finally, the close proximity of the wakefulness center to the oculomotor nuclei suggests a reason for the tendency of the eyelids to drop when sleep is impending.

It is worth noting, before closing this section, that once the monophasic cycle is set up in human individuals it becomes a bona fide rhythm of the cortex, wakefulness center, or both, going on partly independently of whether sleep actually occurs. In the extensive studies of Kleitman (*et al.*) of prolonged wakefulness, every aspect of the rhythm keeps up, for some time at least, even though an individual gets no sleep. The temperature and activity, for example, drop at night and go up in the daytime. A subject is more awake, says Kleitman, on the third afternoon of prolonged wakefulness than he is on the second night. Thus has the sleep mechanism been demonstrated to possess periodicity even when wakefulness is forcibly extended far over the normal period.

ACTIVITY AND DRIVES

Turning now from sleep and waking, let us consider the gross activity of organisms without respect to whether or not they are asleep or awake when they are active. Activity, so conceived, has been measured by two general methods. The first (Fig. 136) makes use of the stabilimeter (Richter), a cage arranged on pivots or suspended by springs in such a way that any movement of an animal in the cage, even though exceedingly slight, can be registered by appropriate levers on a smoked or waxed paper. As ordinarily used, the stabilimeter gives records of the amplitude of movement, its frequency, and time of occurrence. The second method employs a circular cage or floor which moves, in the manner of a treadmill, with movement of the animal. From counting devices attached to the apparatus, the number of revolutions run by the animal in any given period of time may be determined, and this is taken as a measure of activity. This second method has been the one most often used in studies of animal activity.

Drives.—In the present section, the relation of bodily activity to drives will be taken up, for this relation is an important one. Implied by the word *drive* here will be the simplest meaning of the term: primarily, the need of the organism for food, water, and sexual satisfaction. In later chapters, the question of what a drive is, from the physiological point of view, will come up and its definition will have to be considered

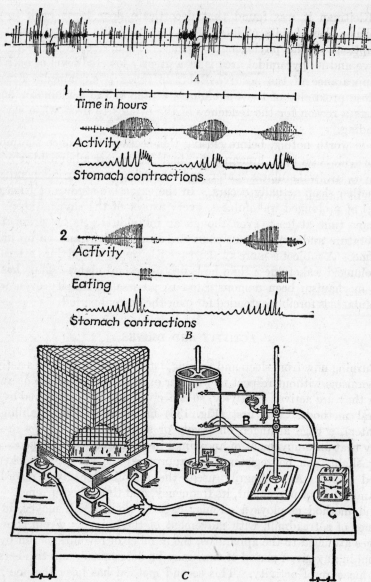

FIG. 136.—A. Kymograph records showing the relation between gross bodily activity and eating.

B. Schematic representation of the relation between stomach contractions and gross bodily activity.

C. Activity cage and recording kymograph. A, magnetic marker activated by activity cage; B, time marker activated by electric clock C. (*From C. P. Richter. Animal behavior and internal drives. Quart. Rev. Biol., 2, 307–343, 1927. By permission of the publishers.*)

in some detail, but for the present a more naïve conception of it will suffice.

Hunger.—Several experiments with rats and with human beings demonstrate the fact that bodily activity and hunger are closely related. Rats, if allowed to eat freely, display rather regular rhythms of activity and feeding, which occur, on the average, about every four hours. The activity almost always begins first, and only after it has continued for some minutes does eating take place; thereafter activity soon ceases. Similar findings, moreover, have been reported for human subjects studied while asleep, but in this case, instead of studying eating or verbal reports of hunger, records of stomach contractions were taken (Wada). Shifts of sleeping position and other more minor movements, it was found, preceded or attended episodes of gastric motility.

Having established this close connection of hunger or gastric contractions with bodily activity, one may ask which is the cause and which the result. One might be inclined to believe that the gastric contractions are the cause of the bodily activity (Richter), especially in view of the common belief that stomach contractions are the basis of hunger (see Ch. XXI). In view of the fact, however, that in the rat activity *precedes* eating and in man bodily motility very frequently *precedes* gastric contractions, it is difficult to hold such a view.

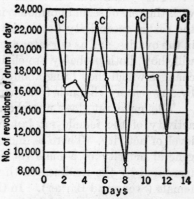

FIG. 137.—Rhythms of gross bodily activity corresponding to estrual periods in the female rat. The dots marked *C* correspond with the presence of cornified epithelial cells in the vaginal smear which indicates that the animal was "in heat." (*From G. H. Wang. The relation between "spontaneous" activity and oestrous cycle in the white rat. Comp. Psychol. Monogr., vol. 2, No. 6, p. 27, 1923. By permission of Williams and Wilkins, publishers.*)

The preferable conclusion is that the two have a common origin in conditions influencing the nervous system. More extensive evidence for this conclusion is found in a later discussion of hunger.

Sexual Drive.—Gross bodily activity is also intimately related to sexual drive, at least in some of the infrahuman animals. In female sexual functions, the relation is particularly striking. The female rat has a sexual cycle in which ovulation (p. 422) and sexual receptivity occur rather regularly at 4- to 5-day intervals. Correlated with this cycle is a prominent rhythm of somatic activity which shows up well in measurements of the number of turns run in a rotating drum (Wang, Slonaker; Fig. 137). At the peak of the cycle, a female rat may run as much as

10 miles a day, whereas on other days only a fraction of a mile will be run. The period of greatest activity, it has been shown by direct observations, corresponds to the time of "heat," or sexual receptivity. If at this time, the female is copulated and made pregnant, no further periods of heat will be seen throughout the length of pregnancy (about 20 days); and throughout this period activity remains at a very low level. Thus it is clear that the activity is directly dependent upon conditions having to do with sexual receptivity.

Here, again, the question comes up as to what the cause of the activity is. This question is answered quite clearly in a section below dealing with the role of sexual hormones in activity; the gross bodily activity and the sexual receptivity both arise from hormonal conditions determined in the ovaries, and as our later examination of the basis of sexual behavior will show, both probably are elicited by the hormones and the metabolic changes which they bring about directly affecting the brain, rather than by any sensory channels from particular organs of the body.

The male rat does not show the periodicity characteristic of the activity of the female rat but maintains, rather, a relatively constant level of activity. There is, moreover, little or no relation between the general activity of a male rat and the strength of its sexual drive as measured by the readiness with which it will avail itself of a receptive female (Stone and Barker). In this respect, therefore, there is no important relation between activity and strength of drive. Of interest also is the fact that reduction in sexual drive has no visible affect on activity, for animals allowed a period with a female rat in "heat" are just as active in a revolving drum as before.

THE ENDOCRINE BASIS OF ACTIVITY

The relation between the sex and hunger drives leads us to inquire about the part chemical conditions of the internal environment may play in general bodily activity. In view of the importance, moreover, of the thyroid and adrenal glands in the metabolism of the body and of the pituitary gland in regulating many of the glandular functions we should be inclined to expect them to be closely related to activity—and so it turns out. The gonads, too, which are primary factors in sexual drive, prove to take part in the control of activity.

The Gonads.—The ovaries, whose cyclical activities govern sexual receptivity in the female, are quite crucial determinants of activity. Removal of the ovaries, Richter finds, reduces activity to about one-fifth the normal level and completely eliminates all signs of cyclical functions, as described above (Fig. 138). A similar reduction in activity takes place in castrated male rats. Whereas, moreover, before such operations, there are marked individual differences in rats with respect to activity level and females show a higher level of activity, on the average, than males, such differences are abolished by ovariectomy or castration. All animals seem to be reduced to a rather uniform, but very low, level of activity. Suggested by this fact is the possibility that a considerable part of individual differences among human beings, in respect of 'pep' and general activity, may be governed by hormones from the gonads. It is dangerous, however, to carry over such a generalization, without subjecting it to an experimental test, which in this case is rather difficult. It is possible, too, that the revolving-drum method of measuring activity is not a sensitive enough measure for indicating individual differences at low levels of activity (Stone).

Of considerable interest is the fact that the hormone, or at least, one important hormone, producing activity in the female rat has been iden-

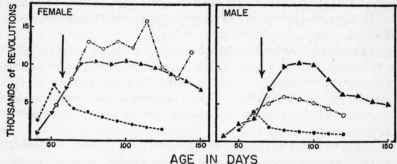

Fig. 138.—Effect of amniotin (estrin) injection upon the activity of normal and gonad-ectomized rats. Triangles, uninjected normal rats; open circles, injected gonadectomized animals; closed circles, uninjected gonadectomized rats. (*After C. P. Richter and C. G. Hartman.*)

tified. *Estrin*, the chief hormone of the ovary (a member of the general class of estrogens), when injected into ovariectomized female rats, prevents the degeneration of the reproductive tract, which normally occurs after removing the ovaries, and, at the same time, maintains activity at its normal level (Richter and Hartman). Moreover, injections of this hormone into castrated male rats, while it does not prevent atrophy of the sexual organs, has a similar effect in bringing bodily activity back to near its normal level for males. Quite striking, therefore, is the dependence of bodily activity upon an adequate supply of sexual hormones.

The Adrenal Glands.—That activity is not entirely controlled by one particular hormone but is dependent upon a number of factors is seen in the fact that extirpation of the adrenal glands also reduces activity. Such a reduction is quite marked, being on the average about 90 per cent. Apparently responsible for this effect is the *cortex*, rather than the medulla, of the adrenal gland; for the administration of *cortin*, the extract of the adrenal cortex, rectifies the effects of adrenal extirpation, so far as general activity is concerned. If, however, the quantity of salt (sodium chloride) fed the adrenalectomized animals is greatly increased, the activity level will also rise, although it will not recover completely. The relation of the adrenal cortex to the metabolism of sodium and to the retention of water in the body has already been mentioned (p. 38), and the chemical conditions of the internal environment influenced by the adrenal cortex are undoubtedly quite complex.

The Thyroid Gland.—Also making for a reduction in activity is the experimental removal of the thyroid gland (Richter). In this case, however, the effect is not so great as when the adrenal glands or gonads are taken out. In thyroidectomized rats, as in the other experiments, the level of activity could be restored to normal by feeding extracts of the gland. The thyroid hormones, therefore, are also factors in activity, probably through the control of general metabolic rate in the various tissues of the body.

The Pancreas.—A similar control is exercised by the pancreas, except that this gland, when removed, has a more profound influence upon activity than any other gland. Its extirpation causes activity to be reduced by 98 to 99 per cent. The pancreas, it will be remembered, secretes insulin; this acts on cell membranes to allow food materials, particularly sugar, to pass through them, and thereby is a very crucial factor in the metabolism of all cells in the body, particularly of the brain. Then, too, pancreectomy is accompanied by marked acidosis, which as we have seen, is itself a sufficient condition for greatly reduced neural excitability.

The Pituitary Gland.—Removal of the pituitary body or cutting the stalk that connects it with the hypothalamus also causes a considerable reduction in the general activity level of rats (Richter). In this case the effects are to be explained, in part at least, by the influence of the pituitary gland on the growth and secretion of other glands. After removal of the pituitary, the adrenals, thyroid, and gonads show more or less atrophy, and these glands, we already stated, are all factors in activity.

Another point to be made concerning the effect of the removal of the pituitary is that the changes in activity include not only a reduction in its level but also, in females, a change in its rhythm. Whereas the normal female rat shows a 4- to 5-day activity cycle, the hypophysectomized rate tends to show a 14-day rhythm. To explain this finding, Richter offers the suggestion that the 14-day cycle is a multiple of the 4- to 5-day cycle and that it comes about because the amplitude of the changes in the ovary which are expressed in the 4- to 5-day rhythm is so reduced that it only makes itself evident on the average every three cycles.

This hypothesis, Richter says, is upheld by the fact that in animals not showing the 14-day cycle there seemed to be a 9- or an 18-day rhythm, which would represent two or four normal ovarian cycles, respectively. The suggestion is not unreasonable because it is known from other data that the ovary is normally stimulated by the hormones of the hypophysis (p. 429).

THE NEURAL CONTROL OF ACTIVITY

When the results of studies on the relation of endocrine and chemical factors to activity are viewed as a whole, it seems that no one chemical condition is responsible for activity, although any one factor such as estrin, cortin, or insulin may, when lacking, have a profound affect on activity. This is perfectly reasonable when it is realized how complex are the chemical processes required to sustain nerve cells at their normal level of functioning—and it is to nerve cells that one must look for the immediate source of the changes in activity described, for gross bodily activity represents motor nervous activity. One may turn, therefore, to the question of what functions or structures of the nervous system are of primary importance in the instances above. It may, of course, be taken for granted that the general metabolic rate of the cerebral cortex and the brain will be related to activity; but it may be that there are more specific mechanisms for activity than that.

Frontal 'Activity' Areas.—It has been reported from time to time by those casually observing the behavior of animals after cortical operations that lesions in the anterior part of the frontal lobes are accompanied by great restlessness and generally increased activity (see Beach). From such observations it was suggested that the frontal areas of the cortex (see p. 551) had, as one of their functions, the part of inhibiting other nervous processes, particularly those of a motor character. In every group of animals (usually monkeys) studied, the majority would be made more active by the frontal lesions, but a few would stay the same or even become less active (Jacobsen). In order to account for such variability, a somewhat less specific mechanism than centers of "inhibition" in the frontal areas was proposed: the increase in activity, it was suggested (Jacobsen), comes of the fact that the animal which is partially decorticated is somewhat more distractable and therefore reacts more readily to external stimuli.

Recently the question has been reopened by several studies in which, in contrast to visual observation of behavior, quantitative records of activity before and after operation were taken, usually by the revolving-drum technique. The rat (Richter and Hawkes; Beach), the cat (Langworthy and Richter), and the monkey (Richter and Hines) have been studied in this manner. The results, unfortunately, have been of a somewhat complicated character and need some detailed discussion.

In their study of the rat, Richter and Hawkes came to the following conclusions: Removal of one frontal pole tends to increase the activity of all animals but affects less active rats more than more active ones. Upon removal of the other pole, thus making a bilateral operation, the increase in activity is very marked. The rats do not run themselves to death, but they come near to it. Along with the hyperactivity goes a greatly increased food intake and a considerable increase in irritability and savageness, the reasons for which are not known. Then, upon examining the sizes of the various endocrine glands in the hyperactive and normal rats, it was found that the pituitary glands of the operated rats were smaller and their ovaries larger than those of normal rats.

From these findings, it was clear to Richter and Hawkes that removal of the frontal poles of the rat's cortex (possibly including some of the striatum) causes hyperactivity; but the reasons for the effect were not so clear. It might be that the crucial areas inhibit the growth and secretion of the gonads or of other glands and that when removed the increased activity results from the greater production of hormones. The increased size of the ovaries in operated animals supports this conclusion. The hypothesis, on the other hand, that the frontal areas inhibit nervous functions or that their removal makes the animal more distractible, and thus more active, is not ruled out.

The conclusions reached by Richter and Hawkes have to be modified somewhat by the later research of Beach. He found that lesions anywhere in the brain may either increase or decrease activity, although when in the frontal part of the brain they more often increase activity and do it in greater degree. Prominent in his findings is the same result that was met in the earlier more casual researches, that not all animals are made hyperactive by the frontal-area lesions. Beach, too, did not observe any increase in savageness in his animals. With such results considered it appears that, although the frontal areas have something to do with activity, in what way and why the same results are not obtained in all animals are problems for further research.

Experiments with the cat, carried out by Langworthy and Richter, appear to present very clear-cut results (see Fig. 139). Unilateral lesions lead on the average to a doubling of activity, and bilateral removal of the frontal pole results in a very remarkable increase in activity, on the average by a factor of *ten times*. Some animals may, indeed, run more than one hundred times as far per day as they did before operation, and, as a consequence, they may exhaust themselves and die. The hyperactivity is often accompanied by a ravenous appetite, but it is not known whether that is a direct consequence of frontal-pole removal or an indirect result of the hyperactivity; this, naturally, increases the demands of the body for energy.

A survey of the work with rats and cats leaves no doubt that there is a genuine and dramatic increase in activity following removal of the frontal poles in these animals. For a more refined picture of what particular areas of the frontal lobes are responsible for these results, however, we must turn to experiments with monkeys, which have brains

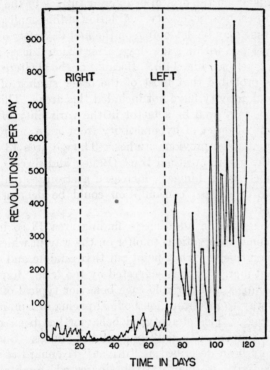

Fig. 139.—Effect of removal of the prefrontal areas upon activity as seen in the record of a cat subjected first to right, then to left, prefrontal lobectomy. (*After O. R. Langworthy and C. P. Richter.*)

that are more highly organized and in which it is more possible and plausible to speak of specific areas than it is in lower animals.

All who have studied the problem in monkeys agree that hyperactivity, like other symptoms of frontal-lobe lesions, is much more pronounced in bilateral than in unilateral lesions; indeed, it is controversial whether or not the latter produce any significant effects whatsoever.

The results of Richter and Hines with objective means of recording activity indicate further that hyperactivity follows destruction of one particular part of the frontal area (Brodmann's area 9) more than that of any other, but that the addition of a larger part of the frontal area (areas 10, 11, 12; see Fig. 26) will somewhat augment the effect. Kennard *et al.*, who also studied the question by objective methods, conclude that separate ablation of area 8, area 9, or areas 10, 11, 12 induces hyperactivity but that all these areas must be removed to produce maximal hyperactivity. This study indicates equipotential rather than focal representation of the areas involved in activity.

Recently Ruch and Shenkin have shown that still another region, area 13 (of Walker) on the orbital or inferior surface of the frontal lobe, is of primary importance in activity. Ablation of this small area produces hyperactivity that may be detectable on the first day after operation and that is well developed within a few days, after which it lasts permanently at a very high level (see Fig. 140). Because of the sheltered position of this area, it is probable that most of the other studies of removal of frontal areas and activity have not included this area. This, Ruch and Shenkin suggest, may well be a factor in the variability of occurrence, degree, and time of onset of hyperactivity from large prefrontal lesions that have characterized previous studies. Though area 13 is known to be related to the gastrointestinal tract (Bailey and Sweet), no marked hyperphagia (increase in hunger), increased gastrointestinal motility or increase in rate of oxygen consumption could be demonstrated after lesions in this area.

Ruch and Shenkin, in addition to finding area 13 so important in activity, have some observations to offer on the way in which activity is changed postoperatively. They point out that random and spontaneous activities are not increased as is suggested by the term "hyperactivity," but that the complex and variable cage behavior typical of unoperated monkeys gives way to incessant, methodical pacing or running from end to end of the cage. This stereotyped behavior has been recorded for periods of 2 or 3 hours with only momentary pauses. Such behavior has appropriately been described as "driven" (Kennard *et al.*). Thus, though total activity is quantitatively increased, qualitatively some kinds of activity are reduced and replaced by locomotor activity. This, Ruch and Shenkin point out, cannot be explained in terms of "generalized inhibition" or of "increased distractibility," as early experimenters had suggested.

A paradoxical result of lesions of the frontal areas, finally, is that hyperactivity may not appear until as late as 3 weeks after operation. And the stage of hyperactivity may be preceded by a period of considerably reduced activity, as measured by objective methods and by certain ill-defined behavior changes. Kennard *et al.*, for example, speak of the monkeys' appearing "confused, lethargic, slow, and difficult to arouse." Ruch and Shenkin note that fear and aggressive patterns of response are reduced and that the animals are unresponsive to environ-

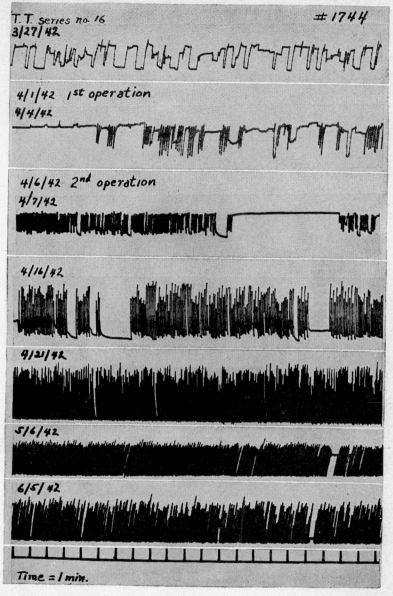

FIG. 140.—Effect upon activity of removal of area 13 on the orbital surface of the frontal cortex. Successive kymograph records represent the preoperative activity, activity following operation on one side, and activity at different intervals after operation on the other side. (*From T. C. Ruch and H. A. Shenkin, 1943. The relation of area 13 of the orbital surface of the frontal lobe to hyperactivity and hyperphagia in monkeys. J. Neurophysiol., 6, 352. By permission of the authors.*)

1ent and human presence. Acceleration of running is the main response o unusual stimuli. Particularly in animals subjected to removal of rea 13, periods of complete immobility alternate with bouts of pacing hat become progressively more rapid in rate and longer in duration. 'hus the two types of symptoms, hyperactivity and apathy, coexist, specially in the first postoperative days. This fact leads one to believe Ruch and Shenkin) that the prefrontal areas are not merely inhibitory n function but contribute in a much more complex manner to the paterning of behavior.

From this brief review of the facts as they stand at present it is clear hat a lesion of a phylogentically new part of the cerebral cortex, the rontal "association" areas, can alter the level of behavioral activity both 1pward and downward. No defect of motion occurs and no reaction 3attern is permanently abolished, but the energy devoted to the char-.cteristic locomotor pattern is greatly increased at the expense of other .ctivities. Much remains to be learned about the significance and nechanism of this relation. Further research along this line may throw ome light on disorders of activity and hyperactive states found in 3atients with neurological and psychiatric disorders.

General References

KLEITMAN, N., 1939. *Sleep and wakefulness.* Chicago: Univ. Chicago Press. Pp. 638.

SHIRLEY, M., 1929. Spontaneous activity. *Psychol. Bull.*, 26, 341–365.

CHAPTER XIX

INSTINCTIVE BEHAVIOR

Instinctive behavior is not easily defined. Many years ago it was conceived as "the faculty which animals have instead of intellect which yet makes their behavior seem intelligent." Such a definition, however, has become inadequate with our abandonment, in recent years, of a mentalistic conception of adjustment. Yet even in a strict behavioral frame of reference, there are no strict criteria by which we can classify certain phenomena as instinctive and others as not. The principle most often followed in practice, it seems, is that of calling any behavior instinctive which is somewhat complicated and *whose mechanisms are not understood by the observer.* Instinctive behavior, therefore, gets defined in terms of the ignorance of the observer.

There are reasons, of course, why we cannot readily learn the mechanisms of some kinds of behavior. If a behavior pattern is determined by a number of different external stimuli, rather than by a single stimulus, as is the case of reflexes or even of fairly complex discriminations, we cannot help but be confused about its cause unless we vary these different stimuli in systematic experiments. Then, too, if an important or crucial factor in the behavior is some condition within the organism—*e.g.,* the body temperature or some particular hormone—we fall easily into believing in some "inner urge," which has very frequently been implied in the concept of instinct. It turns out, indeed, upon experimental analysis, that these two kinds of factors, *i.e.,* determination by multiple stimuli and internal needs (drives), characterize instinctive behavior. With a knowledge of this fact the concept of instinct is no longer necessary, except as a conventional rubric for referring to rather complex motivated behavior. Fortunately, the experimental work of recent years has led us to an understanding of some of the activities of organisms formerly called instinctive, although we have by no means answered all the questions that arise concerning them.

PERCEPTUAL FACTORS IN INSTINCTIVE BEHAVIOR

We shall be concerned, for the most part, in this chapter with the internal factors at the basis of instinctive behavior, exclusive of sexual behavior (see Chap. XX), because it is in respect of the motivational (internal) factors that experimental work with instinctive behavior has

396

been most illuminating. Worth considering briefly, however, is the problem of what stimuli govern various instances of instinctive behavior. Lashley has recently discussed this problem in some detail, summarizing and interpreting most of the important facts, and the following discussion will, therefore, draw heavily upon his writings.

Sensory Deficit.—Many instinctive activities lead to ends which are of remarkable perfection. The spider's web, for example, consists of regularly spaced strands arranged in a specific pattern, and it can be spun again and again with the same perfection. The same is also true of nest building in birds; certain birds build nests that are characteristic of their species, so long as the appropriate materials for building are available. But, although the product of the instinctive behavior is the same from time to time, the behavior itself may be quite variable and follow no stereotyped pattern; the behavior cannot be said, therefore, to be reflexive. This fact suggests, instead, that there is a 'sensory need' which impels the animal to work until the need is satisfied; or, putting it another way, the animal reacts to the *absence* of the stimulus situation presented by a nest or web, for example, and behaves somewhat randomly until, through its work, a satisfactory stimulus situation is obtained. In the case of a rat building a nest, the nature of the 'sensory need' can be seen from the fact that the nest takes a form that will give low conduction of heat beneath the animal, contact of its sides with the body, and, to some extent, the exclusion of light; temperature and light in this case appear to be of primary importance.

Sensory Cues.—Other instances of instinctive behavior often have a more complex sensory basis. Copulatory activity of the rat, for example, does not depend upon vision, olfaction, or tactile sensitivity alone, but rather upon the combination of these factors, since the elimination of any one does not interfere with the behavior (Stone). When vision alone is employed, the stimulus to copulatory behavior is an object having approximately a certain size and presenting jerking movements, such as the female rat normally presents. Similarly, in the retrieving of eggs to a nest by gulls, the important property of the stimulus is that it be of a rounded or oval *form*, regardless of size (Borovski). Thus in these two instances a definite visual perception figures in the instinctive behavior. How such a visual perception can be aroused by internal conditions, which we shall consider below, cannot be explained at present, except by saying that there is, in the innate neural equipment of an animal, the ability to perceive form. Of this we can be sure; experiments have shown that rats can perceive, without previous training or experience, some of the form and brightness relationships seen in learning (Hebb). Thus we may conclude that in instinctive behavior specific behavioral reactions are brought into play which are innately connected with particular aspects of a stimulus situation, even with the form and combination of the stimuli in it.

Certain general principles can be stated regarding sensory determinants of instinctive behavior. Sensory stimuli, first of all, are often *alternatives* to each other in calling forth instinctive behavior. The male rat, for example, may exhibit copulatory behavior, either on the basis of the visual stimulus which the receptive female rat presents or in reaction to olfactory stimuli characteristic of the receptive female. In other instances, sensory stimuli must be present in *combination* to elicit instinctive behavior. Thus the gull needs not only an 'egg' of a particular shape and texture, but also the stimulus of a nest with which it is familiar, for it to accept the egg and sit on it. In other cases, finally, various stimuli may be reacted to in *succession*. As Lashley has pointed out, a mother rat may retrieve a stuffed skin, but when she discovers the stitches in it, she pulls at these, subsequently discards the skin, and fails to 'nurse' it as she would a real rat pup; or in the migration of salmon, which we shall consider below, the path back to the spawning grounds is determined first by reaction to chemical conditions of the water and by the pressure of moving water and later by the temperature of the water. In any event, the instinctive behavior consists of patterns of behavior which are set by the constitution of the nervous system to come into play when the appropriate stimulus conditions are present, and in this respect instinctive behavior is hardly any different from reflexive behavior except that instinctive reactions are somewhat more intricately organized and the stimulus conditions are somewhat more complex and difficult to uncover.

The Internal Environment.—One great difference, however, between reflexive and instinctive behavior is that the latter is dependent primarily upon conditions within the organism. True, the internal environment—the endocrine balance, blood-sugar level, oxygen supply, pH, and the like—must be of a certain character in order for any behavior to take place, but instinctive behavior arises much more directly from factors in the internal environment. When all other behavior of the organism is normal and when the appropriate external stimuli, mentioned above, are present, instinctive behavior requires, usually, some special factor or sets of factors in the internal environment. It is this aspect of the mechanisms of instinctive behavior which is difficult to understand, and it is this to which we shall pay particular attention in the following sections.

OBSTACLE AVOIDANCE

For a long time it was a mystery how bats were able to avoid obstacles without using vision. When one observes them flying at night or in dark

laces, it is plain that they perceive the position of objects quite as clearly
s if they were using vision. A recent series of experiments by Galambos
nd Griffin has solved this problem.

A room was set up in which wires stretched from the ceiling to the
loor provided standard obstacles for bats to avoid. The wires, indeed,
vere arranged in such a way that the probability of bats striking them by
hance could be computed and the significance of a score better than that
ould be determined. When an animal struck the wire, the experimenter
vas informed of the fact by the noise of the vibrating wire.

Just to make sure that the animals were not making use of visual cues,
hey were blindfolded and their accuracy of obstacle avoidance tested.
Vision, it was found, played no part in the adjustment. Then the possibility that hearing was being used was tested; the ears of the animals
vere plugged to keep out sounds. This procedure seriously affected the
nimals and brought them, in fact, to a chance level of performance.
The conclusion was indicated, therefore, that auditory cues were enabling
hem to avoid the obstacles. The next question, then, was the source
f the cues. These, it was thought, might be sounds made by the
nimal itself, for bats often make soft cries while flying. To test this
ypothesis, the mouths of the bats were taped shut so that they could no
onger vocalize. This produced the same effect upon obstacle avoidance
s deafening the bats, and it appeared that the animals were localizing
he position of objects by sending out sounds which were reflected from
he wires and perceived through hearing.

A further analysis was conducted to determine just what frequencies
f sounds were being used in this manner. With an apparatus for determining the presence of different frequencies, even though so high as
o be inaudible to the human ear, the experimenters found that bats in
pproaching obstacles emitted a supersonic sound in the neighborhood
f 50,000 cycles per second. Later they showed that the bat's ear was
ensitive to these very high frequencies, as one might well expect knowing
hat these must be employed in obstacle avoidance. Such frequencies
ave properties much more like those of light than do lower frequencies
o which the human ear is sensitive; they are reflected more perfectly
rom a surface, do not round corners as much as lower frequencies, and
ast sharper shadows when obstructed by objects. As a result, such
requencies can form the basis of a localizing adjustment much better
han can low frequencies and are admirably suited to the purposes of the
at. The ear which is nearer to the wire reflecting the sound will, pre-
umably, be stimulated more intensely than the ear farther away, and
n the basis of this difference in intensity the animal can perceive the
lirection of the obstruction and avoid it.

Thus a reaction that has been hard to explain upon any terms in which man is accustomed to think has been shown to have a sensory basis essentially comparable to man's visual mechanisms for avoiding obstructions in his environment.

MIGRATION

The migratory behavior of many animals, particularly that of birds and fishes, has long puzzled the student of animal behavior. To the layman, the explanation of such behavior has often been a matter merely of ascribing to such animals instincts of various kinds which tell them where they are, where they want to go, and how to get there. The scientist naturally pushes such an explanation aside because it says nothing; he inquires instead about the specific factors involved in migration. Some progress has been made in answering that question, but owing to the practical difficulties encountered in attempting to experiment with migration, there is still much to be learned.

Homing.—The fact that pigeons when released many miles from home will quickly find their way back home is well known and has been put to use for military and other purposes by entrusting pigeons with messages. Other species of birds besides pigeons have also been shown to be capable of homing behavior. It is certain, moreover, that birds can home when they must cover territory that they have never seen before; homing cannot, therefore, be ascribed to familiarity, through learning, with landmarks in the path homeward.

Attempts to discover the basis of homing have so far met with little success. It has been shown without much question that memory of the direction of transit away from home cannot guide back home, for this factor has been eliminated experimentally by disorienting the birds. It is not feasible, unfortunately, to test whether visual cues are responsible for their homing, because birds will not fly without the use of vision. There is some evidence that they make use of rivers and waterways in choosing their course of flight and that this factor may aid them in homing, but it is doubtful whether this can be the sole or even the principal factor in homing flight over unfamiliar territory.

The Seasonal Migration of Birds.—We are not so much in the dark concerning some of the factors ordering the northward and southward flight of birds that migrate from one territory to another in different seasons of the year. One of the important causes of such migration has been traced to changes in the length of the day and its effect upon the glands of birds. In one experiment two groups of birds were chosen and subjected to different conditions of illumination: one group was given illumination for decreasing lengths of time each day just as the day hortens in the fall of the year; the other group was given an artificial day that gradually lengthened over a period of time, simulating the change in length of day that occurs in the spring. The first group when released did not move away from the vicinity; many of the animals of the second group did.

Correlated with this difference in the migratory behavior of the two groups was a difference in the amount of development of their gonads. The first group had minimally developed gonads, whereas the second group showed considerable gonadal growth similar to that found normally in birds in the spring. As the next chapter will show in some detail, this relationship of light stimulation to gonadal development takes place through the visual stimulation affecting the pituitary gland which in turn stimulates the gonads. The gonadal growth, it is suggested, causes the birds to migrate because it affects their reaction to the temperature of the environment. Gonadal hormones, we have already seen, cause activity to be increased and probably also increase body metabolism. This may cause animals to choose regions of lower temperature as they fly and therefore to establish a northward course. Similarly, a reduction in the output of the gonadal hormones may result in animals' choosing regions of higher temperature and thus cause them to take a southward course of migration. All this is uncertain, of course, but the fact that light and hormonal changes direct the migration appears to be established.

The Migration of Fishes.—Another case of migratory behavior which has been studied with some success is the migration of salmon. Their place of birth and early growth is far up in the headwaters of streams. In their second year they migrate downstream to the ocean and there spend two or three years. After that they reenter a river, usually the one from which they came, and proceed up the river and its tributaries to its headwaters and there spawn and die.

Not all the phases of this cycle have been experimented upon, but from some observations and from correlated physiological changes in the salmon with their migratory behavior, one can construct what appears to be a good picture of the factors at work in the migration. The young salmon, in the waters where it has been born, gradually loses the pigmentation in its skin which serves to protect photosensitive receptors below this pigmentation (Roule). With loss of this pigment, the fish is stimulated by light and reacts negatively, *i.e.*, avoids light. Since the upper streams are shallow, this light-avoidance reaction takes him gradually downstream to the deep ocean where he is free from photic stimulation. Because the waters of the river emptying into the ocean are somewhat colder, contain somewhat more oxygen, and are less salty, the salmon tends to stay in the general region of the ocean into which the river runs.

Eventually the salmon matures in its sexual development, and it gonads put out more sexual hormones. These raise the activity an probably also the metabolism and lead to the choosing of colder water much as the sexually mature bird chooses colder climates, and als raises the requirements for oxygen. In addition, a rheotropism, *i.e.*, strong swimming reaction against the direction of streaming water, come into play; for what reasons it is not clearly known. The fish then head upstream, and as it comes to each branching of the river, it chooses th one which is of the colder temperature. This has been established b measurements of the temperature chosen by salmon in their upstrear migration (Ward). Certain, too, is it that such factors as the siz of the stream or the speed of its flow do not determine the choice. Even tually the salmon arrives at one of the headwaters of the stream—usuall the one that is coldest. There it lays its eggs and dies, thus closing on cycle and beginning another. Because of the factor of temperatur in the route of the migration it turns out that salmon tend to return fo spawning to the same places in which they were born, and thus what ma seem to be an instinct or a phenomenal memory for their place of birt turns out to be explicable in terms of reactions to particular stimuli i their environment.

HOARDING BEHAVIOR

An instinctive behavior that can be observed in many animals, mos conspicuously in such rodents as chipmunks and squirrels, is the hoardin of food in seasons of the year when it is relatively plentiful. The anima psychologist often sees essentially the same behavior in the rats of hi laboratory, and recently this observation has been put to use by subject ing the hoarding behavior of rats to controlled tests in which the factor causing it could be studied (Wolfe). Animals were placed in circum stances where food was available some distance from their home cage an their tendency to hoard the food could be measured by counting th pellets of food that they carried back to their cages. This work ha not had time to go far yet, especially in the line of discovering wha particular physiological factors are at work in it, but what has alread been learned is of some value and points the way to future physiologica experimentation.

Adult rats which, so far as is known, have been provided with a libera supply of food throughout their previous lifetime, tend to do som hoarding if given the opportunity. Such control hoarding, as it i called, is not, however, very great. It may be due to deprivation having taken place without the experimenter's knowledge, but that is question yet to be studied. The principal factor in producing an appre ciable amount of hoarding, at any rate, is deprivation of food (Morga *et al.*). When rats are deprived of food, they may hoard as many as several hundred pellets in an hour, carrying each of them a distance of a yard or more. It is interesting, moreover, that hoarding behavior does not occur in deprivation until the deprivation has accumulated over some period of time. Starvation for 24 hr., although sufficient to make an animal hungry, does not ordinarily cause a normal adult rat to hoard. With several repetitions of the 24-hr. starvation, however, hoarding makes its appearance. This fact points not to hunger itself as the basis of the hoarding but to physiological changes, possibly the depletion of certain reserves in the body, that take some time.

A similar conclusion can be drawn from the effects of satiation upon hoarding which has been produced by previous deprivation. When animals are hungry, their hoarding is not at a maximum, no matter how severe or prolonged has been the deprivation. Their desire to eat appears to conflict with their tendency to hoard, and since both cannot be done at the same time, they give preference to eating. Twenty-four hours after their food supply has been restored and they have been satiated, in the sense that they have all they want to eat, their hoarding will be considerably greater than under the most extreme conditions of deprivation. Obviously satisfaction of hunger, at least in the sense of filling the stomach, has not abolished hoarding, and the causes of hoarding therefore lie deeper than that. The physiological basis of the behavior takes some time to remedy. What that basis is, unfortunately, is not yet established, but future experiments on this aspect of the problem may reveal it.

Whatever the crucial physiological factor or factors are they can be changed by subjecting animals to extreme deprivation in infancy (Hunt). Rats starved for about 24 hr. at a time over a period of days just after they have been weaned will, when subjected to food deprivation in adulthood, hoard more than normal animals. The infant deprivation, therefore, leaves the animal more susceptible to the effects of factors producing hoarding. For this relationship to obtain, the deprivation must be conducted relatively early in infancy, for animals subjected to the same schedule of infant deprivation only about two weeks after weaning do not display the effect.

One can interpret this finding in two ways: either that in infant frustration the capacity of the animal to store materials which when depleted cause hoarding is reduced (Morgan *et al.*), or that the deprivation has had a 'purely' psychological effect in reducing the tolerance to deprivation (Hunt). The first interpretation is certainly the one to be preferred in any final analysis, for the fact that the infant deprivation must take place before a certain age is not easily understood in psychological terms and, moreover, the physiological psychologist thinks of a psychological explanation only as temporary, pending a more complete knowledge of physiological factors.

There can be no question, however, but that factors which we ordinarily call psychological affect the hoarding. In one experiment, frustration of animals in obtaining food proved to raise considerably the amount of hoarding (McCord). During deprivation, pellets were placed in a crate below the floor of the cage where they would invoke the efforts of rats to get them and yet be quite inaccessible. When subsequently the hoarding of animals subjected to frustration was compared with those deprived to just as great an extent but not frustrated, it was found to be greater. Thus psychological factors do enter into the behavior. The basic point, nevertheless, is that the hoarding is the result of food deprivation and particularly of general physiological effects of deprivation more basic than those involved in eating.

HIBERNATION

Like migration and hoarding, hibernation is a seasonal type of instinctive behavior. It occurs in many mammals during the winter months when supplies of food are low, the temperature is low, and the animal is therefore called upon to conserve its bodily resources to the greatest degree possible. The animal usually finds a secluded place in which it will be protected from being preyed upon, as well as from the cold, and there spends the winter months in a deep stupor resembling sleep. When the cold lets up and the chances of obtaining food are better, the hibernation ends.

The causes of hibernation as well as the physiological conditions found in it are to be found in the two factors already mentioned: lack of food and fall in the environmental temperature. Mammals are normally warm-blooded creatures who keep their body temperature at a high level compared with that of the environment. To do this, however, they must expend a great deal of energy and maintain a high level of metabolism. Such energy expenditure is difficult to keep up when food runs out and the environmental temperature is low. The animal consequently 'solves its problem' by giving up its high metabolism and becoming more or less a cold-blooded animal whose temperature and metabolic rate are governed by the environment. Since the irritability of the nervous system, general physiological processes, and general activity level are dependent upon temperature, the result of this concession to the environment is the stupor of hibernation.

This is the general picture of hibernation. All the evidence at hand supports it in just about every detail (Kleitman). The normal body temperature of a hedgehog, for example, is about 34°C., and while the environmental temperature is not too low it maintains this and behaves in a normal manner. When the environmental temperature falls to between 14.5 and 17°, however, the body temperature fluctuates between 15 and 30° and the hedgehog behaves as though half-asleep. Then, below an environmental temperature of 14.5°C., the animal goes into hibernation and its body temperature stays about 1° above the outside temperature. The accommodation of body temperature to environmental temperature is therefore clearly correlated with hibernation. It has likewise been shown that when squirrels are starved and made less able, consequently, to keep up their body heat they will go into hibernation more readily than otherwise.

Other physiological changes during hibernation are very much what one would expect from this general picture of hibernation. The metabolic rate is much below normal; the blood-sugar level is also down somewhat. The acidity of the blood is considerably greater than in normal conditions. This is to be explained on the ground that at lower temperatures the blood can carry more carbon dioxide; it is itself a factor, however, in lowering nervous excitability and keeping neural activity low, as has been pointed out before. The heart rate is, as one might expect, very low. It gradually decreases with lowering of the external temperature down to 17°. Between 17 and 14°C., which is the critical region of onset of hibernation (see above), it may decrease to about 10 or 15 per cent of its former value, and with still greater lowering of the external temperature it gradually slows even more.

The relation of the endocrine glands to hibernation also falls into the same scheme. The general sympathetic system, which functions as an energy expender (see Chap. XVII), particularly the adrenal glands innervated by that system and closely related to furnishing the brain and muscles with sugar, is functioning at a very low level. Adrenalectomy, which will ordinarily prove fatal to a normal animal, leaves one in hibernation unaffected. Injection of adrenalin will awaken a hibernating animal briefly from its hibernation, so also will the administration of an extract of the thyroid. Both hormones, it will be recalled, raise the metabolic rate. Insulin, on the other hand, may induce hibernation or favor it, apparently because it reverses the action of adrenalin, causing lowering of metabolism (in the long run) and a storing, rather than a burning, of the body's food supplies.

Putting all these facts together, there can be little question that hibernation is closely associated with a fall in the temperature and metabolism of the body in response to a lowering of external temperature. There remains, however, the further question of why the animal accommodates its body function to the environmental demands. A suggestion for the answer to this question comes from the observation that in hibernation there is a pronounced increase in lymphoid tissue of the body.

This is known to be quite toxic and when injected can produce loss of appetite, fall in body temperature, and reduction in metabolic rate. Such an increase in lymphoid tissue can be due to a lack of vitamin D. On the basis of that clue, hedgehogs were fed doses of this vitamin at a time when they normally would be hibernating. The animals as a result did not hibernate, even though they were kept at temperatures well below those ordinarily invoking hibernation. Animals to whom the vitamin was not fed or in whom the feeding was discontinued hibernated. This striking result, unfortunately, was not based upon a very large number of animals, and the experiment should be repeated before it can be fully accepted.

NEST-BUILDING BEHAVIOR

Two other closely related types of instinctive behavior are easily studied in the laboratory and have therefore been rather extensively investigated. They are maternal and reproductive behavior; the latter is taken up in the next chapter. Maternal behavior may be said to be made up of several instinctive patterns—nest building, cleaning of young, brooding, and retrieving the young. All these are open to semiobjective methods of study, but nest-building behavior can be measured quantitatively by either of two methods: placing strips of paper around a drum and determining the number that are selected by the rat for the building of a nest; or making available to the nesting rat a roll of paper which can be unrolled by the rat and the number of turns automatically counted.

Nest building is performed by both female and male rats, and it is not, therefore, primarily associated with maternal behavior. Male rats may, as a matter of fact, build larger nests than females. The physiological mechanisms of nest building are such that the behavior is most likely to be called out in female rats, but this will be explained in a moment. It is important to note first the relationship that exists between activity and nest building (Richter). It is, taking the general case, an inverse one; the greatest amount of nest building taking place when activity is low, and vice versa. This fact leads us to expect that activity and nest building are polar aspects of the same processes, and other evidence confirms this expectation.

Nest Building and Estrus.—In this connection we may note the relation between the estrus cycle and nest building. During estrus when, as we have seen, running activity and general movement is highest, we find that nest-building activity is lowest; during the diestral period, on the other hand, when activity is low, nest building reaches its highest level. There is, then, in the female rat a cycle of nest-building behavior that corresponds to the 4- to 5-day estrus cycle except that the peaks of the bodily activity and nest building are inversely correlated. Both aspects of the estrus cycle are related, as we shall see, to changes in body temperature and to the mechanisms of temperature regulation.

Endocrine Function and Nest Building.—With a knowledge of the relation between activity and nest building, we could predict the facts which have actually been obtained concerning the role of the endocrine glands in nest building (Richter; Fig. 141). Extirpation of the hypophysis produces an increase in nest building of nearly 200 per cent. Removal of the adrenal glands results in a 34 per cent increase; of the gonads, a 50 per cent increase; of the thyroid, about 100 per cent increase. As in the case of running activity, so here it is thought that the effects of hypophysectomy are mediated principally through secondary atrophic

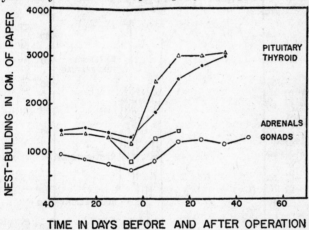

FIG. 141.—Effect of removal of various glands upon nest-building behavior in the rat. (*After C. P. Richter*, 1937. *Hypophyseal control of behavior*, p. 265, *Cold Spring Harbor Symposia on Quant. Biol.*, **5**, 258–268.)

changes in the other glands just mentioned. The fact that the changes in nest-building activity do not occur for several days after hypophysectomy lends weight to this belief. Since the greatest change, as far as any other one gland is concerned, follows thyroidectomy, it would seem that changes in metabolic level are the principal cause of the increase in nest building brought about by hypophysectomy.

Temperature.—As we have noted before, the thyroid controls to a very great extent metabolism and energy expenditure in the body. Reduction in thyroid output can be expected to result in a lowered metabolism attended by a lowered heat output. It is this latter which is suspected of being crucial in nest building. In a series of experiments designed to test this notion, rats were subjected to different external temperature, so as to bring about varying degrees of heat loss from the body (Kinder; Fig. 142). At low external temperatures the loss was great, and correlated with it was a greatly increased amount of nest-building activity. On the other hand, rats maintained at a high external temperature such as to prevent much heat loss from the body showed a marked reduction in nest-building behavior.

Nest building is, of course, a part of the behavior pattern accompanying pregnancy and nursing, and we find that immediately after impregnation there is an increase in nest building (see Fig. 143). This behavior, it will be noted, is correlated with the dropping out of the estrual rhythms and the periods of great activity every 4 to 5 days. Toward the end of

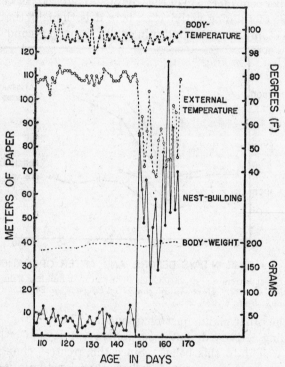

FIG. 142.—The relation of external temperature to nest-building behavior in the rat. (*Based on work by Kinder. After C. P. Richter, 1937. Hypophyseal control of behavior, p. 265, Cold Spring Harbor Symposia on Quant. Biol.,* **5**, 258–238.)

pregnancy, nest building increases greatly and is maintained at a very high level until about 20 days after parturition when the estrual rhythms begin again and when the young rats are normally weaned. Bringing these facts into relation with the "temperature hypothesis," we note that pregnancy is characteristically attended in women by difficulties in keeping temperature constant and that this is doubtlessly related to glandular changes which accompany pregnancy.

To establish the relationship of nest building to the mechanisms of temperature regulation is not by any means to have explained this instinctive behavior. Nest building is not a simple act but rather an intelligent one. How it is that deficient body temperature brings into play the nest-building sequence of behavior must be understood in terms of the effect of thermal conditions upon neural activities.

In the present state of our knowledge, we know that there are definite centers for the regulation of body temperature. In the hypothalamus there seem to be separate centers for cold and heat, the anterior hypothalamus reacting to heat (parasympathetic) and the posterior region

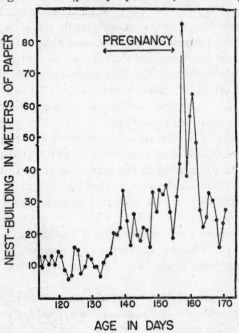

Fig. 143.—Increase in nest building during pregnancy. (*After C. P. Richter*, 1937. *Hypophyseal control of behavior, p. 265, Cold Spring Harbor Symposia on Quant. Biol.*, **5**, 258–268.)

responding to cold (sympathetic). Recent research has also shown that there are specific regions sensitive to temperature changes in the ventral portions of the cerebral hemispheres. Whether these areas are related particularly to nest building is not known, although it is certain that the neopallium of the dorsal cortex plays some role in nest building, as the next section will show.

MATERNAL BEHAVIOR

Nest building is a part of the complex of behaviors which make up the maternal pattern, but since considerable attention has been given to it in research it has been treated separately. Now, however, let us turn to the broader aspects of maternal behavior.

Brooding and Nursing.—In addition to nest building we may recognize certain other rather discrete maternal activities, chief of which are the cleaning of pups at parturition, nursing, retrieving of pups when they get out of the nest, and certain other adaptive responses such as moving the nest when adverse conditions of temperature or tactual stimulation disturb the mother.

Beach has recently carried out an extensive study in which these various aspects of maternal behavior were observed and rated in both normal and operated rats, the purpose of his research being the determination, if possible, of what neural mechanisms were involved in maternal instinctive behavior. On the basis of the notion that the cortex subserves intelligent functions and the subcortical centers mediate instinctive and reflexive activities, it has been commonly held that the cerebral cortex is not concerned in instinctive behavior. To test this supposition Beach confined his study to operations of the cerebral cortex. His results may be summarized as follows:

When operated and normal rats are compared with respect to maternal behavior expressed both during pregnancy and after parturition, operated animals are uniformly inferior in the performance of all maternal activities, particularly when the lesions involve more than 20 per cent of the cortex. The inferiority of the operated animals is in respect of the perfection of their behavior, not in which kinds of behavior are performed. Neither does there seem to be a localization of any aspect of maternal behavior. On the contrary, the amount of disturbance of maternal behavior was proportional to the amount of cortical tissue destroyed.

The detailed results of Beach's study are worth enumerating: Nest building in pregnant rats is impaired both qualitatively and quantitatively by cortical operations. Cleaning newborn pups and gathering them into the nest are not done so well by operated animals as by normal controls. Normal animals adapt more readily to disturbing conditions such as turning a fan upon the nest or placing an electric heater near the nest; they more frequently move their nest and their young to a better position in the cage. Finally, the retrieving activity of operated mothers when their young are experimentally removed from the nest is slower than that of the normals and tends to be less perfectly carried out.

We may conclude, so far as maternal behavior in the rat is concerned (and no other good studies seem to be available), that the instinctive behavior is dependent to a great extent upon the cerebral cortex but that all parts of the cortex participate in each aspect of maternal behavior. Information concerning the importance of subcortical centers is lacking.

There are a few scattered observations concerning the hormonal basis of maternal behavior, and since these do not lead to any systematic conclusions they need be summarized only briefly. *Prolactin*, the hormone associated with mammary secretion and nursing, has received some attention (Riddle). When given to certain fishes, it induces spawning. So also will the luteal hormones, with which prolactin is related physiologically (see Chap. XX). Prolactin will likewise induce brooding in birds and causes them in some instances to take care of foster young when they would not otherwise do so. Although it is generally thought that the anterior pituitary exercises its control over instinctive and motivational activities through its effect on other endocrine glands, several well-controlled studies agree to the fact that hormones of the anterior pituitary are directly concerned in certain aspects of maternal behavior. Injection of extracts of the anterior pituitary gland causes young virgin female rats to retrieve young rats and to show other general signs of maternal behavior.

Work on the question of the endocrine basis of maternal behavior is at present inadequate, and more extended research is required in the future before any valuable conclusions can be drawn. It looks at present as though the endocrine relationships were quite complex and that a variety of hormones may produce maternal behavior, but careful work might show some crucial endocrine agents. There is no evidence as to whether endocrines affect most directly central neural centers, as seems to be the case in sexual behavior, or whether their control of maternal behavior is exercised through peripheral changes affecting the nervous system through afferent pathways.

CHAPTER XX

MATING BEHAVIOR

More attention has been given to mating behavior in the researches of recent years than to any other field of motivated behavior. As a result there is today a considerable literature abounding in facts from which a comparatively complete picture of the psychology and physiology of mating behavior can be constructed. Therein lies the excuse for a whole chapter on the topic in this book. We shall see, moreover, that the facts of mating behavior provide an excellent basis for forming general conceptions of the mechanisms of motivated behavior, indeed, much better than can be obtained from existing knowledge concerning other types of motivation.

THE SEX HORMONES

Many of the facts of mating behavior can be understood in their full significance only when set in the background of the sexual hormones at work within the body. For this reason it is best to begin with a consideration of the sexual hormones. It would be confusing, however, to present a complete description and system of notation for them, because their various interrelationships, though not completely understood, have been worked out in more detail than their functions in sexual behavior. The discussion of the hormones to be presented, therefore, will be simplified accordingly.

Gonadal Hormones.—The primary organs of sex, the gonads, are the ovaries in the female and the testes in male animals. It is upon the endocrine functions of these organs that other secondary sex characteristics, such as the structure of the reproductive organs, distribution of hair, and skeletal structure, depend. Attesting this fact are many experiments in which the reversal of secondary sex characteristics has been brought about by the administration of gonadal hormones. Although femaleness and maleness depend upon the hormones produced by the gonads, even the gonads themselves possess a potential bisexual composition; for it is possible to bring about reversals in their structure by the administration of hormones, and the structure of both ovaries and testes is similar. These organs, indeed, are derived from a common primordium. It appears, however, that in normal embryonic development the sex of the gonads is first determined by genes and only later do

412

gonadal hormones influence the development of both the gonads and the secondary characteristics (see Willier).

The principal ovarian (gonadal) hormones are the estrogens and progesterone. The *estrogens* are a group of hormones that have common physiological properties; the most widely known of them is estrin. *Progesterone,* on the other hand, is a pure hormone which is responsible for changes in the mammalian uterus related to pregnancy (gestation) (Allen *et al.*).

The origin of these hormones may be indicated by reference to cyclical changes in the ovaries which may either coincide with the seasonal cycles of the year or go on at some independent rate. An ovary consists of a mass of connective and epithelial tissue in which are embedded a number of follicles (see Fig. 144). These follicles, as well as the ova which they contain, are in an immature condition in the prepuberal female (*i.e.,*

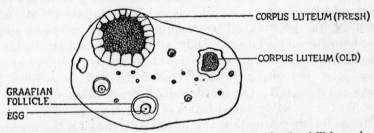

Fig. 144.—Diagram of section through the human ovary showing follicles and corpus luteum, the principal sources of endocrine secretion in the ovary. (*After Shull. From G. A. Baitsell. Human biology, p. 117. New York: McGraw-Hill, 1940.*)

before puberty) and in certain stages of the adult female cycle. Under the influence of the gonadotropic hormones of the pituitary to be considered below, a follicle, with the ovum in it, grows or "ripens." As it does, it secretes estrogen which, when it reaches a certain concentration in the blood, brings about, among other things, changes in the epithelium of the uterus and vagina. When the follicle and ovum are fully matured, the follicle ruptures and discharges the ovum into tubes leading to the uterus. Thereupon the ruptured follicle undergoes retrogressive changes which are accompanied by reduction in the secretion of estrogen. The cavity of the follicle from which the ovum was discharged, however, is replaced with a mass of cells, known as the corpus luteum, which secretes the hormone, progesterone. This brings about further changes in the uterine lining favorable to the maintenance of pregnancy. If pregnancy follows, tropic hormones secreted by the placenta, which connects the embryo with the uterus, cause the corpus luteum and its hormone, progesterone, to be maintained throughout the term of pregnancy. If pregnancy does not occur, the corpus luteum degenerates and the production of estrogen and progesterone is returned to its original level; then, new immature follicles begin to grow and repeat the cycle.[1]

The principal gonadal hormone of the male is testosterone and is derived from the testes. It is only one, however, of a number of chemically related male hormones. These taken as a class are known as the androgens and are found in the testes, the blood, and the cortex of the adrenal gland. The androgens appear to be in the male what the estrogens are in the female, i.e., the primary hormones of the gonads; but in both cases other tissues besides the gonads are capable of secreting them. Androgen activity of the testes is regulated like the estrogen secretions of the ovaries by gonadotropic hormones of the pituitary. Unlike the ovaries, however, the testes do not seem to possess an intrinsic cycle, but vary their androgen secretion only with factors that influence the activity of the pituitary body.

Gonadotropic Hormones.—The gonad-stimulating hormones of the female arise from two principal sources: the pituitary gland and, in pregnancy, the placenta. There appear to be two principal gonadotropic hormones of the pituitary body, a *follicle-stimulating* and a *luteinizing hormone;* these facilitate maturation of the ovarian follicles and of the formation of the corpus luteum, respectively, and are derived from the anterior pituitary. The gonadotropic hormone of the placenta is very much like the gonadotropic hormones of the anterior pituitary in that it stimulates follicle maturation and luteinization and for this reason has been called the *anterior-pituitary-like hormone.* In the male, the anterior pituitary body secretes one or more gonadotropic hormones which stimulate the formation of spermatozoa in the testes and the secretion of androgens.

It is worth noting in passing that the gonadotropic hormones of the prehypophysis (anterior pituitary body) and the gonadal hormones are reciprocally related. That is to say, gonadotropic hormones of the pituitary stimulate the secretion of estrogen and androgen by the respective gonads, but a high concentration of gonadal hormones in the blood inhibits gonadotropic activity of the pituitary. The net effect of this antagonism is to bring about a comparative equilibrium in which the hormone production of the gonads is relatively constant (male) or varies in a cyclic manner from controlled high and low points (female).

THE CHARACTER OF SEXUAL BEHAVIOR

Since a considerable part of the present chapter is concerned with the relation between sex hormones and behavior, it is best to turn at this

---

[1] It is well to note that the secretion of estrogen is not performed exclusively by the ripening follicles. The corpus luteum and the placenta also appear to secrete estrogen.

point to a review of the nature of sexual behavior, so that we may have in mind both the character of the sex hormones and of sexual behavior when we consider the relation between the two. Patterns of sexual behavior differ a great deal in different species of animals and in the two sexes, but we need note only briefly the behavior that appears in those animals which have been commonly used as subjects in the study of the physiological basis of sexual behavior.

Birds.—Sexual (mating) behavior in birds may be divided into two types, primary (copulatory) and secondary (courtship) behavior. Courtship precedes and leads up to copulatory behavior. It consists of several rather distinct activities, among them billing and cooing. In billing behavior the bills of the male and female are interlocked in such a way that the lower beak of the female is usually below that of the male, the upper half being in the mouth cavity of the male. With their bills thus interlocked, the birds move their heads up and down with vigor and quickness which suggests excitement. Interspersed with this billing may be various vocalizations, charging and strutting, all characteristic of sexual behaviors. The latter have much in common, but charging is more characteristic of some animals (*e.g.*, pigeons) and strutting of others (*e.g.*, turkey and peacock). "Birds in the act of charging, ruffle the neck and back feathers, lower and slightly spread the wings and tail, tilt the body upward at a sharp angle, and move forward rigidly in sharp spurts, thus giving the charging character to the action. The response is often accompanied by deep rolling, muffled vocal expressions" (Carpenter, p. 72). Such secondary behavior prefaces copulatory behavior and perhaps serves as a stimulus to it.

Courtship behavior merges into copulatory behavior when the female assumes a submissive and receptive posture, consisting of a slight spreading of the wings, extension of the tail, and flexing of the legs. These constitute posture which is conducive to copulation. The behavior of the male, on the other hand, becomes dominant. He mounts the female and makes a balanced adjustment with his feet and wings, in some cases by grasping the feathers of the female's neck with his beak. Then, copulation occurs and is followed by a period of inactivity, after which the sequence of mating activities may be reenacted. There are, of course, several variations in patterns of sexual behavior in the same animals and in different animals, but the highly organized character of the mating behavior patterns is a remarkable fact worthy of special note (Carpenter).

Mammals.—The mammalian animals whose mating activities have been most extensively studied are the cat, rabbit, guinea pig, and rat. The male sexual behavior of all these animals is quite similar, consisting chiefly in mounting, clasping the neck of the female in the mouth, and copulatory movements. Patterns of mating behavior are in each case highly organized and are relatively stereotyped sequences, but they differ markedly in the different animals, as is indicated by the following descriptions (Bard). Receptive behavior of the female rat consists simply of tense crouching for brief periods interrupted by quick darts about the home cage and by an extremely great amount of running activity. When mounted, the female rat assumes a particular posture which allows the male to copulate successfully. In the receptive female rabbit and guinea pig, there is simply a well-defined reflex pattern to the tactual stimulation called out by the male's mounting her. It consists of an elevation of the rump, together with a tense receptive posture, and in the rabbit, an adjustment of the tail. Along with this reflex pattern, the guinea pig frequently emits a characteristic vocalization.

Whereas the female mating pattern of the rodent, just considered, is rather simple, receptive behavior of the cat is much more highly organized and conspicuous. It begins with courtship, which leads to copulation which in turn is followed by an after-reaction (Bard).

The courtship behavior includes playful rolling, excessive rubbing, a curious slow vocalization (the estrual call) and crouching and treading. The estrual crouch is a most specific posture. Resting on chest and forearms with pelvis raised somewhat and with tail elevated and turned to one side, the animal tends to execute treading movements of the hind legs. It is in this posture that the male is accepted. Many estrual cats crouch and tread quite spontaneously in the absence of any specific external stimulus. Others do not show this behavior unless they are in the presence of a male or receive some stimulation of the external genital region. . . . In most animals [the after-reaction] consists of more or less frantic rubbing, squirming, licking and rolling (Bard, p. 554).

Bisexual Behavior.—It is important to note that there are certain rudimentary forms of behavior which are not specific to either sex, and further, that animals of one sex often display the characteristic primary and secondary sexual behavior of the opposite sex. As an illustration of the point, certain behavior common to both male and female cats may be noted. When the genital regions of either the male or the female cat are rubbed or touched, the pelvis and tail will be elevated and sometimes light stepping movements will occur similar to those seen in the courtship behavior of female cats. This, however, is not the typical receptive pattern, for it does not include lowering of the foreparts of the body and partial flexion of the hind legs which are integral to the female crouch. Such a response seems to be the rudiment of sexual behavior, but it does not seem to be associated with sexual drive either in the male or female.

Coupled with this fact are observations of various birds and mammals which indicate that males often show feminine copulatory behavior when aggressive males attempt to mount them, as they will, and that females when especially receptive may often show mounting behavior characteristic of males. Such observations accord with the potentially bisexual character of the gonads and with mating reflex patterns common to both male and female, and they *suggest* a constitutional rather than an acquired basis of bisexual and homosexual behavior (Stone).

Experience and Sexual Behavior.—Observations on mating behavior in different animals under various conditions lead one almost inescapably to the conclusion that patterns of mating behavior are not organized through experience but are the result of the maturation of certain neural connections laid down in the constitutional structure of the organism and evoked by certain exteroceptive stimuli and hormonal conditions of the blood. The facts to be presented later in this chapter will support this conclusion, but here we may note that mating behavior appears in various animals in full-fledged form when no opportunity has been provided for the gradual acquisition of the behavior. In one experiment, for example, female rats were kept in isolation until sexual maturity and until signs of sexual receptivity were evident; then they were placed with aggressive male rats. Their sexual behavior was comparable to that of experienced female rats (Stone). Tests of the behavior of male rats that have been maintained in isolation and observed when first presented with an opportunity for sexual behavior leads to a similar conclusion (Beach). Experience no doubt plays some role in the primates and man, particularly in the refinement of sexual behavior (Bingham), but we must think of mating behavior patterns as constitutionally organized. Indeed, the precision and adaptiveness of such complex behavior puts it in a class with instinctive activities.

SENSORY DETERMINANTS OF MATING BEHAVIOR

External Stimuli.—Many senses make their contributions to the control of mating activity. Vision, somesthesis, and olfaction appear to play the dominant roles, but hearing and even kinesthesis are of some importance. Although we lack direct experimental evidence, it would appear that billing behavior in birds contributes to sexual excitement through the tactual, kinesthetic, and perhaps gustatory stimulation to which it gives rise; and the various vocalizations characteristic of courtship behavior in both mammals and birds seem clearly to be an excitant to consummatory (copulatory) sexual activity (Carpenter). The role played by tactile stimulation in the elicitation of sexual reflex patterns has already been indicated. Olfactory stimuli seem particularly important in certain of the mammals (*e.g.*, dogs and rats) in connection with the secretions of the female genital tract during sexual receptivity, for these present special olfactory stimulation associated only with physiological conditions conducive to mating. Visual perception of the receptiveness of a mate, finally, can also bring about mating behavior. Charging and strutting in a bird, for example, may serve to induce receptivity in the mate; the crouching and treading behavior of the female cat, or the behavior pattern of the receptive female rat, presents the male with a visual stimulus to mounting behavior.

The studies of Beach are especially enlightening in respect of the role of olfactory and visual factors in governing the sexual behavior of the male rat. He has shown that female receptive behavior, which has been described above, may engage the visual attention of the male and thereby elicit aggressive sexual behavior in him. Similarly, olfactory cues arising from the vaginal secretion, in evidence in the receptive female, are adequate, in the absence of other cues, for induction of copulatory behavior in the male rat. Thus, in connection with sexual behavior, there are unique external stimulus conditions which, by virtue of the character of the organization of the nervous system, give rise to sexual behavior.

In normal behavior, no one sensory modality appears to be important, but instead the various senses cooperate to present an integrated pattern of mating behavior. It has been shown, in fact, that the destruction of the nonauditory labyrinth, the enucleation of the eyes, or the removal of the olfactory bulbs does not abolish it in either males or females (rabbit). It is possible that there may be an exception to this statement in the case of kinesthetic impulses coming from the hind legs, for in one experiment with rabbits paralysis of the hind legs abolished sexual excitement (Brooks), but this result is understandable perhaps in terms of the primary importance of hind-leg movements and posture in the mating behavior of many animals.

Internal Stimuli.—Later we shall see that much prominence has been accorded the local theory of the hunger drive, *i.e.*, the theory that hunger depends upon sensory excitation arising from contractions of the stomach. It is therefore a question of especial interest whether sexual behavior depends upon afferent impulses from the sexual apparatus. There are now several experiments that render a definite answer to this question. Normal mating behavior continues to appear in female rats after the removal of the uterus and vagina, in spite of the fact that such an operation completely deprives the animal of both the afferent impulses from the sexual apparatus and the necessary organs with which to carry out copulatory behavior (Ball). Similarly, it has been shown that following complete interruption of both the sensory fibers innervating the sexual apparatus and the sympathetic motor fibers which play a prominent role in its function, female cats enter into mating behavior that is normal in every respect (Bard). Similar findings also apply to the male cat. Injury to the lower part of the spinal cord thereby causing the genitalia and the cutaneous regions surrounding them to be completely insensitive does not impair sexual aggressiveness in any way (Root and Bard). Thus the experimental evidence shows conclusively that in certain animals, at least, sexual drive and behavior do not depend upon sensory impulses from sexual organs, and we are forced, consequently, to deny that a local theory can hold for sexual behavior. On the contrary, the relation which holds between hormones and sexual behavior and which will be brought out in subsequent paragraphs points to the theory that sexual behavior depends primarily upon the erotization of the nervous system.

FACTORS IN SEXUAL DEVELOPMENT

Light.—In taking up migratory behavior it was indicated that the seasonal variations in light affect maturation of the gonads and in that way guide migratory behavior. Such photic influences, a host of experiments show (Rowan), also play their part in mating behavior. When, for example, in one experiment, a day was artificially lengthened, a male pheasant not only assumed prematurely the secondary sex characteristics —*e.g.*, changes in plumage, which are normally associated with breeding— but also presented typical mating behavior, the mating call, treading behavior, and copulation. Studies of other animals, especially some extensive work with the ferret, have indicated that mating behavior and premature gonadal development may be induced by an artificial increase in the number of light hours in a day (Bissonnette).

Not only is light known to influence the maturation of mating behavior, but the mechanism through which it acts is also understood, at least in general. It includes the eyes and visual impulses to the pituitary body, which result in raised production of the gonadotropic hormones and consequently of accelerated gonadal development (Rowan). One fact supporting this theory is that blinded animals do not show the effects of artificial illumination upon sexual behavior. Extirpation, furthermore, of various visual centers of the brain shows that only the visual pathways to the subthalamus, and thus presumably the hypothalamus and hypophysis, need be intact for light to play its role in hastening sexual maturation (see Clark *et al.*).

Adrenal Glands.—The secretions of the cortex of the adrenal glands also are of some importance in sexual development, as is shown by the fact that injection of extracts of the adrenal cortex into immature rats hastens markedly the appearance of sexual maturity (Carey and Britton). It is not known whether the important principle in this effect is an androgenic substance, known to be secreted by the adrenal cortex, or whether it is some other hormone. There is evidence, however, that the effect is mediated through the pituitary, for the injection of corticoadrenal extracts causes hypertrophy of the pituitary gland. We therefore seem to have in this case a chain of causal effects leading to maturity of sexual behavior: the adrenal secretions stimulate the hypophysis; the hypophysis accelerates growth in the gonadal glands; their secretions in turn bring about sexual behavior, the maturation of the genital apparatus, and other secondary sexual characteristics.

The Gonads.—The secretions of the gonads appear to be the condition *sine qua non* for the development of sexual behavior (Stone). Excision of the gonads (castration) in young rats and other animals permanently prevents the development of normal sexual behavior (Shapiro). As will be shown at a later point, castration in adulthood does not always abolish sexual behavior, but if it is performed before sexual maturity neither sexual behavior nor physical maturity will occur.

Prehypophysis.—As one might expect from the preceding statements, the anterior pituitary gland governs the development of sexual behavior and of the gonads and secondary sexual apparatus. The administration of hormones of the prehypophysis to young chicks, for example, will usher in adult physical characteristics within a very few days, and accompanying this physical development are such adult behavioral characteristics of sexual aggressiveness as crowing and treading (Domm and van Dyke). Likewise, by the transplantation of pituitary tissue in rats sexual maturity may be so accelerated that the development of secondary sex characteristics and sexual behavior appear at a time when they are usually weaned (Smith). Hypophysectomy in rats and other animals, on the other hand, prevents the normal development of sexual behavior (Stone). Thus normal sexual maturity has been shown to depend upon the anterior pituitary, and factors influencing its activity therefore affect sexual development.

It is interesting to note, moreover, that the reciprocal relationship which already has been stated to hold between the hypophysis and the gonads participates in regulating the rate of sexual development. Gonadal secretions inhibit gonadotropic activity of the pituitary, but in their absence, *i.e.*, when the gonads have been extirpated, the anterior pituitary undergoes unrestricted hyperdevelopment. This relationship is demonstrated by the fact that the hypophyses of gonadectomized animals are, when transplanted, more potent in accelerating sexual maturity than are hypophyses of normal animals (Engle).

The maturation of sexual behavior does not depend upon the maturation of the secondary sexual apparatus (genitals); rather the two kinds of development issue from one common basis, gonadal growth. It has been noted in rats that copulatory behavior appears before the apparatus for successful copulation is complete, and on the other hand, the organs of intromission are in some cases perfected before sexual behavior makes its appearance (Stone). Similar observations upon young chimpanzees support this finding. Young chimpanzees engage in a number of playful activities that are unmistakably sexual in nature and indeed they may include attempts at copulation with the sexual postures and rhythmic movements characteristic of copulation—all this before the sexual apparatus is mature. Such sexual behavior is, as one might expect, much less persistent and less frequent than is similar behavior subsequent to puberty (Bingham). We may therefore conclude that the maturation of the sexual organs and of the nervous pathways essential to sexual behavior depend upon one common factor, the growth of the gonads and the associated gonadal hormones.

PERIODIC ASPECTS OF MATING BEHAVIOR

As has already been noted, mating behavior is associated in some animals with particular conditions of lighting which go along with the seasons of the year. The periodic character of sexual activities, however, is evident in other ways than this. We may, in fact, distinguish three different, although not mutually exclusive, periods or cycles of such activities.

Life Cycle.—There is, first of all, the single long period of mating activity that occurs only once in the individual's life span. This may be long or short. The usual situation in human individuals is that such a period is introduced with the maturation of the gonads (puberty) and continues throughout life until it is terminated comparatively suddenly as in the menopause of women or rather gradually as in the sexual senility of men. In either case, the diminution of sexual activity and drive is normally associated with deteriorative changes in the gonads. Rats show a similar life cycle of sexual activities. Certain of the fishes, however, salmon, for example, have a relatively short period of mating activity that occurs only once in the life of the animal. In the salmon, the breeding period is an integral part of the life pattern of activities and subsequent to it the animals die.

Seasonal Cycles.—Every animal has its life cycle of mating activity, but superimposed upon this may be seasonal cycles. The rise and wane of such activity is consistently correlated with the growth and involution of the gonads, but the number and length of seasonal cycles varies in different animals. In the dog, for example, there are two seasons of heat (in the female), one in the spring and another in the fall; they each last about 6 weeks. In man, reproductive activity is not limited to any particular portion of the year, although it is possible that sexual drive may be higher in one part of the year than another, for birth statistics show a higher incidence of fertility in the late spring than any other time of year. Seasonal cycles sometimes apply only to the female of a species, and sometimes to both sexes.

Estrus Cycles.—Males undergo periodic change in sexual activity with respect to the life cycle and perhaps also to the seasons of the year. The third type of sexual cycle, however, males do not have; this is the estrus cycle and is seen only in the female mammal. Some of the physiological and hormonal changes associated with it have already been described, but the relation of behavioral functions to them may now be considered.

Consider first the female rat. It has a cycle of 4 to 5 days. During the major part of this period it is completely unreceptive to the advances of the male and will in fact be aggressively antagonistic. For about 6 hours of this cycle, however, it is receptive, *i.e.*, it is in estrus or "heat." The period of receptivity is usually correlated with changes in the vaginal mucosa, particularly with the appearance of cornified epithelial cells. The correlation is not perfect, however, for such changes, like sexual behavior itself, appear to be caused by hormonal conditions.

The complete cycle may be outlined as follows: During anestrus, *i.e.*, the interval between estrus, follicles of the ovaries and the ova which they contain gradually mature. With such maturation, estrogens are produced in ever-increasing amounts. When, after a period of time, they have reached some threshold concentration, the estrogens bring about the characteristic changes in the uterus and vaginal mucosa. High concentrations of estrogen likewise call forth changes in the nervous system which give rise to the behavior of estrus. When the follicle is fully matured it expels its ovum (or ova), and thus the peak of estrus is correlated with ovulation (Young, guinea pig). Upon ovulation the follicle undergoes degenerative changes, and estrogen production is correspondingly reduced until the beginning of another cycle.

Rats.—Among the most important behavioral signs of estrus are hyperactivity, special patterns of behavior, and sexual receptivity. Most animals are much more active during estrus than in anestrus, but in none is the activity so striking as in the rat. This animal, when placed in a revolving activity cage, will run ten to one hundred times the distance in one day that it will normally run on anestrual days (Wang, Slonaker). The rat's courtship behavior, on the other hand, is not very conspicuous as compared with other animals, but seems to consist principally of short periods of inactivity interspersed with fitful hops and runs about the cage. Upon being approached by a male, the estrual female rat puts up little resistance and readily allows the male to mount.

Monkeys.—The estrus cycle of primates is parallel in essential respects to the human menstrual cycle. (Fig. 145). Whereas infra-primate animals lack menses, female monkeys and chimpanzees have them. The length of the cycle is also about the same in the primates, and ovulation occurs at about the same time, *viz.*, about midway between the menses. Although the causes of menstruation are still obscure, the phenomenon seems to be associated with the low point of the estrus cycle in respect of the secretion of estrogens and progesterone. Ovulation, on the other hand, represents the estrual high point in the production of these hormones.

In rhesus monkeys the height of sexual drive is reached immediately preceding or coincident with ovulation (Ball and Hartman). The study in which this was determined employed as measures of sexual receptivity the typical behavior of a female monkey in estrus: (1) the receptive female goes toward and is in general sociable with the male, whereas during anestrus the usual behavior is one of avoidance; (2) various attempts to attract the attention of the male may be made; and (3) the receptive

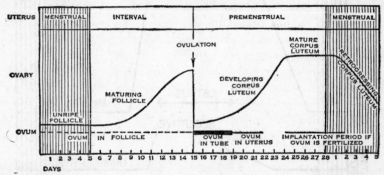

Fig. 145.—Scheme of the events taking place in the ovary and in the uterus during the estrual cycle. (*After Haggard. From G. A. Baitsell. Human biology, p. 323. New York: McGraw-Hill,* 1940.)

female may assume the specific receptive posture, thus "presenting" herself to the male. Careful observations of such indications of sexual receptivity and of sexual behavior show that although behavior is not lacking in any phase of the estrus cycle it rises markedly in the period of three or four days just preceding ovulation and after that quickly subsides to its resting level—a finding consistent with the observations on lower animals.

Chimpanzees.—A similar study of the relation of sexual drive and physiological changes has been made in chimpanzees (Yerkes and Elder). As Fig. 146 indicates, the menstrual cycle in the chimpanzee lasts for about 5 weeks. During a good part of this period the genitalia are characterized by reddening and swelling (this also occurs in monkeys). Such local physiological changes probably parallel the changes in the vaginal mucosa which are related to estrus in lower animals, except that in this case the change is of longer duration. Within the period of maximal swelling, estrual receptivity makes its appearance, rising to its greatest intensity at or about the time of ovulation. At this time copulation and various secondary aspects of sexual behavior also appear, these being limited strictly to a third of the cycle at and around ovulation.

In the chimpanzee, changes in behavior associated with estrus are not limited to purely sexual activities, but also include other social relations, particularly social dominance (Yerkes). During anestrus, the male chimpanzee is normally dominant over the female in such matters as who is to partake first of food. During the period of estrus and of maximal genital swelling, the male defers to the female, allowing her to become dominant in getting food, and if the amount of available food is restricted,

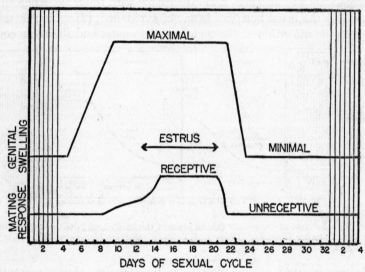

Fig. 146.—Relation of genital swelling to estrus and to sexual receptivity in the chimpanzee. (*After Yerkes and Elder.*)

she will get most of it. Thus a reversal of the usual social relations between the two is correlated with estrus, and social behavior of greater breadth than that of a sexual nature is changed by the hormonal conditions underlying estrus.

Man.—Attempts have been made to determine the relation of sexual drive to the events of the menstrual cycle in human individuals. Such attempts meet with difficulties, however, because of the many factors affecting reproductive behavior in man and because of barriers to the attainment of accurate information concerning such matters (see Stone). The best data available agree in placing the greatest sexual drive in the neighborhood of menstruation. As Fig. 147 indicates, moreover, there are two peaks, one before and one following menses (Davis). This state of affairs, it is to be noted, is not consistent with the data secured from lower animals, and doubt has been expressed as to whether the so-called sexual desire is based on any physiological conditions; may it not instead be the outcome of social conventions or perhaps of affective psychological states associated with the menses (Tinkelpaugh)?

Even though we may question whether the peaks of sexual drive to be seen in Fig. 147 are comparable to estrual sexual activity in animals, it is nevertheless true that in human beings there is no such striking restriction of sexual activity to a limited period of the menstrual cycle as we have found in chimpanzees and lower animals.   There are several possibilities to explain this fact: Hormone levels may be maintained in man at an adequate level for "erotization" of the nervous system throughout the entire cycle; or hormones may not be of such basic importance in

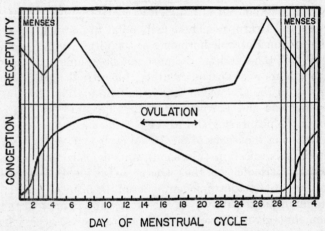

Fig. 147.—Relation between sexual desire, ovulation, and frequency of conception in women as shown by answers to questionnaires. (*After K. B. Davis.*)

the organization of sexual desire in man as in lower animals; or social conventions and the setting up of habitual attitudes in human individuals may be sufficient, in lieu of basic hormonal determinants, to instigate and maintain reproductive behavior. Which of these possibilities, or others, may be correct, can only be a matter of speculation at this time, and we are led, therefore, to await the acquisition of experimental material capable of settling the question.

Photic Stimulation and Estrus.—We have already considered evidence to the effect that the changes in the number of light hours in a day are important in controlling seasonal cycles of sexual maturation and behavior.   Light also appears to affect estrus cycles, presumably through the mediation of the prehypophysis.   Careful records of the time of day at which estrus begins in guinea pigs (vaginal-smear method) indicate that it is essentially a nocturnal phenomenon and occurs early in the

evening (Young *et al.*). Similarly, the burst of bodily activity characteristic of estrus in the rat typically occurs at night (Browman). That it
is light (or darkness) which is important is shown by the fact that the
relationship can be reversed by experimental reversal of light-dark
conditions.

Such facts point superficially to the theory that it is the absence of
light which aids the onset of estrus. An alternative interpretation,
however, is that estrus tends to appear in darkness as a result of the
accumulation of the effects of light. In support of this supposition is
the fact that one can maintain the vaginal signs of estrus, *i.e.*, cornifica-
tion of vaginal epithelium, for 5 or 6 days by administering constant
light (Browman), and, moreover, by such a device the period of sexual
receptivity can be prolonged, although the estrual running activity cannot
(Hemmingsen and Krarup).   These facts point to photic influences upon
the secretion of gonadotropic hormones of the pituitary in regulating the
cyclic activity of the ovaries. It must not be assumed, however, that
such influence is more than contributory, for estrual rhythms will continue normally in the absence of any visual stimulation (Browman).

The Hypophysis and Estrus.—A natural question, at this point, is
the relation of the pituitary gland to the periodicity of the female gonads
in the production of the estrus or menstrual cycle. There is considerable
evidence upon this question (Marshall), and it leads to the conclusion
that the primary periodicity of the estrus cycle is a function of the ovaries,
not the pituitary. Gonadotropic hormones of the pituitary are, of course,
necessary to maintain the activity of the ovaries and to prevent them from
retrogression, but given these, the cycle of the ovary which has been
described is governed by the ovary and only influenced within narrow
limits by the pituitary.

An interesting and informative experiment in this connection has
been presented by Richter. The stalk of the pituitary which supplies
nerve fibers from the hypothalamus and midbrain to the pituitary was
sectioned in female rats and its effect upon the estrus cycles of activity
studied. The usual cycle of 4 to 5 days disappeared in most animals,
it was found, but instead there appeared a new cycle, relatively constant
in each rat, of about 13 to 18 days. The peaks of these cycles were
observed to coincide with ovulation. This new 'estrus cycle,' Richter
thought, was a multiple of the 4- to 5-day normal estrus cycle, and
further, it was theorized, severance of the nervous connections of the
pituitary body had reduced either the gonadotropic secretions of the
gland or its reciprocal relations with the ovaries in such a way that
gonadal activity was reduced, not in terms of cycle length, but in respect
of level, with the result that full follicle maturation, ovulation, and sexual
receptivity did not appear in some of the cycles.

Pregnancy and Estrus Cycles.—In all infrahuman animals, sexual drive is notably lacking in the female during pregnancy. In rats if copulation during estrus results in fertilization and pregnancy, no further estrual periods of heat will occur throughout gestation. A few hours after birth of the young a period of estrus ensues, and impregnation may in some instances take place at this time (postparturitional heat). Immediately following this, however, the mother goes into anestrus and does not display heat again until the end of the nursing period 18 or 20 days later. In spite of the lack of sexual drive or estrus cycles throughout these periods, it would seem that ovarian cycles continue in pregnancy, for it is the common rule that the term of pregnancy in nearly all animals is some multiple of the estrus cycle. Parturition seems to be associated, in fact, with the culmination of a cycle, for ovulation and postparturitional heat follow it closely. The hormonal causes of parturition, however, are obscure.

There is no direct experimental evidence as to why sexual drive is diminished in pregnancy. We know that estrogens are produced during pregnancy by the placenta and possibly also by the corpus luteum; these are associated in the estrus cycle with "heat." For the absence of sexual drive despite the presence of estrogens, two reasons, both supported indirectly by experimental facts, may be suggested: (1) Progesterone is the prominent hormone of pregnancy. Progesterone, under certain conditions, is known to counteract the effect of estrogen in raising the excitability of the uterus (Allen), and it is quite possible that progesterone is antagonistic to estrogen in producing sexual drive (*cf.* Boling *et al.*). (2) There is also evidence that prolonged action of estrin reduces heat (Ball). In an experiment in which estrin was injected in rats over a period of two months, estrus cycles were inhibited and sexual receptivity was kept at a very low level. What the reasons are, however, for this action of estrogen as contrasted with its normal role in the ovarian cycle of producing heat, are not known. (There was some evidence in this experiment that ovarian cycles continued unabated but that they never were expressed in conspicuous estrual periods). Likewise, we cannot at the present time state the hormonal basis of diminution of mating activity during the nursing period after birth.

THE EFFECTS OF CASTRATION ON SEXUAL BEHAVIOR

It was implicit in much of the foregoing discussion that sexual behavior, particularly in the female, depends upon gonadal hormones. The evidence for this belief may now be presented, first by reference to the effects of extirpation of the gonads and later by considering experiments in which gonadal hormones have been administered.

Ovariectomy.—It is well established that monkeys and lower mammalian animals become sexually unreceptive after complete removal of the animal's ovaries (Ball). If animals are castrated while in estrus, sexual behavior may be elicited for some short period of time following the ovariectomy, after which all sexual receptivity will disappear permanently. If activity records are used as an indication of sexual drive, there is also indication that the gonadectomy has permanently abolished sex drive, for the usual cycles of activity (4 to 5 days in the rat) are completely lacking. Thus previous statements to the effect that sexual behavior depends upon the secretion of estrogen by the ovaries are upheld by the experiments upon ovariectomy.

In women, however, the matter is not nearly so definite. There are on the one hand numerous observations that sexual desire undergoes no diminution following double ovariectomy (Frank), and yet other comparatively good studies claim a gradual reduction in sexual desire and in the capacity to carry out reproductive behavior properly (Clauberg and Schultze). It seems quite certain in any event that ovariectomy does not promptly and permanently abolish sexual desire in all women; and we are again confronted with a discrepancy between man and lower animals such as we found in the case of the periodic waxing and waning of sexual drive in relation to the menstrual cycle. Again it can only be suggested that social conventions among human beings are capable of governing sexual receptivity and further that the actual successful completion of copulatory behavior does not necessarily depend upon hormonal conditions.

Male Castration.—Whereas ovariectomy immediately abolishes sexual behavior in female animals, castration in male animals seems to be comparable to human ovariectomy in not eliminating sexual drive. In birds (Carpenter) and rats (Stone), with which the most careful experiments have been carried out, copulatory ability withstands castration and diminishes only slowly in the period subsequent to it. It was found in rats, for example, that at the end of one month after castration only 33 per cent of a group of castrates had ceased to copulate; after two months, 45 per cent; and in subsequent months, more and more animals gradually lost their sexual drive (Stone). Why it is that copulatory ability is not crucially dependent upon the presence or absence of the gonads is not yet understood, but other facts which will be introduced later suggest possible answers to this question. A similar finding has been obtained in man (Stone), and in this respect man and animals do not seem to differ.

In connection with the possibility suggested above that social factors and habituation may serve to sustain sexual drive, it is worth noting in passing that in Stone's study of castration in the male rat the copulation of castrates did not prevent the waning of sexual desire; *i.e.*, exercise of the copulatory apparatus and habitual copulation, after castration, were followed eventually by the disappearance of sexual aggressiveness.

Male rats show no periodicity of sexual behavior or of activity, and as stated elsewhere (p. 388), the normal male rat maintains a relatively uniform activity level in a revolving drum from day to day. Following castration, however, activity is reduced to about one-fifth its normal level (Richter). Moreover, about the same amount of loss in activity follows castration carried out before puberty and after it (Gans). Thus the male gonads govern activity somewhat independently of its relation to sexual behavior. It has been suggested that postcastrational fall in activity level is associated with the accumulation of fat (Hoskins); and it is true that observers have generally found a reduction in metabolic rate following castration (Commins and Stone). These and other inter-relations of the gonads with other endocrine glands, appetite, and neural activity still need to be worked out in greater detail.

Hypophysectomy.—In contrast to the fact that sexual drive tapers off only slowly following male castration, extirpation of the pituitary body is followed by the complete disappearance of male copulatory behavior (Wiesner and Sheard). These two facts taken together are very important, for they indicate that in the case of the male sex drive the secretions of the gonads are not fundamental but that some factor associated with pituitary activity is. It is not necessary to conclude that the hypophysis itself secretes the crucial hormone, for we know that it governs the activity of several other glands, of which the adrenal is perhaps the most important in this connection. Nor is it necessary to conclude that the androgens secreted by the testes are not crucial to sex behavior, for the adrenal cortex also secretes them, and there are several other related chemical substances in the blood, some of whose sources are unknown, which can be converted into androgens. We may recall here that hypertrophy of the adrenal cortex or injection of the corticoadrenal hormone accelerates sexual maturation in male animals. What we can conclude is that the factors (hormonal?) governing sex behavior in the male are under the control of the pituitary and that this factor is not secreted exclusively by the gonads.

In turning to the effects of hypophysectomy upon sexual drive in females, one meets with a result similar to that found in males. Hypophysectomy causes a prompt disappearance of sexual receptivity, but for that matter, so also does gonadectomy in this case, and one can believe simply that ovarian activity depends upon the secretion of the pituitary body. Examining the physiological correlates of this effect, one can find that in hypophysectomy the ovaries rapidly retrogress and the secondary sex apparatus, whose integrity depends upon the ovaries, changes back to a prepuberal stage of development. A comparable situation obtains in the male.

GONADAL HORMONES AND MATING BEHAVIOR

The discussion of the effects of gonadal hormones upon sexual behavior logically follows that of the relation of castration to such behavior. The use of hormones in such studies has naturally been limited by their availability in comparatively pure form. This problem fortunately has been solved for an ever-increasing number of hormones by virtue of the great strides which have been made recently in the field of hormonal chemistry. A considerable number of hormones, particularly those of importance in sex physiology and behavior, have been obtained in pure form and their chemical structures ascertained. Consequently in recent years a considerable amount of work concerning the relation between sex hormones and sex behavior has been made possible, and it is to be expected that greater advances will be made more rapidly in the next few years. The material that we have and which is now to be summarized throws considerable light, as it stands, upon the very crux of the problem of the physiological basis of mating behavior patterns.

Reactivation of Castrates.—There is, first of all, the question as to whether gonadectomy in male and female animals can be remedied by the administration of hormones manufactured by the gonads. The answer is in the affirmative. Castrated male guinea pigs whose sexual drive has diminished significantly subsequent to castration are largely restored to their precastrate level of sexual aggressiveness by treatment with testosterone (an androgen) (Seward). Likewise, the administration of estrogen to castrated female rats brings about estrus, although such estrus may not be completely identical, physiologically or behaviorally, with normal estrus (Ball). Finally, castrated female monkeys have been reactivated by injections of estrogenic hormones; in this case, moreover, a definite relation between the amount of hormone injected and the degree of sexual responsiveness induced was demonstrated (Ball). Thus there is proof that estrogen activates sexual behavior in the female and androgens do the same in the male.

The results of Young and his collaborators, who have carried out an unusually extensive series of experiments with guinea pigs, deserve particular mention in this connection. One of the very interesting results of their research is the discovery that, in the guinea pig, estrogen and progesterone administered in sequence are more effective activators of sexual behavior and of estrual physiological conditions generally than is estrogen alone (Boling *et al.*). Estrogen alone will, to be sure, induce heat in the spayed female, but estrogen and progesterone seem to act synergetically to produce a better result. This fact makes us question, therefore, whether the hormonal activation of sexual behavior is a matter of only one hormone, although it happens that both estrogen and progesterone are ovarian substances. A further fact is that in heat produced by estrogen injection an inverse relationship between the time elapsing before heat and the period of the duration of the heat was obtained (Collins *et al.*). This result led Young and his coworkers to suggest that estrogen involves the activation of some all-or-none mechanism, a suggestion which contrasts with the findings, in monkeys, that the degree of reactivation is related to the amount of hormone injected.

That other hormones in addition even to ovarian hormones may be important in sexual behavior is indicated by an experiment in which it was found that the sexual excitability of castrated females who were kept in rather constant estrus by the use of estrogen (Ball) was raised by the addition of the gonadotropic luteinizing hormone of the pituitary.

Senility.—Although the injection of gonadal hormones will reinstate mating behavior in castrated animals, experiments designed to determine whether a similar reactivation can be accomplished in senile animals have so far yielded negative results (Hoskins *et al.*). Sexual behavior was not directly observed in these experiments, unfortunately, but the decrease in running activity that accompanies the senile waning of sexual drive was studied, and the injection of male hormones was of no avail in reinstating such activity. Besides this experiment there is an extensive literature which records the failure of attempts for more than a hundred years to reactivate human individuals; indeed, the modern evidence on this question speaks univocally for the conclusion that no such reactivation by gonadal hormones is possible (Stone). It appears, therefore, that the waning of sexual desire which takes place in senility is not due to a lack of gonadal hormones but to changes elsewhere, possibly in the nervous system or in other more widespread areas in the internal environment.

Hormones of the Opposite Sex.—Another interesting question is that of whether a hormone of one sex will reactivate a castrated animal of the opposite sex. Answering this question is the fact that in one experiment the sexual receptivity of castrated female guinea pigs was reinstated by treatment with testosterone (Seward); similarly castrated male rats have been activated by estrogenic hormones (Ball). To explain these remarkable results, it has been suggested that the gonadal hormones stimulate the pituitary and that this gland in turn secretes a principle that brings in sexual behavior. Such a hypothesis, however, is not required, if it is assumed (Ball) that the estrogens and androgens both effect the reinstatement of the mating patterns by directly influencing the nervous system and that the type of mating pattern is determined not by the activating hormone but by the organization of the neural patterns.

Bisexual Behavior.—The fact that gonadal hormones may activate sexual patterns in castrated animals of the opposite sex raises the interesting question of what relation exists between the gonadal hormones and homosexual or bisexual behavior. Contrary to frequent assertions that homosexuality and bisexual behavior are acquired through experience, the experimental material in animals on this question indicates that both male and female sexual behaviors are in varying degrees part of the behavioral repertoire of each sex. This bipotentiality for sexual behavior, as we soon shall note, is consistent with the basically bisexual character of the gonads mentioned earlier in this chapter.

Changes in the sexual apparatus, as well as bisexual behavior, may be induced in rats by the injection of ovarian hormones (Kun) and by testosterone (Ball). Such behavior, however, is not associated exclusively in either sex with any one particular gonadal hormone, although the evidence on this question is based more upon females than males. In one experiment (Ball), male rats were castrated at weaning age and were given estrogen for several weeks and finally were subjected to tests of sexual behavior. It was found that males when mounted by sexually aggressive females would assume the basic female posture, and to this extent they exhibited bisexual behavior, but they never displayed the rest of the female pattern. It was necessary to inject much more estrogen into castrated males than into castrated females to obtain this rudimentary female mating pattern, but it is nonetheless singular that it appears. It is also interesting that the addition of progesterone to estrogen somewhat enhances the bisexual behavior of the male rat.

In a comparable study (Ball), except that the animals were not castrated in this case, the effect of testosterone injected into female rats over a period of months was determined. Throughout this period masculine sex behavior (mounting) definitely increased. Such a result seems to indicate that the rudiment of the male copulatory pattern (mounting) is possessed by the normal female rat, and that, although the threshold for this pattern is high, it can be lowered by appropriate injection of testosterone.

As clear as these two experiments may seem, one cannot say that it was the use of the hormone of the opposite sex which induced the bisexual behavior, although it would seem that this hormone is probably more effective than one of the same sex. Nevertheless, in a very extensive experiment (Young and Brewster), conducted with castrated female guinea pigs, homosexual mounting behavior was observed in estrus produced by both female and male hormones. The following hormones and combinations of hormones were used: estrogen alone, estrogen and progesterone, androgens alone, and androgen, estrogens, and progesterone. It was found that the most effective combination of hormones was estrogen followed by progesterone, precisely the combination necessary for optimum estrus in the female guinea pig. Thus it seems clear that homosexual behavior was at a peak at the same time that heterosexual behavior was. The conclusion to be reached from this result was that both the male (mounting) and the female ("receptive") patterns of sexual behavior are possessed by the female guinea pig, and that the two different neural organizations underlying them are both stimulated by estrogen and progesterone acting in synergy. Thus both male and female hormones are capable of inducing both male and female behavioral reactions in both sexes, although there are individual differences in this respect. Certainly, therefore, so far as the evidence from lower animals is concerned, we must grant the fundamental bisexual organization of individuals in respect of both gonadal hormonal secretions and neural patterns of sexual behavior.

THE NEURAL BASIS OF SEXUAL BEHAVIOR

As has been plain in the preceding discussion, there are yet many problems to be settled with respect to the hormonal basis of mating behavior, but the evidence as it stands is nevertheless definite with respect to two major problems: patterns of mating behavior do not depend upon afferent impulses from the copulatory apparatus; and on the other hand, they are crucially dependent upon certain hormonal conditions of the blood. We have not, of course, ruled out the possibility that hormones may activate certain sexual patterns by producing changes in some organs of the body which in turn give rise to afferent impulses in the nervous system, but the facts point to the direct erotization of the nervous system by hormones.

There is one possibility, however, which experiments to date have not definitely excluded. That is the possible effect of sex hormones upon the olfactory sense organs (see Seward). Sex hormones are known to induce changes in the nasal membranes, and it is a question whether such changes might provide an afferent basis for sexual drive. Such a hypothesis does not appear particularly attractive, and moreover, it has been shown in at least one case that an animal with complete genital denervation and removal of the olfactory bulbs is capable of normal mating behavior. In any event, we may turn now to the consideration of the role of the central nervous system in the organization of patterns of sexual behavior.

The Spinal Cord.—So long as autonomic innervation of the sexual organs is intact, by mechanical stimulation of the genital regions one can obtain in a spinal animal the reflex erection of genital tissue and even ejaculatory responses. This much of sexual behavior requires only the spinal cord. One may observe, furthermore, certain of the elementary skeletal reflexes which seem to be related to sexual behavior in spinal preparations, but such responses, for example, lifting of the tail, are to be found in normal animals of both sexes and are not properly regarded as a distinctive part of either the male or female patterns of sexual behavior (see Bard). If one concerns himself, however, with the copulatory pattern or with estrual patterns such as the estrual crouch or treading in the cat—*i.e.*, patterns which are activated hormonally—these are found not at all to be organized at the spinal level. For example, estrual patterns have not been obtained in the female guinea pig after the injection of estrogen and progesterone when the spinal cord and brain have been surgically divided from each other (Dempsey and Rioch). Similar results have been obtained in spinal cats (Bromiley and Bard). Thus we must look to supraspinal levels for centers that govern the sexual pattern induced by the gonadal hormones. Section at any level below the middle of the midbrain, however, presents the same picture, and thus the neural center for the hormonal organization of the sexual pattern must lie above the middle of the mesencephalon.

Hypothalamus and Midbrain.—The results of experiments with animals subjected to injuries at levels above the middle of the mesencephalon vary a great deal according to the species of animal used and according to sex of the subjects. In spite of such differences, however, we may reconstruct a picture which makes a great deal of sense and is enlightening as to the centers important in the organization of sexual behavior.

In an experiment with ovariectomized animals brought into estrus through the administration of estrogen and progesterone, Dempsey and Rioch obtained the following results: Subjects which were decerebrated in such a way that the cut in the brain stem passed definitely behind the mammillary bodies gave no evidence of estrual behavior when injected with the appropriate hormones. If, on the other hand, the decerebrate section passed anterior to the mammillary bodies, typical estrual responses to an aggressive animal followed hormone injection. The peripheral point of the cleavage of the brain stem was in both cases between the superior and inferior colliculi. These data point definitely to the posterior hypothalamus and the anterior mesencephalon as the loci of estrual patterns activated by gonadal hormones.

Work with the female cat under similar conditions of gonadectomy and hormone injection leads to a rather similar conclusion (Bard). In this work, the surgical technique was different from that of Dempsey and Rioch in that instead of decerebration direct lesions were made in the hypothalamus. It was found that rather extensive damage in the caudal hypothalamus sometimes abolished estrual behavior in spayed cats injected with estrogen, but sometimes it did not. The experiments have not cleared up this variation in the effects of hypothalamic lesions on different animals, but it has been suggested, in line with the findings of Dempsey and Rioch, that the anterior mesencephalon in connection with the caudal hypothalamus—*i.e.*, the region of the mammillary bodies—is the important region in estrual behavior and that the hypothalamic lesions that have been made so far do not give consistent results because they do not invade the mesencephalon. It should be pointed out, however, that the hypothalamus is important in so many of the basic homeostatic functions of the organism, such as temperature control, metabolism, and blood pressure, that great caution must be exercised in interpreting the effects of hypothalamic lesions upon sexual behavior, for any disturbance of the essential functions could very well abolish sexual behavior without proving that the organization of estrual behavior, apart from its dependence upon autonomic functions, resides in that area.

The Cortex and Striatum.—Observations of the decorticate female cat support the belief that estrual behavior is mediated at some subcortical level; for the estrual pattern of behavior, which is so striking in the cat, fully survives complete decortication (Bard). One must not think, however, that this is the case for all animals. In the pigeon, mating patterns are not disturbed by extirpation of the cortex, but if in addition to decortication the corpus striatum is also extirpated, then courtship behavior is greatly diminished and copulatory patterns are not executed at all (Rogers).

A similar picture is presented by the *female* rabbit, except that the importance of the striatum has not been investigated. Complete extirpation of the neocortex and of the olfactory bulbs leaves the mating pattern quite intact in this animal. In the *male* rabbit there is this difference: the neocortex is not essential for mating behavior, but the additional destruction of the olfactory bulbs abolishes it (Brooks). Apparently copulatory behavior in the male rabbit requires olfactory cues, whereas this is not the case in the female. If a sizeable amount of the neocortex is left intact, however, then one may destroy the olfactory bulbs without any such disturbance of mating behavior in the male. Thus it appears that olfactory cues per se are not essential so long as other cues remain available to the animal (Stone).

A very careful study of the effect of cortical lesions upon sexual behavior in the rat has been carried out by Beach (Fig. 148). The cortex is apparently much more important in the rat than it is in any of the other animals discussed above, but its role can best be understood in terms of a loss of perceptual capacity as is also the case with the male rabbit. Beach's work was restricted to male rats, so that his results probably cannot be generalized to apply also to the female. His findings may be summarized as follows: The removal of small portions of the cortex up to about 20 per cent of its mass does not abolish copulatory behavior in the male rat. With more extensive destruction of the cortex, copulatory behavior is reduced or abolished and this roughly in proportion to the magnitude of the lesion. The actual pattern of behavior is not disturbed in any way, however, but instead cortical injuries seem to reduce the readiness with which the behavior may be elicited. The results, therefore, do not point to the cortex as the seat of the organization of copulatory behavior, but instead they lead one to believe that inability to recognize the sex object seems to be the important factor in the loss (Lashley). Such an interpretation is consistent with the part that the cortex plays in the more complex processes of learning and thought.

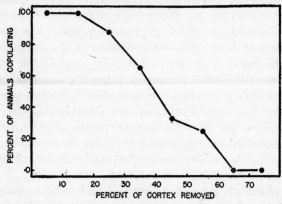

FIG. 148.—Relation between extirpation of the cortex and copulatory ability in male rats. (*After F. A. Beach,* 1940.)

Erotization of the Nervous System.—Our present knowledge concerning the foci of neural processes concerned in these various patterns of sexual behavior can be summarized by stating that in females the organization of estrual behavior appears to depend upon a portion of the brain stem in the region of the mammillary bodies and that insofar as higher centers of the nervous system play a significant role they do so as mediators of the perceptual processes which lead to the arousal of the subcortically organized sexual pattern. Although conclusive proof is still lacking, the most acceptable hypothesis as to the way in which these subcortical centers are activated is that the gonadal hormones act directly on these centers rather than upon any afferent mechanism.

General Reference

STONE, C. P., 1939. Sex drive. Pp. 1213–1262. In *Sex and internal secretions.* Ed. E. Allen, C. H. Danforth, E. A. Doisy. Baltimore: Williams & Wilkins.

CHAPTER XXI

BODILY NEEDS

No particular occasion for using the term *needs* has arisen in previous chapters concerning motivated behavior, although the conditions in the internal environment which were shown to govern instinctive and mating behavior could have been called needs. Psychologists, however, usually make considerable use of the concept of need or drive, and because we are about to take up several types of motivated behavior to which this terminology has become attached, it is best that the terms should be introduced and defined.

It is customary to draw a distinction between *viscerogenic* and *psychogenic needs;* some prefer to speak of *primary* and *secondary needs.* Psychogenic, or secondary, needs are held to be the result largely of learning and are regarded as so complex in nature that there is little profit at present in attempting to deal with them at the physiological level. The viscerogenic, or primary, needs are regarded as arising primarily from activities in the alimentary and urogenital tracts. Since, however, certain aspects of instinctive and motivated behavior are known to have their roots in the endocrine glands, the circulatory system, body temperature, and general metabolism, it would probably be more appropriate to refer to such needs as *biogenic.* It is these with which we are concerned here.

It is important to understand that even the biogenic need or drive, as used by psychologists and in this book, may have three meanings (*cf.* Adolph): It may refer, first of all, to the fact that an animal has been deprived for some period of time of something essential to its existence. Thus an animal which has gone without food for some time is said to possess a hunger drive simply by virtue of its deprivation. For many purposes, deprivation is the only convenient way of knowing that an individual is needy. Words denoting need may also refer to the conscious experience of a human observer. When one speaks of being hungry, he often means, in the language of introspection, that he has a *sensation* of hunger. Need may indicate, finally, an urge or craving that is expressed in the behavior of an animal. Thus an animal is thirsty when it drinks or hungry when it eats.

The needs considered in this chapter will be those connected with the activities of breathing, drinking, eating, urination, and defecation. In the following chapter a general survey of the problem of motivation and also of the concepts of greatest value in the field will be presented.

RESPIRATORY BEHAVIOR

Breathing is such a fundamental activity of the organism and is ordinarily carried out so regularly and dependably that we are prone to ignore its psychophysiological significance. To be sure, respiratory behavior is not very relevant to most phases of psychology, for it probably plays an exceedingly minor role in learning and seldom enters into conscious experience. Respiration is, nevertheless, motivated behavior. Indeed, it is a model of such behavior in that it is relatively simple behavior whose mechanism is much better understood than other mecha-

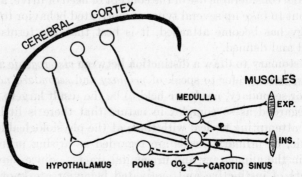

Fig. 149.—Centers and pathways involved in respiration. The inspiratory and expiratory centers of the medulla are primary and are controlled both by chemical stimulation of carotid sinus receptors and by direct stimulation. In addition, the pons reciprocally inhibits inspiratory impulses, and highest activities in the cortex and hypothalamus affect the bulbar respiratory functions.

nisms of motivation; and its study offers some suggestions for the interpretation of other facts of motivation.

Respiration displays, first of all, the periodicity which is so often characteristic of other drives. The two important phases in its periodicity are *inspiration* and *expiration*, i.e., the alternate inhaling and exhaling of air. Both of these activities are regulated by several centers located at different levels of the cerebrum (see Fig. 149). The lowest and most vital level of regulation is in the medulla. Here there are two centers, one for inspiration and another for expiration. Then in the pons there is another center whose function is to regulate the periodicity of the bulbar centers. In the cortex, finally, is vested the integration of respiration with 'higher' psychological processes; several parts of the cortex are probably concerned in some way in respiration, but the principal cortical center appears to be in the orbital gyrus near by, and presumably associated in function with, the speech area.

The activity of the neural centers concerned in respiration is partially controlled by direct chemical stimulation. It has long been known that the bulbar respiratory centers are sensitive to carbon dioxide, and since a rise in carbon dioxide in the blood lowers pH it was formerly suggested that the over-all pH of the blood is the stimulus to respiration. Recent studies, however, show carbon dioxide per se, not the general pH of the blood, to be the crucial factor in regulating the bulbar centers of respiration. Whether such is also the case for higher centers has not yet been determined, but the sensitivity of the bulbar center to carbon dioxide is so great that this mechanism must be taken as the fundamental one.

Although direct stimulation of the medulla may be primary, there are also peripheral mechanisms controlling the behavior. The inspiratory act produces afferent impulses in the vagus nerve, and these, when they reach the medulla, inhibit inspiratory behavior and cause contraction of the expiratory muscles of the chest. The physiological mechanism in this case appears to be one of reciprocal innervation previously described for spinal reflexes, and it is as a result of this mechanism that breathing behavior is periodic in character. Worth noting, too, is the fact that the pontine nuclei for respiration perform a parallel function; nervous impulses put out by the bulbar centers during inspiration cause the pontine nuclei to send back impulses which inhibit the inspiration and actively produce expiration.

Besides these reciprocal mechanisms there are two other factors in controlling respiration: chemical and mechanical stimulation of receptors in the carotid sinus and aortal arch. Chemical receptors in these places are activated by increases in the carbon dioxide content, and perhaps also the pH, of the blood, just as the bulbar respiratory centers are stimulated by carbon dioxide. When one makes careful comparisons, however, of the effects of chemical stimulation of the aortic and carotid receptors with the effects of similar conditions upon the bulbar centers, it is clear that the bulbar nuclei are by far the most important. The control of respiration exercised by mechanical stimulation of the carotid and aortic pressure receptors is simply a means of adjusting respiration to changes in blood pressure; when pressure decreases the respiratory rate increases, and conversely.

This completes the sketch of the major physiological factors in respiration. From it we see that respiration, a very primitive and essential motivated behavior, has the following mechanism: The need is for oxygen, but the control of behavior designed to obtain more oxygen for the body is vested for the most part in carbon dioxide (p. 100). This affects behavior by stimulating peripheral receptors and, more directly, centers of the nervous system controlling behavior. The different phases of the behavior are also controlled by both peripheral and central mechanisms which are relatively complete in themselves and are only slowed or hastened by changes in carbon dioxide. This picture of central and peripheral processes in respiration is a rather good model, it appears, for other kinds of motivated behavior as well.

EVACUATION

We ordinarily think of defecation and urination as reflex acts which human individuals, and sometimes animals, learn to control by acquiring voluntary cortical mechanisms. Such a conception of these behaviors is not incorrect, but it should be enlarged to take in the fact that they arise from needs and are, therefore, motivated.

For one thing, they are both periodic. The stimulus, which is the accumulation of materials in the bladder or colon, builds up over a period of time; then the behavior takes place, and the cycle is repeated. In rats, for example, urination is performed rather regularly at 2-hr. intervals and defecation occurs about every 5 hr. (Richter). During the quiet phase of the cycle the need undergoes deprivation in the sense that the conditions for the behaviors are building up which in the other phase of the cycle are satisfied.

In addition to these motivated aspects of evacuative behavior, there is the further fact that it often has the character of highly complex instinctual reactions. Dogs and cats, for example, usually seek a particular set of environmental conditions in which to carry out such behavior and display highly specialized reactions with respect to these conditions. They must find dirt, sawdust, or some similar material in which a hole can be dug, and then follow the behavior by attempts to cover the excrement. They also assume particular stances in performing such behavior, depending upon the sex of the animal. All these reactions fit into a complex pattern whose motivated character cannot be mistaken. Little is known of the physiological basis of these patterns, and more research along this line is called for. All that can be said at present is that the primary stimulus for the behavior arises in the accumulation of materials in the bladder and colon, from which sensory fibers carry impulses to the central nervous system. The need in this case has its basis in a peripheral stimulus.

THIRST

We do not yet know the physiological basis of thirst but only certain physiological factors influencing it. Part of the reason why we know so little about it is due to the way in which early psychologists and physiologists regarded it. They tended to think of thirst as a conscious experience, and when they found the immediate conditions giving rise to the thirst experience—*viz.,* dryness of the mouth and throat—they were content. Such an approach to thirst is sadly inadequate, for it leaves out not only the question of the physiological factors governing dryness of the throat, but it entirely disregards thirst conceived as a general bodily state which can be altered and which can lead to different sorts of behavior in search of and in partaking of water.

Thirst as a Sensation.—The most widely known theory of thirst, offered by Cannon, and sometimes called the *local theory*, deals with thirst as a conscious experience. According to this theory, thirst is dependent directly upon the state of the mucous membranes of the tongue, mouth, and throat. It holds further that thirst reflects the body's need of water because a lowering of the amount of water in the blood affects the constitution of the saliva secreted into the mouth and throat. Going into details on this point, Cannon notes that the amount of water in the blood is held relatively constant from time to time even though water is needed, but that constancy of water in the blood is maintained at a sacrifice of water in the tissues of the body. The salivary glands are part of these tissues and, as a consequence, are influenced by very slight changes in the blood. Thus the dryness of the throat will be a rather sensitive index of the body's need for water.

In support of the point that thirst depends upon buccal dryness, Cannon has presented and referred to several experiments. These, briefly, show that thirst can be alleviated by simply taking water into the mouth and not necessarily into the digestive tract, by chewing gum and thereby stimulating salivary secretion, and by cocainizing the receptors of the surfaces of the mouth and throat so that they are insensitive to the stimulus of dryness. All such facts point quite clearly to dryness of the throat as the basis of the thirst which is recognized in conscious experience.

Thirst as Craving for Water.—In spite of these and other similar facts, it has by no means been demonstrated that an organism depends upon dryness of the throat for the regulation of its water intake or that there is not thirst quite apart from conscious experience. Dryness of the throat does, of course, lead in some instances to drinking, but it is possible that other peripheral and central mechanisms also participate in behavior in search of and in the drinking of water. A most telling experiment which heavily emphasizes this point of view has been performed by Montgomery. He removed the salivary glands of dogs, so that, if these governed dryness of the throat, which in turn was the sole determiner of thirst, one should expect the operation drastically to increase the amount of water intake. Such, however, was not the case; the average daily water intake of animals without salivary glands was the same as that of normal animals. In this result we find good reason to suspect that a craving for water apart from conscious experience is controlling thirst

behavior. Cannon, it may be remarked, has attempted to explain
Montgomery's result in such a way as to support a local theory of water
intake by supposing that in the absence of the salivary glands the secretions of the mucous membranes of the mouth and throat serve the purpose
of informing the organism of its needs for water. This interpretation is
possible but not particularly convincing, and other work taken up below
points so definitely to other mechanisms of thirst that Cannon's explanation of Montgomery's results can do little to preserve the status of a
purely local theory of thirst.

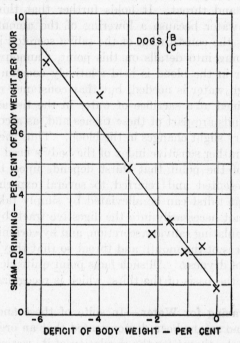

Fig. 150.—Amounts of water ingested in sham drinking of fistulated dogs during steady
deficits of water content. (*From E. F. Adolph. The internal environment and behavior:
Water content. Amer. J. Psychiat., 6, 1365–1373, 1941. By permission of the publishers.*)

That thirst is something more than dryness of the throat is shown in
studies of the relation between water deprivation and water intake
(Adolph; Bellows). The total deficit of water produced in the body by
deprivation was determined by measuring the difference in body weight
of a dog under normal conditions of free intake of water and after deprivation. Then, when the animal was given an opportunity to drink, it
displayed a very accurate 'ability to estimate' the extent of its body's
need for water as measured in these terms. The amount of water ingested
in a 5-min. period was directly proportional to the amount of water
deficit that had been accumulated (Fig. 150), and the relationship was

clearly proved by using several subjects and varying amounts of deficit. Such a result, it is to be emphasized, is not explicable in terms of a local theory of buccal dryness, for the first few swallows of water do away with whatever dryness exists before drinking, and yet drinking goes on beyond that to an extent in accordance with the need of the tissues for water.

More interesting information along this line comes from similar experiments in which the esophagus of dogs was brought out to the surface and the water which they drank had no access to the body (Bellows). In such sham drinking, just as in the normal case described above, the amount of water ingested was directly proportional to the deficit of water previously brought about by deprivation. Here, as above, it may be concluded that dryness of the throat is not the governing factor in thirst as measured in terms of the amount of water consumed.

To see what factors do relieve thirst, the experiments with sham drinking were taken a step farther. Since the operations made the stomach as well as the esophagus accessible, water could be placed directly into the stomach without passing it through the mouth. An amount which, through previous measurement, was known to be the quantity the animal with the same extent of water deficit would drink if given the opportunity was placed directly in the stomach. Then, after varying periods of time, the dog was allowed to drink, and the amount of water consumed was measured as usual.

The following very interesting results were obtained. If permitted to drink immediately after placing the water in the stomach, the dog drank an equal amount, just as if it had not been 'prewatered.' After a wait of 10 min., some water would be drunk but not so much; if required to wait 15 min., it drank no water at all. Similar results were also obtained in a normal animal given water through a stomach tube.

Taken together with the other facts above, these results lead to some very important conclusions about thirst as the craving for water. First of all, in addition to the fact that dryness of the throat does not regulate thirst, neither does sheer *amount* of water in the stomach, for when an adequate amount of water to compensate a deficit is placed in the stomach, an animal does not stop drinking. From this fact it can be argued that sensory impulses from receptors (mechanical?) in the stomach do not regulate the thirst. For this reason and because in sham drinking the amount consumed is governed by the severity of the water deficit, it can be argued that drinking behavior is regulated by water deficit more or less independently of the disposition of the water drunk. It is as if with some given deficit a clock in the nervous system were wound up to some particular amount relative to the deficit and then when the opportunity was presented unwound itself in drinking without regard for the consequences of the drinking. Taken out of the metaphor, the point, briefly, is that thirst is the consequence of water deficit but that the drinking behavior itself is, for the time being at least, the satisfaction of the need.

That is not to say, however, that there is no other way of satisfying thirst. If water remains in the stomach or intestines for some short period of time, it accomplishes some specific effect that relieves thirst. The failure of dogs with fistulas of the stomach to drink 15 min. after water was put in their stomachs points to that conclusion. What the specific effect is, however, we do not know. It could be simply the absorption of some amount of water; or it might be the production of some hormonal condition in the blood. In any event, water in the gastro-intestinal tract does something, presumably by way of the blood, which

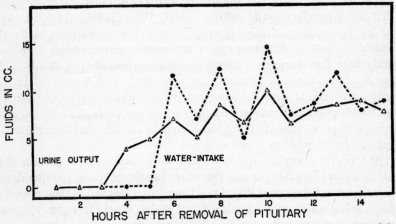

Fig. 151.—Polyuria and polydipsia in the rat following removal of the posterior lobe of the pituitary body. Note the primacy of the polyuria. (*After C. P. Richter.* *The internal environment and behavior: Internal secretions,* 1941, *Amer. J. Psychiat.,* **97,** 878–893.)

reduces thirst. If it is a change in the water content or other conditions of the blood, it may be presumed, or is at least plausible, that the allevi-ation of thirst has come about through direct effects upon the central nervous system. Of all this, however, we know very little, and research concerning it is plainly needed.

Pituitary Hormones.—Turning our attention now to other physio-logical factors known to be involved in thirst, we may note first that there is a hormonal factor in the secretion of the posterior lobe of the pituitary body which appears to be fundamentally related both to water metabo-lism and to thirst (Fig. 151). In a series of experiments, Richter has found that injury either to (1) the hypothalamic nuclei which send fibers to the pituitary body, (2) the pituitary stalk which carries these fibers, or (3) the posterior lobe of the pituitary, which secretes in response to nerve impulses in such fibers, will produce both excessive excretion of urine and

a greatly increased water intake, known technically as polyuria and polydipsia, respectively. By a careful analysis of his records, he came to
believe that the polyuria came first as the result of the withdrawal of the
antidiuretic factor, known to be secreted by the posterior lobe, and that
the polydipsia following it was the result of the loss of water from the
body, *i.e.*, the creation of a water deficit. If that is the case, these
experiments add nothing new to our knowledge of the mechanism of
thirst except that they show the pituitary to regulate, via excretion in the
kidneys, the general amount of deficit of water in the body.

General Metabolism.—There are several indications that thirst is
closely related to normal body metabolism. Extirpation of the entire
hypophysis, for example, does not produce so great an effect upon thirst
as removal of the posterior lobe described above (Richter). This, it has
been suggested, is explained by the fact that the anterior pituitary contains several hormones regulating body metabolism. For when they are
absent, metabolism falls and with it there is a decrease in thirst measured
in terms of water intake. Just why there is this connection is not clear,
but the fact of it is further demonstrated by injecting hypophysectomized
animals which are eating little food with extracts of the anterior pituitary.
Under these circumstances, food intake rises markedly and with it water
intake; indeed, the polydipsia characteristic of animals with lesions of the
posterior pituitary gland is reinstated.

There are, in addition, other experiments conducted with normal dogs
in which water intake was closely associated with food intake (Gregersen).
It was found, for example, that most of the water drunk during a 24-hr.
period is consumed within a few hours after eating. If the time of feeding
is delayed, water intake is reduced, and water intake increases following
feeding no matter when it occurs. Cannon has explained this result by
assuming that in taking food into the digestive tract an organism loses a
great deal of water from its blood in the various secretions of the stomach,
liver, and intestine and that such a loss of water is reflected in decreased
salivary secretion and dryness of the throat. Such an explanation is not
so satisfactory in the light of Richter's findings that polyuria does not
occur unless food is ingested, which would mean that digestive nutrient
materials in the blood probably have more to do with the thirst associated
with food intake than the loss of fluid through secretions into the digestive tract.

HUNGER: GASTRIC FACTORS

Just as was true in the case of thirst, the problem of hunger has often
been regarded largely as one of understanding the basis of conscious
experiences of hunger. Both the classic experiments on hunger and the
conventional theory of hunger have been presented from this point of

view, largely under the influence, in modern times, of Cannon. Recently, however, emphasis has shifted both in research and in theoretical approach to the conception of hunger as an urge or craving created by the deprivation of food and relieved, as well as measured, by food intake. Most of the present discussion will be based upon that point of view, but Cannon's conception of hunger as sensation will first be considered.

Hunger as a Sensation.—The most widely known experiments dealing with the immediate physiological basis of hunger experience were performed by Cannon and Washburn. Their problem in these experiments was simply to determine what happens in human individuals when they report feelings of hunger. They were led to suspect that contractions of the stomach were the essential factors because of the known physiological fact that contractions tended to occur in an empty stomach and from previous theories that these contractions were felt as conscious experience. They therefore studied such gastric contractions by two methods: (1) X-ray observation of the behavior of the stomach for periods preceding, accompanying, and following the usual time of eating; and (2) pneumographic recordings of gastric motility from a balloon swallowed in the stomach taken together with introspective reports of the subject's feeling of hunger. Both methods concurred in showing that when an individual reports hunger, gastric contractions are taking place, and therefore that the conscious experience of hunger arises from sensory stimulation in the stomach.

Although Cannon's theory of the sensory basis of the experience of hunger is undoubtedly correct, it has led to considerable confusion, largely because it does not deal with any desire for food apart from that arising from stomach contractions. Such a desire Cannon considered as *appetite*, which he regarded as learned. The idea became prevalent, accordingly, that all unlearned cravings for food were the outcome of hunger contractions. This notion, recent research shows, is not correct. It is important, therefore, to recognize that the local theory of hunger applies only to the conscious experience of contractions of the stomach and that hunger, conceived as a physiological state leading to the taking of food, demands some other type of theory to account for it.

Hunger as a State.—There are many facts of an observational or experimental nature which argue conclusively against the theory that gastric motility is essential to hunger defined as a craving (unlearned) for food. There are instances, first of all, in which individuals without stomachs give all the signs of normal hunger. One such case of a human patient in whom it was necessary to remove the stomach completely and to connect up the esophagus and intestine was studied carefully and found to report the desire for food at intervals in much the same way as a normal individual (see Hoelzel).

More crucial than this clinical case is an experiment conducted with rats in whom the stomachs had been experimentally removed (Tsang). Such animals were just as hungry as normal animals in all respects except one. They learned a maze with food as incentive just as quickly as normal rats; they showed as much activity in connection with the time of feeding as normal animals; and they made as high a score in an obstruction apparatus often employed to measure the strength of a drive. The principal difference between the operated and normal animals was that the operated rats ate more frequently than the normals and could not withstand repeated 24-hr. deprivations so well as normal subjects. Explaining this effect is the fact that the removal of the stomach greatly reduces the capacity of an animal to store food, for even though the intestines will undergo some enlargement into an artificial stomach they cannot fully compensate for the lack of the stomach. Considering that fact, then, the experiment indicates quite clearly that the factors causing the animals to desire food were not dependent upon the stomach.

Other experiments have attacked the same problem by depriving rats surgically of the afferent pathways from the stomach to the brain, thereby eliminating sensory impulses from the stomach. In two such experiments conducted by different researchers (Bash; Morgan and Morgan), it was found that, except for a few animals which die as a result of surgical effects, rats in whom the vagus nerves carrying sensory impulses from the stomach to the brain were sectioned display normal behavior with respect to food. Whereas the normal rat usually takes food about every 1.8 hr.; so does the operated animal; activity of both normal and operates is characteristically similar before, during, and after eating; finally, measures of drive strength by means of obstruction techniques or speed of learning show no essential differences due to vagotomy (Bash). The conclusion to be reached from these studies is that neither the presence of a stomach nor sensations from the stomach are necessary to the physiological mechanisms of hunger, regarded as a craving measurable in terms of food intake and other forms of overt behavior.

CHEMICAL FACTORS IN HUNGER

As was pointed out in the previous chapter, gross somatic activity appears along with gastric motility and with eating. It is noteworthy, moreover, that a great percentage of the time somatic activity *precedes* eating. Such activity, presumably, is correlated with stomach contractions (Richter); in man, at least, such a correlation has been established (Wada). The possibility suggested by this fact and by the negative conclusions reached above concerning gastric motility itself is that both

gastric and somatic motility may be governed by a common physiological factor. Since the physiological origin of hunger must rest in some
way upon depletion of the bodily reserves of material for energy expenditure, the most logical possibility is that this factor may be chemical in
nature.

Blood-sugar Level.—It is known that gastric motility is normally
under the control of the central nervous system via the vagus nerve which
innervates the stomach, but it has been observed that in cases of denervation of the stomach gastric motility can also occur 'spontaneously'
(Cannon). Since sugar is such a fundamental material in the organism's
metabolism, the question has been raised as to whether variation in the
blood sugar may be associated with gastric motility, general somatic
activity, and hunger.

Several experiments directed toward the correlation of blood-sugar
level with gastric motility and with hunger sensations in human individuals have yielded different results. It was found in one case that there
was a tendency for blood sugar to be lowered preceding periods of hunger
and to rise with satiation (Carlson). In another study the inhibition of
stomach contractions with the injection of glucose was observed (Bulatao
and Carlson). In a more recent experiment (Scott *et al.*), which seems
to have been very carefully performed, there was no indication that
blood-sugar level varied in any significant way with the onset of periods
of activity and of hunger.

In contrast to this finding there is the well-established fact that when
hypoglycemia is produced by the injection of insulin there is an increase
in gastric motility. Indeed, as blood sugar falls, following insulin injection, some critical point of hypoglycemia is reached at which the activity
of the alimentary tract is greatly heightened (Mulinos). Other experiments have shown that correlated with the increase in gastric motility
there is an increase in the amount of food eaten. This fact has been
demonstrated both in man (Freyburg) and animals (Morgan and Morgan)
under rather dependable conditions.

In support of the notion that there may be a chemical factor that is
common to somatic activity, food-seeking behavior, and gastric motility
is the additional observation, in connection with the injection of insulin,
that the increase in hunger associated with hypoglycemia is in no way
dependent upon sensations arising from gastric contractions. This was
demonstrated by showing in successive steps that gastric motility which
is produced by insulin injection is mediated by the vagus nerve and that
sectioning this nerve will separate the effects of insulin on the body from
any action upon the gastric motility (M'Crea *et al.*). When, therefore,
animals with vagotomized stomachs were subjected to insulin hypoglycemia, it was found not only that hunger increased, as was indicated

by the amount of food ingested, but that the increase in hunger in vagotomy was greater than in the normal animal (Morgan and Morgan).

There is also the interesting fact about insulin hypoglycemia that the extent to which insulin influences hunger is dependent upon the amount of sugar in the diet (Morgan and Morgan). When dietary sugar is high, insulin does not augment hunger, but tends on the contrary to decrease it. Conversely, a low intake of sugar is correlated with pronounced increases in hunger when insulin is administered. This effect seems explicable in terms of the amount of sugar stored in the body, and it probably indicates, therefore, the direct importance of blood-sugar level in hunger induced by insulin.

Hunger Hormone?—Even though experimental alternations of blood-sugar level are correlated with the drive for food, the fact that one cannot satisfactorily demonstrate spontaneous changes in blood-sugar level in relation to food demand leads to skepticism of a hypothesis that blood-sugar changes are the primary chemical changes involved in food demand. We may have to look elsewhere for the common factor in hunger. There are, in fact, several lines of evidence that point to the presence of some specific hormone as the agent which sets into play the various behavioral activities associated with hunger.

There is first of all the fact that blood transfused from a starving to a normal dog will induce gastric tonus and hunger contractions in the latter (Luckhardt and Carlson). Carlson, who verified this fact, found that evidence of induced gastric motility lasted for a limited time of 10 to 30 min., comparable to periods of normal gastric contractions. Correlated with this fact is another, that hemorrhage of blood vessels is accompanied by a similar increase in gastric contractions. In another experiment, blood from a recently fed animal when transferred to a starved animal caused inhibition of stomach contractions for 5 or 6 hr. at a time (Templeton and Quigley). From such facts it can be concluded that when the storage of nutrient reserves of the organism is depleted a "hunger hormone" is liberated into the blood.

Other evidence concerning a hunger hormone comes from the periodicity of contractions of alimentary tissue isolated from neural influences. In one experiment, for example, a section of the small intestine was transplanted to a position under the skin (in dogs) where it could be nourished by blood and also freely observed (see Bash). This tissue was found to contract and to secrete juices at intervals of $1\frac{1}{2}$ to 2 hr. and just at the same time that the stomach was contracting. Another set of observations, conducted upon a patient who had small intestine transplanted to the vicinity of the esophagus, yielded similar results. Inasmuch as the transplanted tissue in each case was not under nervous control, humoral stimulation must have been responsible for its behavior. It seems, therefore, that some hormone, by directly activating the smooth muscle of the digestive tract, may be responsible for some of the behavior associated with hunger.

It is not unreasonable, of course, that such a hunger hormone may also stimulate the nervous system, and thereby be responsible also for the somatic activity correlated with gastric motility. The evidence with respect to sexual behavior indicates that hormones may directly affect the nervous system and bring about sexual behavior in the absence of afferent impulses from the sexual organs. Also, in the case of respiration, a particular chemical substance stimulates a particular center to activity. We have no information, unfortunately, as to whether a hunger hormone or any chemical conditions basic to hunger may likewise directly activate or facilitate hunger mechanisms in the brain, but the possibility should be considered seriously and subjected to investigation.

Just as the evidence above points to a hormone or chemical substance giving rise to hunger, there is, on the other hand, some indication that there may also be a chemical substance which leads to the satiation of hunger. Like the facts above, it depends upon observations of stomach contractions, but we can assume that under normal circumstances gastric motility is closely related to hunger. Dogs were operated and their stomachs surgically altered in such a way as to obtain a pouch of stomach tissue completely independent of the rest of the stomach, of food entering the main portion of the stomach, and of neural innervation. Observations of this isolated pouch revealed that whenever, from time to time, activity appeared in the intact portion of the stomach and in the intestines, the pouch also showed motility, just as might be expected from the observations indicating a hunger hormone. If, during such periods of motility, sugar were injected directly into the bloodstream, it exerted no observable influence upon the motility. If, on the other hand—and this is the important result—sugar were administered by mouth, it caused inhibition of the activity of the pouch after it had had time to reach the small intestine. From this fact, it has been concluded that, since no direct neural or mechanical relation could have produced the inhibition, some hormone which, when circulated in the blood, causes inhibition of gastric contractions must have been liberated in the intestine by the presence of sugar. Since, moreover, the direct injection of sugar into the bloodstream itself did not produce this effect, the hormone must not be sugar but some substance released from or secreted by the intestine under the influence of sugar. We have, then, evidence for a 'satiation hormone,' but its nature we do not know. Unanswered also is the question of whether such a hormone affects the nervous system and reduces the desire for food (*cf.* Young).

SPECIFIC HUNGERS

The problem of the basis of hunger is complicated by the fact that there are, not one, but many hungers. In both man and animals one finds hungers for particular elements of the diet such as salt, fats, or vitamins that cannot be ascribed to learning but must depend upon the physiological condition of the organism. Such specific hungers make themselves evident in the preferences of organisms for different kinds of foods as they are affected by the elements in which the organism may be deficient or well supplied. These specific hungers constitute even better proof than any considered above that there are mechanisms of hunger independent of gastric contractions, and they force us to consider how specific chemical conditions in the body may cause an organism to seek and select one dietary element more than another.

Self-selection of Diets.—One of the best indications that there are specific hungers aside from the experience of hunger as a general hunger is the ability of organisms, when given the opportunity, to select a diet that contains all the elements necessary for its survival. This ability is probably much better expressed in children than in adult human individuals, for after there has been considerable experience with food, and habits have been set up, the natural preferences of an organism are probably obscured. An experiment with children, however, demonstrates that they usually select an assortment of foods such as is required to meet their bodily needs (Davis). If observed on any one day, they appear not to follow this rule, for they may choose only one food and eat that exclusively, just as if they had an overwhelming hunger for some essential material in that food. Over a long period of time, however, the preferences shift from one kind of food to another with the result that a balanced diet is obtained solely by following the individual's preferences.

A similar situation obtains in rats (Richter). If these animals are presented with several dishes of food, in each of which is one element— e.g., salt, sugar, or fat—that is necessary for the normal functioning of the body, they will eat from each dish an amount which is just about correct for their needs. Indeed, if one wanted to know what kind of diet rats should be fed to keep them in the best of health, he could determine the proportions of the preferences displayed under these circumstances and use them to mix the complete diet.

Order of Preference.—One can see the manifestation of specific hungers not only in the selection of a well-balanced diet but also in the way preferences change with starvation and with the kinds of foods that have been eaten previously (Young). For example, if a rat, after having been starved for several hours, is given its choice of sugar, wheat, or fat, it will spend most of the first few minutes eating sugar and ignoring wheat and fat; the result of normal starvation, obviously, has been to increase the hunger for sugar over that for wheat or fat. After a time, however, the hunger for sugar appears to be satisfied, for the rat will then turn to the other foods and prefer them above the sugar, and thus once one specific hunger has been satisfied another specific hunger which was formerly less strong becomes the dominant one.

As one might expect, however, the picture changes if the animal has been starved of only certain elements rather than all food. If a rat is deprived for some time of all fat and then is offered it, it will take the fat in preference to wheat or sugar, and only when the hunger for fat has been satisfied will it turn to eating sugar and wheat. In other experiments, rats that were fed all the wheat they wanted but were put on short rations of sugar preferred sugar, and animals that had had plenty of sugar but little wheat chose wheat. There can be no doubt, consequently, that deprivation of specific elements of the diet is reflected in the kind of food which the organism will choose.

Vitamin Deficiency.—Vitamins, unlike the materials just discussed, are not used up directly in the work of the body but are nevertheless quite necessary for such work to go on. It is of interest, therefore, to inquire whether there are also specific hungers for them. Experiments directed toward this problem have shown that in some cases such a specific hunger exists and in other instances does not. After deprivation of vitamins A or D, for example, rats give no evidence of recognizing these elements in the food presented to them, for they choose a diet containing them no more than they do a diet which is lacking in them (Wilder). Vitamin B, however, is quite another matter, for when deprived of it rats show a most remarkable hunger for it. Either the taste or smell of vitamin B will be recognized by them and the material containing it ingested avidly. If the vitamin is in weak water solution, for example, they will drink inordinate amounts of the solution. Their specific hunger for the vitamin is especially interesting because vitamin-B deficient animals otherwise lose their appetite for almost all other foods and eat very little.

Although one may speak of *vitamin B* as a matter of convenience, we know that it is not one but several vitamins, some of which have been identified and others about which we have only probabilities. Two well-known factors in vitamin B are thiamin (vitamin B_1) and riboflavin, and it is possible to deplete an animal of one and not of the other. When appropriately tested, rats show that they can have a specific hunger for each of these factors, for they can recognize and choose the diet containing the factor of which they have been deprived.

Not only that, but along with the appearance of a specific hunger for the vitamin there are changes in specific hungers for other foods depending upon how these are related to the action of the vitamin factors in the body. Thiamin, for example, is necessary for the utilization of sugar in the body, and thiamin deficiency therefore reduces the demand of the body for sugar; on the other hand, it forces the body to make better use of fats, for its expenditure of energy and the body's demand for fats are raised in such deficiency. These physiological consequences of thiamin deficiency, moreover, are paralleled closely by the specific hungers of thiamin-deficient rats. The hunger for sugars is much reduced, whereas that for fats is considerably increased.

The picture is much the same for riboflavin. This factor in vitamin B is required for normal protein metabolism in the body, and without it the

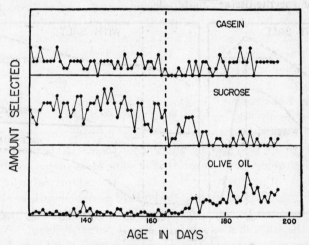

Fig. 152.—Effect of removal of the pancreatic gland on selection of elements of the diet by rats. Vertical dashed line indicates the day of operation. Note that with the diabetes created by pancreatectomy there is a decrease in hunger for sugar and an increased choice of fat (olive oil), which the animal can better dispose of. (*After C. P. Richter and E. C. H. Schmidt.*)

body cannot make the greatest use of its proteins. Riboflavin deficiency is accompanied, accordingly, by a reduced hunger for proteins; then upon restoring riboflavin to the diet, the eating of proteins returns to its normal level.

Pregnancy and Lactation.—The way in which specific hungers are changed with 'normal' changes in the physiology of the body is to be seen in the relation of specific hungers to the demands of pregnancy and of the nursing of young. During pregnancy, the mother's need of many minerals, particularly sodium, phosphorus, and calcium, is greatly increased because of the demands of the growing fetuses dependent upon the mother for food. For the same reason she needs more fats and proteins, because these are required in the building of tissues. Sugar, however, is of no more importance than usual and may, in fact, be less necessary, because the mother tends to expend less energy in muscular activity and to maintain a somewhat lower metabolic rate.

All these changes in the physiological requirements of the body during pregnancy are reflected in the shifting of preferences for foods in this period. Specific hungers for minerals are much stronger; those for fat and protein are also raised somewhat; but the intake of sugar is reduced. The same general conclusion applies also to the mother's preferences during the nursing period following birth, for the task required of the mother is much the same as in pregnancy. After the young are weaned and the physiological demands move back to normal, so also do the hungers for specific dietary materials.

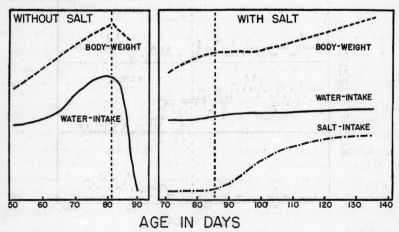

AGE IN DAYS

Fig. 153.—Increased salt intake following adrenalectomy and the dependence of the adrenalectomized animal on salt for survival. (*From C. P. Richter.   The internal environment and behavior: Internal secretions, 1941, Amer. J. Psychiat.,* **97,** 878–893.)

Minerals and Glandular Functions.—Several experiments, finally, show us how some of the endocrine glands figure in the specific hungers for minerals (Fig. 153). The cortex of the adrenal gland, it will be recalled (p. 38), governs to a considerable degree the amount of sodium excreted from the body, and its extirpation is followed by a marked fall in the concentration of sodium in the blood and tissues. In this way lack of cortin creates a physiological need for salt. Reflecting this need is the fact that rats in whom the adrenal glands have been destroyed show a greatly increased preference for salt. Their salt intake will jump to several times its former value if unlimited quantities of salt are available, and at the same time their sensitivity in detecting solutions containing salt is increased several fold. Indeed, after adrenalectomy a rat can detect concentrations of salt in solution so small that it is not possible for the rat to drink enough of the solution to satisfy its physiological need for salt.

Another case of a specific hunger for a mineral can be studied in parathyroidectomy. The parathyroid gland, it will be remembered, governs calcium and phosphorus metabolism in the body in such a way that the greater the amount of parathormone present, the more calcium and the less phosphorus is found in the blood. If, then, the parathyroid glands are removed, there follows a deficiency of calcium and an excess of phosphorus, and the preferences of the animal subjected to such parathyroidectomy reflect these changes in the demands of the body. A great avidity for calcium appears and the intake of calcium is increased by three or four times, whereas a marked aversion for phosphorus develops. Then, upon transplanting parathyroid glands into such rats to restore their supply of parathyroid, the preferences of the animals shift immediately to normal proportions.

Theory of Specific Hungers.—All the evidence that has been reviewed leaves no question but that, depending upon physiological conditions in the body, there are specific hungers for particular dietary elements. This fact raises more questions, among them: How many specific hungers are there? What are their physiological mechanisms? As regards the first question, we know that in rats there are at least 11 specific hungers. Listing them in terms of the materials toward which they are directed, we have: carbohydrates (sugar), fat, protein, thiamin, riboflavin, oxygen, salt, phosphorus, sodium, calcium, and water. The appearance of oxygen and water in this list may seem strange, but they have been placed in it because the states of the body in which they are lacking can be called hungers just as much as can those which lead to the ingestion of the other materials.

More important, however, is the question of how hungers are specific, *i.e.*, how the deficit of a particular material in the body affects the nervous system and behavior of an animal in such a way that he is enabled to select the needed material. A theory proposing an answer to this question has been offered by Richter and Young, the two most prominent researchers in the field. They suggest that chemical deficiencies in the body, because they affect all the tissues of the body and their metabolism, must also influence events in the olfactory and gustatory receptors. In particular it is suggested that these receptors have their thresholds lowered for the particular substance needed, and as a result its presence in food can be discovered by the animal. Such a theory is plausible, although it might be questioned whether the lowering of receptor thresholds is enough to explain the craving of the animal for the material; at any rate it is the best that we have at present. No one has proposed that the central nervous system reacts differently to various chemical deficiencies, but this possibility must also be kept in mind.

THE NEURAL BASIS OF HUNGER

The Richter-Young theory, unfortunately, is not readily put to a test. No relation between specific hungers and lowered thresholds of the gustatory receptors can be demonstrated, but it can be shown that the gustatory receptors are concerned in the selection of specific foods. When the taste nerves of adrenalectomized rats are sectioned, they give up their former habit of compensating for their adrenal insufficiency by eating large quantities of salt, quickly lower their salt intake as though they could no longer recognize this material, and as a consequence die (Richter and Hawkes). Thus it is clear that in this case the taste receptors are necessary for the preferential discrimination. We do not know, however, just how the specific hunger affects either the receptors or the central nervous system to bring about the discrimination, and research along this line is called for.

There is also relatively little information concerning the functioning of central mechanisms in hunger and the behavior arising from hunger. One can recall at this point the experiments on the frontal lobes (p. 392) in which rats and cats were often observed to be made ravenously hungry by lesions of the frontal lobe, which also markedly increased somatic activity. We do not know, unfortunately, whether the increase in hunger is independent, or the consequence, of the increase in activity resulting from the operations. Then, too, there are autonomic centers in the frontal lobe, and it is a possibility that these alter autonomic functions in such a way as to change hunger. Besides these observations in animals, there are reports of human patients who have shown various abnormalities of hunger in connection with injuries to the frontal lobes. Occasionally, too, abnormal conditions of thirst and hunger accompany lesions of the hypothalamus, apparently because this center is of primary importance in regulating the chemistry of the body. The whole question, however, of neural mechanisms in the behavior of hunger is open in both man and animals and invites research.[1]

[1] Work in progress at the Yale Laboratories of Physiology and Physiological Chemistry (Ruch et al.) conducted with rats and monkeys indicates that certain lesions of the hypothalamus and mesencephalon produce a great increase in food intake and body weight. The first striking symptom to follow operation is an enormous increase in food intake. Preliminary researches reveal no abnormality of the metabolism of the animals which might be indirectly responsible for the changes because of the role played by the hypothalamus in metabolism, and it appears, therefore, that the lesions directly affect the animals' hunger for food, which in turn causes them to take on weight. This line of research is very promising, but at this writing it is not far enough along to be described in more detail.

CHAPTER XXII

SURVEY OF ADAPTIVE BEHAVIOR

Whereas most of the chapters of this book have considered the facts of physiological psychology according to the particular topic under consideration, this one will be of a more general nature and will consider general theoretical questions related to motivation and learning. The facts of motivation reviewed in the last four chapters are greatly in need of being drawn together into a general conception of the nature of motivation in order that their fullest significance for psychology can be perceived, and also in order that they may be fitted into the picture of learning and related functions which will emerge in the chapters to follow. Before approaching the physiological material concerning learning, the student ideally should have a thorough knowledge of the psychology of learning, but that requires a volume in itself (see Hilgard and Marquis, and McGeoch). The best substitute is a survey which brings out the most important theoretical concepts for physiological psychology. This chapter, accordingly, attempts in the first place to formulate a physiological theory of motivation, and secondly, to present a general theory of learning, memory, and thought. As such, it incorporates the viewpoint of the writer much more than does any other part of the book.

Theories of Adaptive Behavior.—Some writers have divided the theoretical viewpoints concerning adaptive behavior—the term that will be used to cover motivated behavior, learning, memory, and higher thought processes—into two general classes: association theory and field theory. As with all classifications this one is not perfectly adequate, but on the whole it is fair and useful.

In modern association theory, the basic terms of discourse are stimulus (S) and response (R). The phenomenon used as a model for the theory is the conditioned reflex, which presumably can be represented adequately in these terms. With S's and R's, and the assumption that the strengths of S-R bonds are increased and decreased by the manner in which S's are combined, the attempt is made to explain all adaptive behavior from simple conditioning to reasoning. Thus the association theorist effectively disposes of the nervous system as unnecessary for his purposes. He knows, of course, that it exists, and presumably the bonds between S's and R's are there, but for theoretical purposes these might just as well be in a vacuum. For him, too, the motivation of an organism can also be represented by an S arising somewhere inside it; thus hunger is

457

regarded, after the notions of Cannon, as a stimulus arising in the gastro-intestinal tract.

Whereas association theory is behavioristic, rather than physiological, field theory may be characterized as "perceptionistic." It points out that most learning takes place under circumstances in which an organism has a goal, is faced with certain barriers to that goal, and perceives, or attempts to perceive, the relation of objects in its environment to its goal. Field theory holds insight and reorganization of the perceptual field to be basic to motivation and learning. Although such notions appear, offhand, to be somewhat mentalistic and, indeed, run the danger of being more obscure and less demonstrable than the scientific mind wants to tolerate, field theory, in emphasizing perceptual processes, is tacitly more physiological than association theory, because perceptual processes must occur in the nervous system and cannot be thought of merely as bonds connecting stimulus and response.

It is not necessary, fortunately, to hold to either of these viewpoints and to bar the other. Psychological facts supporting points in both theories are available, and physiological evidence, likewise, disproves neither. Association is certainly a basic principle of learning; on the other hand, it is doubtful if any but very special cases of learning do not involve central neural processes of perceptual organization, which it is necessary to recognize as such. The associationistic concept of an internal stimulus as the basis of motivation, however, appears to be grossly inadequate. To explain exactly how and where these conceptions of motivation and learning are valid or inadequate and just how they may be integrated into an over-all picture of adaptive behavior will now be attempted.

SURVEY OF MOTIVATION

The discussion can begin with a survey of the problems and concepts of motivation. The general outline of the survey is as follows: Motivation must be thought of in terms of patterns of nervous activity which arise not merely from receptor stimulation but also, and perhaps even more important, from the direct influences of chemical conditions in the blood. This pattern of nervous activity differs according to the factors giving rise to it, whether these are lack of food, water, or the presence of sex hormones. Each pattern of activity may produce more or less general activity, but also specific forms of behavior. In addition, the pattern involves the set or predisposition to perceive environmental stimuli in certain ways and to give certain responses to these stimuli. Such perceptions and responses may be said to be the goals of the motivated organism and contribute in part to the reduction of the pattern of nervous activity that, physiologically speaking, is the motive.

Motivation as a Stimulus Condition.—The facts have already been presented in previous chapters to show that motivation is not solely a matter of stimulation of receptors in some particular part of the body. Hunger, for example, is more than the result of gastric stimulation. Animals and human beings, it was shown (p. 447), are impelled to eat in the absence of stomach contractions and, indeed, of a stomach; it is difficult, moreover, to argue that such desire for food exists only through learning. There is strong indication, indeed, that chemical conditions in the blood are more basic to hunger than gastric contractions and that these conditions lead both to central neural excitation and to gastric contractions. To clinch the argument are the well-established facts of specific hunger in which animals and human beings desire not food in general but particular kinds of food, and no one can argue that such selection is accomplished in terms of gastric stimulation.

Sexual drive, also, provides very striking proof of the nonstimulus basis of motivation. Various evidences of sexual drive (see p. 418) can be seen in the absence of stimulation from the primary sexual organs; on the other hand, sexual drive clearly depends upon the presence of certain hormones in the blood, and it is quite probable that sexually motivated behavior is brought about by direct excitation of the nervous system. Similar arguments apply also to thirst-motivated behavior, as has been seen in Chap. XXI. It is necessary to formulate our conception of motivation, therefore, in terms broader than the doctrine of the reflex and of local stimulation of internal receptors.

H.M.F.—Without denying the fact that local stimulation can figure in motivated behavior, it must be argued first of all that one essential physiological factor in motivation is the chemical or humoral condition of the blood. We can call this the *humoral motive factor* (briefly, the h.m.f.). In the case of sexual drive, we know in part what the h.m.f. is, but in hunger we are still trying to identify it.

There are three possible ways, it appears, in which the h.m.f. may affect the brain.

1. The h.m.f. may affect the brain by direct stimulation. In this case, it is to be presumed, the nervous system differs somewhat in its various parts in respect of its reactions to factors in the internal environment; thus one h.m.f. may excite certain neural systems, and other h.m.f.'s may excite other sets of neurons. The female sex hormones present a good example of this point, for experiments indicate that they directly excite centers of the brain stem and thereby bring out patterns of female sex behavior.

2. The h.m.f. may influence the nervous system by stimulation of internal receptors. A good example of this kind is the activation of carotid-sinus receptors by the carbon dioxide content of the blood.

Whether or not there is such an influence in other kinds of motivation we do not yet know, but the possibility must not be excluded. Richter and Young, it will be recalled, have proposed to explain the phenomena of specific hunger by assuming that bodily deficiencies affect the gustatory and olfactory receptors.

3. The h.m.f. may influence the brain by producing changes in effectors which in turn excite receptors. The h.m.f. in hunger, for example, probably causes contraction of gastric and intestinal musculature, and because there are receptors in these muscles, afferent excitations to the brain are produced. Similarly, the h.m.f. may effect vasodilation in certain tissues and thereby excite sensory fibers in the blood vessels. We do know that certain sex hormones, for example, have a special affinity for influencing sexually erogenous tissues, although cases of such an influence figuring in motivation are not clearly established.

THE CENTRAL MOTIVE STATE

Next, although a nonphysiological psychologist may be perfectly content to get along without referring to the nervous system, it is quite clear that the nervous system is the locus of integration into which motivating factors pour and from which patterns of motivated behavior emerge. We might as well, then, recognize such neural integrative activity and give it a name, the *central motive state* (briefly, the c.m.s.).

The origin of the c.m.s. has already been indicated in referring to the ways in which the h.m.f.'s may influence the nervous system. In addition, too, the effect of stimuli arising from purely local conditions, as in the emptying of the stomach which is in part the cause of stomach motility, must be recognized.

The Properties of the C.M.S.—These may be derived from our general knowledge of motivated behavior.

1. The c.m.s. appears to be partly self-perpetuating. That is to say, there is some reverberatory activity (see p. 64) in the neurons involved in the c.m.s., such that neural activity, once it has been initiated, tends to continue. In this respect the c.m.s. is no different from the c.e.s. obtaining in reflex action and giving rise to such phenomena as afterdischarge, facilitation, and recruitment. Lashley, among others, has pointed out, for example, that although gastric contractions are distinctly periodic affairs, a rat running a maze in search of food does not run in fits and starts according to the contractions but shows a continuous and maintained motivation in search of food. Some of the reverberation maintaining the c.m.s. may be a purely central affair accounted for in terms of recurrent neural circuits; some of it, on the other hand, may be caused by circular, reflexive activity—*i.e.*, the c.m.s. may lead to gastric

contractions, to changes in the sexual organs, or the like, and these may, in turn, send in afferent stimulation which builds up the c.m.s.

2. In addition to reverberation, we must postulate three behavioral properties of the c.m.s. One of these is general activity. As we have already seen in previous chapters, an increase in body activity goes along with the need for food and water and, in female animals, is dramatically correlated with sexual drive. Although some have argued that such activity arises from local tissue conditions associated with the drive in question, the facts may be interpreted as indicating that both local behavioral changes (*e.g.*, stomach contractions) and general activity are the outcome of a c.m.s.

3. Another property of the c.m.s. is that it evokes specific forms of behavior. Gastric contractility may be considered as an example, although not the most important one. Much better are the various forms of 'heat' behavior seen in birds and in certain female mammals. The sexually excited male bird, for example, carries out patterns of strutting and vocalization. The female cat, as has already been described in detail, presents a special 'heat' posture, participates in treading, and gives other specific behavioral evidences, including its cries, of being in heat. These specific forms of behavior do not depend upon any especial environmental conditions and appear to be the expression of the c.m.s.

4. A further aspect of the c.m.s. is what may be called a *set* or potentiality for presenting various patterns of behavior when the appropriate stimulus conditions in the external environment are available. This is the priming property of the c.m.s. A hungry animal, for example, eats when food is in front of him, but does not exhibit the behavior involved in eating in the absence of food. The sexually excited female gives a 'receptive' behavioral reaction when mounted by a male; or conversely, the sexually motivated male mounts the receptive female when she is present but does not show mounting behavior in the absence of the female. Thus there are forms of behavior that depend not only upon the presence of the c.m.s. but also upon external stimulus conditions, and in the absence of these, the c.m.s. can be said to prepare, prime, or set the organism for these forms of behavior when they become possible.

These three behavioral aspects of the c.m.s.—general activity, specific behavior, and the readiness to perceive and react to stimulus situations in particular ways—are obviously intimately related to each other in such a way as to form an effective means of eventually remedying the condition which motivated the animal. In many ways, however, the priming aspect of the c.m.s. is its most important feature for the psychologist. It is this which makes motivated behavior appear so purposive, for it is the set to perceive and react in certain ways which defines the goal. The hungry animal, for example, 'wants' to eat, and its motivation is really as simple as that. The general activity is necessary and useful in enlarging the possibilities of finding food, but the set or readiness to eat is clearly what determines the habits learned in obtaining food.

Satiation.—The question of what reduces motivation (c.m.s.), though probably not particularly relevant to the role of motivation in learning, is, nevertheless, of physiological interest. It is not, however, easy to answer, for there are at least four conceivable ways in which the c.m.s. might be eliminated.

1. The first is by eliminating the h.m.f. in the internal environment which gives rise, in cases where it operates, to the c.m.s. Thus if an animal lacks calcium, and this lack by influencing the brain causes calcium to be eaten, the eating would stop when enough calcium to eliminate the h.m.f. had been eaten, digested, and taken into the blood. This would be the simplest and most direct method of motive reduction, except that in view of the considerable time between eating materials and their utilization in the blood an animal would in this way always get more of the desired material than it actually needed. Moreover, the experimental facts indicate that although the h.m.f. may start the c.m.s., it does not finish it. Dogs with esophageal fistulas drink water in proportion to the amount they need, not until the water has gotten into the bloodstream and offset what they need (see p. 443). Similarly, rats eat about as much sugar as they need within the first few minutes of eating and then turn, long before the sugar has been utilized, to other kinds of food. There are so many examples of this kind available that it is quite clear that in most cases motivation is reduced by mechanisms other than by the remedy of the condition which caused the motivated behavior.

2. Now there are several possible ways in which the c.m.s. might be reduced at least temporarily by factors other than elimination of the h.m.f. One is the liberation in the stomach or intestine of some hormone which 'signals' to the brain that the materials needed are on their way, so to speak, to the blood. In studies of gastric activity such materials have already been demonstrated; placing sugar in the small intestine, for example, causes gastric contractions to cease quite abruptly, and this result is known to be a humoral affair because it occurs in a denervated stomach (see p. 450). Water placed in the stomach, likewise, has been shown to allay thirst in a much shorter time than is required for the water to be absorbed into the blood and directly relieve the dehydrated condition; this effect, presumably, is a humoral one. Thus it is likely that one way of reducing motivation (c.m.s.) is by humoral messengers liberated into the blood to 'tell' the brain that relief is on the way.

3. Still a third possibility may be suggested, that the stimulation of receptors incident to behavior instigated by the c.m.s. may reduce the motivation. The taste of sugar, for which an animal is hungry, may, for example, reduce the motive to eat sugar. Or, in a somewhat more familiar example, the taste of water in the mouth may reduce thirst. Common experience indicates that in this latter case motivation is at least temporarily reduced. How general a mechanism this may be and by what neural means it operates, we do not know, but such sensory stimulation may be regarded as reducing the motivation in at least some instances.

4. The final possibility to be mentioned is that behavior resulting from the c.m.s. is motive reducing. Thus, in hunger, eating activity may reduce hunger. In thirst, too, the drinking of water, aside from its effect on the receptors of the mouth or in the gastrointestinal tract, may reduce the c.m.s. The experimental facts, indeed, indicate this conclusion for thirst, for in fistulated dogs the amount of water drunk in a given period is directly proportional to the negative water load (p. 442) whether or not this water goes into the organism and has any effect upon reducing the negative water load. It does not seem reasonable that this fact has anything to do with the excitation of buccal receptors, since a mouth that is wet is wet, and there can be no quantitative relation between amount of stimulation and the amount of drinking, which we know is proportional to negative water load. Thus it appears that the drinking behavior itself is satisfying.

A similar situation appears in the case of sexual behavior. Here there is no material to be taken into the body. Satisfaction of the motive (c.m.s.) takes place when a certain sequence of behavior has been completed, ending with the orgasm and the various behavioral components concerned in it. Thus, in this case, too, reduction of the c.m.s. is accomplished, it would appear, by prosecuting the specific behavior issuing from the motive state.

This point, it may be noted, is like that made earlier with respect to set. A motive primes the organism for behavior which, at least in part, satisfies the motive.

Emotional Motivation.—All that has just been said refers to motivated behavior arising from conditions within the organism: the depletion of food reserves, loss of water, and the accumulation of sex hormones. To refer to this class of motivations we may use the term *biogenic*, previously suggested as more adequate than the term *viscerogenic* which is frequently employed. With certain modifications, the analysis above may also apply to behavior which has an emotional motivation and, in the normal learning of animals and human beings, is as important, if not more important, than biogenic motivation. The principal difference, of course, is that in one case h.m.f.'s participate in producing the c.m.s., whereas in the other, the c.m.s. is produced by some external stimulus, *e.g.*, a noxious stimulus or some situation that the organism perceives as harmful.

The c.m.s., however, has the same general properties in emotion as in hunger.   (1) It tends to persist, presumably through recurrent nervous circuits.   In an earlier chapter, we have seen that the reverberatory character of emotional reactions is the outcome largely of cortical contributions to the emotional state, for animals without the cerebral cortex get over their emotion more quickly upon the withdrawal of the emotional stimulus than do normal animals.   (2) The emotional state (c.m.s.) has relatively general patterns of behavior associated with it.   Foremost of these is the general autonomic involvement which has already been described in some detail for emotion (Chap. XVII).   Then, too, there tends to be general somatic activity, seen in the running of a scared animal or the restlessness of an angry or frightened animal.   (3) There are also specific forms of behavior called out by emotional stimuli. The cat crouches, bares its teeth, and spits when presented with a dog. The startled organism executes special postural changes which have been described.   These specific forms of behavior associated with emotional motivation are somewhat variable from time to time, but are nevertheless relatively fixed properties of the emotional motivation. (4) Finally, completing the parallel with biogenic motivation, central emotional states supply a set or preparation for reaction to stimulus situations.   The cat faced with a dog not only displays certain special emotional reactions, but becomes primed for the whole series of reactions that are needed for fighting; these may be set off by the snarl or continuing approach of the dog.   Illustrations of this sort could be multiplied but they are hardly needed; mere casual observation of human beings or animals in emotional situations will reveal that the organism is set or primed for a number of different reactions in addition to those being displayed at the moment.

The problem of how emotional states are reduced is somewhat simpler than that of biogenic c.m.s.'s.   The principal factor, obviously, is the withdrawal of the stimulus situation that produces the emotional state. Even this is not entirely adequate, for the reverberatory property of emotion makes it outlast, sometimes for a considerable period, the presentation of the emotional stimulus.

The Neural Basis of the Motive Set.—A word is in order about the neural basis of set, since the concept of set will become important in later discussion.   Although the c.m.s. is certainly not to be regarded as localized in any particular part of the nervous system, it is perfectly legitimate to expect certain parts of the nervous system to be more concerned with one aspect of the motive state than with another.   We have seen, for example, that fragments of emotional behavior are mediated by neural centers below the thalamus. The walking and running patterns, we know from a study of reflex behavior, are also organized at relatively low neural levels. Fragments of sexual behavior in animals also occur below the thalamic level.

The organization of the specific forms of behavior, however, seems generally to take place at the hypothalamic level. There have been localized the specific patterns of facial expression in emotion, and there have been found the specific forms of sexual behavior which issue directly from the c.m.s. Thus both the general and specific behavioral properties of motivating states appear to be organized at subcortical levels.

The other two properties of neural activity in motivation which have been enumerated, however, depend much more upon the cerebral cortex. As was mentioned in an earlier chapter, the emotional reactions of the decorticate animal are much more easily elicited and subside much more quickly than do those of the normal animal. Moreover, the decorticate animal does not give evidence of perceiving the fuller implications of the motivating situation; thus, for example, although the decorticate dog snarls when its tail is pinched, it does not direct its emotional behavior toward the site of pinching, as the normal animal will do. In this case the emotional state does not bring in the set or preparation for reacting to the place of the pinch. Similarly, studies of the effects of cortical extirpation upon mating behavior show that in the absence of the cortex, or even a large part of it, the various perceptions normally associated with sexual drive are lacking. This holds even though the more specific and reflexive mating responses are not destroyed. A similar situation exists in the case of sleep, where, through the complex influences of the cerebral cortex, the normal polyphasic rhythm of infancy is transformed into the diurnal rhythm; but upon decortication, the animal relapses to its normal, more primitive, subcortically determined, polyphasic habits of sleep.

The conclusion, then, is this: The *set* aspect of motivation, *i.e.*, the potentiality of perceiving various aspects of the external situation and reacting to them in an organized way, is dependent chiefly upon the cerebral cortex. Without the cortex, the motive state eventuates only in the immediate general and specific forms of behavior associated with the c.m.s., or humoral motivating influence giving rise to it; the more complex perceptions and organized responses which issue from the priming property of the c.m.s. are lacking.

SURVEY OF LEARNING

In this and later sections of the present chapter the attempt will be made to summarize the basic conceptions of learned behavior which have emerged from the studies of such behavior conducted, in large part, without physiological questions in mind; in brief, we shall try to get a bird's-eye view of learned behavior that will provide a basis for the interpretation of the physiological material which appears in later chapters. This survey will differ in some respects from that which others might use in summarizing the same field; this difference will be due partly to the fact that different interpretations have been placed upon learning phenomena and, in addition, to the emphasis upon the physiological aspects of learning, which is our immediate concern here.

The outline presented here is in part original with the writer and in part representative of the thinking of present-day physiological psychologists.

The fact that there are different theories of learning adhered to by different psychologists seems to arise chiefly from the kind of behavior taken for the study of learning. Philosophical psychologists of a century ago, introspecting and analyzing human learning as casually observed, came to conceive of learning as the formation of a bond or association between ideas through the simultaneous presentation of the stimuli which evoke the ideas. And this is very much the conception of learning at which a layman might arrive after some thought on the matter. The first experimental studies of learning (Ebbinghaus) took the case of memorizing nonsense materials and obtained results that supported this conception.

Some time later two different groups of workers studied cases of learning in animals in which the subject was placed in a puzzle box and had to discover the correct solution to the problem; a latch had to be pushed, a string pulled, or two sticks fitted together to make a rake with which to secure food. In one set of experiments, cats and lower mammals were used. They exhibited more or less random behavior in the situation until they had solved the problem; then, on subsequent trials, the correct response appeared in less and less time. Thus learning appeared to take place by trial and error in which the correct responses, because they were rewarded, came to be learned. In other experiments, however, primates, not cats, were observed in problem boxes (Köhler); they seemed to exhibit very little overt trial-and-error behavior, but instead 'studied' the situation, and then, as if by insight, carried out the correct solution. From these experiments arose a different conception of learning than that deduced from lower animals; learning takes place by spontaneous changes in perceptual organization, i.e., by insight.

Still another experimental situation appeared as a model for understanding learning. Pavlov noticed that the sight of food would cause a dog to salivate—so regularly, in fact, that salivation could be considered a reflex to the sight of food. Then, when a bell or light was presented repeatedly just before the presentation of food, salivation occurred before the dog had even seen food. The interpretation of this fact made by Pavlov and later by many American psychologists was that the bell or light had been substituted for the sight of food in evoking salivation. This situation, one of substitution, was taken as the prototype of learning, and attempts were made to explain all learned behavior in terms of it. This principle of substitution was essentially the same conception of learning as that held by the early associationists, with the exception that for the Pavlovians it referred to behavior alone, and the notion of ideas, held by the associationists, was regarded as an unnecessary mentalistic assumption.

Now, there has been much discussion as to which of these principles is the basic one for theories of learning. Sometimes it has been assumed that one, and only one, must be; but there is today a growing realization that no one type of learning situation is the model for all learning, nor is any one principle taken from such a situation explanatory of all learning. The concept of the *idea* has been readmitted to psychological discourse under the name *symbolic process*, of which we shall hear more later. The principle of substitution is accepted as fundamental, but not exclusively so, in learning. Also to be given status as essential concepts in learning theory, pending a more satisfactory explanation of these concepts than has so far been advanced, are perceptual reorganization (Lashley) and selection of behavior through trial and error (Hilgard and Marquis). These latter factors in learning can be taken together as different aspects of a principle of effect, which will presently be discussed.

The Principle of Substitution.—A general statement of the principle of substitution is that one stimulus presented repeatedly at the same time as, or in close succession with, a second stimulus tends eventually, in a greater or lesser number of trials, to evoke the same effects in the organism as the second stimulus. There is hardly an instance in human or animal learning in which this factor cannot be seen at work. Yet there is hardly an instance in which the substitution is complete or in which other factors are not also at work.

Probably the best example to be found of simple substitutive learning is the conditioned eyewink; by repeatedly presenting a flash of light just before or with a blast of air on the cornea of the eye, the winking reflex evoked by the puff of air becomes attached to the flash of light. Even in this case, however, very significant differences in the form, amplitude, and latency of the unconditioned response to air and the conditioned reaction to light have been found (see Hull). It has also been reported (Liddell) that the constitution of saliva secreted in a salivary-conditioned response to light or a bell is different chemically from that produced by the sight of food, a fact which indicates that the motor impulses going to the salivary glands are somewhat different in the conditioned and unconditioned reactions. Thus, even though substitution is a good principle, if indeed not the most fundamental of all in learning, it refers, at best, to an incomplete substitution of effects.

Substitution of Sensory Effects.—In accordance with the behavioristic bias of many modern psychologists, the principle of substitution has usually been applied to reflexes and motor responses; a stimulus comes through conditioning to call out a response that was formerly only an unconditioned reflex. We should not overlook the fact, however, that the principle applies also to sensory processes in the brain; in this case, we may speak of sensory conditioning or conditioned sensations. Or, putting the statement in mentalistic terms, we may say that images or ideas, as well as responses, may be conditioned. Such effects are probably not so easily conditioned as are reflex reponses, but they are nevertheless important in understanding learning.

As a casual argument for conditioned sensations, we may cite the introspective fact, recognized by most people, that a stimulus often arouses in us an 'image' of other stimuli that were previously associated with the stimulus. More sound and trustworthy evidence, however, comes from experiments on the question. In one, human subjects were presented with a tone (unconditioned stimulus) and a light (conditioned stimulus) for 60 trials, and afterward they were tested with the light alone; most of the subjects reported hearing a tone (Ellson). They were, in fact, often unable to tell whether a tone had actually been presented. Other experiments are also available on this point (see Ellson), but need not be detailed here.

Then, too, there are data from animals which indicate, indirectly, the existence of sensory conditioning. In one study (Brogden), dogs were presented with combinations of bell and light, and a conditioned withdrawal reaction to shock was set up with one of the stimuli as the conditioned stimulus. In some animals the conditioned stimulus was the bell and in others it was light. In either case when tested with the other stimulus, which had never been directly associated with the shock, but only with the conditioned stimulus, the animals responded with conditioned reactions. Secondly, there is the fact, often spoken of as latent learning, known to us both in subjective experience and in animal experiments (Blodgett). Rats, for example, which are allowed to explore a maze without being rewarded show that they have learned something about the maze by the great speed with which they come to run the maze correctly once they are rewarded for doing so.

It seems clear, therefore, that the principle of substitution applies to sensory effects in the brain just as it does to behavior (Fig. 154). It is only fair to assume that in this case also the principle of substitution holds only imperfectly and that the conditioned sensation is not a perfect reproduction of the neural effects caused by the unconditioned stimulus. It may be, in fact, that the conditioned sensation is an even less perfect reproduction, especially in respect of its strength, than is the conditioned response. Research has not given us information on this point. It might be supposed, however, that in general conditioned sensations are more difficult to form and maintain than conditioned responses. The difficulty of some experimenters (see Ellson) in obtaining conditioned sensations would seem to indicate this. Then, too, human individuals give the impression more often of possessing conditioned responses to stimulus situations than they do of conditioned sensations (images, ideas).

The Principle of Effect.—This principle is illustrated best by the behavior of a hungry animal in a problem box or maze. When first

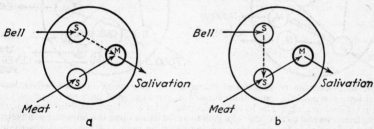

Fig. 154.—Diagram illustrating two neural routes by which conditioning may take place. *a*, Motor conditioning in which connection is formed between sensory representation of the conditioning stimulus and the unconditioned response; *b*, sensory conditioning in which the connection is made between the sensory processes of the conditioning and unconditioned stimuli. (*From N. R. F. Maier and T. C. Schneirla. Mechanisms in conditioning. Psychol. Rev.*, **49**, 117–134, 1942. *By permission of the American Psychological Association.*)

placed in either of these problem situations, its behavior is more or less variable, *i.e.*, the animal does almost everything, in his repertoire of behavior, that could be done in the situation. Some acts, such as pushing a lever or running down particular alleys of the maze, result in food being presented to him, and after a greater or lesser number of trials these acts are retained while other members of the original random behavior are eliminated. In a word, acts are learned according to the effect they have.

Although most clearly seen in the maze or problem box, the principle of effect can also be shown to apply to conditioning situations despite the fact that these appear superficially to involve only substitution. In the case of a dog being conditioned to avoid shock by raising its paw when a sound signal is presented, it can be shown that the first responses to the shock are more or less random responses involving the whole animal, but, since flexing the leg always terminates the shock, this response is retained and other elements dropped out according to whether they are irrelevant to the avoidance to shock, *i.e.*, the effect. If, on the other hand, the flexing of the paw will not avoid shock, the animal does not learn to lift its paw. Thus is the learning of the paw-flexure response determined by its effect in avoiding shock. Thereafter, by presenting a bell or light signal before the shock, paw flexure becomes conditioned to the signal by the principle of substitution (see Fig. 155).

Motor Organization.—It should be pointed out that the variable behavior in trial-and-error learning consists of a number of organized responses. To be sure, there is an element of general activity in such behavior, but there are different patterns of behavior which appear to be

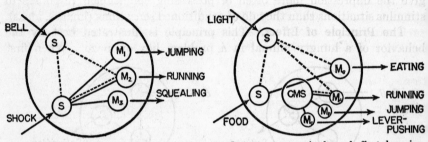

FIG. 155.—Scheme of the neural changes that may occur in law-of-effect learning. Dotted lines are possible connections formed in learning; solid lines represent connections existing before learning. The left-hand diagram is for avoidance conditioning, e.g., the rat running from one end to the other of a grill to avoid shock upon the sounding of a bell. The right-hand diagram is for a problem-solving situation such as a light-dark discrimination (Yerkes-Watson box) in which an animal pushes through the lighted door. Two principal points are that already existing connections may be greatly strengthened (see cases where dotted line parallels unbroken line) and that a central motive state (*CMS*) may be jointly conditioned with the conditioning stimulus to a response (see right-hand diagram).

arranged in some kind of hierarchy attached to the motivating situation. Thus an animal faced with the problem of escaping shock on a grill may first jump into the air and repeat this a few times before giving it up, then it may turn to biting the grill and showing 'aggression' toward it, then, finally, this may be given up for running along the grill. Most experiments are so arranged that this last pattern of behavior is the one rewarded. Problem situations requiring different motivation and solution may be arranged differently, but in each of them the essential point is that in a motivating situation there is a hierarchy of responses,[1] each organized in its own way, which occur in turn.

Following the line taken in discussion of motivation, we may look upon this hierarchy as the group of responses that, by innate neural dis-

[1] Some students of learning regard the different responses of the hierarchy as having a natural order or prepotency. Running, for example, may be the first response elicited by shock, and then, if that does not work, jumping may be the next response in order to be tried. If this is the case, the hierarchy is certainly differently arranged in different animals and varies from time to time, for the order in the hierarchy cannot be demonstrated in any other than a statistical way.

position or by previous learning, emerge from the c.m.s. They may be regarded partly as specific forms of behavior arising from the motivation and partly as patterns dependent upon the priming property of the motivation, since they depend somewhat upon the external stimulus situation and upon the possibilities for behavior which it presents.

Perceptual Organization.—Paralleling the conception of a hierarchy of responses elicited by a motivating situation is the conception of trial-and-error perceptual organizations (perceptions). The description of problem solving in primates given by Köhler and mentioned above brings out the idea that the subject studies the situation, sees it first one way and then another until one 'manner of looking at it' gives the solution. Such learning has been called learning by insight, and some have argued that it is a basic principle in all learning. Because this conception smacks of mentalism and cannot be broken down into stimulus-response terms, it has not been fully utilized in formulating theories of learning. To the physiological psychologist, however, it is hardly more difficult to conceive of the organization of nervous activity at the sensory or perceptual level than it is on the motor side. The evidence for such perceptual organization, moreover, is becoming increasingly weighty.

Only a few examples can be cited here. Krechevsky, in experiments in which animals could select either visual or spatial (tactual-kinesthetic) cues for the solution of a problem, found that some rats formed visual 'hypotheses' and others spatial 'hypotheses.' This fact could, of course, be clearly demonstrated by observing the choices of animals in many trials in which the visual cue would take them in one direction in the maze and the spatial cue in another. Evidently the animals were ordering their behavior in respect of some definite perception.

Lashley taught rats to discriminate between rather complex visual figures. When they had mastered the situation, he tested them on a number of visual figures, differing somewhat from those with which they were trained, to determine to which aspects of the stimuli they had learned to react. He found that animals tended to 'select' some part of the figure (perhaps a curved stroke in the corner of a figure with many irregular forms on it) and to discriminate on the basis of this feature of the stimulus. Rats trained on the same problem, moreover, tended to select different aspects of the figure. They had not learned, therefore, to react to the figure as a whole but had 'perceptually organized' the figure, picking out some aspect or part of it as a cue.

Finally to be mentioned is another experiment by Lashley which makes the point even more convincing. Rats were trained to choose the larger of two circles and therefore to make a size discrimination. Thereupon, a triangle was substituted for the larger circle. The rats continued to choose it, trial after trial, even though it differed in form from that which they had learned. After 200 further trials with the (small) circle and the (larger) triangle, they were tested with a small circle and a triangle of the same size (in surface area). They failed to show a preference, indicating that they could not discriminate the two. When tested again with the two circles one larger than another, they chose the larger. When tested, finally, with a small triangle and with a large circle, they chose the circle. All this indicated that, despite continued long practice with figures which differed in form, they still reacted to the difference in size, because of their original training to select size, and had learned nothing at all about the form of the two. The animals apparently were seeing the figures all the time as different in size, not in form.

In applying the conception of perceptual organization to learning, Lashley supposes that the rule is the same as in variable behavior. An animal 'sees' a situation according to one organization, and behaves accordingly; if he has been right, he tends to learn to assume that organization the next time he is presented with the situation. If he makes a perception which is irrelevant to the 'real' solution of the problem, that perception, like unsuccessful behavior, is not learned. Thus a principle of effect operates in selecting perceptual organizations just as it does in the selection of a pattern of response. In the untrained animal faced with a problem situation, there is a varying perceptual organization, just as there is a varying motor organization.

The Principle of Expectancy.—Closely related to the notion that perceptual organizations, as well as behavior, are fixated in learning is the concept of expectancy which has recently been introduced into learning theory to account for some of the phenomena of learning not otherwise explicable in the simple terms of substitution or of trial-and-error fixation of behavior (Hilgard and Marquis). An example of the operation of expectancy can be seen in experiments with monkeys in which, after being trained to secure a banana as reward for solving a problem, animals rejected lettuce leaves when these 'unexpectedly' were presented in place of the banana—despite the fact that under normal circumstances the lettuce is acceptable to the monkeys (Tinklepaugh). Essentially the same phenomenon has been demonstrated in rats (Elliot) and chimpanzees (Cowles and Nissen). The results of some conditioning experiments also lead to the factor of expectancy in learning, but these require too involved an argument to present here (see Fig. 156).

Worth considering briefly is the systematic relation of the three principles mentioned and the theory of the percept. The principles of substitution and effect are most widely accepted as basic principles of how learning takes place. For some, however, it has seemed attractive to reduce the principle of effect to a special case of the principle of substitution. This can be done by supposing that, because a successful act terminates the formation of additional percepts and the execution of other responses, that act occurs most often in any given motivating situation and therefore becomes most closely associated with it. Others argue that there is some factor aside from mere association which strengthens the tendency to carry out successful acts.

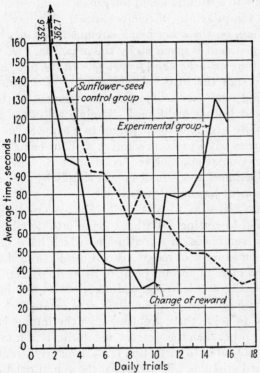

FIG. 156.—The effect of change of reward upon maze performance, illustrating the role of expectancy in learning. (*From M. H. Elliott. The effect of change of reward on maze performance of rats. Univ. Calif. Publ. Psychol.*, **4**, 19–30, 1928. *By permission of the publishers.*)

At present the principle of expectancy is offered as a secondary principle deriving from the principle of effect. The expectancy is regarded as some neural process which stands for the successful act and serves the same function. Thus, if a perception or an act results in the expectancy of reward, that perception or act is learned as if the reward had actually occurred, in which case, of course, it would be said that the principle of effect had been operating. The principle of expectancy, it is to be noted, introduces the concept of a central neural process which represents the rewarding act, *i.e.*, the act for which motivation primes the organism. Thus, try as we may to rid ourselves of so-called mentalistic conceptions, they have pushed their way back into our thinking, this time because an adequate theory of learning cannot, apparently, be formulated without them. We shall hear more of them later.

EXTINCTION AND FORGETTING

Learning, as we ordinarily understand it, refers to the acquisition of new adjustments to a situation, and the principles governing this acquisition are called the principles of reinforcement. We have just discussed them. There are, on the other hand, circumstances in which an innate or acquired adjustment is given up by the organism. Of these, the two most important are *extinction* and *forgetting*. In the first, an adjustment is given up through the repeated presentation of a stimulus situation without its being reinforced; subjecting an organism to the conditioned stimulus, without the unconditioned stimulus, will after a time usually cause the formerly acquired conditioning to disappear, or similarly, the animal that carries out a problem solution without being rewarded tends subsequently to stop attempting the 'solution' behavior. In forgetting, an acquired adjustment tends to disappear simply by the passage of time after the adjustment has been learned.

The question arises as to what principles govern these phenomena of extinction and forgetting. Without going into detail concerning the answer, we can summarize the conclusions which have been supported by the experimental work of recent years directed toward its solution.

The first and most important point to be made concerning extinction is that it is actually *new* learning. Monkeys observed during intervals in which they are not rewarded for their acts or are forced to wait for an opportunity to solve their problems give the impression of learning to do something other than the 'correct' act during that interval (Wendt). Animals being subjected to extinction trials, similarly, seem to learn that an unconditioned stimulus will *not* follow the conditioned stimulus, just as in the conditioning series they learn the contrary. Extinction thus becomes a different sort of learning than the acquisition of response, but it is still a kind of learning.

The relation of extinction to learning is further explained in this way: When a conditioned stimulus is presented without the unconditioned stimulus—*i.e.*, when a learned response is evoked without reward or reinforcement—other stimuli present at the time, whose effects have formerly been overcome by the conditioned stimulus, have a chance to come into play. Some of these stimuli will be those occurring in the internal environment and acting as distractors. Others will be the kinesthetic stimuli within the organism which regulate postural tonus and tend to maintain the existing posture of the organism (*cf.* stretch reactions, p. 313). The reactions to these stimuli, as they occur from time to time, become associated with the conditioned stimulus, and a new conditioning consequently takes place. The net result is that animals learn *not to respond* to the conditioned stimulus, to which they formerly learned to respond, but learn, in addition, to do something else.

A similar argument can be applied to forgetting. In this case it may be assumed that stimuli in the normal environment of a subject are 'similar' to the conditioned stimulus and that these become associated with behavior other than that learned. Because extinction is the consequence of this fact, the organism when put back into the conditioning situation shows evidence of forgetting.

As a way of summarizing in a few words this explanation of extinction and forgetting in terms of learning, a *principle of interference* has been suggested (Hilgard and Marquis, p. 108). This term implies that the loss of a new adjustment takes place by new learning's interfering with old and that the same general principles govern both. Illustrating the principle of interference is its analogue in unlearned behavior, reciprocal inhibition, in which one response, by virtue of conditions that we have already discussed (p. 67), becomes dominant over another. Whether or not such a principle is completely adequate to explain these and other related phenomena is still a question. Some have suggested that, in addition, it is necessary to posit a *principle of adaptation* in which unreinforced responses tend to become weakened in their attachment to conditioned stimuli. However that may be, it is important to realize that relearning is also an important aspect of such changes in learned behavior.

We may note, in passing, the role of extinction in the original learning of behavior requiring the principle of effect. Such learning we have seen involves variable behavior, *i.e.*, a number of different responses that occur, one after the other, with some repetition, until the one appropriate to the problem appears. An examination of such variable behavior, moreover, indicates that it consists of a hierarchy in which one is strongest, another less strong, and so on. The problem, then, is why the first response tried is given up and another one tried. To answer this we must assume that some process of extinction operates in giving variable behavior. Thus a response that is unsuccessful is unlearned or weakened in strength, thereby allowing a response which was formerly lower in the hierarchy to come to the head of the list; variable behavior, consequently, is the result of the extinction of different natural responses of an organism in a problem situation.

SYMBOLIC PROCESSES

In the era of mentalism that characterized philosophic psychology, man's mental processes were conceived to be made up of the sensations arising from present stimulation together with images of sensations with which they previously had been associated. This conception involved two main points, the image as a mental process representing previous sensations and the association of these images with sensations because they had previously been aroused together.

Implicit Behavior.—When, early in the present century, the phenomena of conditioning became known, the first of these notions, the image, was discarded and in its place was put response; the second notion, however, that of association through contiguity, was retained in the form of the principle of substitution, which states that one stimulus comes to stand for another in the evocation of responses. As a result, a mentalistic psychology of sensations and images was transformed into a behavioristic psychology. Since that time much effort has been expended in attempting to explain all the phenomena of learning, problem solving, reasoning, thinking, and even consciousness in terms of stimulus and response and the principle of substitution.

Neither the stimuli nor the responses assumed in such explanations appear in overt behavior—it takes only a brief inspection of human reasoning to show this. They were therefore assumed by behaviorists to occur implicitly, *i.e.*, at such small magnitude as to be unobservable but nevertheless present. This approach to the explanation of higher thought processes has been called the motor theory. Some have believed it alone sufficient to account for all mental processes, but experimental work of the last few years, both physiological and nonphysiological, has pointed to the existence of intervening central processes in the brain that are not necessarily manifested in implicit behavior.

Symbolic Processes.—Such central processes we may call *symbolic processes* because they are events in the brain which stand for and, as far as the determination of behavior is concerned, serve the same purpose as the neural events arising from afferent stimulation or leading to implicit response. The most elementary case of the symbolic process is the conditioned sensation. At a somewhat higher level are the symbolic processes indicated in the principle of expectancy. A stimulus, instead of leading merely to some response to which it has previously become attached through conditioning, is regarded as also giving rise to central neural processes which reproduce in part those elicited by the stimulus with which it has become associated. Thus the symbolic process turns out to be the neural counterpart of what the early associationists called an idea. It may also be regarded, however, as the representative of motor effects which do not actually take place but which, without the intervention of behavior, may serve to evoke other motor effects or symbolic processes. In this sense, the symbolic process refers to what the older psychologists called 'set' or 'determining tendency.'

To accept symbolic processes, however, is not to deny that implicit behavior can occur and that such behavior can play a role in determining later overt behavior. The symbolic process and implicit behavior can be taken as two complementary functions in adjustment.

Symbolic processes, moreover, are not limited solely to very complex adjustments. The principle of expectancy, derived from conditioning, appears to refer to such a process, and it is probable that symbolic functions are at work in a good many cases of conditioning.

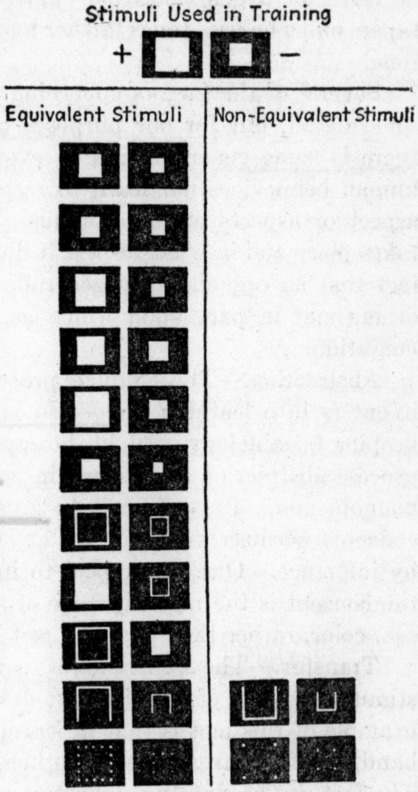

EQUIVALENCE

The final topic which needs to be taken up here preparatory to approaching physiological problems in learning is that of *equivalence*. This notion is applicable, in general, to three different aspects of learning: the sensory, the motor, and the central neural aspects of learning. We have different terms to apply to equivalence in each of these aspects of learning.

Generalization.—It is a demonstrable fact that when an organism learns to react to a particular conditioned stimulus it has also learned to respond similarly to other stimuli having certain characteristics in common with the conditioned stimulus (see Fig. 157). If, for example, a rat or human being learns to avoid shock when a 1,000-cycle tone is presented, it will make the shock-avoidance response when either 900- or 1,100-cycle tones are

Fig. 157.—Examples of equivalent and nonequivalent stimuli. Monkeys were trained to choose the left member of the uppermost pair of stimuli. They were then tested with other pairs and showed a preference for the left-hand member of each pair marked equivalent but no preference for either member of the pairs designated nonequivalent. (*From H. Klüver. Behavior mechanisms in monkeys, p. 175. Chicago: University of Chicago Press, 1933. By permission of the publishers.*)

presented. The learning has therefore taken place not to the particular tone of 1,000 cycles but to tones in general. The phenomenon is accordingly called generalization. It is a case of the principle of equivalence because the tones other than 1,000 cycles are equivalent to it in that they evoke the learned response.

Such equivalence, however, is not an absolute affair, for the tones other than 1,000 cycles, are not quite so effective as the conditioning tone in bringing out the response. Indeed, if one uses some measure of the strength of the conditioned response, such as its frequency or amplitude, he can plot a generalization curve around the 1,000-cycle tone which tapers off as he uses tones farther and farther away from the conditioning tone.

Several of the factors governing generalization have been studied in some detail, but for our purposes only one main point need be made: there is some generalization in every case of learning. An animal or human being does not learn to react to a stimulus per se but to some aspect or aspects of the stimulus. In just what aspect generalization takes place and in what respect it does not occur depend partly upon the fact that an organism can generalize more easily in some ways than in others and in part upon which aspects of the stimulus are varied in conditioning.

Abstraction.—The symbolic process in the form of an image, wherever it enters into learning, may also be generalized. For the purposes of keeping terminology straight, however, it is convenient to call this latter process abstraction and to retain generalization to refer to the sensory phenomenon. It is difficult to give an example of the abstraction (or concept) because we never get at symbolic processes directly but only by inference. One can appeal to introspection, however, and say that the concept is the mental image of some quality or aspect of an object, *e.g.*, color, rather than of the object itself.

Transfer.—The principle of equivalence applies not only to the stimulus aspects of learning but also to those of response. A common example of this fact is that in learning a skilled act with the use of one hand, one also learns to use the other hand without ever giving it practice. The fact can be simply demonstrated by testing proficiency with the left hand before and after training with the right hand has taken place. Many other instances of such a transfer of training have been demonstrated in animal learning. One such striking example is of a monkey that had learned to solve a problem with one hand and then had that hand paralyzed by damage to the motor cortex representing it; when, after the operation, the animal was given the problem again it immediately used the other hand, which had not been involved in the original learning (Lashley). Thus is there not only equivalence of stimuli but also equivalence of response.

Equipotentiality.—When we meet with the results of extirpation of neural centers we find a similar principle of equivalence applicable to neural structure (see Fig. 158). A rat that has learned to discriminate visual patterns while its visual cortex is intact may continue to discriminate well when a very large proportion of its visual cortex is removed. Since we know that the visual cortex is absolutely necessary for learning, it is clear that the remnant of the cortex mediating the postoperative discrimination is functionally equivalent to the whole cortex. Similarly, a rat which uses only one eye in learning shows perfect retention of that

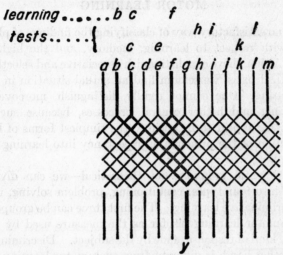

Fig. 158.—Diagram illustrating the problem of the equivalence of stimuli. An association is formed with *y* by stimulation of receptor cells *bc-f*. Thereafter any similar pattern of receptors (*ce-k*) will excite reaction *y*. The assumption of a fixed neural trace, as indicated by the heavy lines, fails to account for such equivalence. (*From K. S. Lashley. The problem of cerebral organization in vision, p. 305. In Biological Symposia, Vol. VII. Lancaster: Jaques Cattell Press, 1942. By permission of the publishers.*)

learning when it is tested with that eye covered and the other one now seeing.

General References

HILGARD, E. R., and D. MARQUIS, 1940. *Conditioning and learning.* New York: Appleton-Century. Pp. xi + 429.

McGEOCH, J. A., 1942. *The psychology of human learning.* New York: Longmans. Pp. xvii + 633.

YOUNG, P. T., 1936. *Motivation of behavior.* New York: Wiley. Pp. xviii + 562.

CHAPTER XXIII

MOTOR LEARNING

There is no satisfactory way of classifying the findings of physiological researches with respect to learning, memory, and the higher thought processes. Although we can distinguish associative and selective learning on a theoretical basis, we seldom find an actual situation in which only one is operating. One cannot rigidly distinguish, moreover, between simple learning and higher central processes, because such so-called higher processes appear to be basic to the simplest forms of learning, as the introduction of the principle of expectancy into learning theory has demonstrated.

On experimental grounds—not theoretical—we can divide animal experiments into four types: conditioning, problem solving, maze learning, and discriminative learning. The first three can be grouped together as forms of motor learning insofar as the measure used by the experimenter is the kind of response made by the subject. Discriminative learning, on the other hand, is different from such motor learning in that the kind of response made by the animal is secondary and that the aspect of the stimulus situation to which he responds is the thing measured. Here, accordingly, the discussion will be outlined in terms of this distinction.

Human learning and memory, from the experimental point of view, are in a class by themselves, because the prominence of verbal instruction and of linguistic performance gives to them an entirely different character. If the psychological theory of learning and its physiology as well were more advanced than they are, the differences between human and animal learning might appear more superficial than real; but at present it seems best to deal with them on an operational basis.

In a last chapter, finally, we shall deal with the problem of central symbolic processes as they have been studied from the physiological point of view in animals and human beings. By taking them up separately, it should not be implied that such processes are not involved in the cases of motor learning, discriminative learning, and human memory, but the problem, as well as the evidence bearing upon it, is important enough to take a separate chapter.

CONDITIONING

Subcortical Conditioning.—It is well known that in the higher animals possessing true cortices the cerebral cortex is the part of the nervous system most responsible for the organism's ability to learn. It was

480

assumed for a long time, in fact, that there could be no learning in the absence of the cerebral cortex. Pavlov, the father of the conditioned reflex, presented some experiments that appeared to support this conclusion. Recently, however, it has been demonstrated that animals can be conditioned in the absence of the cortex, and, indeed, in the absence of the entire brain, for spinal animals are capable of adaptations which can be called conditioning. Today the problem is not whether the cortex is necessary for learning, but rather just what role is played by the cortex and subcortical centers, respectively, in conditioning and learning.

Decorticate Conditioning.—As indicated above, there are several experiments showing clearly that the cerebral cortex is unnecessary for conditioning to occur (Poltyrew and Zeliony; Culler and Mettler; Girden *et al.*). Both dogs and cats, lacking all shreds of cortex, have been conditioned to respond in some manner to visual, auditory, and cutaneous stimuli as conditioning stimuli. Whether or not it is also true that monkeys and primates can learn in the absence of the cortex is not known, for the appropriate experiments have not been carried out, owing largely to the extreme difficulties encountered in keeping such organisms alive and healthy when deprived of their cortices.

But although decorticate cats and dogs are capable of conditioning, there are significant ways in which their conditioned behavior differs from that of normal animals (Culler and Mettler). The stimuli employed in conditioning must be more intense than in training normal subjects; in addition, many more trials are required to establish the conditioned responses than is the normal rule. More important than that, however, the decorticate animal does not develop the refined conditioned responses of the normal animal, but develops only gross undifferentiated responses to the conditioning stimulus.

Consider the example of conditioning a dog to lift its paw, when a sound is presented, to avoid shock. This is the example which has been most carefully studied in the decorticate animal (Culler and Mettler). The first part of such conditioning in the normal animal, it will be recalled, consists of yelps, struggling, and variable behavior. It is this behavior which first becomes attached to the conditioning sound; moreover, if the procedure is so arranged that an animal cannot avoid shock no matter what it does (Brogden, Lipman, and Culler), its conditioned behavior will consist of this gross behavior with only slight modification. If lifting the paw brings escape or avoidance of shock, however, the animal will, in the later stage (selective) of conditioning, come to give this response to the auditory signal.

In the decorticate animal this second stage does not occur. The animal when conditioned gives only the gross behavior characteristic of the early stage of learning in the normal animal. In a word, the decorticate animal displays associative learning, but not selective learning. The principle of substitution is operative, but not the principle of effect. The conclusion to be drawn from this result, consequently, is that the cortex is necessary for selective learning but not for associative learning. This conclusion, obviously, is an important one, but a word of caution needs to be said concerning it. The experiment was based upon one dog which had been successfully decorticated and lived in good health to be conditioned. Further work might cause us to alter the conclusion, but at present we can accept it tentatively. It is supported, fortunately, by results of another kind which will be discussed below.

Curare Conditioning.—Curare is a drug which when injected into the bloodstream almost completely paralyzes somatic muscle. It is for this reason that it has been used in experiments with conditioning. Curare also has the property of depressing the excitability of the cerebral cortex, apparently with little or no effect upon subcortical tissues. At any rate, comparison of the excitability of the cortex and of motor nerves in curarized and normal states shows the cortex to be greatly depressed by curare and the motor nerves to be unaffected (Culler *et al.*). It is to be concluded from this fact and from others to be taken up presently that curare can be used as a cortical depressor, thus functionally decorticating an animal. Its effects consequently give us another means of studying cortical functions, and several experiments, therefore, have been conducted with respect to the effects of curare upon conditioning.

The first experiment to be carried out (Harlow and Stagner) employed the usual conditioning procedures while an animal was under the influence of curare. Since the drug effectively paralyzed the animal, it could not be told whether any conditioning took place or not. After more trials had been given than are ordinarily required for normal conditioning, the effects of the drug were allowed to wear off and the animals tested in the normal state for any memory of the conditioning procedure under curare. There were no effects.

But the question was unanswered whether or not there had been any conditioning under curare. To answer it, Girden and Culler devised a means of observing the little response of muscle that is left after curarizing. They teased out a muscle of the leg, which always contracted when the shock was applied to it in the normal dog, leaving the blood and nerve supply intact, and found that, even under curare, there was a definite twitch of the muscle upon applying shock. They then presented a series of conditioning trials with a sound immediately preceding shock and found that conditioning would occur, thus demonstrating that the curarized animal could be conditioned.

The really striking fact appeared, however, when the animal was tested after curare had worn off and no evidence of conditioning could be found. Conditioning accomplished under curare, apparently, did not carry over to the normal state. Next, they reversed the procedure, conditioning an animal in the normal state and testing it under the influence of curare. The comparable phenomenon appeared; normal conditioning did not carry over to the curarized state. In each case, however, the animal would show conditioning when put back into the state in which it had been conditioned. Thus is it demonstrated that two different neural systems can exist independently of each other, so far as conditioned behavior is concerned, one obtaining in the normal state, the other under curarization.

The interpretation of this state of affairs naturally depends upon whether it is valid to suppose that curare suppresses the cortex without interfering with subcortical functions. If so, it can be said that curare conditioning is subcortical and is suppressed by the cortex; normal conditioning in turn can be regarded as cortical, dropping out when curare suppresses cortical functions.

To test this supposition, Girden repeated the experiments described above in animals which had been subjected to removal of their auditory cortices. These areas were chosen because the conditioning stimulus in the experiments was sound, and by removing the areas the role of the cortex could be eliminated in both the curare and normal states. In accordance with the theory, it was found that such animals did not show the division between normal and curare conditioning which turned up uniformly in previous experiments. Conditioning accomplished under curare carried over to the normal state, and vice versa. Thus the interpretation that curare suppresses cortical functions and that this factor was responsible for the split personality of the dog was supported. Moreover, it was shown that the auditory cortex, in particular, was responsible for this effect.

A final point considered in the curare experiments was whether the dissociation of conditioned responses holds as well for autonomic behavior as it does for somatic responses. The evidence on this point is contradictory. Harlow and Settlage, on the one hand, studied conditioned pupillary responses, controlled by the autonomic system, and concluded that conditioning performed in one state carries over into the other and thus that dissociation in curare is limited to somatic conditioning. Girden, on the other hand, armed with extensive observations of pulse rate, blood pressure, and, to some extent, pupillary responses, finds that, if the curarization is deep enough, such conditioning is like somatic conditioning in that it will not carry over from the normal to the curarized state or vice versa. In view of the fact that autonomic conditioning plays such an important, though indirect, role in many types of learning because it is involved in anxiety and emotional responses, the final answer to this question is of some importance. It is a common finding in clinical psychology, for example, that emotional conditioned responses remain long after memory for the events connected with the original conditioning situation has been lost or repressed.

One of the main points to be made from these experiments with curare is that the cerebral cortex can prevent the acquisition of learning at subcortical levels and suppress the expression of such learning once it has been acquired. Such inhibitory functions of the cortex are, of course, not new to us in physiological psychology. In studying posture, we found that many reflexive reactions were inhibited by the cortex; the functions of the extrapyramidal system, in fact, must be understood largely in terms of such a concept of inhibition. To this fact may be added two recent observations. Rats having a natural aversion to light show a markedly increased aversion when their visual cortices are removed (Abelmann and Morgan). The reflexive movements of the eyes which cats and other animals show in response to moving striations in the visual field are improved somewhat by extirpation of the visual cortex (Smith). Later we shall see that the concept of cortical inhibition also applies to other cases of learning.

The Conditioned Eyewink.—It was just concluded that autonomic responses are normally conditioned at a subcortical level independently of the suppressing influence of the cortex. This can also happen, it appears, in the case of some somatic responses: It has been reported, at any rate, in the instance of conditioned eyewink (Marquis). Dogs were conditioned to give an eyewink to light by pairing a light and a puff of air to the cornea. Then they were subjected to extirpation of the striate area of the cortex. Upon postoperative testing, they still retained the conditioned reaction acquired preoperatively. This fact is especially interesting because many other learned reactions (see Chap. XXIV) to visual situations are abolished by such an operation. It appears, however, that in this case the conditioning was accomplished from the very first at a subcortical level, the cortex exercising no inhibiting influence on it, so that there was no effect of cortical destruction. Other areas of the cortex were probably not responsible for the conditioning because extirpations in these areas likewise had no effect upon the retention of the conditioned reaction.

It may be noted in this connection that the conditioned eyewink is about the purest case of simple associative (or substitutive) learning known to us. There are, to be sure, significant differences in the latency and form of the conditioned and unconditioned reactions, but in general the conditioned response reproduces the reflex response quite well. In other conditioning situations, on the other hand, the operation of the principle of effect is more suspect, for rewards for the response are more easily identified and the reaction is modified selectively in a manner determined by its effectiveness in avoiding harm or achieving reward. Here again, therefore, we may point out that subcortical learning is associative and not selective (*i.e.*, not influenced by reward).

Spinal Conditioning.—As already stated, one cannot obtain such refined conditioned responses as the withdrawal of a leg to avoid shock in the decorticate animal, but general activity can be conditioned in the absence of the cortex. Since some kind of conditioning, if only of an elementary character, can be established in the decorticate animal, the possibility that conditioning might even take place in the spinal cord has also been investigated. The first attempts were made with spinal rats (Prosser and Hunter), and in them it was possible to obtain a sort of adaptation of reflex behavior by eliciting the reflex quite often, but no changes that could be called real conditioning were observed. Successful spinal conditioning, however, has recently been reported in the dog (Shurrager *et al.*). In order to obtain it, it was necessary to dissect out muscles from the leg, as was done in some of the curare experiments, and observe very small twitches in the muscles. The conditioning procedure consisted of applying pressure to the tail and then following it by shock to the limb in which the muscle was being observed. After a number of trials, conditioned responses could be observed in the form of twitches in the end of the muscle. Investigation of the behavior of these conditioned responses under various conditions led the experimenters to believe that they were observing true conditioned responses. If they are correct, it can be concluded that substitutive conditioning can occur in the spinal cord alone, just as it does in higher subcortical centers.

NEURAL PATHWAYS IN CONDITIONING

In addition to the experiments reported above, there are several that attempt to determine just what routes are traveled in the nervous system in the establishment of conditioned responses and thereby the locus of conditioning. These experiments make use of the paralysis of muscles involved in the conditioned response, the extirpation of parts suspected of functioning in conditioning, and the electrical stimulation of various parts of the nervous system as a substitute for either the conditioning or unconditioned stimulus. These studies, as we shall see, throw some additional light on some of the problems raised in the previous section.

Is Response Necessary for Conditioning?—The attempt has been made in two studies to determine whether an unconditioned response must actually take place in order for conditioning to occur (Light and

Gantt; Kellogg *et al.*). In both of them paw flexure to avoid shock was used as the unconditioned response, and it was prevented from occurring during the conditioning trials by crushing the nerves going to the limb muscles. Both studies agree in finding that, after time had been allowed for the nerves to regenerate and the animals tested with the conditioned stimulus, conditioned paw flexure occurred. It happened, however, that during the original conditioning sequence a generalized conditioned response developed similar to that which ordinarily occurs in the early stages of conditioning paw flexure and that this was of some avail in relieving the animal of the painfulness of the shock. Thus the principle of effect was allowed to operate, and it is probable that, in the conditioning training, responses of the animal tended to become focalized around the limb. Thus when the limb became functional again it is understandable that it was involved in the conditioned responses.

A somewhat more satisfactory answer to the question of whether the unconditioned response is necessary to conditioning comes from work with glandular responses. In one study, morphine was used as the unconditioned stimulus for salivation, but actual salivation was prevented by atropine (Crisler). In this case it was demonstrated that conditioning took place without the conditioned salivation's occurring. Similarly, when acid in the mouth was the unconditioned stimulus and salivation was prevented by atropine, conditioning was shown to have occurred when tests were made without atropine (Finch). In these instances, therefore, it is clear that the unconditioned response need not be a part of the conditioning process. Salivation differs from leg retraction, however, in that it does not depend, in any important degree at least, upon the differentiation of response through the principle of effect. More important in this type of conditioning than simple effect or substitution is the principle of expectancy, for salivation appears to be just the consequence of the expectancy of the unconditioned stimulus for salivation. Such an expectancy is reinforced not by the response, as is true of leg flexure, but by the presentation of the unconditioned stimulus.

That some central neural processes are basic to such conditioning is shown in several experiments in which conditioning was studied in relation to whether the unconditioned response is produced by direct activation of the effector or by neural activation. The injection of pilocarpine, for example, causes the secretion of saliva, but this response cannot be conditioned (Kleitman; Finch) for the reason that it has its action on the effector rather than upon the central nervous system. The same is true of hyperglycemia caused by the injection of adrenalin (Gantt; Loucks) or of the secretion of gastric juices from injecting histamine (Katzenelbogen *et al.*). Conditioning can occur, however, when morphine is used to produce salivary secretion because it has its effect by acting upon neural centers (Kleitman).

Summing up the results upon the question of the role of the unconditioned response in conditioning, we may come to the following conclusions: The unconditioned response need not occur if the central neural events leading to its occurrence are brought into play and provided that the principle of effect is not necessary for its appearance.

Where effect is important, *i.e.*, where the kind of response made alters the stimulus situation, it is probable that a general response pattern focalizing on the specific response is of help, although the specific response, it is clear, does not need to occur.

Role of the Motor Pathways.—From the work with responses produced or inhibited by drugs comes the suggestion that the central processes representing the response to be conditioned must be present in order for conditioning to take place. The question which logically follows that point is: Where must such central processes be? Experiments relevant to this question have been carried out and have given an answer which depends, again, upon whether the learning involves only the principle of substitution or also that of effect.

In substitutive learning, conditioning cannot be obtained if electrical excitation of the final common path is substituted for the unconditioned stimulus in producing the behavior to be conditioned. In one experiment (Loucks and Gantt), for example, electrical stimulation of moderate intensity, sufficient to evoke the unconditioned response, was applied to the motor pathways of the spinal cord. No conditioning was obtained. When the intensity of the electric current was increased, however, to the point where neural effects spread in the spinal cord to the sensory pathways, conditioning followed. This finding is not surprising, because sensory effects were produced by the electric stimulus comparable to those which would have been obtained by an unconditioned stimulus, for which the electric current was substituted.

Falling in line with these observations is another finding. Electrical stimulation of the motor areas of the cortex was substituted for shock in an attempt to condition paw flexure in a dog to an auditory stimulus. With extensive training, however, no conditioned responses developed. This result was like that obtained with activation of the motor pathways in the spinal cord. The conclusion to be drawn is that neural activity eliciting the unconditioned response must be produced at some point in the nervous system preceding the beginning of the final common path.

By introducing reward into the procedure of the experiment last mentioned, it was possible to get a different result. Just as before, a buzzer was sounded and paw flexure elicited by electrically stimulating the motor areas, but in addition food was presented to the animal after each flexure.   In contrast to the previous results, this procedure brought about good conditioning.

But it is not clear just what this finding indicates with respect to the neural processes involved in conditioning.   The psychologist might say that the bell came to arouse an expectancy of food and because the paw flexure, with a little coaching, led to food, it was learned selectively according to the principle of effect (Maier and Schneirla).   But what is expectancy in neural terms?   Presumably it involves impulses spreading to the motor areas and tending to evoke behavior of a kind that confirms the expectancy.   At any rate, the introduction of reward must introduce neural activity proceeding and spreading to the motor areas.   It cannot be claimed, therefore, that these results demonstrate the efficacy of

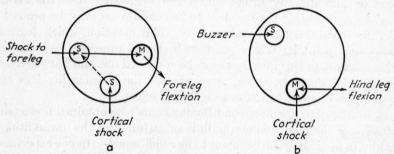

Fig. 159.—Diagram illustrating connections formed in experiments with electrical stimulation of the brain as conditioned stimulus. *a*, Cortical shock in sensory areas is capable of being conditioned to foreleg flexion; *b*, shock to the cortical point for foreleg flexion does not form any conditioned response. (*From N. R. F. Maier and T. C. Schneirla. Mechanisms in conditioning. Psychol. Rev.*, **49**, 117–134, 1942. *By permission of the publishers.*)

electrically evoking the unconditioned response in the motor areas. About the most that can be said is that in this way the animal is aided in his selection of an appropriate response (see Fig. 159).

Sensory Functions in Conditioning.—Turning from the motor to the sensory side of neural pathways, we find the results of experiments coming out as we might expect.   When, for example, the procedures described above were again altered so that a shock was combined with motor-area stimulation, conditioning to the buzzer was obtained.   This, of course, was not unexpected, for conditioning would be obtained with the cortical stimulation, but this, since it directly evoked the flexure, without intervening random activity, aided in the conditioning (Loucks).   In another case, electrical stimulation of sensory nerves was substituted for either the conditioned or the unconditioned stimulus and conditioning occurred.

It has also been shown that the sensory activity arising from movement of a limb could be used as a conditioned stimulus for learning (Loucks).   By electrical stimulation of the motor area a *hind-limb* movement was produced, and this was a signal that shock would be applied to the forelimb if it were not lifted. Conditioning occurred, the kinesthetic excitations from the hind limb apparently acting as the conditioning stimulus.

Of greater importance is the fact that electrical excitation of the visual areas of the cortex can be substituted for the conditioning stimulus in the production of either salivation (food reward) or leg withdrawal (shock avoidance). Here, obviously, direct activation of the sensory cortical areas has taken the place of their excitation by way of the visual receptors and optic pathways.

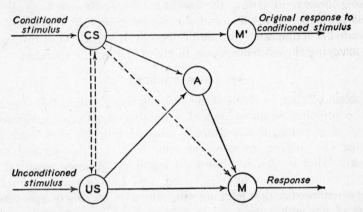

FIG. 160.—Schematic diagram of the possible relations of areas and pathways involved in conditioning. There are four possible points of convergence of pathways in conditioning at which neural changes representing conditioning might occur: *CS*, the center excited by the conditioned stimulus; *US*, the center excited by the unconditioned stimulus; *A*, some association center or pathway; and *M*, the motor center for the unconditioned response. (*From E. Hilgard and D. Marquis. Conditioning and learning, p. 319. New York: Apple-ton-Century, 1940. By permission of the publishers.*)

One result that is striking but not easily interpreted is that electrical stimulation of the cerebellum may serve as the *unconditioned* stimulus, in conjunction with sound as the signal, for a movement of the foreleg (Brogden and Gantt). Such cerebellar stimulation evokes movement of the same sort as excitation of the motor cortical areas, and it is note-worthy, therefore, that in contrast to the experiments with such cortical stimulation conditioned responses were formed. Indeed, conditioning was as rapid as it is in normal circumstances, and other characteristics of the conditioned response were as in normal conditioning. The inves-tigators conducting the experiment gave convincing proof that their electric current had not spread from the cerebellum to the cortex or brain stem. What we should like to know, then, is whether by neural conduction sensory effects in the cortex or thalamus were produced comparable to those evoked by shock.

As matters stand at present, we can reach this conclusion: The locus of conditioning, which depends upon the cortex, is not in the final common path of the behavior which is conditioned. Perhaps it is there in the case of subcortical conditioning such as occurs under curare or with the sensory areas of the cortex extirpated, but the experiments required to test that possibility have not been done. In cortical conditioning, the central counterparts of the conditioned and unconditioned stimuli appear to be necessary. This being the case, the locus of the connections which are formed in conditioning—if, indeed, they have a locus—must be in one of three places: the centers representing the unconditioned stimulus, those representing the conditioned stimulus, or in some area (association?) between these and the motor areas. This conclusion is represented in a diagram (Fig. 160) drawn by Hilgard and Marquis, who after surveying the evidence, come to about the same conclusion.

PROBLEM SOLVING

Problem solving, in its most general meaning, is almost synonymous with the principle of effect: out of a number of variable responses or patterns of response, that pattern is selected which is most capable of satisfying the motive operative at one time. In this general sense, problem solving is seen in almost all learning. A more practical and limited meaning of the term is to be used here, however. Problem solving is regarded as that learning which involves making one response or a series of particular responses to achieve a goal. It is distinguished from conditioning and from discriminative learning in that there are no definite stimuli acting as cues. It is different from maze learning because the principal feature of it is not running the shortest and most correct pathway but making more highly skilled responses than running. The simplest examples of problem solving as used in this way are the rat's learning to depress a lever that releases food or the cat's pulling a string that admits it to a box containing salmon.

Physiological work with respect to problem solving has been conducted for the most part with three different animals, the rat, the monkey, and the chimpanzee. The last two, being primates, have considerably more ability than rats in problem solving, and their brains are rather alike and differ from that of the rat. It is advisable, consequently, that we consider the material on problem solving in relation to the type of animal, whether rat or primate, used for experimental study.

THE RAT

Most of the work with rats has been carried out by Lashley and has involved two general classes of problems. The first we may call unskilled because it requires no manipulative ability but only that an animal thrust its weight on a platform. Representing such an unskilled problem is the *double-platform box* which consists simply of two pedals placed near the center of a box, each of which must be pressed before the animal is admitted to food (Fig. 161). In the normal exploratory behavior of a hungry rat, these pedals will be pressed accidentally, and all that the animal must learn to be successful is to select the pushing response, rather than running or some other aspect of general behavior.

The second class of problem requires more skill (Fig. 162). As before, the rat must strike upon the general type of response which is correct,

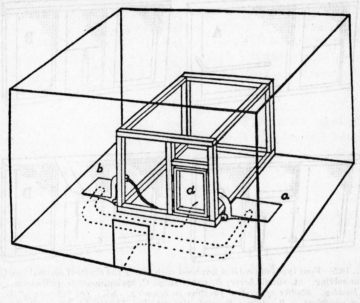

Fɪɢ. 161.—The double-platform box for use with rats. When the platforms *a* and *b* are pushed successively, the door *d* opens. (*From K. S. Lashley. Brain mechanisms and intelligence, p. 27. Chicago: University of Chicago Press, 1929. By permission of the publishers.*)

but in addition it can greatly increase the speed with which it attains the goal by improving its skill in making the response. Several varieties of problem box fitting into this class have been used: in one, a lever—not a large platform—must be depressed, thereby releasing the latch of a door which admits the animal to food; in another, there is a paper strip which must be cut or torn by the animal before he can obtain food; in a third, the door opening to food can be opened only by pulling a handle; a fourth requires that a chain be pulled. All these are manipulative, or skilled, solutions.

Physiological study of these two classes of problem-solving behavior has been limited to the study of their dependence on the cerebral cortex;

the principal question raised in such studies has been whether problem solving depends upon some particular cortical areas. The procedure, therefore, has been to make lesions of variable size in different parts of the cortex and to ascertain what effect these had upon problem solving. By making the lesions before the animals are presented with the learning situation, their effect on learning can be established. By operating after learning, however, their effect upon memory can be determined. These effects, it so turns out, are not exactly the same (Lashley).

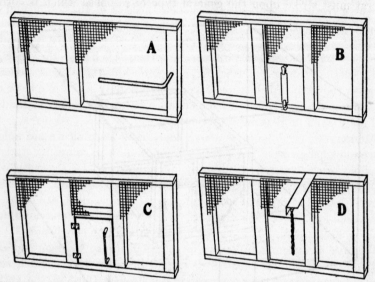

Fig. 162.—Four types of problem box used with rats in the study of cortical functions in problem solving. *A*, simple lever; *B*, paper strip; *C*, spring door; *D*, pull chain. (*From K. S. Lashley. Studies of cerebral function in learning. XI. The behavior of the rat in latch-box situations, p. 9. Comp. Psychol. Monogr., Vol. 11, No. 52, 1935. By permission of the Johns Hopkins Press, publishers.*)

Learning.—Two general conclusions come out of the study of effects of cortical lesions upon learning to solve problems in rats: (1) retardation in rate of learning is proportional to the mass of the lesion, not its locus, although only lesions of considerable size have any significant effect upon it; (2) skilled learning is more easily affected than unskilled learning. The basis for these conclusions can be seen in the following experimental facts.

Lesions of small or moderate size, including all those up to about 60 per cent of the cortex, do not affect the rate of a rat's learning to solve the double-platform box. Lesions larger than this tend to cause some retardation. It must be remembered, however, that removal of the cortex in such large amounts has serious effects upon the health of the animal and deprives it of a large proportion of the sensory and motor areas of the cortex. The result is serious interference with the basic sensory-motor capacities of the animal, and this probably explains the effect upon learning.

Learning of the skilled problems, on the other hand, is considerably retarded by more limited destruction of the cortex. Lesions of 30 per cent or less may show up in the rate of learning. But such limited lesions do not need to be in any particular part of the cortex; damage to one part appears to be as important as damage to another. Instead, there is a quantitative relation between the size of the lesion and the amount of retardation of learning that it produces. Statistical correlations expressing this relation range between .48 and .72, depending upon the type of skilled problem investigated. Thus, the effect of cortical lesions upon the learning of more skilled problems depends, not upon the locus of the lesion, but chiefly upon its size. We have met this kind of relation before in connection with mating behavior, and we shall see it even more in later sections.

Memory.—From the facts above concerning learning we are able to determine what parts of the cortex *can* function in learning; by studying the effect of cortical lesions upon memory, however, we ascertain what areas of the cortex *have* participated in normal learning. Studies of this type, so far as problem solving in the rat is concerned, are restricted to the double-platform box and the relatively unskilled behavior that it entails. From them, however, come some interesting conclusions.

Whereas, in learning, only very large lesions impair learning capacity, relatively small lesions will abolish memory for the habit. Such small lesions, however, must be confined to the frontal third of the cortex; lesions in other parts will have no effect. This fact makes us conclude that the frontal cortical areas are crucially concerned in the learning that takes place with the cortex intact. But notwithstanding such 'localization,' animals that have lost their memory of the solution because of frontal injury are quite capable of relearning the solution in a normal number of trials. This checks with the fact that only extremely severe lesions retard learning. Putting all these items together, we come to the general conclusion that the frontal cortex normally participates in learning to solve the double-platform box, but that in its absence other areas of the cortex, or possibly subcortical centers, may take over the capacity for learning.

We, of course, are interested not only in what parts of the cortex function in, or are necessary to, problem-solving learning, but also how they perform their functions. Throwing light upon this aspect of cortical functions are some general observations of the behavior of rats that lack some cortex in problem-solving situations (Lashley; Krechevsky). One conspicuous effect of cortical damage is impairment of exploratory behavior; this naturally is important in the animal's rate of learning because it is only by exploration that an animal hits upon the solution. One can also say that partially decorticate rats do not display the same aggressiveness, the same vim and vigor, in trying to solve the problem as do normal rats. They display, furthermore, much more stereotyping and, conversely, considerably less versatility in their behavior. Once they have struck on one solution of the problem, for example, even though it may not be the most efficient solution, they tend to repeat the same movements used in this solution, whereas the normal animal will by degrees eliminate useless movements and change to the most expeditious and energy-saving solution.

These facts may be looked at in several ways. We might say that the principle of effect does not operate so efficiently in the partial decorticates; normally the more effective response is 'stamped in' more than a less effective one, but after cortical damage, this difference in the amount to which the two responses are 'stamped in' is lessened. This view of the results of cortical damage fits in with the conclusion, reached in the section on conditioning, that the cortex, though not necessary for associative learning, is essential for selective learning.

On the other hand, the fact that animals display greater stereotyping and less versatility might be regarded as indicating a reduction in the rate of extinction. The point has previously been made that an animal varies its behavior, at least in part, because a response which is tried but is unsuccessful becomes extinguished, i.e., is learned not to be made, thus allowing some other response to become dominant. Such extinction is, of course, subject to the same principles as normal learning, but it could be that cortical damage has an especially important effect upon extinctive learning.

Other ways of looking at the effect of cortical lesions upon the character of problem-solving behavior are, on the one hand, that there is a deficiency in attention and interest—these terms unfortunately are not clear themselves and need further explication—and, on the other hand, that the motor mechanisms for organizing highly skilled behavior are interfered with. At present, no final conclusions can be drawn with respect to these views. This aspect of physiological research in the mechanisms of learning is, indeed, only in its infancy, and in the future we may expect more light to be thrown upon it.

PRIMATES

Some of the problems that have been employed in studying primates are as simple as those presented to rats and consist only of the pushing of a bar or the pulling of a string to secure reward for the animal. Because primates possess greater motor dexterity, however, they can be given other problems requiring more skill, *e.g.*, undoing a latch, turning a crank, or using rakes to procure food. More than that, because it turns out that primates have capacities not possessed by lower animals for organizing a complex series of acts, they can be presented with problems requiring a series of acts to be executed in a particular order. For the solution of one problem, for example, it was necessary for the monkey or chimpanzee to undo a latch, pull a rope, and turn a crank, in that order. Thus we can distinguish three types of problems in primate investigations: unskilled, skilled, and seriatim. Problems of the latter type involve psychological processes not required for simpler learning and such processes are taken up in detail later, but some reference to seriatim problems is also in order in this section.

A general statement about the effects of cortical lesions upon problem solving in primates to be made at the outset is that the cortex posterior to the central fissure is not nearly so important in problem solving as that anterior to the central fissure, *viz.*, the frontal lobes. This we know to be true despite the fact that parietal and temporal areas have not been investigated so fully as we might like. Lesions in such primary receptive areas as the striate cortex, of course, have some retarding effect upon learning, but it is possible to assume that such effects are due to disturbances of a sensory nature comparable to mutilating the receptor organs which project to the areas. The frontal lobes, at any rate, are the areas of primary importance in problem solving. In the present discussion, these may be divided into three areas: the motor area, the premotor area, and the prefrontal ('association') areas.

Motor Areas.—These are important chiefly because they begin the final common path for skilled movements, and the paralysis of skilled movement which results from their extirpation naturally interferes with problem solving (Jacobsen). If, after a monkey or chimpanzee has learned to solve a problem, its motor areas are bilaterally removed, there is serious impairment of ability to solve the problem, and it might seem as though these areas had some part in the memory for the solution. A simple check of whether paralysis or amnesia (loss of memory) is the cause of the disability is available, however. As we already have seen (p. 338), the disturbance of skilled movements which follows motor-area lesion in monkeys is gradually effaced with time, and after several months the paralysis largely disappears. When monkeys are tested, then, for memory of problems learned prior to operation, they show perfect memory for the solution. Thus the temporary interference with problem solving, we may conclude, has been the outcome of the inability of the animal to carry out the coordinated movements necessary for the solution, not of his amnesia for the correct solution.

Premotor Areas.—The effect of premotor ablation may be characterized as a disintegration of the pattern of movement in problem solving. A 'premotor monkey' which, prior to operation, has learned some simple skilled act, such as undoing a latch or pulling a rope, shows fragmentation or disintegration of this act, not a true loss of memory for it. The monkey may, for example, walk over to the rope and take hold of it, showing full well that he 'knows' its significance in solving the problem, but then he may fail to follow through by pulling it. Similar phenomena appear in other kinds of problems. In each case, the *way* of performing an act, not what to do, is lost.

Important, however, is the fact that this ability may be regained by retraining the animal. This taken together with other facts about the premotor area make one wonder whether there is any real loss of memory occasioned by its extirpation. These areas, it will be recalled, are essential structures in the postural organization of behavior and their ablation introduces an awkwardness into skilled behavior. It may be such a disturbance of posture, and its effect upon skill, which gives the appearance of a fragmentary amnesia. The effacing of the disability by restraining, it might be argued, could be the animal's learning how to compensate for its motor disability. If, aside from this disturbance of motor skill, there is any loss of memory, the premotor areas are still not of considerable importance in problem solving, for an animal can accomplish the solution without these areas.

Prefrontal Areas.—Perhaps the best way of stating the effects of complete removal of the prefrontal areas is to say that seriatim functions are almost, if not entirely, destroyed. By *seriatim* functions is meant the organization or synthesis of skilled acts into an orderly series. The monkey, after extirpation of the premotor areas, gives clear evidence of being able to learn specific unskilled or skilled acts and, if these have been learned prior to operation, of remembering them. This is true even in seriatim problems, where a series of skilled acts is required. But although the animal executes the movements which the problem requires, he does not perform them in the correct sequence. If the problem requires pulling a rope, pushing a lever, and undoing a latch, in that order, the animal may show that he remembers what to do, because he makes each of the responses, but he has forgotten how to do them in that order. Not only has he forgotten the order, but he cannot relearn it. Thus it is the seriatim aspect of the problem, not the component skilled or unskilled acts, which the animal is unable to learn or to remember.

This distinction between seriatim and nonseriatim memories will prove important at a later point where it will be possible to give it some interpretation. For the present, it is sufficient to record the fact as it appears in primates with prefrontal ablation.

MAZE LEARNING

The maze has been one of the most widely used instruments for the study of animal learning. Its difficulty can be easily varied by changing its form and length, and it is well suited to the rat as a laboratory subject because it does not require skilled movements for its solution. It has, therefore, been extensively used in the physiological study of learning in the rat.

But though it is convenient, results obtained from it are not always easy to interpret. For one thing, we do not know just what sensory cues are employed by animals in solving it, unless we go to a great deal of trouble with special tests, which at best are not very satisfactory. Another difficulty is that we cannot determine easily to what extent simple factors of responding to external stimuli, and more complex factors, such as the seriatim factors discussed above, are operative in the learning. Indeed, systematic studies of maze behavior indicate that there are so many factors in maze learning that, if it appears that maze learning or memory is altered as a result of brain lesions, we are unable to put forth any certain interpretation of the effects.

The Cerebral Cortex.—Several studies, carried out chiefly by Lashley, have examined the role of the cerebral cortex in learning. The general procedure in all of them has been to destroy areas of the cortex before and after learning has taken place. In the principal experiments (Lashley),

Maze III

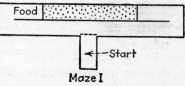

Maze II

Maze I

Fig. 163.—Three mazes of graded difficulty used in Lashley's studies of cortical functions in maze learning. (*After Lashley. From L. W. Crafts et al. Recent experiments in psychology, p. 160. New York: McGraw-Hill, 1938.*)

three mazes of differing complexity were used: a 1-cul maze, a 3-cul maze, and an 8-cul maze (see Fig. 163).[1] The effect of cortical damage, it was found, depended upon which of these mazes was used.

To interfere with learning of the easiest maze, the one with one blind alley, relatively large lesions are required, and there is no particular area

---

[1] *Cul* is a common abbreviation used by psychologists to indicate cul-de-sac, or blind alley.

whose ablation is any more important than another. Just as in the
rat's learning of the double-platform box, the learning of such simple
mazes proceeds just as rapidly after small damage to the cerebral cortex
as before; indeed, the relation between cortical damage and rate of
learning is comparable in the two cases, the statistical correlation being
.20. This fact is understandable when it is realized that the double-

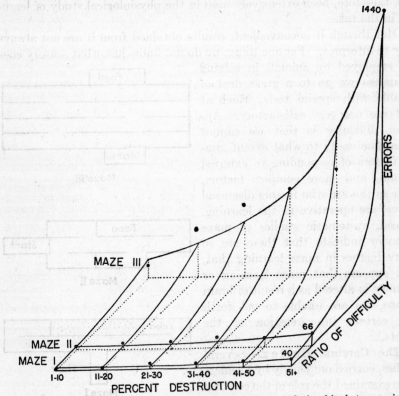

FIG. 164.—Three-dimensional graph of results showing relationship between size of
cortical lesion, difficulty of the maze, and degree of retardation resulting from the lesion.
(*After K. S. Lashley. Brain mechanisms and intelligence, p. 74. Chicago: University of
Chicago Press*, 1929. *By permission of the publishers.*)

platform box requires only a simple path of movement as does the
1-cul maze.

In more complex mazes, however, the effect of cortical lesions upon
learning is considerably greater, and here again no one cortical area
is of significance. Only the mass of the lesion appears to be related to
the amount of retardation in learning. Thus, the statistical correlation
between size of lesion and learning rate is .58; in the 8-cul maze it is .75.
Resulting from these experiments are the conclusions (Fig. 164) that (1)
the ability to learn a maze does not depend upon any particular part

of the cortex, (2) learning ability after cortical lesions is in proportion to the mass of cortical tissue remaining, (3) the relation between mass and learning ability is more predictable, the more difficult the maze to be learned.

Quite similar conclusions apply to the effects of cortical damage upon the memory of mazes previously learned. Retention of a very simple maze habit, the 1-cul maze, is not disturbed by lesions varying in size up to about one-third of the cortex, but injury of larger size impairs memory somewhat without preventing its reacquisition by additional training. The retention of moderately difficult mazes (3 cul) is affected by smaller lesions and in greater degree when the lesions are large; retention of the very difficult habit (8 cul) is impaired by lesions of 20 per cent or less of the cortex. In all instances, there is no relation between locus of damage and effect, just as in the case of learning. The statistical relation between size of lesion and the severity of the amnesia is .69 with the 8-cul maze. Finally, the size of lesion required to produce some disturbance of memory is, in general, smaller than that necessary for learning to be impaired.

In addition to these facts, another one of some importance has been brought out recently by Erickson. Other things being equal, the effect of cortical lesions upon learning ability is less in bright rats than it is in dull ones. In the experiments demonstrating this point, all the rats were subjected to cortical lesions of the same size, *viz.*, about 20 per cent of the total cortex. Upon comparing preoperative learning scores with postoperative tests of retention, it was found that the animals which had learned most rapidly were affected least by the operation, whereas very slow learners were upset a great deal more by lesions of the same size. Thus the more intelligent rats seemed able to do without the given amount of cortex more easily than the duller ones.

Subcortical Mechanisms.—Relatively extensive experiments concerning subcortical centers, particularly those in the thalamus, have been carried out (Ghiselli and Brown). Subcortical lesions were made in various portions of the thalamus by electrical currents delivered through a stereotaxic instrument (p. 237); then learning rate in the operated rats was compared with normal subjects. From this procedure it was learned that lesions anywhere in the thalamus could affect learning ability but that injuries in the sensory and association nuclei lying behind the anterior group of nuclei are most important. The anterior thalamic nuclei, it will be remembered, are associated with the hypothalamus and the more primitive parts of the cortex, and it is doubtful that they are concerned in learning activities. It is reasonable, however, that the other nuclei should bear the same relation to learning as the cortex since this area is concerned with relaying impulses to and from the cortex. It is significant that, although no statistical correlations were computed in this study, the amount of retardation of learning was roughly proportional to the size of the thalamic lesions made.

Mass Action.—In the monkey the prefrontal areas proved to play a very special role in problem-solving learning and memory, but in the rat, as we have seen, all the experiments fail to reveal any particular cortical or subcortical centers for either problem solving or maze learning. In every case, the site of a lesion is of special importance, and if the lesion affects learning or memory, it is in proportion to its size. Thus the facts of maze learning as seen in the rat face us with the conclusion that, in this animal, the cortex functions as a whole, not in parts. A name has been given to this fact by Lashley: *mass action*. This refers simply to the fully demonstrated fact that the mass of cortex, rather than locus, governs learning and retention in the rat.

There is no denying the fact of mass action; but what interpretation can we make of it? There seem to be three possibilities. (1) There is some general learning function exercised by the cortex as a whole which cannot be analyzed into the contribution of the parts. Such a conclusion is what the facts of mass action, taken at face value, appear to point to. (2) It is possible, on the other hand, that particular sets of neurons participate in different aspects of learning and memory but are greatly dispersed over the cortex. One can conceive, for example, of two different learned behaviors involving two completely different sets of neural connections but of these two systems as being so overlapped and dispersed in the cortex as to make it impossible to sort the systems from each other by the methods of extirpation. (3) The third possibility is that learning a maze may involve several different pathways but that the many factors concerned in maze learning do not allow us to uncover this fact by the experiments so far conducted. Thus visual learning might involve the visual cortex, and somesthetic learning the corresponding cortex, and so on, but if all kinds of learning are operative at once, as they undoubtedly are in the maze, cortical lesions would find no one of them crucial but of increasing importance according to the number eliminated.

For convenience in writing, we should have names for these three possibilities. The first refers to a *general factor*, the second to *dispersed specific factors*, and the third to *localized specific factors*. The three possible sets of factors explaining the empirical fact of mass action need not be mutually exclusive; indeed, it is probable that all three of them are operative. So it seems, at any rate, from a series of experiments testing the validity of these three possibilities.

The General Factor.—The first experiment was conducted by Lashley (*cf.* Tsang) to determine crucially whether a *mass* factor plays a part in cerebral learning activities. The procedure, briefly, was to compare the maze learning of blind animals with that of animals lacking the visual cortex and, similarly, to test the effects upon retention of blinding and of striate extirpation. By this means, he could hope to determine whether, in addition to visual functions, the visual cortex contributed any general mass-action factor to learning; for, if the visual cortex has visual functions only, blinding should affect maze performance as much or more than striate ablation, whereas if there is a mass-action factor, striate extirpation should have more severe affects than blinding alone. The results supported the latter alternative, for the striate lesions had more severe consequences for learning and retention than did simple blinding.

It has been questioned, however, whether Lashley's experiments did not suffer from defects that would make this conclusion untenable (Finley). Many of his striate lesions, it has been pointed out, considerably exceeded the limits of the striate area and thus, by running over into other cortical fields, probably caused sensory disturbances other than those of a visual nature. It is also possible that the residual vision, left after destruction of the visual cortex (see p. 214), is a greater hindrance to an animal in learning than no vision at all, for it has recently been shown that the natural aversion of the rat to light is markedly increased following striate destruction (Abelmann and Morgan). This factor could cause an animal to make an unnecessarily large number of errors. There is the fact, too, that Lashley's experiment has recently been repeated by Finley with different results. In her experiment, lesions of the visual cortex were little, if any, more important than blinding. In many respects, her experiment was more complete and crucial than Lashley's. She used, for example, a larger number of cases; her animals were run both in the dark and in the light; fewer of her lesions were so large as to overrun the visual areas. The chief criticism to be leveled against her experiment is that too many of her lesions were considerably *smaller* than the visual areas. Thus, whereas Lashley tended to overrun the area, she tended to undershoot it. The experiment, although of great importance, is not, unfortunately, an easy one to do well enough to decide the question of whether there are general effects of operation upon the circulation and health of the brain as a whole. The issue cannot, therefore, be considered settled at the present time.

Dispersed Specific Factors.—It is similarly not easy to test the possibility that maze learning depends on several types of cerebral function involving neural systems dispersed on the cortex; there are no experiments bearing upon it directly. There are, however, certain well-known facts which allow us to believe that such factors are operative, at least within certain limits. In the rat the electrostimulable areas (see Fig. 165) are spread over a considerable part of the cortex, covering most of the anterior half. This indicates that the area concerned in strictly motor functions is of considerable size. The somesthetic sensory projections, similarly, although not perfectly delimited, cover a rather sizable portion of the lateral and dorsal surface. Little is known of the extrapyramidal areas of the cortex, but in the primates these are distributed over a large section of the cortex, consisting chiefly of the premotor areas and the parietal areas. In view of the encephalization that takes place in other respects between rats and primates, they can be no less dispersed in the rat. Thus, from the dispersal of these three different systems, it is easy to see that cortical lesions are not likely to eliminate any one of them discretely, should one of them be more important in learning than another. Then if it be granted, as seems

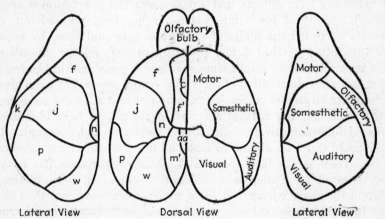

Fig. 165.—Areas of the rats' cerebral cortex. On the right, functional areas; on the left, cytoarchitectural areas as determined by Fortuyn and modified by Lashley. $f, f', c,$ and $n,$ motor; $j,$ somesthetic; $p,$ auditory; $w, m', aa,$ visual; $k,$ olfactory. (*After Lashley. From N. R. F. Maier and T. C. Schneirla. Principles of animal psychology, p. 322. New York. McGraw-Hill, 1935.*)

reasonable, that several such systems are concerned in learned behavior, it would really be quite unexpected if learning were related to cortical functions in any other than a purely statistical way, *i.e.*, in the manner seen in mass action.

Localized Specific Factors.—A large part of the facts of mass action are undoubtedly to be accounted for on the basis of the great number of specific factors involved in maze learning. Assume, for example, that in solving a maze an animal, taking its route through the maze, uses several different sensory cues at various times and that the connections through which it learns a response to a particular cue are located in some sensory area of the cortex. Then, the more cortex one removes, the more of these connections will be destroyed, and the greater will be the deficit in maze learning or retention. Or assume, similarly, that some animals use one sensory cue predominantly and others some other type of cue predominantly, but, at the same time, that the experimenter does not know which animal is which. Whether or not a lesion damages the particular area mediating the learned response in each case becomes, then, a matter of probability, and the greater the size of the lesion, the greater the likelihood of destroying the area through which learning takes place. In either case we might expect learning and memory for maze performance, as studied in the experiments described earlier, not to appear as dependent upon particular loci, but to be related to mass of lesion.

Both of these assumptions are validated by experiments bearing upon them. It is known, in the first place, that animals vary among themselves in the cues of which they make use in solving maze problems. One way of testing that is to remove different cues, after an animal has learned a maze, and see what effect this procedure has on his memory. In experiments in which rats were trained in the light and subsequently tested in the dark, for example (Dennis, Finley), it was shown that some animals were considerably disturbed and others were not. Another test is to provide two different solutions of a problem, one employing

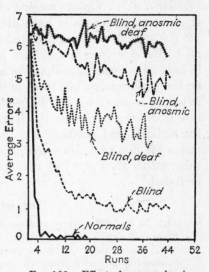

Fig. 166.—Effect of sensory deprivation upon maze learning. (*After Honzik. From L. W. Crafts et al. Recent experiments in psychology, p.* 147. *New York: McGraw-Hill,* 1938.)

visual cues and another positional ones (tactual-kinesthetic); in this case, some rats take one 'hypothesis' and other animals the second 'hypothesis' (Krechevsky).

The second assumption that cortical lesions of increasing size deprive the animal, in increasing amounts, of necessary sensory cues can be tested by studying the effects of the destruction of sense organs upon learning (see Munn). Here one finds results essentially comparable to those of mass action (see Fig. 166). If animals are blind while learning a maze, the lack of vision has little or no effect upon their learning. The same is true if one destroys the olfactory bulbs. Combining anosmia and blindness, however, makes a great deal of difference; animals are appreciably retarded in their learning of maze problems. It is a little difficult to make more extensive combinations, but even this result points rather definitely to the conclusion that in sensory deprivation, as in

cortical destruction, there is a 'law' of mass action. In the former case
however, it is plain to be seen that no mass factors are concerned, but
on the contrary, only specific sensory factors.

There is more to learning, of course, than having sensory cues available, but other factors have not been studied and explicitly defined. In
one case, however, what might seem to be a relatively complex factor
viz., the ability of animals (rats) to estimate distances in a maze, has been
demonstrated to be localized mainly in rather well-defined frontal areas
(Stellar *et al.*). Various aspects of the maze situation were so controlled
that external cues could have little if any control of the behavior, and
yet the animals were required to run down a pathway with alleys leading
off to the side from it and turn into the correct alley. Lesions placed
in cortical regions other than the anterior areas had no appreciable affect
on the performance, but those in the anterior areas, even if rather small,
impaired memory for the discrimination and, it appears, prevented the
rats from ever relearning it. This capacity, it is believed, is related to
the seriatim and symbolic functions considered elsewhere, but it illustrates the fact that when one factor in maze learning is considered at a
time, rather than many of them together, localization of functions may
be found.

General References

LASHLEY, K. S., 1929. *Brain mechanisms and intelligence.* Chicago: Univ. Chicago
     Press. Pp. xii + 186.
LASHLEY, K. S., 1934. Nervous mechanisms in learning. Pp. 456–496. In *A
     handbook of general experimental psychology.* Ed. Carl Murchison. Worcester:
     Clark Univ. Press.

CHAPTER XXIV

DISCRIMINATIVE LEARNING

Whereas in conditioned behavior an organism makes a response when a stimulus is present and no response when it is absent, discriminative behavior consists of making one response to one stimulus and some other response to another stimulus. Sometimes two responses made to two different stimili may merely be opposites of each other, *i.e.*, an animal may lift its leg when a light is turned on and keep his leg on the ground when a bell is heard; in other instances the responses may be quite different. The former case, it can be seen, is a case of conditioning in which responding is conditioned to one stimulus and not responding is conditioned to another and, for this reason, is called differential conditioning. In other types of discrimination an animal may turn left in response to one stimulus and right with respect to another; or it may jump through a door presenting one stimulus and avoid other doors presenting other stimuli.

It would be well if, in approaching discriminative learning, the reader keeps in mind the statements made in an earlier chapter concerning perceptual organizations in learning. The most important point to be remembered here is that the stimulus instigates activity in the brain which is not a simple reproduction of the stimulus but has a pattern of organization of its own. In this organization certain aspects of the stimulus, such as its size, form, shape, or even some of its particular details, may become the dominant factors in guiding behavior. The organization shifts, moreover, from time to time, in much the same way as behavior, before learning, is variable. Later, apparently by a principle of effect, the organization which is most often and most strongly reinforced comes to be the perception learned. This conception seems well validated by facts previously presented.

Turning now to the subject at hand, we may note that vision is the modality in which discriminative learning has been most extensively studied in relation to physiological activities. It will, therefore, be especially emphasized in the following summary. The aspects of visual learning which have been studied include brightness, movement, flicker, and form. These we shall take up in order.

BRIGHTNESS DISCRIMINATION

The discussion of brightness-discrimination learning centers around two points: the relative difficulty of the discrimination, *i.e.*, the relative

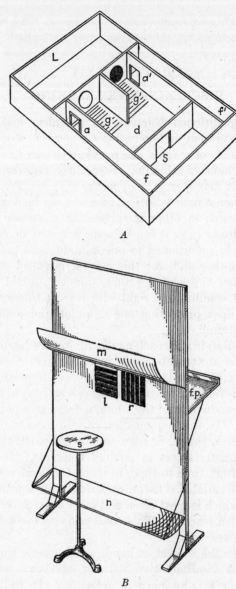

A

B

FIG. 167.—*A*, apparatus for studying brightness discrimination in rats.   *s*, starting box;
d, point at which discrimination is made; *g*, *g'*, electrified grids from which shock is given if
wrong choice is made; *aa'*, door to food compartment *f* or *f'*; *L*, light. *B*, "jumping"
apparatus for studying visual-pattern discrimination in rats.   *s*, stand from which rat
jumps to left (*l*) or right (*r*) card; *n*, net into which animal falls if wrong choice is made; *f.p.*,
food platform where reward is given for correct response. (*After Lashley. From L. W.
Crafts et al. Recent experiments in psychology, p.* 159. *New York: McGraw-Hill,* 1938.)

difference in brightness to be discriminated; and roles of the subcortical and cortical mechanisms in the learning. The first factor has been studied by comparing the rate of learning a simple dark-light discrimination, in which the brightness difference is rather large, with the rate of learning to distinguish two lights of moderately different brightness (Fig. 167). Then this factor has been set in relation to the second by comparing the effects of extirpation of different cortical and subcortical regions upon the rate of learning these two discriminations.

Light-dark Discrimination.—The results of experiments with light-dark discrimination may be summarized as follows. In normal rats, learning the discrimination depends upon the striate cortex, for when it is removed after learning all memory for the discrimination is lost (Lashley and Frank). Upon retraining, however, the animals learn the discrimination again in about the same number of trials as was required originally.

These results, it will be noted, are similar to others that have already been discussed. The loss of memory following striate extirpation is like the amnesia for conditioning which occurs upon curarization or like the amnesia for problem solving which follows removal of the frontal areas. Similarly, such amnesia means only that the area is used normally, not that it must be used, for without it learning in a normal number of trials will again take place. Thus as in curare and frontal ablation, some parts of the brain other than the striate cortex can take over light-dark discrimination when the striate cortex is lacking. A similar conclusion about cortical inhibition is also indicated; *i.e.*, the cerebral cortex, while functioning in learning, 'inhibits' the activity of lower centers in learning. Giving additional evidence of this inhibition is an observation already mentioned, that the light aversion of the rat is greatly increased by removal of the striate cortex (Abelmann and Morgan).

Differential Discrimination.—As one might expect, it is more difficult for a rat to learn to discriminate lights of different brightnesses than to distinguish a light from a dark stimulus, and the difficulty is increased the nearer the two lights are in brightness. This fact is relevant to the results of extirpation of the visual cortex upon learning and remembering a differential discrimination.

Since removal of the visual cortex blots out traces of light-dark discrimination, it is not unexpected that striate ablation also completely abolishes memory for the differential discrimination. Unlike the light-dark discrimination, however, the number of trials required to learn the differential discrimination following the operation is appreciably more than it formerly was. This greater difficulty in learning is related principally to the difficulty of the discrimination and not in any appreciable degree to impairment of sheer discriminative capacity, for studies of the differential threshold following striate removal show only slight deviations from the normal (Lashley, Mead). The visual cortex, therefore, is not necessary for very easy brightness-discrimination learning, nor for good performance in differential discrimination, but it is important in the learning of difficult discriminations.

Just how and why the visual cortex plays this type of role in visual learning we do not know—at least not definitely. It may be suggested, however, that the difficulty in learning a differential brightness discrimination is linked with the fact that in the absence of the visual cortex animals are unable to discriminate any patterns except those of the very simplest character and under the most optimal conditions. Pattern perception is naturally of some advantage to an animal in orienting itself in the discrimination situation. If, as suggested, its loss is the basis of the difficulty in learning brightness discriminations, we may consider the effect a secondary one.

The primary and crucial importance of the visual cortex in the learning of brightness discriminations is corroborated by the fact that the extirpation of other cortical areas, even in large amounts, has no effect upon either the learning or retention of brightness discriminations. Thus, it appears, the visual area and no other cortical area is of any importance in this aspect of learning.

Subcortical Mechanisms.—To establish the participation of the visual cortex in normal learning is one step in isolating the mechanisms of brightness-discrimination learning. To determine the centers responsible for learning in the absence of the visual cortex is the next step. In view of the fact that lesions of nonvisual cortical areas interfere neither with retention nor with learning of a brightness discrimination, it is to be supposed that the alternate mechanisms in the discrimination are subcortical. For the purpose of investigating this possibility, studies have been made which employ the stereotaxic instrument and are, therefore, capable of making subcortical lesions without appreciable damage to cortical tissues.

The superior colliculus, such methods reveal, is the subcortical visual station of primary importance in learning a dark-light brightness discrimination in the absence of the visual cortex (Ghiselli and Brown). Although the learning of the discrimination is not retarded by extirpation of the striate area of the cortex or of the thalamocortical radiations to this area, destruction of the superior colliculus, *in addition to the visual cortex*, is followed by abolishment of the discrimination and of the capacity to relearn it. Thus is the role of the superior colliculus indicated.

More of the subcortex than the superior colliculus, however, is involved in learning of the light-dark discrimination; this has been shown by investigating the role of the corpus striatum and of various thalamic nuclei besides those which are primarily of visual function (Ghiselli and Brown). Indeed, destruction of any thalamic nuclei, except those of the anterior group, brings about some retardation in the rate of learning—this in spite of the fact that the cortical areas to which many of these thalamic nuclei project have been shown to have no significance in the learning. No particular thalamic nuclei appear to be essential for learning, but each seems to contribute something to the rate of learning; in general, the amount of retardation appears to depend not upon the position of a lesion but upon the extent of the thalamic destruction. The anterior thalamic nuclei and the corpus striatum, however, do not bear any significant relation to the learning of the light-dark discrimination.

The explanation of this fact is not yet clear. There are, of course, many interconnections between thalamic nuclei which may serve associative functions; indeed, there are thalamic nuclei whose sole purpose appears to be that of association. Their functions, however, are not easily separated from the functions mediated by the somesthetic nuclei which make up such a large part of the thalamus. Why it is that either association or somesthetic nuclei should be essential to good learning of a light-dark discrimination is a problem.

MOVEMENT DISCRIMINATION

Brightness and pattern are the aspects of visual stimuli which have been most thoroughly investigated in connection with neural mechanisms, but some facts are available concerning the movement aspect of visual stimuli. Even with relatively prolonged training, the discrimination of movement by animals (cats) lacking the visual cortex is not nearly so good as in normal animals (Kennedy; Morgan); the visual cortex is of primary importance in movement discrimination, although some discrimination is possible without it. Just as in brightness discrimination, moreover, discrimination of movement is lost following removal of the visual cortex, but may be relearned again upon further training. But in this case the training required for relearning is much longer, and even then the level of performance is inferior to that of the normal animal. Thus, in movement discrimination, as in brightness discrimination, there is a loss of the habit, and relearning is possible following striate destruction, but in the case of movement, the ability of subcortical mechanisms to take over the cortical functions is very incomplete, and movement perception is deficient in the absence of the visual cortex.

PATTERN DISCRIMINATION

Cortical Functions.—As was detailed in an earlier chapter, the capacity to discriminate patterns is almost entirely dependent upon the visual cortex. It is no wonder, then, that complete striate ablation causes loss of memory for pattern discriminations and leaves the animal without ability to relearn any except the very simplest differences in patterns (p. 215). Partial striate ablations of limited size, however, do not impede the rate of learning pattern discriminations so long as a small part of the binocular projection area is intact (Lashley). Nor do they disturb memory for pattern discriminations. But when the intact part of the area is so small that an animal cannot "see" enough of the patterns to discriminate them easily, some impairment in rate of learning is seen, and if the area is very small the discrimination will never be relearned (see p. 215).

Cortical areas outside the striate region, however, are of little significance in the learning of figural discriminations, for such discriminations as triangle versus circle are unaffected by extrastriate cortical lesions. It is interesting, however, that pattern discrimination of considerable complexity is disturbed by lesions in regions outside the visual cortex. Learning to discriminate an upright F from an inverted F, for example, requires more than a normal number of trials after such lesions (Kirk).

Subcortical Functions.—The same stereotaxic methods that were used in studying subcortical functions in brightness-discrimination learning have also been applied in the case of figural discrimination (Brown and Ghiselli). In this case destruction of the lateral geniculate body prevents an animal from ever learning the discrimination because, obviously, such destruction keeps visual neural impulses from getting to the cortex and is therefore equivalent to removal of the visual cortex. The superior colliculus, on the other hand, is not required for such learning, and its destruction does not impede the formation of a pattern discrimination in any detectable way.

It is interesting, however, that the pretectal nuclei are essential to good pattern learning. Animals in which they have been destroyed require a number of trials in excess of that taken by normal subjects to learn pattern discrimination. The pretectal nuclei, it will be recalled, are reflex centers sending pathways to the oculomotor nuclei and having to do with adjustments of the head and eyes. It is quite unexpected, therefore, that they should have any part in pattern learning. The fact that they do will require further experimentation before it can be interpreted.

Nonvisual thalamic nuclei, exclusive of the anterior group, also play some part in learning to distinguish patterns, just as they do in brightness discrimination, but they are not so important as the pretectal nuclei. After destroying the pretectal nuclei, about five times the normal number of errors are made in learning the figural discrimination, whereas after destruction of the main thalamic nuclei, learning requires only about twice as many errors as are usual in normal cases. This fact, like its parallel in brightness discrimination, cannot at present be satisfactorily interpreted.

Remaining for mention is a still more elementary part of the visual system, the retina. Although the lateral geniculate bodies and the visual cortex are anatomically organized in a spatial representation of the retina, it is believed that no such orderly arrangement of fibers is to be found in the optic nerve. Partial section of the optic nerve may therefore be presumed to produce a rather indiscriminate interruption of fibers representing all parts of the visual field. Significant, therefore, is the fact that partial injury to the optic nerves results in a retardation of the rate of learning of either brightness or pattern discrimination (Brown and Ghiselli). The extent of retardation, in general, is correlated with the extent of the injury. Such injury, it is to be presumed, is equivalent to causing elementary sensory defects, and the results, consequently, indicate the relation of rate of learning to sensory efficiency.

NONVISUAL SENSORY LEARNING

Only a few data are available concerning the learning of sensory discriminations in modalities other than vision. Part of them are derived from the rat, the rest from primates.

Rats.—In the rat neither the auditory nor the somesthetic areas of the cortex have been well delimited, and various difficulties have been encountered in devising satisfactory techniques for the study of auditory and somesthetic discriminations.

One experiment concerning the learning of an auditory localization, *i.e.*, the position of a sound source, has been performed in rats (Pennington). It showed that rats could learn the auditory localization just as readily after their auditory cortices had been removed as before. Lesions placed elsewhere in the cortex did not interfere with such learning either. So far as we can judge, auditory localization is comparable to light-dark discrimination in that it can be learned with the use of subcortical centers.

In one available study of tactile discrimination in the rat (Smith), results also comparable to light-dark discrimination were obtained. Rats were taught to distinguish between two sandpapers of different roughness and were subsequently operated in such a way that various lesions, taken together, covered the entire cortex. One area when removed caused partial or complete loss of the discrimination, and this was presumed to be the somesthetic projection area. Animals that lacked it, however, were capable of relearning the discrimination in relatively few trials, and it appeared consequently that other cortical or subcortical centers could, if necessary, take over the function normally subserved by it. Considerably more work on this problem is indicated, but these results so far lead us to conclusions similar to those obtained in brightness discrimination.

Primates.—The neural centers involved in somesthetic learning and memory have been more extensively investigated in primates than in the rat. The primates, for example, have been required to learn differences not only in the roughness of objects but also in their form. Thereby are provided data comparable to those obtained in vision where the discrimination of brightness and of pattern has been examined. To understand these data, the chief features of the somesthetic system of the monkey and chimpanzee should be reviewed briefly. The somesthetic nuclei of the thalamus project, it will be remembered, to the precentral and postcentral gyri, although the latter gyrus is the most important. In addition, the lateral nucleus of the thalamus relays impulses from the somesthetic nuclei to the posterior parts of the parietal lobes, these latter sometimes being called the somesthetic 'association' areas.

Kinesthetic Discrimination.—One can begin with the facts about kinesthetic weight discrimination (Ruch). Monkeys were trained to discriminate differences in weight, and the effect upon retention of the discriminative habit was measured after removal of the precentral, postcentral, and posterior parietal areas, taken separately and together. The results were as follows: After the separate removal of any one of these areas, there was some loss of memory for the discrimination, but after retraining, the discriminations could be mastered again. The memory loss was much slighter in the case of removal of the precentral and postcentral areas than after destruction of the posterior parietal areas. With combined lesions of the precentral and postcentral areas, there was still only a moderate loss of memory for the discrimination, and this was easily effaced by training. A combination of the postcentral and parietal 'association' areas, unfortunately, was not performed.

But, interpreting the facts available, we can conclude that the learning of a kinesthetic discrimination by normal animals does not depend in any critical degree upon any small localized area of the cortex. The somesthetic functions of the cortex are spread over wider areas than are those of vision, and all these areas must participate in normal learning, for injuring any part of them causes some amnesia. In view of the slightness of the effects, however, it is to be doubted whether the learning is as much a cortical affair as is, for example, the learning of a brightness discrimination.

Filling out our picture of cortical functions in somesthetic learning, and answering some of the questions left unanswered by the experiments with monkeys, are observations of chimpanzees in the learning and retention not only of kinesthetic discriminations, but also of tactile intensitive discriminations and of tactile pattern discriminations. In these observations we find evidences that between the monkey and chimpanzee there has been some corticalization of somesthetic functions, for the effects of cortical lesions upon learning and retention of kinesthetic discriminations are more severe in the chimpanzee than are comparable lesions in monkeys.

Tactile Discrimination.—The same general statements apply to the discrimination of tactile roughness as were made above in connection with kinesthetic weight discrimination (Ruch). Destruction of the posterior parietal areas, first of all, causes a severe loss of retention for the discriminations, much more so, indeed, than the same lesion in the monkey. The amnesia can be overcome by further training in the discrimination, but more trials are required for regaining the habit than are taken by monkeys. Extirpation of the entire parietal lobe, *i.e.*, of the postcentral gyri and posterior parietal lobules, deprives the chimpanzee of memory for kinesthetic and tactile habits. Only after prolonged retraining can the discriminations be reestablished, showing in addition to amnesia a loss of normal ability to learn the discrimination. More than that, the fundamental discriminative capacity has been altered, for when, after retraining, thresholds are determined, these turn out to be considerably worse than the usual values for normal animals.

Interpretation of such results as these is always difficult because one cannot be sure in distinguishing between discriminative capacity and learning. One obviously depends upon the other, and which is fundamental is not easily determined. We can conclude, therefore, only that normal learning of the tactile and kinesthetic discriminations depends in the chimpanzee upon the parietal lobe, that in its absence learning can occur, presumably via subcortical centers, but that such learning is inferior to the normal in rate and ultimate level of performance reached.

Tactile Form Discrimination.—Distinguishing the form of objects, *i.e.*, stereognosis, is more critically dependent in the chimpanzee upon the cortex and, indeed, upon a limited cortical area than is either tactile intensitive or kinesthetic weight discrimination (Ruch). Ablation of the posterior parietal lobule alone, for example, is sufficient to cause complete amnesia for stereognosis. In the case of complex form discriminations, no amount of retraining will yield mastery of the discrimination, although with less difficult discriminations retraining is effective. If subjected to long retraining, a chimpanzee whose posterior parietal lobule has been removed, for example, may learn again to distinguish a cone from a pyramid, but the capacity to discriminate a pyramid from a wedge, which are much more alike than a cone and pyramid, is never regained no matter how many trials are given the subject.

This finding indicates (1) that stereognostic learning depends upon the posterior 'association' area when it occurs in the normal animal; and (2) that after removal of the area some other structure takes over part, but not all, of the learning function. We do not know whether this other structure is subcortically or cortically located. It is possible that the relearning of simpler stereognostic discriminations after removal of the posterior parietal area is carried out by the postcentral cortex; but to establish this point would require observations with animals lacking the postcentral areas in addition to the posterior parietal area and, unfortunately, such observations are not available. The alternative possibility is that subcortical centers perform the learning function in the absence of the parietal 'association' areas—they seem to carry out such a function in kinesthetic discrimination—but the first possibility seems more probable.

The parietal 'association' area, it may be observed, is similar in certain respects to the visual cortex. Insofar as stereognostic discrimination is forgotten and can be relearned postoperatively, one parietal area functions in the way the visual cortex does in brightness discrimination. In respect of the more complex pattern discriminations which can never be relearned, it functions as does the striate cortex in pattern vision. Thus, even with the corticalization that appears to have taken place between the monkey and chimpanzee, somesthetic learning has not been so highly corticalized in the chimpanzee as has vision in the rat.

EQUIVALENCE

It has already been pointed out in an earlier chapter that one can distinguish three types of psychophysiological equivalence in adaptive behavior: equivalence of stimuli, equivalence of response, and equivalence of structure. All three of these can be reduced, it appears, to equivalence of structure. When, in the example given earlier, an animal generalizes from a 1,000-cycle tone to another of considerably different frequency, it may be assumed, on the basis of a place theory, that the tones, to which it responds in the same way as it did to the tone to which learning took place, stimulate different parts of the ear and therefore of the cortex (see Chap. XI). Again, when an animal uses one eye in learning a visual discrimination, but thereafter displays perfect ability to make the discrimination when using the other eye, it is clear that the two retinae are equivalent in respect of the learning. In transfer of training, on the other hand, when the learning of a skill transfers from one hand to the other, different neural centers and pathways, as well as the actual muscle responses, are functionally equivalent in the learning

The phenomenon of equivalence is one of the most perplexing problems to be faced in arriving at a conception of the neural mechanisms of learning, for it renders difficult the understanding of just what changes in neural structure can be the basis of learning. We tend to think of the nervous system as a complex of synaptic connections and to assume that learning takes place through the formation of new connections (see later section). But how can connections be the basis of learning when completely different neural structures than those directly exercised in learning also show that learning has affected them? This is the problem which is addressed in the discussion and survey of the present section.

Binocular Equivalence.—One approach to the neural mechanism of equivalence has been the study of binocular equivalence, *i.e.*, the transfer of learning 'from one eye to the other' as described above. This study has been carried out in two different animals, the rat and the pigeon.

Because in rats the fibers of the optic nerve partially cross at the optic chiasma and the two eyes are, therefore, represented in the same parts of the cortex and colliculus, the first explanation of binocular equivalence which comes to mind is in terms of the fact that the two eyes have common connections with the same cortical areas. As one step in testing this hypothesis, the fibers of the optic nerves were cut longitudinally at the optic chiasma, so that there would no longer be the common ending of the optic fibers in the thalamus. When, after such an operation, rats were tested for binocular transfer, no changes in the ability to transfer could be discovered (Levine).

This possibility being eliminated, the next step was to cut the fibers of the corpus callosum, a structure that might possibly provide a connecting link between the two visual cortices. This too had no effect upon binocular transfer (Lashley). Unfortunately, however, the section of the callosum was not performed in the same animals that had been subjected to the section of the chiasma. It is, therefore, possible that in the first experiment common connections in the corpus callosum could have effected the transfer and that in this last experiment the common endings of optic fibers in the thalamus could have mediated it. In addition, the possibility that fibers may connect the two lateral geniculates is still untested, although there is at present no evidence for it. So far as the studies with rats go, therefore, the possibility has not been eliminated that binocular transfer takes place by means of common connections of the endings of the two eyes.

In birds, however, the problem of binocular equivalence has received a more definite answer (Levine). Pigeons trained to discriminate patterns, color, or brightness show binocular transfer under some conditions and no such transfer under others. When the patterns are placed directly in front of them and they are trained while using only one eye, they show not the slightest indications of memory when tested with the other eye being used. On the other hand, when the stimuli used in discrimination are placed just beneath their heads, they exhibit perfect binocular transfer. The significance of the effect of the position of the stimuli upon binocular transfer, it is thought, is that in the first case the bird is using monocular portions of the retina, and where binocular transfer occurs the binocular parts of the retina are in use.

Related to these interesting facts is the nature of the bird's visual system. Optic fibers from each eye are completely crossed at the chiasma and end up, therefore, entirely on the opposite sides of the brain. In the bird the superior colliculi mediate pattern vision (Layman), and the crossing of the visual fibers means that there are no common connections in the superior colliculi. Interconnections comparable to those of the corpus callosum exist, however, at least for the most medial parts of the colliculi, by means of a commissure running between the colliculi of the two sides.

Because the visual system is completely crossed and the only known connections between the two central representations of the two eyes are to be found in these interconnections, it is possible to use the bird to test whether connections are the basis of binocular equivalence. Levine has done this by cutting the fibers connecting the two colliculi, and the result was that binocular transfer could no longer be obtained—this despite the fact that conditions of training and testing were those that always permitted transfer in normal animals. The conclusion, of course, is clear, that in this case—the only case in which the basis of binocular transfer has been successfully determined—the transfer depends upon common connections between the centers whose functions are equivalent.

Equipotentiality.—Now, in the many experiments that have been carried out involving extirpation of parts of the cortex, it is a very common thing to find one part of the cortex or one part of a sensory system equivalent to other parts of the system in respect of learning and memory. Such an ability of one part to subserve the functions of another has been called *equipotentiality* by Lashley. This term has also been used in embryology to designate the fact that in the first stages of division of cells one can separate them and obtain from them two organisms, perfect in every detail, where without the separation only one organism would have been obtained. It appears, therefore, that each set of separated cells was equipotential in respect of subserving the functions normally carried out by all of them. So it is in neural functions.

Several illustrations of the application of the principle of equipotentiality to learning and memory are in evidence in the available experimental literature. Consider, for example, the effects of partial destruction of the striate areas upon retention of a simple brightness discrimination (light-dark). Rather extensive injuries to the area can be sustained with little or no loss of memory (Lashley). Indeed, probably less than one-twelfth of the visual area need remain intact for such perfect retention. With smaller remnants of the visual cortex there is some amnesia for the discrimination, but it can quickly be effaced by relearning so long as a very small part of the area is left. Thus it appears that the majority of the visual area is not necessary for the retention of a habit that was learned while the entire area was functioning. The small part, then, is equipotential with the whole.

Equipotentiality, likewise, characterizes the function of the striate area in pattern vision. Memory for simple visual patterns is not disturbed by destroying up to 90 per cent of the striate areas so long as a small part of the projection area of the binocular visual field is undamaged. Thus, although the memory for such patterns is localized in the striate area and does not remain without it, yet it is not localized in any particular part of the area.

Similar facts are demonstrable in other cortical areas. Conditioning to tones, although abolished by complete lesions of the auditory areas, remains unimpaired if a small part of the area is intact (Girden). In the experiments upon problem solving and its dependence upon the prefrontal areas, it was found that the complete removal of the area upon one side did not impair problem solving whereas bilateral removal does (Jacobsen).

Equipotential Cortical Units.—In the section that follows, theories as to how equipotentiality may be explained will be considered. Here, however, we may go on to inquire about its properties and its relation to various psychological functions. One interesting problem, for example, is the size of the units of equipotentiality (*unit* meaning the proportion of a system normally concerned in a function) necessary to continue subserving that function without impairment.

The size of the equipotential units, it appears, varies with both the neural system and the types of psychological functions involved. In the visual discrimination of brightness and of form, for example, the unit is less than 10 per cent of the size of the visual cortex. In somesthesis, however, almost any damage to the primary or secondary projection areas causes some amnesia, although a learned discrimination can be carried out when there has been appreciable damage to the areas. The size of the equipotential unit, relative to the total cortex involved, appears, nevertheless, to be larger than it is in simple visual learning. A similar situation obtains with the frontal areas, concerned in complex problem solving, for although one whole area on one side can be removed without deficit, invasion of the other tends to show up in performance. Thus equipotential units may be of different size in different functional systems.

Probably more important than the neural system is the relation of size of the equipotential unit to the psychological functions involved. This can be illustrated in vision in two ways. First is the fact that complex visual learning involves larger equipotential units than simple visual learning. The rat's memory or ability to learn the discrimination of an upright F from an inverted F, it will be remembered, can be disturbed by lesions outside the visual cortex, as well by injuries within it (Kirk), whereas simple discriminations depend only upon the striate area. Even within the striate area, the equipotential unit is larger in more complex visual discriminations than in the simpler ones, as can be shown by the amount of damage to the area necessary to destroy the discriminations or make them impossible to relearn. In the somesthetic areas, also, it will be remembered, the capacity for complex discriminations of the forms of objects perceived stereognostically is disturbed by smaller lesions than those necessary to interfere with the simple discrimination of weights.

Another experiment illustrates the relation of equipotentiality to the complexity of the problem to be learned or remembered (Lashley). Normal rats were trained to discriminate the largest of *three* circles— a problem that requires more training than does the discrimination of the size of *two* circles. Following destruction of the larger part of the striate area, the ability to avoid the smallest circle was retained, but the two larger circles could no longer be distinguished; nor could this ability be regained by additional training. If, on the other hand, such an animal was preoperatively trained in the opposite way—*i.e.*, was taught to choose the smaller circle—after operation they would eliminate the largest circle and confuse the two smaller ones. It is to be concluded, therefore, that in complex psychological functions the cortex is less equipotential than it is in the simpler functions, or putting it another way, equipotential units are larger in the first than in the second instance.

One final point should be mentioned. The less equipotentiality found in a cortical area—*i.e.*, the larger the equipotential units—the more a quantitative relation holds between the amount of damage to the area and the impairment of psychological functions subserved by the area. In the visual discrimination of simple figures, for example, there is almost an all-or-none law holding between striate lesion and memory for the discrimination because only a small area needs to be intact for memory to remain. In somesthesis, however, or in more complex visual discriminations, the quantity of damage done is related more directly to the amount of impairment of functions. In view of what was said above, therefore, one can expect very complex functions to depend quantitatively upon the amount of intact area concerned in these functions, and this expectation has, in general, been upheld by the results.

THEORIES OF THE NEURAL BASIS OF LEARNING

In this closing section we turn to the general problem of what changes in the nervous system underlie, and are responsible for, learning. We shall not be concerned here with what parts of the nervous system are involved in learning, for that has been the subject of the preceding pages. We want to know *what* happens, rather than *where* it happens.

There are, unfortunately, no experimental answers to this question. No one has directly observed any changes in the brain which can seriously be ascribed to learning. We are consequently limited to the theories that have been proposed, but we can see what they have to say and consider in each case how plausible they may be.

Levels of Discourse.—For many years it was customary for neurophysiologists to distinguish the properties of the synaptic nervous system from those of nerve trunks. Inhibition, after-discharge, facilitation, recruitment, and other phenomena had been seen in the reflex but not in bundles of peripheral nerve fibers. It was tentatively accepted that such properties must be generated at the synaptic junctures of nerve fibers, but the quest never ended for phenomena in the individual nerve fiber which might help or completely explain these so-called synaptic phenomena. The studies of recent years, many of which were mentioned in the earlier chapters of this book, finally rewarded this hope, and now it is possible to understand the general physiology of the nervous system, to a very considerable degree, in terms of individual neurons.

Many students concerned with the physiological basis of learning have followed in the footsteps of the neurophysiologists. Although learning is seen in the functioning of the nervous system as a whole or nearly so, it has been their hope that learning would be explicable if enough were known about individual neurons and their connections. Up to now they have not had the success that has come to neurophysiologists. Indeed, as we shall see, some have given up the hope and come to believe that learning must be the outcome of properties generated by neurons in the mass (Lashley); a few seem to feel that the fact of the nervous system's being an assemblage of neurons is more or less irrelevant to perception and learning (Köhler).

So we have today two types of neurophysiological theories of learning, one considering individual neurons and another disregarding them and stepping to a higher level of discourse. These two levels of theory have so far gone without names, but the differences between them are perhaps best indicated by the terms *molecular* and *molar*, used in the same general sense as they are in chemistry, *i.e.*, with respect to individual units and masses of such units, respectively.

'Molecular' Theories.—In addition to the fact that they consider what happens in neurons in learning, these theories have another important characteristic in common: they rest on the premise that learning is the laying down of new pathways in the nervous system in the sense that connections are made in a telephone exchange. They are, therefore, *connectionistic.* We shall see, on the other hand, that the molar theories may or may not be connectionistic.

Neurobiotaxis.—The theory of neurobiotaxis has previously been mentioned (p. 32) as applying to the embryonic development of the nervous system. In that context, it makes use of the fact that the growing nervous system exhibits gradients of metabolism and especially of electrical potential; it also assumes that electrical gradients exert an effect upon the direction of growth of nerve fibers, the net outcome of which is that neurons grow in the direction from which the stimulation comes and, consequently, make synapses with the cells generating the stimulation.

It is only a short step to apply this same theory to learning. An organism learns, of course, only when it is subject to stimulation with the consequent electrical activity of certain nerve cells. These cells, therefore, can serve to guide the growth of other nerve cells to them, thereby improving the synaptic relations between them and bringing about better synaptic transmission. This, in brief, is the basic notion of the neurobiotactic theory of the formation of connections in learning. A formal statement of the theory has been given by Holt as follows: "Dendrites grow towards an active neurone or nerve bundle provided that the neurone from which the dendrite grows and the neurone towards which it grows are in excitation simultaneously or in close succession" (Holt, p. 26–27). This theory, it may be remarked, appears to be as capable of application to learning as it is to embryonic development. The reader will recall, however, that there is some doubt about how well it applies to embryonic development (Weiss), and until this question is settled, the value of neurobiotaxis as an explanation of learning must also remain in doubt.

Synaptic Resistance.—Merely being aware of the fact that a synapse is a break or gap between nerve cells is enough to make us suppose that it is a point where 'transmission' of nervous impulses is most difficult and thus meets the greatest resistance. So it was observed in the early days of nerve physiology, and the most recent findings (*cf.* Gasser) fully confirm such a conception of synaptic resistance. When considered with respect to learning, it might easily be supposed that in learning synaptic resistances are lessened so that impulses are transmitted over synapses that were formerly blocked. Such a reduction in synaptic resistances would readily give us the new connections needed to explain learning (Fig. 168).

A synaptic-resistance theory of learning, it is to be noted, is not necessarily an alternative to such a theory as that of neurobiotaxis, but may be complementary to it. The neurobiotactic notion assumes implicitly that the farther apart two nerve endings are, the more difficult

is 'transmission' from one to the other, and by supposing that lessening
the distance improves transmission it assumes essentially that 'resistance'
is lowered.   The synaptic-resistance theory, on the other hand, does not
necessarily require neurobiotaxis.   Some have suggested that the frequent
passage of an impulse over a synapse, as can be assumed in learning,

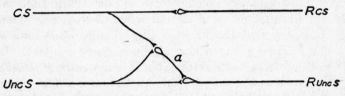

FIG. 168.—Diagram of theory to account for conditioning in terms of alterations of
synaptic threshold.   Before conditioning, it is assumed, impulses from *CS* can not excite *a*,
but with impulses arriving at *a* simultaneously with impulses from *Unc S*, the excitability
of *a* increases so that eventually impulses from *CS* alone can excite *a* and thus the unconditioned response, *R Unc S*.   (*From E. Hilgard and D. Marquis.   Conditioning and learning,
p. 329.   New York: Appleton Century, 1940.   By permission of the publishers.*)

causes chemical changes in the synaptic space which allow an impulse to
'cross' more easily.

Fiber Conductance.—A theory proposed before the all-or-none law
was established was that the frequent passage of an impulse over a fiber
increased its conductivity and thus the 'chances' of an impulse traveling
a route without interruption.   This theory, it is easy to see, is parallel

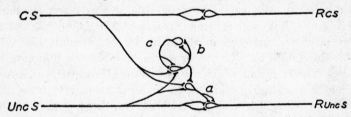

FIG. 169.—Diagram of theory to account for conditioning (learning) in terms of closed
chains of neurons.   Synaptic summation is assumed to be necessary for the excitation of
neurons *a*, *b*, and *c*, so that before learning, *CS* alone cannot excite *a* or the unconditioned
response.   By paired activity in *CS* and *Unc S*, however, the revereberatory circuit *b-c* can
be activated by summation.   The revereberatory activity can, in turn, summate with
impulses coming directly from *CS* to excite *a* and thus the unconditioned response, *R Unc S*.
(*From E. Hilgard and D. Marquis.   Conditioning and learning, p. 331.   New York: Appleton-Century, 1940.   By permission of the publishers.*)

to the synaptic resistance theory, differing from it only in that the change
in resistance occurs within the fiber rather than at the synapse.   Although
its original statement has been discredited by the all-or-none law, it is
not altogether implausible.   The implication of modern neurophysiology,
it will be recalled, is that nerve fibers divide into fibrils in the region of the
synapse, thereby delivering smaller impulses to the synapses than are
found in the fibers.   If, in any way, it should happen that the size of these
fibrils could be increased by use, fiber conductance—and indeed synaptic

resistance—would in a very real sense be changed, since the impulses stimulating across the synapse would be larger and more effective.

Reverberation.—Another suggestion is that learning results from residual excitation outlasting the learning situation (Fig. 169). This theory makes use of the recurrent or reverberatory nerve circuit (p. 64) which has been adequately demonstrated to exist and to take an important part in the production of several reflex phenomena. The theory requires, however, that the reverberatory circuit, when once set into motion, never ceases going so long as the memory is intact. It is not possible to disprove this supposition, but it is not entirely plausible that in sleep, unconsciousness, and throughout the lifetime of an individual in which memories last there should be such uninterrupted activity of groups of neurons.

Resonance.—From time to time it has been proposed that neurons have resonant properties similar to those of the strings of a piano, *i.e.*, in some way or other there is some temporal relation between the impulses of two neurons joined in synapse which is optimal for synaptic transmission, and that in learning neurons which are initially so out of tune that there is no 'conduction' between them are brought into tune, or resonance, so that they subsequently constitute a pathway which formerly was blocked. There are several ways in which such resonance can be conceived, but to explain them would take us into a more prolonged digression than would be profitable at this point (Rashevsky). Suffice it to say that there is some experimental basis, both in the excitability cycle of neurons and in the behavior of neurons with different forms of stimulation by alternating waves, to make the notion of tuning plausible. That neurons which are out of tune, however, can have their properties so modified in learning as to bring them into tune, thereby making synaptic transmission possible between them, is purely a matter of speculation.

Thus run the so-called molecular theories of neural changes in learning. Others besides these could have been included but would have added little of value to the discussion. None of the theories is especially attractive, none has any direct experimental evidence for it, and none has been disproved. All of them, it may be said again, rest on the assumption that learning involves the establishment of new connections in the nervous system, the task of the theory being to explain how the connections are formed.

'Molar' Theories.—Theories of this class are less concerned with what kind of specific changes may occur in the nervous system in learning than they are with the construction of general models of neural activities in learning which will be broad enough to explain some of its general phenomena. Two of these theories may be called connectionistic because they assume that the changes occurring in learning are to be found in particular neurons and synapses and that thereby new pathways are formed. The second two to be mentioned, however, deny this assumption, because their proponents find it difficult to explain the phenomena of equivalence in terms of it and offer instead suggestions that learning consists, not of new *pathways*, but of new, or altered, *patterns* of neural activity.

Drainage Theory.—According to this theory (McDougall) the centers and pathways involved in learning are regarded as having properties much like those of a system of interrelated tanks and pipes filled with water. Two tanks of water, for example, may be arranged one above the other, and the pipe from which water flows out of the upper tank may connect with the pipe from the lower tank in such a way that, so long as the faucet from the higher one is closed, no water will flow from the lower one, but upon opening this faucet the passage of water through its pipe sucks water from the lower tank. On the basis of this hydrostatic analogy, the theory of drainage proposes that when impulses flow out from one center they suck or drain impulses from another center in which there is also activity, and as a result the latter comes to send nervous activity over the path to which formerly only the first led. Such a theory says nothing about the actual causes of the drainage but argues simply that it is analogous to hydrostatic drainage.

Irradiation Theory.—Pavlov, the pioneer student of the conditioned reflex, is the author of an irradiation theory of the neural processes in learning. Conditioning, according to him, takes place exclusively in the cortex, but this assumption need not be accepted in order to hold to other aspects of his theory. These are as follows: Excitations arising from the conditioned and unconditioned stimuli proceed to their respective places of projection in the cerebral cortex. Then they irradiate, like the spokes of a wheel, from their points of arrival in the cortex, diminishing in intensity as they spread. The excitations initiated by the conditioned stimulus are the weaker of the two groups; they flow toward, or are drawn toward, the center of stronger excitation, *i.e.*, the place where excitations from the unconditioned stimulus are arriving. Then, as a consequence of the repeated presentation of the two stimuli, a path is worn from the conditioned-stimulus center to the unconditioned-stimulus center, and the conditioned stimulus comes, thereby, to bring about the same neural effects as the unconditioned stimulus.

Gradient Theory.—Lashley, in considering the problem of arriving at a satisfactory molar theory of learning, lays great stress on the phenomena of equivalence of stimuli, structure, and response. He points out that Pavlov's theory is essentially a connectionistic theory in that it holds learning to take place in particular places in the cortex (nervous system). Such a theory, he argues, cannot account for equivalence of structure. Thus, if the discrimination of patterns requires specific localized changes in the visual cortex, how can it be that a very large part, and yet no particular part, of the visual cortex may be removed without impairment of the discrimination? Equipotentiality, he feels, cannot be explained if learning is merely the laying down of new pathways.

As alternatives to connectionistic theory, Lashley has suggested two possible ways in which learning might occur, without the formation of connections and with equivalence accounted for. The first, a gradient theory, is applicable to the generalization (equivalence) one finds in

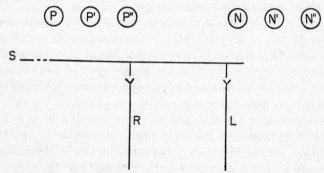

FIG. 170.—Diagram to illustrate neural processes in learning in terms of gradients. *P* and *N* are positive and negative stimuli, respectively, to which an animal has been trained. *P'* and *P''* are equivalent positive stimuli, and *N'* and *N''* equivalent negative stimuli. The stimuli, *P* and *N*, are assumed to set up a potential difference or polarization gradient along the line *S*, and the final common paths *R* or *L*, alternative responses, become conditioned to the high or low end of this polarization gradient. Conditioning, then, is in terms of gradients of activity rather than in terms of particular cells activated. (*After K. S. Lashley. Brain mechanisms and intelligence, p.* 169. *Chicago: University of Chicago Press,* 1929. *By permission of the publishers.*)

brightness discrimination, in which a rat, for example, learns to respond, not to a circle of particular size, but to the larger (or smaller) of two circles though their actual sizes are varied. The point of the theory is simply made (Fig. 170); in learning, a response comes to be attached to the gradient of differences between two stimuli, the direction of difference in neural activities being the determining feature of the response. To bolster this suggestion he cites the work of Child in embryology which indicates that gradients of neural activity (physiological gradients, p. 31) are capable of governing somewhat the growth of neurons and thus the structure and functioning of the nervous system.

Pattern Theory.—The importance of physiological gradients in embryonic development has come into question in recent years, accompanied by a dissatisfaction with the applicability of a gradient theory to learning. Lashley, therefore, offers a conception which is made possible and plausible by the latest information concerning cortical neural structures and functions.

Because the best studies of cortical structure have failed to show the existence of any appreciably long association fibers, he adopts the premise that impulses spread across the cortex by means of very short internuncial fibers. These short internuncials serve as a continuous pathway over which impulses may spread like a ripple on the surface of water. The impulses, moreover, will really move in such ripples or waves because, we have reason to believe, impulses in internuncials are rather well synchronized (p. 67), and in the wake of each wave there must be a period of inactivity—the trough of the wave—by virtue of the refractory periods of the neurons involved.

The next point is an important one: Series of waves will spread over the cortex in fronts and directions depending upon the pattern of the exciting stimulus; the series of waves proceeding from different points and different directions will meet and form interference patterns—*i.e.*, one wave will come to a point where another has just been, consequently find that point refractory, and be unable to pass it. The effect will be a very complicated pattern of activity on the cortex, similar to that seen in a pool of water when one has initiated waves simultaneously in different parts, or like the pattern of sound obtained in a room by reflection of sound waves from walls coming back and meeting each other. Such interference patterns will depend in character, not upon the particular points from which activity was initiated in the cortex, but rather upon the *form* of the excitations in the receptive area. If these patterns are constant, some cells somewhere in the cortex will be excited with one form, whereas other cells will always be excited with some other form. The association of their activity with particular responses can then be learned in a simple connectionistic way, which may be explicable by one or another of the 'molecular' theories proposed above.

This, briefly, is Lashley's suggestion for a theory of the neural processes concerned in learning, a theory that will account for equivalence of stimuli and response as well as for equipotentiality. He does not go into the question of the nature of the changes constituting learning, but far more important than this is the success of the theory in dealing with equivalence, which is of more immediate relevance to physiological psychology than what physical or chemical change may occur at a synapse.

CHAPTER XXV

MEMORY IN MAN

The study of learning and memory in man, as it depends upon physiological events, is a rather different affair than it is in animals, because human beings cannot be treated under the same controlled experimental conditions as can animals. In place of the controlled surgery possible in animals, we must rely upon the accidents of nature, which, in the form of gunshot wounds, tumors, infections, and the like, produce uncontrolled and fortuitous damage to the nervous system. Because this damage seldom involves particular functional areas of the cortex but invades part of this or that area, we are unable to correlate psychological changes with any particular neural structures. Indeed, because human brains are not always obtained in connection with our studies, we often do not know very accurately what parts have been damaged.

Then, on the psychological side, there is the fact that the previous histories of patients suffering from such damage are uncontrolled and, at best, very incompletely known. Sometimes various clinical tests of intelligence and of personality can be administered before and after neurological damage. One can also note prominent disorders of memory or abnormalities of behavior seldom seen in normal individuals, and this is of value. But we never know exactly how habits have been learned, and the variation in the experiences of different individuals is so great as to make comparison difficult.

The consequence of these difficulties is that our information on man concerning neural functions involved in memory and adaptive behavior above the level of reflexes is much less satisfactory than that obtained from animals. There is only a superficial classification of memory disorders with considerable disagreement both about the nature of defects following cerebral damage and the relation of the defects to different parts of the cerebral cortex. There is nothing to do, however, but make the best of it and to survey the material as it stands at present, even though much of it is tentative.

CLASSIFICATION OF MEMORY DISORDERS

A great variety of terms has been employed in an attempt to describe and denote the kinds of memory losses that occur in human patients suffering from cortical injuries. These terms, unfortunately, have not always been used in the same way, and it is necessary, therefore, to be somewhat arbitrary if one is to use a consistent terminology. That which is presented here represents as nearly as possible the most common usage.

Losses of memory can be classified according to two general criteria: whether they are sensory or motor and whether they concern linguistic or nonlinguistic functions. Those which have to do with language are called *aphasias*. They may be termed sensory aphasias, if they consist of the inability to appreciate spoken or written language, or motor aphasias, if the memory loss is of the ability to speak or write language. Sensory forms of nonlinguistic disorders are known as *agnosias*, whereas motor forms of these difficulties are called *apraxias*. Thus can we recognize four main classes of memory disorders. For the purposes of a more specific analysis of them, however, it is useful to subdivide these main classes further. Doing this gives us the following outline of memory disorders (see Weisenberg and McBride):

Sensory Aphasia
    Auditory aphasia (word deafness): difficulty in understanding the meaning of words and language as heard.
    Visual aphasia (word blindness, alexia): disturbances of the perception of the meaning of language as read.
Motor Aphasia
    Manual aphasia (agraphia): difficulty in writing language.
    Speech aphasia (word muteness): inability to express language vocally or to think in terms of it. Head distinguishes four types of speech aphasia:
        Verbal: "defective power of forming words, whether for external or internal use."
        Syntactical: "lack of that perfect balance and rhythm necessary to make the sounds uttered easily comprehensible." Articles and prepositions binding words together tend to be dropped or slurred.
        Nominal: inability to use words as names and failure to appreciate the nominal character of words.
        Semantic: disturbances of the connected sequence of verbal or written expression.
Agnosia: disturbances in the perception of the significance of sensory stimuli or defects of imagination.
    Astereognosis: "difficulty in the recognition of objects or forms by touch."
    Auditory agnosia: "psychic deafness for noises and music deafness" (sensory amusia).
    Visual agnosia: disorders of visual recognition of
        1. Objects or pictures.
        2. Color—not color blindness or color defect but "difficulty in understanding colors as qualities of objects, a faulty color concept, and an inability to evoke color images."
        3. Visual cues orienting the person in space.

Apraxia: disturbances of the memory of movements

  Limbkinetic: The patient "appreciates the nature of the movement but cannot carry it out with ordinary skill." It is thought to be a loss of innervatory memories for complex forms of movement.

  Ideokinetic: a disorder attributed to a break between the kinesthetic processes and others of the brain; consists of loss of memory of how to make movements.

  Ideational: faulty conception of the movement as a whole. The patient, for example, is unable to strike a match.

  Constructive: "In typical cases the patient experiences difficulty in laying out sticks to copy a given design, in building with blocks, in drawing" and so on.

THE LOCALIZATION OF MEMORY FUNCTIONS

Such an outline as that given above indicates the types of memory loss that may follow cortical injury and serves as a descriptive device for

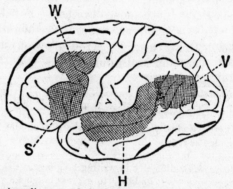

Fig. 171.—Side-view diagram of the human brain showing supposed localization of language centers of the cortex. *W*, area whose injury is said to give amnesia for writing words (agraphia); *S*, area for spoken words (aphasia); *V*, area for recognition of printed words(word blindness); *H*, recognition of spoken words (word deafness). Localization is probably not so definite as the diagram would indicate but tends to focus on these areas. (*After Donaldson. From W. H. Howell. Textbook of physiology, p. 233. Philadelphia: Saunders, 1937. By permission of the publishers.*)

specifying, more objectively than is possible in uncontrolled verbal description, the particular losses of any patient. There is the question, however, of whether such different types of aphasia are independent of each other and related to different cortical areas. Is there, in a word, localization of different kinds of memories?

This problem has engaged the attention of neurologists and clinicians for years. Some have argued for very strict localization of such functions (Henschen; Kleist; see Fig. 171). Others believe in only a limited localization at most. This view has usually taken the form that one memory function may depend more upon one area than another but that almost any memory function involves many aspects of the activity of the brain as a whole (Head). A more extreme view approaches the position that there is no localization at all in the cerebral cortex (Goldstein) except for the primary sensory and motor areas and these are more concerned with the handling of sensory stimulation and response, respectively, than with the intervening and higher order memory functions.

Probably the best basis for decision between these various views is the recent work of Weisenberg and McBride who studied a series of cases extensively both in respect of the kind of cortical damage done and in respect of losses of memory. They found in their observations little reason to believe in pure memory defects as given in the outline above, but believe the safest classification of memory disorders as they actually occur in patients is in the following four categories: *receptive, expressive, receptive-expressive,* and *amnesic aphasia.* The first two denote what the terms suggest, *viz.,* disturbances of sensory and motor memory functions, respectively, and the third involves the mixture of the two. From an analytical point of view the fourth, amnesic aphasia, is a type of expressive memory disorder, involving the inability to recall, as distinct from the inability to recognize, the names of objects. It is given a place of its own in the classification, however, because it appears in pure form without being accompanied by other types of receptive or expressive defects.

Receptive Disorders.—Many of the older workers in this field believed that there were special association areas for sensory functions located in the vicinity of the primary sensory areas. The areas to which most attention was given were the so-called visual and auditory psychic areas. These areas, also called the visual and auditory parareceptive areas, lie in the parietal and occipital lobes, respectively, immediately adjacent to the primary auditory and visual areas. It was held that damage in one of these areas would present a pure 'associative' defect of word blindness or word deafness as the case might be. Henschen, who was one of the most extreme of the 'localizers,' examined 700 cases of cerebral damage and concluded that there was a discrete localization of visual and auditory language (symbolic) functions in the respective visual and auditory parareceptive areas. Others have supported a similar conclusion.

Many of the earlier conclusions, however, were based upon inadequate psychological examinations of the patients, with the result that all the aspects of the disorder often were not revealed. In the recent studies of Weisenberg and McBride this matter was to a large extent remedied and more conservative conclusions were the consequence. From their work, it appears that cases of pure word blindness and pure word deafness probably do not exist. Usually, if there is one kind of disorder, there is also the other in some degree. One type of disorder, however, may be much more serious than the other, and one type may characterize a patient more than another, even though symptoms of other receptive disorders may be present.

There is, moreover, a considerable degree of functional localization for different receptive disorders. Illustrating this fact well are cases of patients in whom both a knowledge of the nature of the lesions and psychological testing procedures were relatively adequate. In one (German and Fox), the lesion was in the occipital area. The patient was very much affected in visual recognition. She could not, for example, name an orange when presented to her visually but could do it when she was allowed to smell it. She did not have, on the other hand, difficulties of this sort with auditory stimuli. The ringing of a bell, for example, was readily recognized, whereas the sight of it did not give recognition. In the second case (Fox and German), defects appeared in the interpretation and recognition of auditory events. Verbal commands were not well understood when presented orally but could be readily interpreted when presented in writing. Thus visual agnosia was related to occipital injury and auditory agnosia to temporal-lobe damage.

This is not the whole story, for when somewhat more complex receptive memory functions are examined than those illustrated above, it turns out that there is not so much localization of function. In the last case cited above, for example, although there was a distinct difference in the amount to which visual and auditory agnosias were in evidence, there was considerably less distinction to be made between visual and auditory aphasia. This patient found that in listening to or reading language he could follow it successfully for only a short time and then would "begin to miss the meaning of some words, and the mistakes would multiply rapidly. Finally . . . his 'mind became so full of words' that he . . . was compelled to stop" (Fox and German).

Weisenberg and McBride, whose observations are based upon more cases but who had less satisfactory knowledge of their lesions, also conclude that the more complex aspects of receptive aphasia are not very well localized. From an analysis of the primary motor and sensory symptoms displayed by patients and the degree to which they recovered from these symptoms, they had a reasonable knowledge as to what areas were involved and to what extent. They find no clear-cut separation of visual and auditory receptive aphasias and think that there is no very specific localization of damage in receptive aphasia. It appears to them "that in the receptive cases the anterior or motor part of the brain is predominantly implicated but less severely than in the expressive group, and that the posterior part of the brain, while considerably less involved than the anterior, is more likely to be diseased than in the expressive cases" (p. 449).

Expressive Disorders.—A similar situation appears to obtain in the case of the localization of the motor memory functions. Here, too, there is a difference between simpler and more complex memories, the level of complexity in general being defined in terms of the extent to which the memories are believed to be symbolic (see next chapter). Head, for example, distinguishes between *reactive* and *propositional* speech. Reactive or emotional speech tends to be ejaculatory or automatic, representing only some vague feeling of the patient of which the reactive speech is a part. Examples of this type are "Oh! dear me," "Yes," and "Hello." Propositional speech, on the other hand, represents definite objects or actions, as well as relations between them, imagined by the speaker and guiding his speech. This, therefore, involves symbolic processes to a greater extent than reactive speech.

Cerebral Dominance.—One statement concerning the localization of these two varieties of linguistic memory is seldom contested. It is that speech functions in general, and propositional speech in particular, are localized in the dominant hemisphere (see p. 340)—in most individuals this is the left hemisphere—but that reactive speech can be mediated by the nondominant hemisphere. Supporting this belief is the fact that in cases in which there was complete or nearly complete extirpation of one hemisphere (the right) no serious disturbances of language functions followed (Dandy; Gardner), whereas in another case in which the removal of the left hemisphere was carried out, all but elementary reactive speech was abolished (see Weisenberg and McBride). Thus most aspects of speech are localized within one hemisphere, but reactive speech is possible in its absence.

Worth noting in passing is the fact that when the dominant hemisphere is so badly damaged as to abolish all but the simplest speech a great deal of language can be restored through reeducation. It is supposed that under these circumstances the other hemisphere, which normally has little to do with speech, comes into play and takes over the functions lost with the dominant hemisphere.

Localization.—There is the further question of the extent to which the propositional speech functions, which involve symbolic processes, are localized in the dominant hemisphere. The answer to this question seems to hinge partly upon distinguishing further the complexity of different linguistic memories. Head conceives the memories represented by the nominal and semantic aphasia (see above) to involve processes of a higher order—presumably more imaginal activity—than those which are affected in verbal and syntactical aphasias. This being the case, one expects the nominal and semantic memories to be more easily disturbed than the verbal and syntactical. Clinical observations tend to support this expectation.

Concerning the locus of damage in instances of these different varieties of aphasia, Weisenberg and McBride make the conservative statement that "in expressive cases from the clinical standpoint, in the great majority, the lesion is preponderantly in the motor or anterior part of the brain, with less implication of the posterior part." Their data, however, did not allow them to determine accurately the limits of damage in the cortex. The consensus of clinical opinion, beginning with the famous case of Broca (1861), is that speech aphasias tend to center around a region in the frontal lobe located ventrolaterally at the foot of the premotor and motor areas. Few claim that this region is the only region having to do with speech memory, but it deserves the status of a focal area for such memory. Head, who has presented the classic observations on aphasia, agrees essentially with this point of view.

Head goes on, however, to point out that nominal and semantic speech, which he regards as more complex, are not dependent upon this area so much as they are upon another area, consisting of the angular and supramarginal gyri in the region of juncture of the parietal, temporal, and occipital lobes (see Fig. 26). He does not propose any strict localization of these types of memory, but believes it to focalize upon this area. Thus, in summarizing, we may state that the more elementary types of speech asphasia center upon Broca's area and that the more highly evolved aspects of linguistic memory, represented in the nominal and semantic aphasias, are closely related to the angular and supramarginal gyri.

The receptive-expressive type of aphasia distinguished by Weisenberg and McBride needs no separate discussion because it simply denotes cases in which the receptive and expressive memory disorders are combined in the same patients, presumably because of the position and severity of the lesions producing it.

Amnesic Aphasia.—Despite the fact that the only other clear types of memory disorder which Weisenberg and McBride could discover were the receptive, expressive, and their combinations, they were able to give to amnesic aphasia the status of a clear-cut and independent type of disorder of memory. Amnesic aphasia has also been recognized and described by most modern workers who have been equipped with adequate means of testing patients (Harlow). Its chief feature is that the individual loses the capacity to recall the name of an object while retaining perfect recognition of the name when it is given to him. It is indeed remarkable that although there may be really grave disturbances of recall memory for names of objects the patient almost always identifies the correct word if he produces it accidentally himself, or if he hears or sees it. Once he has found it, the patient repeats the word with satisfaction, but soon forgets it and if asked to name the object a few minutes afterward, he is again unable to do so and must be prompted again. The disturbance may consist of inability to recall the name of objects, conditions, qualities, or other aspects of a situation.

It may be noted that amnesic aphasia is about the same type of disorder as is indicated by Head's nominal speech aphasia, and Head, as pointed out above, believed this type of aphasia to concern the highest and most delicate of memory functions. Contained in this conception of amnesic aphasia is the suggestion as to why it is found in relatively pure form, *viz.*, that it represents the most delicate type of memory and is therefore the first to be disturbed when there is any cortical injury. When, consequently, cerebral damage is more severe and involves less complex forms of memory, the symptoms of amnesic aphasia will be blended with the other varieties which make up the general category of receptive aphasias.

Supporting the notion of amnesic aphasia as involving the most complex of memory functions is the fact that it is produced by relatively mild unlocalized damage to the cortex. Indeed, it seems always to be associated with lesions that are rather extensive in locus but not particularly severe. Weisenberg and McBride, for example, present the case of a boy who showed a clear-cut amnesic aphasia which, upon physiological examination, appeared to be associated with a mild infection of the temporal lobe of sufficient severity to interfere with its function but not severe enough to have done any appreciable destruction. The infection was then drained and cleared up. Upon subsequent examination, the amnesic aphasia had cleared up completely.

Categorical Behavior.—Although amnesic aphasia is generally considered to be an inability to recall the names of objects as well as more abstract conditions or qualities, a somewhat different description of it, presented by Goldstein, deserves our consideration. To Goldstein, the chief feature of amnesic aphasia is that the patient has lost, or had impaired, his categorical behavior. This he defines as the ability to recognize an object as a member of a class according to some common property defining that class; or, to put it another way, the ability to abstract or generalize some property or quality of an object and to give the proper name to it. A patient, for example, who shows a loss of categorical behavior may not be able to name a "book" although he may recognize what is done with it and prove it by manipulating and reading the book when it is handed to him. He has apparently lost the ability to name the class of objects of which the particular book is a member. To illustrate further, if told that a book is a book, the patient may thereafter be able to use the name with the particular book to which the symbol has been attached but not to recognize that the name also goes along with other books, *i.e.*, the class of books.

Several investigators disagree with Goldstein's identification of categorical behavior (or abstractive behavior) with amnesic aphasia, but he probably has a point in emphasizing that abstraction is one of the first processes to be interfered with in cortical damage. In support of this view one can argue that abstraction must involve, at least where the relation of language to objects is concerned, the combination of many "images" from past experience and may be expected, therefore, to be most fragile in the event of cerebral injury. At any rate, Goldstein has much evidence from his extensive observation of human patients that the order of loss of memory functions begins with categorical (abstractive) capacities and proceeds toward the more primitive and 'concrete'—as he calls them—levels of responses.

Nonlinguistic Functions.—As was stated before, memories related to language appear to be localized predominantly in one dominant hemisphere, but nonlanguage functions are not. Proof of this fact comes from a study by Weisenberg and McBride of 22 cases in which lesions were restricted to the right (nondominant) hemisphere. In none of them was there any aphasia. The subjects were given several tests of arithmetic and nonlinguistic ability and were compared with control cases matched with them in respect of age and general history except that they did not suffer from lesions. They found the patients to be inferior in all the performances that they tested, particularly in arithmetic and the learning of a maze problem. The defects of these patients, therefore, were marked in nonlinguistic functions but insignificant in the area of linguistic memory. From this study, Weisenberg and McBride concluded that, although linguistic functions are confined primarily to the dominant hemisphere, nonlinguistic memories are not.

In addition, it is worth noting, the nonlinguistic memories are also subserved by the dominant hemisphere concerned in language. Weisenberg and McBride almost always found lesions of the dominant hemisphere producing aphasia also to be accompanied by some decrement in nonlinguistic performance tests. It is not a case, therefore, of language's being dependent upon one hemisphere and other memories on the other hemisphere, but one in which the nonlinguistic memories are mediated by both hemispheres. So far as damage to the dominant hemisphere is concerned, consequently, one cannot expect to see any clear separation of linguistic and nonlinguistic functions.

The Body Image.—There is a type of agnosia that is particularly interesting in relation to questions about the nature of consciousness and self-awareness in man. This is called *autotopognosia* (Pick) or *body-image agnosia* (Shilder), and it refers to an inability of an individual to recognize parts of the body and their usefulness to the individual. A patient, when asked to show his hands, may hunt frantically for them upon the table; or he may be quite unable to imitate the movements of others. Other parts of the body besides the fingers or hands may be affected, of course, and a larger or smaller segment of the body may be implicated. It is important to realize, however, that voluntary paralyses or disturbances of movement are not necessarily related in any way to this type of disorder.

Surveying several of the cases reported in the literature, Schilder has formulated several conclusions about the physiological basis of the disorder. A body image serves the normal individual as a frame of reference for many acts that he makes. It depends, he holds, upon the cortical excitations arriving from various sense organs of the body, achieving in the cortex an organized and unified character. The unity is given to the body image by the angular and supramarginal gyri of the cortex. This area (Brodmann's 39 and 40) is the 'association' area previously mentioned as a focal area for the more complex types of linguistic memory; it lies in the parieto-temporo-occipital region and includes the parareceptive areas of the visual and auditory systems as well as part of the 'association' areas of the somesthetic system (see Fig. 26). The body image, according to Schilder, cannot be divorced from other psychological functions; yet it must be somewhat independent of them, for disturbances of the body image may be very prominent in patients with little or no aphasia or impairment of other nonlinguistic functions.

FACTORS IN MEMORY DEFICIT

Our purpose, of course, in this part of our study is to formulate an adequate picture of the cerebral mechanisms by which memories are formed and function in man. Toward that end we considered in the last section the problem of whether memories are localized in different cortical areas. The answer which we were able to give was equivocal; the kind of memory lost by cerebral damage is related in some measure to the locus of injury, but such a relation is hardly more than a statistical tendency; it is obvious, therefore, that we must look to factors and concepts other than 'localization' for an understanding of the mechanisms of memory.

Levels of Organization of Memory.—One of the reasons why we may not have obtained better localization of memory functions in man is that we may not know what to expect to be localized. Classifications of aphasia, and of memory in general, have been formulated and compared with the positions of lesions, but there is no guarantee that such classifications correspond to the organization of memory functions in the brain. They have been based for the most part on a priori conceptions of how memories ought to be related, drawn from rather mechanical similarities of the habits or the memory situation involved. In general, little emphasis has been placed upon the kind of perceptual organizations involved in the memory.

Now, in an earlier chapter (p. 477), the argument was set forth that even in the most elementary learning situation there is an organizing process in the brain which selects certain aspects of a stimulus situation and ignores others. Thus, aspects of a memory situation apparently important to the classifier may not figure in the memory of the patient at all. Instead his cerebral damage may have obliterated, not a set of connections between stimuli and response, but rather the capacity for general types of perceptual organization, and if these were understood, the relation between locus of lesion and type of memory deficit might be better understood.

All that we can do about this possiblity at the present time is to present evidence that is available for the notion that cerebral injuries affect the level of perceptual organization of which the subject is capable rather than any specific habit. To do that we must make use of material from animal subjects as well as human patients.

First is an experiment by Lashley in which the following results were obtained: Normal rats learned to discriminate the larger of two circles in 20 trials and the largest of three circles in 60 trials. After severe lesions in the striate areas of the cortex, however, the rats could learn to take the larger of two circles in the normal number of trials, but they failed completely, after greatly extended training, to take the largest of the three circles. The line of demarcation to be drawn by cortical damage was not in terms of size discrimination, but in terms of whether the animals could perceive 'larger' or 'largest,' two levels of perceptual organization. Differences similar to this, Lashley has pointed out, exist in striking degree in the phylogenetic series and can be correlated with the evolution of the brain.

In another experiment conducted with monkeys it was found that cerebral destruction damaged no specific habits, but the general ability to make relative discriminations (Klüver). The monkeys were trained before operation to make various sensory discriminations and to react by pulling in a string attached to an appropriate box. After relatively small lesions in several different areas of the brain, the animals appeared to have a complete amnesia for all the habits, pulling in boxes at random, no matter what discrimination was asked of them. The forgetting, however, turned out to be a loss of a general perceptual organization, that of 'comparing,' for when the animals were retrained on one discrimination, they were able—thereupon and without further retraining— to perform perfectly in the other discriminations which they apparently had forgotten.

One cannot go to human material and find instances illustrating the point as well as do these animal experiments. Perhaps the best example, however, is that of amnesic aphasia. We have seen that this consists of loss in the ability to name objects and particularly of the ability to classify objects according to their similarities. It appears therefore to be a disruption of one of the highest levels of perceptual organization, and this fact is correlated with its being one of the first defects of memory to make its appearance with cortical lesions.

Recovery of Functions.—Of considerable importance in understanding cortical functions in memory are the phenomena of recovery. These appear in almost every case of amnesia produced by cerebral damage, no matter how severe the lesion may be and no matter what its psychological effects. Even in the paralysis of voluntary movement which accompanies lesions of the motor area or pyramidal tract there can be some recovery of movement through retraining. In more complex psychological functions, there may also be striking recoveries.

Diaschisis.—Most of the time, the recovery of functions is slow and is clearly associated with relearning, but in some cases, several weeks or months after the injury has been sustained, memories which had been lost suddenly reappear. Such sudden recoveries, coming so long after injury, cannot be ascribed to general physiological shock or to the return of health in nerve cells affected, but not killed, by the lesion. To account for such cases of recovery, von Monakow many years ago postulated the operation of diaschisis. By this he meant that, in an injury affecting one region, impulses which go to other regions and facilitate them are cut off, thereby producing losses of memory dependent upon the regions. At some subsequent time, he supposed, the facilitating effects, thus cut off, were restored and with them the memories related to the regions involved. He did not state just how and for what reason, however, the facilitation lost through injury was brought back into play.

Careful scrutiny of cases supposedly coming under the heading of diaschisis, Lashley holds, shows that some retraining is involved. Sometimes the retraining is aided by intense excitement which facilitates the habit or memory, but the recovered function always seems to be practiced before it is recovered and does not occur spontaneously. It is probable, on the other hand, that in some cases an apparent spontaneous recovery is due to the fact that some general perceptual organization has been destroyed and by relearning some habit in which it is involved, others dependent upon the same organization also appear. A good example of this type is that cited above in which monkeys showing deficit in all comparison behavior had it restored when they practiced one instance of it.

Vicarious Functioning.—Several instances were seen in the animal studies of the loss of memory through operative injury followed by recovery when ample opportunity for relearning was given. The same phenomenon occurs in human individuals; indeed, it is quite the rule where lesions are of limited size and severity. Wherever it occurs, we may state that the memory depended, at least to some extent, upon the area which was damaged but that other areas have taken over the function subserved by the first area. These areas, we might say, function vicariously for those normally concerned.

The theory of vicarious functioning was proposed nearly a hundred years ago in the first experiments of Fritsch and Hitzig (p. 10), and so many instances of it have been uncovered since that there can be little doubt of it. The question has arisen, however, as to what areas participate in such functions and to what extent different areas of the brain, and more especially the cortex, can function vicariously. Some have thought that almost any part of the brain could function vicariously for another, if only there were enough of it left to do so. The experimental facts, however, particularly those obtained with animals, indicate that vicarious functioning is limited to the parts of a system concerned with the general functions in question. Thus recovery of an individual from motor paralysis caused by damage to the pyramidal area, it has been shown, depends upon the premotor area's being left intact (Bucy and Fulton). Likewise, the ability of a rat to learn a brightness discrimination after destruction of the visual cortex depends upon the superior colliculus, which is a part of the visual system along with the striate cortex. In the case of certain problem boxes and maze learning, we do not know what areas enable the rat to relearn after its memory has been destroyed by cortical lesions, but the psychological elements of the problem are not well enough defined to let us decide what systems are primarily involved. As the evidence stands, we may believe that the recovery of memory functions lost through damage depends upon some part of the pertinent system's being preserved.

Mass.—There are, moreover, indications that the degree of recovery possible is related to the amount of the limited system that remains intact. In rats, of course, ability to relearn mazes is statistically correlated with the amount of cortex remaining, but the meaning of that fact is not very clear. For man, however, there are various clinical observations concerning only a given cortical area which give this relation. A good illustration is supplied by Lashley. In reviewing the literature on aphasia, he brought together 18 cases of individuals with lesions in the left third frontal convolution, *i.e.*, in the primary speech area. Ranking these patients with respect to the amount of damage in the speech area and the extent of recovery from aphasic difficulties following the injury, he found a negative correlation of .90; *i.e.*, individuals recovered in almost perfect proportion to the amount of functional tissue remaining intact in the area subserving the function.

This analysis of human cases is paralleled, it is to be noted, by the work from animal studies in which ability to relearn complex visual discriminations depends upon the amount of visual cortex left intact by the operation; and, as was pointed out previously, such a quantitative relation holds when, because the function in question is complex, the 'equipotential unit' is relatively large (see p. 517); otherwise, of course, with small equipotential units, one tends to find an all-or-none relation between damage and amount of possible recovery.

The Factor of Age.—In view of the intimate relation between the neural maturation of an individual and his learning ability, the way in which age is related to the effects of cortical damage upon memory and psychological functions is of especial interest. As with other topics, clinical observations concerning this factor have been recorded from time to time. Hebb has recently surveyed and evaluated these observations and, in addition, added several cases which he himself studied with the best available methods of psychological testing. The present account, therefore, relies heavily upon his findings and his notions concerning them.

The way in which age figures in the consequences of cortical injury depends upon the type of learned functions in question. If one considers simple motor functions, it appears that young individuals are much less affected by interference with the motor areas or pyramidal tracts than are adult individuals. The same has been found to be the case in almost all functions tested in animals, which have been more intensively studied in this respect than human beings. Rats with some 40 per cent of their cortex removed in infancy show practically no retardation of maze learning, whereas the same amount of damage in the adult produces considerable deficit in learning (Tsang). Similar results are obtained in pattern vision, where destruction of the striate cortex in adulthood completely destroys pattern discrimination, yet the same operation in infancy leaves, at least in some animals, residual pattern vision (Tsang).

There is no ready explanation for the advantage of the infant over the adult in these respects. Part of the effect is in the initial effect of the damage, part is in the amount of recovery from the lesion, but the fact nevertheless remains that they are less affected by the damage than adults. The possibility that there may have been regeneration of parts of the nervous system is definitely ruled out in cases where it has been considered and investigated. As alternative possibilities Lashley suggests: "It may be that there is normally a regression of the capacities of lower centers during development and that this regression is prevented by the destruction of higher centers. Or it may be that long continued training can restore not only specific habits but also can build up more general capacities" (p. 751).

Turning to more complex functions, we find, in general, that the difference in amount of impairment goes the other way: individuals who suffer cortical damage in infancy are more affected than those subject to a comparable amount of injury in adulthood. This general statement, however, must be qualified by reference to the kinds of memory defects evident in the respective cases.

The basis for these statements is to be found in extensive tests of cases of infant and adult injury carried out by Hebb. He used a standard intelligence test (Stanford-Binet) which deals with many aspects of memory and mental performance but which can be broken down roughly into verbal and nonverbal items. Individuals, tested at ten to nineteen years of age, but suffering from infant injury, showed impairment of both nonverbal and verbal functions, but, in general, verbal capacity, as measured by vocabulary tests, was the more affected. Individuals having adult cortical injuries, on the other hand, were remarkable for the fact that verbal performance was usually perfectly normal whereas nonverbal capacities were significantly depressed.

Hebb presents reasons for believing that the differences in the two groups of subjects could not be ascribed to a greater frequency of injuries in the speech area in the infant-injury group than in the adult-injury group. It is quite probable, however, that the lesions of the adult-injury group were located where they were more likely to affect non-linguistic than verbal functions, for no evidences of aphasia were to be found in them. If the injuries were in the 'dominant' hemisphere, they were not in the speech areas, and some of them were probably in the nondominant hemisphere where no linguistic defects (according to Weisenberg and McBride) could be expected.

Considering these facts, the hypothesis which comes to mind as best explaining the results is that different areas of the cerebral cortex, including perhaps the two hemispheres, are more interdependent in the development of psychological capacities than they are in the maintenance of these capacities after they have once been developed. Or more specifically, nonverbal capacities are instrumental in the development of verbal memories, but once acquired, the linguistic functions are not affected by injuries that affect the nonlinguistic functions. This is about what Hebb says, in a somewhat different way: Two factors are operative in psychological performance, one "being present intellectual power, of the kind essential to normal intellectual development; the other being the lasting changes of perceptual organization and behavior induced by the first factor during the period of development" (p. 287).

Motivation.—A factor that appears to enter into the performance of both human and animal subjects after cortical damage is a lower motivation for performing the task required. Lashley, for example, tells of a patient who had suffered serious impairment of verbal memories following operation and was being subjected to retraining. After 900 repetitions of the alphabet, he had still failed to relearn it; so he was bet several packs of cigarettes that he could not learn it within a week. After 10 trials the patient had memorized the alphabet perfectly and remembered it until his bet was collected. Other examples of patients who have relearned to use 'paralyzed' limbs only after they had been forced to use the limbs are also on record. In rats, finally, it has been shown that animals lacking the visual cortex learn a brightness discrimination just as quickly as do normals if they are rewarded with food for their successes and punished for their errors with shock, but that they are considerably retarded in their learning if punishment for the errors is omitted (Lashley).

In view of what has been said earlier about the role of central motive states in learning, it is not surprising that cerebral lesions can interfere with motivation in addition to specific memories. Indeed, the motives for many responses are themselves learned, and cortical lesions can be expected to interrupt the neural activities representing them. But even though the factor is known to operate, the extent to which it is important in effects of operations or injuries upon memory and learning capacity is a problem that deserves considerably more investigation in both human and animal subjects.

Availability of Memory.—It has been known from the beginning of the experimental study of learning that failure to give a learned response is no indication that no memory for the response is present. As Lashley has pointed out, a subject may be unable to recall a single item after he has been through a series of nonsense syllables several times, yet the subsequent number of trials required to learn it, compared with that of the totally untrained subject, shows that he has already learned something. Evidently there may be residual memory, which, though nonetheless present, is of insufficient strength to become available for use.

Many of the memory defects that follow upon cortical destruction, Lashley points out, are of this type. The rat, placed in a problem box after considerable cortical destruction, may act in precisely the same manner as one which has never been trained, but upon very brief retraining its memory may be 'refreshened' so that it performs perfectly. The aphasias of human patients, similarly, may seem complete upon first testing, but disappear rapidly after some opportunity for relearning, indicating thereby that the cortical injury simply suppressed the memory below the level of immediate availability. The memory was reduced, one might say, below threshold, but it was not extinguished.

Such a notion of availability is clearly supported both by the ordinary phenomena of learning and forgetting and by the effects of cortical destruction, but the question of why it should be altered by cerebral damage is especially interesting.

Applicable to this question is the concept of *vigilance* formulated several years ago by Head. As proposed, vigilance referred to the general physiological efficiency of the nervous system which affects all activities performed by it. Vigilance fluctuates, he suggested, with sleep and waking—being high in wakefulness and low in sleep—with the influence of drugs and anesthesia, and, most important for the present purpose, with cerebral damage, which lowers vigilance. The level of vigilance, in turn, determines the range and number of responses available in a given situation: with high vigilance, the more complex and most adaptive responses are available; with lowered vigilance only the more primitive, simpler responses can be involved.

Without using the term vigilance, Lashley has recently presented with clarity and emphasis a similar conception. A lesion he suggests, may do two things: The memories that are dependent upon the damaged area will be destroyed and no amount of retraining will reinstate them. On the other hand, the injury may lower the general excitability (vigilance) of the cortex in such a way that, without destroying memories, it may make them less available. In this case, retraining may raise the specific memory to the level of availability, but will not raise the general excitability (vigilance); thus each memory made 'unavailable' by the damage will have to be reinstated in turn by specific training.

This concept promises to have great usefulness for tying together many of the findings concerning the role of the cortex in learning and memory. It is equivalent, we may note, to the possibility of a "general factor" in cortical function as an explanatory factor in mass action, and if experiments concerning this factor should turn out, finally, to support its existence, we have in the concept of availability (or vigilance) a better picture of how such a general factor could operate. It can explain, moreover, why the various findings concerning aphasia point on the one hand to a certain degree of localization and at the same time to general dependence upon the cortex as a whole.

General Reference

WEISENBURG, T., and K. MCBRIDE, 1935. *Aphasia, a clinical and psychological study.* New York: Commonwealth Fund. Pp. xvi + 634.

CHAPTER XXVI

SYMBOLIC PROCESSES

We have already referred to the concept of symbolic process in considering the significance of evolutionary changes in the nervous system and in surveying the general characteristics of adaptive behavior. In each case the references were of a general character and were made merely to round out the topics then being discussed. Here we shall make symbolic processes the principal topic of discussion and attempt to determine just what physiological mechanisms are responsible for them.

Munn has pointed out that symbolic processes have two characteristics: (1) They are representative processes standing for previous experiences in the adjustments of the organism. Applicable to them, therefore, are such terms as reproductive memory, imagination, conception, abstraction, thought, or reasoning. (2) They are unseen processes, their existence being determined only by inference. Neither the stimulus nor the response which we see is symbolic, but only events in the organism which intervene and alter the relation of response to stimulation may be symbolic.

The question arises, naturally, as to how we know symbolic processes are at work, when they are unseen and only indirectly established. There is a ready answer to the question. Only when the response of an organism must be determined by conditions not present at the time of adjustment can it be supposed that a symbolic process is operating. A simple conditioned response does not necessarily entail symbolic functioning, for, although the conditioning is acquired through experience, the stimulus which directs action is present at the time of response. If, however, as is the case in so-called trace conditioning, the conditioned response to the stimulus should be made sometime after the stimulus has been terminated, then we may say that a symbolic process is implied, for the response must have been aroused by the 'trace' or representative of the stimulus rather than by the stimulus itself. Thus, a symbolic process is indicated when the signal or cue for adjustment made is not present at the time of response.

CENTRAL VS. PERIPHERAL BASIS OF SYMBOLIC PROCESS

In the early days of experimental psychology it was taken for granted that mental (or symbolic) processes are events taking place in the brain.

But with the discovery of the conditioned response and the subsequent growth of behaviorism, the so-called motor or peripheral theory of mental processes was put forth. This theory was based upon two concepts, the reflex circle and implicit response. The first was that muscle contractions elicited by efferent excitations stimulated the sensory endings in the muscles and thereby sent afferent excitations back into the nervous system. The second concept, that of implicit response, simply stated that such reflex circles could operate when muscle contractions were so small as to be unobservable by the naked eye. With these devices, higher mental processes could be explained by assuming only that particular patterns of muscle contraction set up patterns of sensory excitation which can be conditioned to other patterns of muscle contraction and that such an implicit reflex circle can go on ad infinitum.

Note that no one has questioned the existence of intervening unseen processes in reasoning, thinking, and the like; only their locus, whether central or peripheral, has been in question. Perhaps the majority of psychologists in recent years have preferred to accept the peripheral theory of symbolic process, largely because it freed them of any uneasiness they might have about the dualistic connotation of 'mental' processes occurring in the brain. In the meantime several experimenters turned their energy to determining empirically, if possible, whether such a theory could be verified. The results that they obtained form the basis of the present discussion.

MAZE LEARNING

Theoretically, symbolic processes need not enter into learning the correct path of a maze, for at various points in the maze there are cues that might serve to direct the subject in this or that direction much as a conditioned stimulus brings out a paw flexure or a flight across a grill. The analysis of factors in maze learning in rats, however, has shown that there are general factors in maze learning not dependent entirely upon specific cues (Tryon). As one observes, either the animal or human subject is not making his choices step by step and running the maze piecemeal but 'knows where he is going' well in advance of each turn. Symbolic processes are therefore suspected of operating in the learning, and the question is raised as to whether they are centrally located or consist of internal cues arising from responses made in running.

Rats.—The question of whether or not symbolic processes of a peripheral nature are involved in maze learning centers around the role of kinesthetic impulses in the learning. If these are unimportant or unnecessary, the symbolic processes involved cannot be said to be peripheral. Experimentation has been concerned, therefore, with testing this point.

There are two ways of going about it, either by eliminating kinesthetic cues in maze running or by requiring that the animal rely entirely upon kinesthetic cues in order to solve the maze. Following the first method, rats have been trained to run a maze correctly and then have been deprived of one or several of their senses. The elimination of any sensory modality, it has been found (Lindley), tends to disrupt the maze memory somewhat, although there is considerable variability from one animal to another depending upon what cues each has preferred to use. And, as was stated before, the more senses removed, the greater the effect upon memory and upon ability to relearn the maze. Kinesthesis, it is to be noted, is no more important than any other sense in the learning and memory of the maze. As a matter of fact, animals in which kinesthesis was eliminated by sectioning the dorsal spinal columns were capable of learning a maze just as quickly as were normal animals (Lashley and Ball). It was established, accordingly, that kinesthetic impulses could not be the basis of any symbolic processes concerned in maze running.

The second approach to the problem, by limiting an animal to kinesthetic cues entirely, has yielded results that serve only to emphasize this conclusion. Since surgical removal of all sense organs beside those of kinesthesis is rather hard on an animal, the elimination of nonkinesthetic modalities has been accomplished by procedures that jumble them so thoroughly as to make them ineffective. The various segments of a maze are interchanged from trial to trial, thereby mixing up olfactory and tactual cues, and the maze is oriented in different positions from time to time to jumble the visual cues. Following such a procedure, it turns out, makes an animal unable to learn any but the simplest maze patterns. If the turns of the maze follow each other in simple alternation —first left, then right, then left, and so on—good learning will occur and this, it may be assumed, is based upon kinesthetic cues (Hunter). With any departure from this simple pattern, however, learning usually does not occur in any satisfactory amounts.

From these experiments two facts, mutually supporting each other, are established: Animals do not need kinesthetic cues to learn a maze; and animals can learn none but the simplest mazes with nothing but kinesthetic cues to rely upon. The conclusion which follows from these facts is clear enough: Whatever symbolic processes are involved in a maze cannot be explained in terms of peripheral events.

Human Beings.—The maze learning of human subjects has been investigated with the same problem in mind, whether or not implicit responses can serve as symbols signaling the correct turns to be made. In this case, of course, one cannot cut the dorsal columns and thereby eliminate kinesthetic functions. An alternative, however, is to make use of sensitive electrical equipment for recording small changes in muscle activity and to determine whether or not there are changes in muscles, unobservable to the naked eye, associated with making the correct choices in the maze. This procedure has been followed in several experiments (see Daniel). The results, unfortunately, do not supply a clear answer to the question raised, but they are, nevertheless, worth reviewing briefly. To understand them properly, it should be remembered that human individuals are ordinarily not asked to run mazes like rats—*i.e.*, with their whole bodies—but use their fingers or a stylus in tracing paths made of grooves.

Muscle tension in maze learning, the results show, is distributed throughout the whole body, but is greatest in that place (arm or hand) used directly in the learning. As errors decrease in the course of learning, tension also decreases for a certain number of trials. But after errors have been reduced to a minimum there is again an increase in muscle tension, which may be ascribed to the fact that at this point the subject usually shifts his attention from eliminating errors to increasing his speed and efficiency in 'running' the maze.

This, in brief, is about all the experiments tell us. They reveal no particular implicit responses characteristic of different points in the maze and the choices to be made, and it is such responses that we are interested in. The level of tension, perhaps, masks such responses so that they cannot be recorded. The mere existence of tension, however, is of little significance, since it must accompany maze performance, and it can very well be an overflow of the nervous processes in the brain directing the maze behavior.

IMAGINATION AND THOUGHT

Since we have no good means of evaluating just how much of learned maze behavior is of the simple conditioned-response variety, more direct approaches to our problem are perhaps called for. These have been taken by studying the situations which we can assume, without much doubt, to involve symbolic processes, *e.g.*, imagination, reasoning, and thought. By instructing the human subject to carry out such processes and at the same time making records with sensitive instruments of his behavior, several experiments have proposed to settle the question of whether peripheral or central events are responsible for symbolic processes. The results obtained have varied somewhat with the methods employed in measuring implicit responses, and they should be outlined for discussion accordingly.

Such methods of detecting small changes in behavior fall into two main groups: First and oldest are those in which some mechanical method of recording and amplifying was used. These were the only ones available before the development of the vacuum-tube amplifier in the 1920's, and the problem of symbolic processes antedates that development. The type of symbolic process in which there was then the most interest was symbolic thinking, and thus the recording of tongue and throat movements was of most concern. In one study a rubber bulb was placed in the front part of the mouth, and by a pneumatic system of tubes and tambours changes in pressure on this bulb could be registered; in another a tambour was put on the tip of the tongue and the pressure against it similarly recorded; in still another a lever was attached to the tongue by means of a metal suction cup and its movements noted. In the more recent experiments these crude mechanical methods have been displaced by electrical devices. These allow electrodes to be placed on, or in the vicinity of, the muscles suspected of being important; the very small currents generated in these electrodes by muscle contractions are then amplified many hundreds of times to as high a level as is required for recording them with ink or photography.

Mechanical Methods.—Unfortunately, the agreement among the various experiments performed with mechanical methods of recording is very poor, and they turn out, consequently, not to give a decisive answer to our problem. Two experiments are in favor of a peripheral theory (Courten; Wyczoikowski). In these, subjects were instructed to think of certain words, and while thinking the movements of their tongues were recorded. In all cases the thinking was accompanied by definite movements of the tongue. Although no evidence was produced that sensory processes aroused by these implicit movements were essential to the continuation of thought, it was believed that these results upheld the peripheral theory of the symbolic process.

On the other side of the question, however, is considerable material indicating that implicit motor activity does not necessarily accompany thought. The most notable and recent of these experiments was conducted by Thorson. She attached a suction cup to the tongue and recorded tongue movements upon a revolving drum while the subject was carrying out her instructions to think of some word or solve some arithmetical problem. Examples of the things they were to think about were 'experimental psychology,' 'duca, rima, rinka, ro,' and the multiplication of 25 by 23. In order to compare the character of the implicit movement with overt response in each case, she took control records of the subjects whispering the words they were thinking. A careful analysis of the records showed that, of 10 subjects studied, only three showed any appreciable similarity between the overt and the implicit patterns of tongue movement. Even in these three subjects the similarity was in evidence only a small part of the time. In another experiment, moreover, she had the subjects carry out the same instructions while singing 'ah' and, in this case, there was no correlation between thought and changes in the vocal musculature.

Thorson was able, in addition, to specify the special conditions under which one could expect movements of the tongue to be associated with thought. The most important ones were: after the tongue had been used in overt speech; thought carried out under distraction, and thus with more than normal effort; when an effort was made to think more quickly than usual; and to some extent during emotional disturbances. These various conditions, it may be observed, are those in which one might expect central processes in the brain to be so intensified that they would 'overflow' into the motor pathways. In view of that possibility, therefore, and of the relatively low incidence of implicit speech movements in thought, Thorson concluded that implicit behavior is not a necessary accompaniment of thought and that, when it does occur, it can be understood as the overflow of central processes.

Electrical Methods.—The negative results of Thorson, as well as some of those in favor of the peripheral theory but obtained by mechanical methods, have been criticized on the grounds that they are not adequate to the problem, *i.e.*, that they are probably not sensitive enough to reveal all implicit movements actually taking place. It is necessary, of course, to be assured that whatever implicit movements are present are recorded, otherwise the results obtained are not crucial to the question. The lack of sensitivity of the mechanical method can be a matter both of amplitude and of the pattern of movement, but electrical methods, it has been argued, are free enough of these inadequacies to provide a sound basis for conclusions.

The most extensive series of experiments using this method have been conducted by E. Jacobson. He measured the action potentials arising from various muscles while subjects were engaged in particular forms of 'mental' activity according to his instructions. In order to make certain that the general level of tension would not interfere with the recording of implicit responses, he took the precaution of training subjects to relax before beginning his observations. In such relaxed subjects, he found, muscle contractions in the tongue and lips almost always appeared in any sort of linguistic thinking, such as mental multiplication, the imagining of 'everlasting,' or the words of a song. Jacobson found, moreover, that the pattern of activity recorded in such cases tended to be very similar to that seen in the same movements executed overtly. Of significance, also, was his finding that the implicit muscular activity related to thinking or imagining was limited, in general, to the specific group of muscles that would have been involved in the performance, had it been overt: implicit behavior appeared in the tongue and throat when linguistic thought was in progress, in the muscles of the eye when the subject imagined a visual object, and in other parts of the body according to the content of thought.

Another study of implicit behavior has been carried out by Max. His results are particularly interesting because he used both deaf-mute and normal subjects and made his records during the dreaming of sleep, as well as under waking instructions. The deaf-mute subject, it may be observed, uses his fingers and hands in communication, whereas normal individuals rely, for the most part, on their vocal musculature.

The onset of dreams in deaf-mutes, Max found, was accompanied by large action currents in the muscles of the arms and fingers, but such was not the case in normal hearing subjects. Thus it appeared that the muscles normally involved in waking linguistic behavior, the limbs in one case and the vocal musculature in the other, were also employed in dreams. Thinking in waking subjects, Max reports further, was accompanied by action currents in the hands in 84 per cent of the deaf subjects and in only 31 per cent of the normal subjects. Max therefore concluded tentatively that "these manual responses in the deaf are more than adventitious effects of irradiated tensions (though the existence of the tension factor is not gainsaid), and that such responses have some specific connection with the thinking process."

These experiments of Jacobsen and Max clearly indicate that implicit behavior usually accompanies mental processes. They do not, however, show that implicit behavior *is* the mental process, and this is the point at issue. To settle it we must know not only that implicit behavior accompanies thought but also that thought cannot occur in the absence of implicit behavior. The data, unfortunately, are not very informative on this point.

One of the strongest arguments against the belief that implicit behavior is essential to the continuity of thought comes from a rather common-sense observation by Lashley. Considering the instance of a pianist playing a fast-moving cadenza, he points out that the speed of the movements is entirely too fast for their pattern to be dependent upon kinesthetic impulses coming back from the muscles concerned, as the peripheral theory of thought would require. If one calculates the speed of nervous conduction from the brain to the fingers and compares it with the interval between the fingered notes, it turns out that the impulses for one response must leave the brain before any excitations arriving back from the response just preceding could reach the brain. The pattern of movements must therefore be temporally organized to some extent in the brain, and the responses, then, must be centrally organized. If this is the case for the pattern of movements in piano playing, why may it not be true also for the elements of thought?

Lashley, bolstered by the studies of Thorson, suggests the opinion that the implicit behavior which accompanies thought is largely the overflow of centrally organized processes. The results which have been obtained so far certainly are subject to that interpretation. If, indeed, a symbolic process is a pattern of cortical activity *representing* experience and movement, one can expect that the symbolic process will be manifested, to some extent, in the movements represented, for it would seem that the same neural patterns must be involved in both the implicit and the overt movements. Much of the material to be presented in the following sections supports this interpretation.

THE NEURAL BASIS OF SYMBOLIC FUNCTIONS

Aside from the question of whether implicit behavior is necessary for symbolic processes or whether they are organized entirely centrally, we may consider the central neural mechanisms which may mediate them. Experiments on this topic have been conducted with rats, primates, and human beings as subjects, and since there are differences both in the structure of the brain and in levels of psychological capacity among these animals, it will be advisable to consider the experiments according to the animals with which they were done.

It will also be convenient to distinguish four aspects of symbolic functions.

1. The first is a *trace process;* this refers to the neural activity that represents a previous sensory experience. It is illustrated by the delayed reaction in which an animal makes a response on the basis of a stimulus that was recently presented to it but is not present at the time of its response.

2. Another aspect of symbolic functions is *expectancy*, this term having the same general meaning as when it was previously discussed under the principle of expectancy. It is probably a complex cortical process involving neural activities representative of previous experience and also a set or preparation for particular types of response. This latter aspect of it is that which, because of the nature of the experimental work concerning it, will be emphasized here.

3. To be distinguished, next, are *seriatim* aspects of symbolic functions. This term, we have seen previously, refers to processes which organize acts in a temporal series of a particular order. Like expectancy, it undoubtedly involves a set or preparation for action, but in addition there is implied the notion of synthesis of action into an orderly series.

4. We may identify, finally, a *reasoning* aspect of symbolic functions. Of such functions it is probably the most highly developed and complex. It is trial-and-error learning conducted entirely at the symbolic level. In it are involved not only expectancies of the outcome of action, but

also representations of previous experience similar to trace processes and serial organizing processes.

Just how these various aspects of symbolic functions may be related to each other, either in terms of psychological theory or in respect of cortical functions, is a question that we should not prejudge. The subsequent discussion will throw some light on it, but will not entirely clear it up. The virtue of the distinction is not that these aspects are mutually exclusive and conceptually pure, but that they have different measures in experimental tests and thus can be separated from each other in practical terms.

THE RAT

As many experimenters have learned by long and tedious work, rats are not supplied with an overabundance of symbolic processes. They never solve any problems designed to measure these processes with any great degree of skill, but after a great deal of training they display just enough capacity for solving such problems to be given credit for a primitive symbolic capacity. This inferiority in symbolic functions parallels the degree of development of the cerebral cortex in the rat.

Trace Processes.—For the study of trace symbolic processes in the rat, two methods have been employed, the delayed reaction and the delayed alternation. In the first delayed-reaction experiments (see Munn), rats were presented with a flash of light but restrained from responding to it until several seconds afterward. Under these conditions they were unable to delay for more than 2 or 3 sec.; indeed, their capacity for delay was so small that it was doubtful whether any trace processes, aside from postural orientation, were indicated. Later, by showing rats the position in which food was hid, it proved possible to obtain delays of as long as several minutes from them. The first results, however, discouraged workers from attempting to study the effects of cortical extirpation upon delayed reaction, and no one has yet made use of the improved method.

The method of delayed alternation, however, has proved more successful. In this method an animal is placed in a simple maze and, after it has made one turn, is given an enforced delay, after which it is required to take a turn in the direction opposite to that of the first choice. Under certain optimal conditions, rats do not have to be taught to make such alternations; for some reason they do it spontaneously (Heathers). They are capable of making the alternation correctly after as much as a minute's delay. To do that, obviously, they must have a 'trace' of the response that they last made.

In one experiment (Loucks) the capacity for delayed alternation survived cortical lesions made in the middle and posterior parts of the cortex, but was abolished by lesions in the frontal third. In a more recent experiment taking advantage of the spontaneous alternation of rats (Morgan and Wood), a similar but even clearer result was obtained. Lesions in a relatively small part of the frontal cortex abolished the delayed alternation, whereas damage in other parts was without effect. The crucial area, it may be stated tentatively, is in the region of projection of the dorsomedial nucleus of the thalamus, and this area is homologous to the area in primates which, as will be seen presently, is concerned with similar functions.

Expectancy.—The effect of cortical lesions upon expectancy processes in rats has also been investigated (Stellar *et al.*). The arrangement of the experiment was as follows: In a maze consisting of a runway from which six alleys led to the left, rats were taught to pass up all alleys except the fourth one, where they could find food. To eliminate all exteroceptive cues and make the animals rely upon their 'memory' of the maze, the alleys were moved up and down the runway and the whole maze was rotated in different positions, from trial to trial; sometimes, on test runs, one or two of the alleys were omitted. In this way the animals were thrown back upon symbolic processes involving an expectancy of where to find food. Having mastered the problem at a reasonable degree of proficiency, they were subjected to cortical lesions of different size and location and their ability to solve the problem tested again. As in the case of the delayed alternation, it

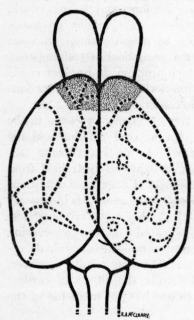

Fig. 172.—Diagram showing approximate position and size of prefrontal areas subserving symbolic processes in rats. (*After E. Stellar et al.*, 1942.)

was found that a relatively small area in the frontal third of the cortex was crucial to optimum performance (Fig. 172); when it was entirely destroyed they were totally unable to solve the problem. Lesions elsewhere had no such effect even when of considerable size.

Reasoning.—There is a test of seriatim functions in the rat which requires that the animal run a maze of the pattern RRLL without being able to depend upon external cues. This pattern of double alternation, it will be observed, cannot be carried out on a purely kinesthetic basis, for right turns are associated with right turns as often as with left turns, and vice versa. Unfortunately, however, this problem has proved so difficult for the rat that it takes most of the lifetime of the rat to learn it, and it has, consequently, not invited study from the standpoint of cortical functions.

To test the most complex of symbolic functions in the rat, however, has appeared feasible. Maier has set up a situation in which a rat first becomes familiar with one part of the problem, then with another, and then is required to put together these two previous experiences in the

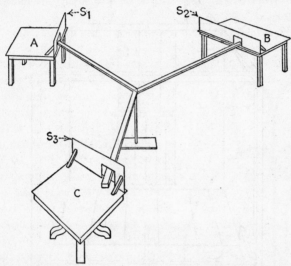

Fig. 173.—Maier's apparatus for testing "reasoning" in rats. A rat is allowed to explore the entire apparatus. Then it is fed on one of the tables and afterward carried to another table from which it must find its way back to the food. The screens S_1, S_2, and S_3 prevent the rat from seeing the food. (*From N. R. F. Maier and T. C. Schneirla. Principles of animal psychology, p. 463. New York: McGraw-Hill, 1935.*)

solution of the problem as a whole (see Fig. 173). In this way, Maier has probably pared down reasoning to its simplest possible elements.

Upon subjecting rats to cortical lesions, Maier has found not a localization of symbolic functions but rather mass action, similar to that found by Lashley in maze-learning experiments. Destruction of 10 per cent or less of the rat's cortex, he found, did not seriously interfere with reasoning ability. Lesions between 10 and 18 per cent, however, gave some reduction in reasoning ability, and ablations greater in extent than 18 per cent completely abolished it. Thus relatively small lesions anywhere in the cortex interfered with reasoning processes. This perhaps could be expected, however, because, as was pointed out above, reasoning involves several aspects of experience and response and thus probably a considerable part of the cortex.

PRIMATES

Both the methods and the results of work with primates on the problem of symbolic functions are similar to those occurring in the studies of the rat. Some of the methods are exactly the same; others are different, because the primate has more highly developed symbolic processes and it can, consequently, solve more complex problems than

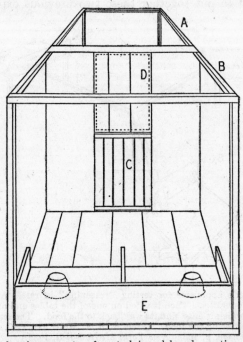

FIG. 174.—Jacobsen's apparatus for studying delayed reaction in monkeys. The animal is placed in compartment A for the delay period; from it, he can see where the food is hidden at E by looking through the screen C. During the delay the opaque door D is kept lowered, and at the end of the delay it is raised and the monkey is allowed to reach into the reaction compartment B to lift the cups. (*From C. F. Jacobsen. Studies of cerebral function in primates, p.* 16. *Comp. Psychol. Monogr., Vol.* 13, *No.* 63, 1936. *By permission of the Johns Hopkins Press, publishers.*)

can the rat. Although the fourfold classification of aspects of symbolic function which was offered above is also applicable to the primate, the available experiments concern mainly trace and seriatim functions. The relation, finally, between symbolic processes and specialized frontal areas is even more striking in the primate than it is in the rat.

Trace Functions.—In monkeys as in rats, trace functions may be tested by determining how long, after a signal has been presented, an animal can still make a correct choice on the basis of the signal (Fig. 174). The usual procedure in the case of monkeys is to present the animal with several cups, show it under which cup food is being placed and then, after some delay, allow it to choose which of the cups it 'thinks' the food is under. One plays, so to speak, a game of hide and seek with the animal, giving it an opportunity to see where the desired object is hidden.

In studying the role of various cortical areas in the capacity to solve the delayed reaction, C. F. Jacobsen found the frontal 'association' areas to be crucial (Fig. 175). Whereas a normal animal can solve the problem after a minute or two, only very short delays are possible in monkeys whose prefrontal areas have been completely removed. The possible delay is so short, in fact, that the animal appears to solve

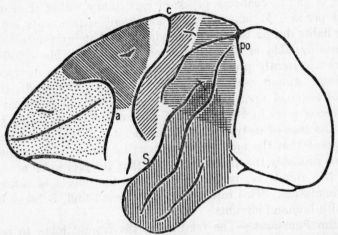

Fig. 175.—Summary of the effects of cortical extirpations in monkeys upon delayed reponse. Extirpation of the various hatched areas had no effect; removal of the stippled area (prefrontal areas) caused permanent disruption of the capacity for delayed reaction. *c*, central sulcus; *s*, sylvian (lateral) sulcus; *po*, parieto-occipital sulcus; *a*, anterior sulcus. (*From C. F. Jacobsen. Studies of cerebral function in primates, p. 44. Comp. Psychol. Monogr., Vol. 13, No. 63, 1936. By permission of the Johns Hopkins Press, publishers.*)

the problem only by keeping its gaze on the correct place throughout the interval. That method of solution, obviously, does not involve symbolic processes. Subtotal extirpation of these areas, Jacobsen found, shortens the time that the animals can delay but does not abolish the solution entirely.

Similar findings were obtained with the delayed alternation procedure previously described for rats (Jacobsen and Nissen). Although monkeys, like rats, do not do particularly well in solving the problem, the normal animal performs well enough to indicate, by this method, the presence of symbolic capacity. After complete bilateral extirpation of the frontal areas, such capacity is abolished. When only unilateral removal is carried out, however, no disturbance results until a second operation is performed to remove the other side.

As the results to be presented below indicate, extirpation of the prefrontal areas interferes not only with trace functions but also with other aspects of symbolic processes. Jacobsen's original interpretation of his findings emphasized the trace functions as primary and the other defects as secondary results of the disturbance of trace functions. This is a possible interpretation, for it will be seen later that all the other problems failed by 'prefrontal' monkeys are those which require traces of acts recently performed.

Recent results, however, lead us to believe that failure of the 'prefrontal' monkey to solve delayed-reaction problems is caused by disturbance of the mechanisms of set or expectancy rather than of trace processes per se. Malmo, repeating Jacobsen's experiments but extinguishing lights during the delay period, found that 'prefrontal' animals were quite capable of normal delayed reactions. This difference in procedure apparently prevented the animals from being distracted by other visual stimuli during the delay interval. The result, then, of prefrontal removal upon delayed reaction appears to represent not a disturbance of trace functions primarily but of the loss of ability to keep a set in the face of distracting circumstances. If that is the case, we must suppose that the memory trace must be preserved by some other area, most probably the visual areas, but that the prefrontal areas serve to keep the animal ready to react despite the effects of intervening visual stimulation. This interpretation, we shall find, is borne out by results with human individuals.

Seriatim Functions.—The relation of the frontal lobes to seriatim problem solving has already been mentioned in an earlier chapter. There it was pointed out that problems consisting of a sequence of three acts to be carried out in a particular order could not be solved by monkeys after ablation of the prefrontal areas.

Another type of test, the so-called *stick-and-platform test*, not previously mentioned, gives us another illustration of this relationship. The essential feature of this test is that a monkey is required to use a short rake in order to secure a longer rake which will enable him to pull in food placed at a distance outside its cage. The problem can be complicated as much as desired by increasing the number of rakes that must be obtained in a particular order of succession, determined by their respective lengths, before the last rake obtained is long enough to use for obtaining food. It may also be made more difficult by placing some of the rakes at one end of the cage and others at the other end of the cage so that the animal cannot see all the steps in the solution of the problem at the same time.

As one might expect, the prefrontal areas are absolutely essential for the solution of these problems (Jacobsen). If these areas are bilaterally removed, no amount of retraining will enable an animal to solve correctly any of the problems, *i.e.*, without manipulating the rakes more or less blindly until the solution is gotten by accident. Destruction of the frontal area on one side, however, does not affect the capacity. This fits into the picture of equipotentiality, previously discussed, showing that the two halves of the prefrontal areas are equipotential in function.

Interpretation.—Before passing on to other aspects of frontal-lobe function, it is well to consider the meaning of the results obtained with rats and with monkeys. In particular we may inquire concerning the relationship of the four aspects of symbolic functions which, for convenience, have been used in this summary.

Trace functions, we have seen, depend on the frontal areas insofar as a set is required for reacting to them, but the traces themselves, it appears, can be mediated elsewhere. So, at least, the tests with monkeys show; relevant experiments with the rat remain to be performed. Since the trace represents the sensory, rather than the motor, side of adjustment we might conclude, consequently, that sensory (trace) aspects of symbolic processes are mediated primarily by the more posterior parts of the brain. The best information available concerning aphasia would seem to fit this conclusion, but we lack, unfortunately, any significant experiments concerning it.

A similar difficulty meets us in dealing with reasoning. In rats, reasoning (so-called) appears to be a function of the total cerebral cortex, whereas the expectancy aspects of symbolic functions are located in the frontal areas. Experiments in monkeys have not been carried out, but the effects of lesions, irrespective of their locus, upon the higher abstractive processes in man point to a similar conclusion. If we suppose that the sensory or trace aspects of reasoning are primarily dependent upon posterior areas and the expectancy or goal-directing aspects reside primarily in the frontal areas (see below), we may believe that reasoning is the outcome of the functioning of the whole cortex. We may hold this conclusion tentatively until more facts on the question become available.

Expectancy has been directly tested in rats and found to depend upon frontal areas, but comparable tests have not been made in monkeys. From some observations, to be presented in the next section, of experimental neurosis in monkeys, however, we have reason to believe that when such tests are performed they will clearly indicate expectancy to depend upon the prefrontal areas. Expectancy conceivably includes both sensory and motor aspects of symbolic functions, but its connotation is more the latter, *i.e.*, a set or readiness for action. Provisionally, therefore, let us assume that these are functions of the prefrontal areas.

The aspect of symbolic processes most clearly dependent upon the prefrontal areas in monkeys is the seriatim function, the capacity to organize and synthesize motor activity in serial order. Neither discrete learned responses nor even, probably, individual images associated with stimulus situations are involved in prefrontal functions, but only their ordering. Experiments do not tell us directly how further to interpret this function, but one can suggest the possibility that it is reducible to expectancy, *i.e.*, to the symbolic representation of the acts to be performed, particularly the final goal act. This seems reasonable because the most plausible way in which acts could be carried out in an orderly manner is by having representations of all of them—or at least the more important parts of them—present at the start. Perhaps the initial expectancy consists of the whole group arranged in a hierarchy of prepotency in which the strongest one can be executed, leaving the next in line, and so on. However this may be, it is possible to conceive, in general terms, of seriatim functions as being basically a matter of expectancy.

To sum up this discussion, we may come first of all to the tentative conclusion that symbolic processes are fundamentally of two sorts, trace (imaginal) and expectancy. One might also call them sensory and motor, or receptive and expressive, respectively. The premotor areas, furthermore, mediate directly only the expressive, motor, or expectancy processes, and the more posterior parts of the brain are primarily concerned with the receptive, sensory, or trace functions. The prefrontal areas, however, can be expected to affect these latter functions because they make ready, or prepare, the reactions to be executed upon the 'signal' to do so by the receptive symbolic processes. This would explain why all aspects of symbolic processes appear to be so intimately related to the prefrontal areas. It is recognized, of course, that these conclusions have been drawn by argument and that they are provisional, but they may serve as generalizations unless and until further experiments force us to revise them.

EXPERIMENTAL NEUROSIS

In addition to the facts brought out above, the study of the symbolic functions of the frontal lobes has revealed a relation between neurotic behavior and symbolic processes that is of considerable importance, even if somewhat unexpected. In order to explain this relation, it will be necessary to begin with some general remarks concerning neurotic behavior.

Varieties of Neurotic Behavior.—The term *neurotic behavior* is used rather freely in both lay and professional parlance to refer to many varied phenomena. All usage, however, has the common factor that neurotic behavior is regarded as emotional behavior. It is possible, moreover, to classify the meanings of the term into three groups.

1. Neurotic behavior may refer to conditioned emotional behavior: the presentation of an otherwise neutral stimulus with an emotion-

arousing situation thereafter leads, or tends to lead, to the evocation of emotion by the formerly neutral stimulus. A good illustration of this type of neurotic behavior in human individuals is the phobia, in which some object, through conditioning, provokes marked emotional reactions. Such behavior, it may be noted, is acquired by the principle of substitution.

2. Neurotic behavior may refer to emotional reactions produced by 'conflict.' Current theory of neurosis, offered by animal psychologists (Liddell, Maier), emphasizes this aspect of neurosis. Conflict is induced by having an animal acquire two learned responses, each under its own strong motivation, which are incompatible with each other and by then putting the subject in a situation where both reactions are called for. Thus, a rat may be taught to jump to a 'correct' door to obtain reward for strong hunger and be taught also that it will be punished severely if it jumps to an 'incorrect' door; then, by presenting the animal with only one door which is 'incorrect,' the animal is torn between jumping and avoiding punishment (see Maier). Or it may learn to choose a circle and avoid an ellipse and later be given an ellipse which is indiscriminably different from either a circle or an ellipse; the animal is, therefore, in 'conflict' as to which response, approach or avoidance, is required. Neurosis produced in this way, it may be pointed out, is related to the principle of effect, *i.e.*, the response most appropriate to reward or effect cannot be selected.

3. One may distinguish neurosis at the symbolic level. In human individuals, this is often referred to as anxiety or worry. Here no emotional stimulus is present, but the emotional response is still exhibited, presumably as a result of the symbolic processes going on centrally. Such neurotic behavior may conceivably be related either to the trace or expectancy aspects of symbolic function. In the first case, lingering memories of previous emotional situations may maintain the anxiety or neurosis; in the second, the expectancy of emotional situations in the future may cause the anxiety. The two possibilities, of course, are undoubtedly always interlinked and inseparable from each other in the actual occurrence of neurosis.

The Frontal Lobes and Neurosis.—Now consider the type of neurotic behavior to be expected in monkeys given the delayed-reaction tests. If a hungry animal is presented with food in full sight but is prevented from getting it by the placing of a barrier between the animal and the food, one can expect the monkey to become emotional because its efforts are being frustrated. One probably should not call such emotional behavior neurotic, however, because there is no learning involved and it is a natural response, but if it is neurotic, then it is of the conflict type. If, on the other hand, in the delayed reaction, an animal is made to make errors by lengthening the delay beyond its capacity for recalling the correct place of food, the behavior is to be regarded as neurotic, since an animal becomes emotional when it makes many errors.   More than that, the neurosis arises from his symbolic processes and, in particular, his *expectancy* of receiving reward.   Indeed, it must be the animal's expectancy that is frustrated, since the food is not visible.

From such reasoning we can expect that by destroying the animal's capacity for expectancy we should abolish its neurotic behavior, and that is what the experimental results show.   Prior to operation, Jacobsen finds, a monkey which has made two or three errors in a row may throw a temper tantrum in which it screams, urinates and defecates, shakes the bars, rolls upon the floor, and shows other manifestations of neurotic rage. The change that comes over the animal after removal of the frontal lobes, however, is truly remarkable.   In some ways the animal is more emotional than before, for like some of the decorticate animals described earlier (p. 371), emotional reactions are displayed more freely.   But, though it may be emotional, it is not neurotic.   As explained before, its greater distractability, apparently, causes it to make many more mistakes than previously, but it now works at the problem trial after trial in a more or less routine manner, without 'blowing up.'   Thus neuroticism of the symbolic type is eliminated by removal of the prefrontal 'association' areas.   As we shall see below, a similar relation holds for human individuals.

PREFRONTAL FUNCTIONS IN MAN

The question of whether the conclusions just drawn are supported by the facts concerning man is one of the reasons for taking up here the topic of prefrontal lobes in man.   Another reason is that the aphasias previously discussed do not seem to depend, in any essential way at least, upon the prefrontal areas; expressive aphasias are related to the speech area, which is more properly considered a part of the motor-premotor complex than of the frontal areas, and the receptive aphasias are, as we have seen, most closely tied to the posterior cerebrum.   Thus, if the frontal areas are not involved in aphasia, there is the question of just what functions they do mediate and how these are related to the types of memory studied in aphasia.   A final point which adds to our interest in the frontal lobes is that in recent years methods have been developed by neurosurgeons for treating patients suffering from neurosis and psychosis by planned damage to the frontal areas; as a result there are now available a number of cases of human individuals who without tumors or other accidental damage to the brain have been subjected to frontal operations.

Operative work on the frontal areas in human patients may be of two types, frontal lobotomy and frontal lobectomy.   In lobotomy, an instrument is inserted through the cortex without appreciable damage to it, and, when its tip is well into the underlying white matter, a knife formerly hidden in the instrument can be made to come out and by rotating it the fibers between the frontal areas and thalamus can be cut in any desired amount and the cortex left relatively intact (see Fig. 176). In lobectomy, on the other hand, the gray matter itself is taken out completely rather than merely separated from the thalamus. As one might expect, the consequences of lobectomy are more serious than those of lobotomy. Lobectomy is usually carried out when the presence of a tumor or infection make such an operation necessary; lobotomy has been practiced as therapy in subjects showing only mental symptoms needing treatment.

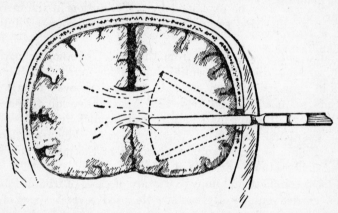

Fig. 176.—The method of performing a prefrontal lobotomy. An instrument is inserted through an opening in the skull and underlying cortex and rotated angularly in such a way as to transect the white matter beneath the cortex without more than slight damage to the cortex. (*From W. Freeman and J. W. Watts. Psychosurgery, p. 83. Springfield: C. C. Thomas, 1942   By permission of the publishers.*)

Intellectual Functions.—It is not easy to generalize the psychological effects of extirpation of all or part of the frontal areas because these are not uniform in all patients, and they are often reported descriptively without regard to analysis or to performance on objective tests. The general picture that they show, however, is in accord with the results of animal work. Patients tend to show deficit in the synthesis of acts into a complete pattern and in mental activities which depend upon such a synthesis. In line with this statement is the fact that one of the most frequent observations of such patients is that they lack the ability for planned administration of their daily or business activities. Examples from several reports will serve to bring this conclusion out and give the reader a more complete picture than can be gotten from general statements.

Lobectomy.—One of the best known studies of frontal-lobe function has been carried out by Brickner. For a considerable time after operation, he had a patient under observation who had been subjected to a relatively complete bilateral lobectomy. The outstanding symptoms of this individual were as follows: The capacity to associate or to synthesize elements of a situation was severely limited; the patient was extremely inattentive and distractable, passing from one thing to another without picking a task and sticking to it until completed. Consequently general learning capacity was impaired, judgment was usually poor, so too was general orientation in situations. Particularly striking was the inability of the patient to appreciate the gravity of a situation, including his own predicament. All these symptoms, however, Brickner sums up in the concept of impairment of "synthesis." Thus he says "all of the interpretable changes may be explained by a diminution in the associative function of synthesizing simple mental engrams [processes] into more complex ones."

A similar conclusion comes from the report of another patient by Karnosh, who describes the essential changes due to frontal lobectomy as a defect in capacity to form complex associations even though simple associations are not impaired, regression from more adult to more childlike manners of thinking and acting, and a much freer expression of primitive emotional reactions, apparently because they are unhampered by the restraints of more complex processes or the motivation to form plans and deliberate on anticipated behavior.

The most complete and objective study of cases of frontal lobectomy has been carried out by Rylander. He used several types of formal tests, including intelligence tests, in 32 cases of frontal lobectomy and compared the results with those of 32 cases of normal individuals matched with the patients in as many respects as possible. His findings may be summarized as follows: The patients showed significant changes in the capacity for logical thinking and for abstraction. Various tests of symbolic thinking which employed the definition of abstract words, the interpretation of proverbs, pictures, and the like showed them to be below normal in this respect. In general the reactions of the patients were much more concrete and elementary and less abstract. Rylander does not place any great emphasis upon the "synthetic" functions of the frontal lobes, but his results can easily be interpreted along that line, especially in view of the lack of any prominent symptoms of aphasia or any of the kinds of specific memory defects discussed above in relation to aphasia.

Other instances of psychological changes following prefrontal lobectomy could be cited but they would make the description repetitious. General agreement seems to exist that thinking, reasoning, abstraction, and synthesis are impaired. These obviously center around disorders of symbolic processes. It is not always possible to state, however, that these are of the expressive rather than receptive variety, because the types of tests employed do not ordinarily differentiate between these. Indeed, as the work with animals indicates, it may appear that the receptive symbolic processes are disturbed when they actually are not, simply because the disorders of synthesis or set overshadow them and prevent them from being used.

Lobotomy.—From the standpoint of mental deficit, cases of prefrontal lobotomy have been much more satisfactorily studied than have those of prefrontal lobectomy. One series of 40 cases was subjected to many types of intelligence tests and the most careful of clinical examinations (Freeman and Watts). This study yielded no significant changes in intelligence. Indeed, if anything, the patients were generally improved by the operation, probably because they suffered before the operation from neurotic and psychotic difficulties that were considerably improved by the operation. It is not strange, however, that lobectomy should affect mental capacity when lobotomy should not, for in the latter case only some of the projection fibers between the frontal areas and the thalamus are interrupted. The main effect of the operation appears to be the destruction of the attachment between symbolic functions and emotional effects, particularly as these are involved in neurotic and psychotic manifestations.

One point of significance concerning the testing of lobotomized patients is worth special notice. Included in the battery of tests given to these subjects was one problem very much like the delayed-reaction problem used with animals. In full view of the patients, coins were hidden under certain ones of a series of cups, and later the patients were asked to find the hiding place. The problem was made more difficult for the human than it had been for the animal subjects by using a lot of cups and hiding several coins at the same time under different cups. It proved to be a very difficult test for both preoperative and postoperative subjects, and few perfect scores were obtained. What was remarkable, however, was the fact that patients after lobotomy not only showed no deficit but performed better than they had before operation. The improvement in performance was ascribed to the generally better emotional condition of the postoperative subjects. That there should be no impairment in this delayed-reaction problem, however, indicated that the operation did not impair trace functions. This finding is in accord with the interpretation made of the 'prefrontal' monkey's performance in delayed reaction.

Neurosis.—In human individuals we find a relationship between the prefrontal areas and neurotic symptoms similar to that found in monkeys. Freeman and Watts have performed prefrontal lobotomies upon a number of patients suffering from neurotic symptoms and have had considerable success in relieving them of their difficulties. As is the case with neurotic individuals, the subjects before operation were characterized by anxiety. In some the anxiety was general and had no particular symptoms except a tendency toward suicide. In others the neurosis had taken the form of some specific phobia, obsessive idea, or compulsive ritualistic behavior. One case was of a conversion hysteria in which the anxiety was accompanied by fancied pain in the back. The principle and underlying disorder in all cases was the anxiety or emotional tension.

In summing up their results in subjecting such patients to prefrontal lobotomy, Freeman and Watts write that even in the most severe and intractable cases

. . . prefrontal lobotomy has succeeded in relieving the underlying emotional tension to a degree where the various symptoms are of little importance in the life of the individual. Indeed, this emotional tension underlies so much of the symptomatology that it would seem as if the operation succeeded more or less specifically in removing the basis for the complaint. There is not infrequently a persistence of symptoms, sensations, ideas, feelings and other phenomena which might be spoken of as the afferent component associated with the tension states (p. 282).

Specific compulsive activities may also continue to exist. "The connecting link, however, in the form of emotional tension seems to be broken down" (p. 282).

On first thought it might seem as though this picture of changes in neurosis with prefrontal lobectomy indicates only that the association of emotional states with various ideas, acts, or other external situations takes place in the frontal lobes. This is not quite the case, however. Patients following prefrontal lobectomy are just as capable of emotional reaction as they were before—indeed, even more so—for release from the restraints imposed by the prefrontal areas seems to make them more ready to express emotional reactions to situations. In this respect they display changes similar to those seen in the emotional behavior of decorticate or partially decorticate animals (p. 371).

Anxiety, however, is not simply emotion. It is the anticipation of unpleasant events to occur in the future. To be sure, the anxious person may not know what it is he anticipates, but the anxiety nevertheless represents readiness to react in a future situation. The emotional tension generated by this anticipation is like the postural adjustments of an individual preparing to carry out some motor task. When understood in this light, the relation of anxiety to the prefrontal areas fits into the same conception that we have already built up of prefrontal function, *viz.*, that of an expressive symbolic process representing action in the future.

Affective Psychosis.—Several types of psychosis in addition to neurosis have been treated with prefrontal lobotomy. Indeed, Freeman and Watts have many more cases of psychotics than of neurotics, and both classes of individuals are, in general, improved by the operations. The psychotic patients may be divided into two main groups: the affective psychoses consisting principally of involutional depression and of manic-depressive behavior, and the schizophrenic psychoses involving hallucinations and catatonia.

In describing the prepsychotic life of individuals who develop involutional depression, Freeman and Watts point out that they characteristically exercise a good deal of foresight, are hard working, exacting, and meticulous and, in general, tend to anticipate a great deal. The precipitating cause of the psychosis may be the menopause (in women) or some illness which when past leaves the individual depleted and exhausted and unable to fulfill his many plans in the manner to which he is accustomed. The psychosis which subsequently develops may take the form of an agitated depression in which there are "marked symptoms of anxiety, apprehension, worry, depression of spirits, agitation, and crying spells" or it may express itself in suicidal ideas and great feelings of guilt and futility.

Such patients when subject to the frontal operations respond, on the whole, quite well. The best recoveries occur in those who show agitated depression, whereas those that complain of bodily ills, or of their inferiority, are not so favorably affected. Apparently this is a more severe form of the psychosis and can probably be cured only by doing more extensive damage to the projections of the frontal lobe than is possible without producing many unfavorable effects.

Personality.—In order to round out the discussion of prefrontal functions it is necessary that a word be said about personality. This certainly undergoes change in prefrontal lobotomy, sometimes very pronounced change. In general, it appears that an individual's natural temperament, free of the restraining effects of the anticipation of consequences of action, tends to be brought out by the operation. Those individuals who have a preoperative history of industry and activity become even more so and after operation are quite tireless, restless, and extremely energetic. Those who tend, on the other hand, to be quiet and rather sluggish become more sluggish. (*Cf.* the effects of prefrontal lesions upon activity in animals, pp. 391 to 456). In addition to these differences in general level of activity, prefrontal lobotomy presents a rather characteristic picture that one would expect to follow the removal of 'planning' functions of the brain. Patients act more vigorously and explosively and tend not to think of consequences before acting. When frustrated or disappointed, they react quickly with sarcasm or anger or when succeeding in what they want, they show unrestrained satisfaction. They become much more responsive to external stimuli and are more distractable. There are, indeed, few signs of internal inhibition of response.

Testing of a representative sample of the patients also reveals general changes in the personality in the direction of extraversion and away from introversion. Much of this is occasioned, of course, by the reduction in the amount of anxiety. Egocentric characteristics such as oversensitiveness to remarks of others or to environmental circumstances are reduced markedly in favor of a more open acceptance of the world and friends.

Theory of Prefrontal Functions.—From their very extensive study of prefrontal operations, the high lights of which have just been reviewed, Freeman and Watts come to a general theory of prefrontal functions which is very much like that obtainable from results with animals. Their point of view and language of description are somewhat different, however, and we can profit, therefore, by considering this theory in their own words (see pp. 302f).

The cerebral cortex may be considered as being divided by the Rolandic [central] fissure into two portions of essentially different function. The parts posterior to the fissure are concerned with the reception of impulses from receptors of various sorts situated all over the body and with the elaboration of these impulses into engrams [neural patterns]. By means of various association centers and pathways, the individual is brought by the post-Rolandic cortex into relation with all that has gone before in his existence. Experience and intelligence, the bases of his behavior, are mediated by this part of the brain.

Just as the post-Rolandic cortex is concerned with the past, the pre-Rolandic cortex is concerned with the future. Aside from certain small areas that mediate voluntary control over muscular movements and the regulation of visceral functions, the rest of the frontal cortex is, according to our hypothesis, concerned with the projection of the whole individual into the future. With the intact brain the individual is able to foresee, to see before, to forecast the results of certain activities that he is to initiate in the future, and he can visualize what effect these actions will have upon himself and upon his environment. [One case] expressed this concept almost directly. When he was questioned about his activities in slapping the nurses and pulling the fixtures from the wall in the hospital, he replied: *"Now that I have done it, I can see that it was not the thing to do, but before hand I couldn't say whether or not it would be all right."*

The patient with normally functioning frontal lobes can presumably define the goal toward which he is working and estimate more or less the nearness to which he approaches it. By projecting himself into the future in his mind's eye, he is calling upon his cortical mechanisms to synthesize past experience as his guide and upon his emotional mechanisms for driving force in the search for satisfaction and the avoidance of distress. Once the goal is set, he is further calling upon his cortical mechanisms to assemble various parts of the problem and to select a proper course from among the many alternatives that present themselves to him at the completion of each separate step.

If this hypothesis is accepted, it makes more easily understandable many of the observed facts concerning frontal lobe disease. Inertia and lack of ambition, reduction in consecutive thinking, loss of what is commonly called self-consciousness, indifference to the opinions of others, satisfaction with performance even though this may be of inferior quality and quantity—these may be considered among the primary results. Euphoria, evasion, bluffing, talkativeness, moria, aggressive behavior, teasing, indecent acts, inattention, poor judgment—these might be classed among the secondary results.

General Reference

FREEMAN, W., and J. W. WATTS, 1942. *Psychosurgery.* Springfield: C. C. Thomas. Pp. xii + 331.

BIBLIOGRAPHY AND AUTHOR INDEX

The following list of names and titles serves as a bibliography and author index. The bibliography is cross-indexed by listing all names in alphabetical order and giving the numbers of titles in which the name appears. Bracketed numbers following a bibliographic reference indicate the page of the text on which the author of the reference appears, except that where the number is preceded by cf., the title which it follows is relevant only to the content of the page which it indicates.

1. Abelman, W., and C. T. Morgan, 1943. The effect of cortical lesions upon light-aversion behavior in the rat (*J. comp. Psychol.*, **36**, 157–168). [484, 501, 507].
   Ades, H. W., see No. 198.
2. Ades, H. W., F. A. Mettler, and E. Culler, 1938. Functional organization of the medial geniculate bodies in the cat (*Amer. J. Physiol.*, **123**, 1–2). [237]
3. Ades, H. W., F. A. Mettler, and E. Culler, 1939. Effect of lesions in the medial geniculate bodies upon hearing in the cat (*Amer. J. Physiol.*, **125**, 15–23). [237]
4. Adolph, E. F., 1937. Rates of adjustment of body water content (*Science*, **86**, 22–37). [442]
5. Adolph, E. F., 1939. Measurements of water drinking in dogs (*Amer. J. Physiol.*, **125**, 75–86). [442]
6. Adolph, E. F., 1941. The internal environment and behavior. III. Water content (*Amer. J. Psychiat.*, **97**, 1365–1373). [437, 442]
7. Adrian, E. D., 1928. *The basis of sensation. The action of the sense organs* (London, Cristophers). [252, 264, 266, 301]
8. Adrian, E. D., 1932. The activity of the optic ganglion in *Dytiscus marginalis* (*J. Physiol.*, **75**, 26–27). [138]
9. Adrian, E. D., 1934. Electrical activity of the nervous system (*Arch. Neurol. Psychiat.*, *Chicago*, **32**, 1125–1136). [138, 301, 382]
10. Adrian, E. D., 1936. Berger rhythm in the monkey's brain (*J. Physiol.*, **87**, 83–84). [cf. 138]
11. Adrian, E. D., M. Cattell, and H. Hoagland, 1931. Sensory discharges in single cutaneous nerve fibers (*J. Physiol.*, **72**, 377–391). [264f., 267]
12. Adrian, E. D., and R. Matthews, 1927. Action of light on the eye. I. The discharge of impulses in the optic nerve and its relation to electric changes in the retina (*J. Physiol.*, **63**, 378–404). [202]
13. Adrian, E. D., and R. Matthews, 1928. Action of light on the eye. II. The processes involved in retinal excitation. III. The interaction of retinal neurons (*J. Physiol.*, **64**, 279–301; **65**, 273–298). [202]
14. Adrian, E. D., and K. Yamagiwa, 1935. The origin of the Berger rhythm (*Brain*, **58**, 323–351). [382]
   Akelaitis, A. J., see No. 710.
15. Allen, E., F. L. Hisaw, and W. U. Gardner, 1939. The endocrine functions of the ovaries. Pp. 452–629. In *Sex and internal secretions*, E. Allen, C. H. Danforth, and E. A. Doisy, eds. (Baltimore, Williams and Wilkins). [413, 427]
16. Allen, L. K., and K. M. Dallenbach, 1938. Minor studies from the Psychological Laboratory of Cornell University. LXXXVI. The effect of light-flashes during the course of dark adaptation (*Amer. J. Psychol.*, **51**, 540–548). [cf. 185]
17. Allen, W. F., 1938. Relationship of the conditioned foreleg response to the motor centers of the brain (*Amer. J. Physiol.*, **121**, 657–668). [cf. 495]
18. Allen, W. F., 1940. Effect of ablating the frontal lobes, hippocampi, and occipito-parieto-temporal (excepting pyriform areas) on positive and negative olfactory conditioned reflexes (*Amer. J. Physiol.*, **128**, 754–771). [151f.]
19. Angell, J. R., 1909. *Psychology* (New York, Holt). [71]
20. Angulo y Gonzalez, A. W., 1932. The prenatal development of behavior in the albino rat (*J. comp. Neurol.*, **55**, 395–442). [126]
   Aristotle [2, 5]
   Arminio, J., see No. 773.

21. Arvanitaki, A., 1939. *Propriétés rythmiques de la matière vivante.* Variations graduées de la polarisation et rythmicités. I, II. (Paris, Hermann). [57]

22. Bailey, P., and W. H. Sweet, 1940. Effect on respiration, blood pressure and gastric motility of stimulation of the orbital surface of the frontal lobe (*J. Neurophysiol.*, **3**, 276–281). [394]

Bain, A. [4]

23. Baitsell, G. A., 1940. *Human biology* (New York, McGraw-Hill). [144, 413, 423]

24. Ball, J., 1934. Sex behavior of the rat after removal of the uterus and vagina (*J. comp. Psychol.*, **18**, 419–422). [428]

25. Ball, J., 1936. Sexual responsiveness in female monkeys after castration and subsequent estrin administration (*Psychol. Bull.*, **33**, 811). [428, 430, 431]

26. Ball, J., 1936. Further evidence of hormonal basis of "heat" behavior (*Proc. Soc. Exp. Biol. N.Y.*, **35**, 416–418). [430, 432]

27. Ball, J., 1937. Sex activity of castrated male rats increased by oestrin administration (*J. comp. Psychol.*, **24**, 135–144). [431]

28. Ball, J., 1938. Partial inhibition of sex activity in the intact female rat by injected estrin (*Endocrinology*, **23**, 197–199). [427]

29. Ball, J., 1939. Male and female mating behavior in pre-pubertally castrated male rats receiving estrogens (*J. comp. Psychol.*, **28**, 273–284). [432]

30. Ball, J., 1940. The effect of testosterone on the sex behavior of female rats (*J. comp. Psychol.*, **29**, 151–165). [432]

Ball, J., see also No. 494.

31. Ball, J., and C. G. Hartman, 1935. Sexual excitability as related to the menstrual cycle in the monkey (*Amer. J. Obst. Gynecol.*, **29**, 117). [423]

32. Banister, H., 1934. Auditory phenomena and their stimulus correlations. Pp. 880–923. In *A handbook of general experimental psychology* (C. Murchison, ed., Worcester, Clark Univ. Press). [254]

33. Barcroft, J., 1938. *The brain and its environment* (New Haven, Yale Univ. Press). [43]

34. Bard, P., 1928. A diencephalic mechanism for the expression of rage with special reference to the sympathetic nervous system (*Amer. J. Physiol.*, **84**, 490–515). [368f.]

35. Bard, P., 1929. The central representation of the sympathetic system as indicated by certain physiologic observations (*Arch. Neurol. Psychiat., Chicago*, **22**, 230–246). [cf. 95–98]

36. Bard, P., 1934. The neuro-humoral basis of emotional reactions. Pp. 264–311. In *A handbook of general experimental psychology* (C. Murchison, ed., Worcester, Clark Univ. Press). [368, 374]

37. Bard, P., 1934. On emotional expression after decortication with some remarks on theoretical views (*Psychol. Rev.*, **41**, 309–329, 424–429). [368f., 372]

38. Bard, P., 1935. The effects of denervation of the genitalia on the oestrual behavior of cats (*Amer. J. Physiol.*, 113, 5). [418, 434]

39. Bard, P., 1936. Oestrual behavior in surviving decorticate cats (*Amer. J. Phsyiol.*, **116**, 4–5). [435]

40. Bard, P., 1940. The hypothalamus and sexual behavior (*Res. Publ. Ass. nerv. ment. Dis.*, **20**, 551–579). [416, 434]

Bard, P., see also Nos. 105, 543, 673.

41. Bard, P., and D. M. Rioch, 1937. A study of four cats deprived of neocortex and additional portions of the fore-brain (*Johns Hopk. Hosp. Bull.*, **60**, 73–147). [151]

Barelare, B., see No. 652.

Barker, R. G., see No. 748.

42. Bartelmez, S. W., 1926. Man from the point of view of his development and structure. In *The nature of the world and of man* (Chicago, Univ. Chicago Press). [119]

43. Bartley, S. H., 1935. The comparative distribution of light in the stimulus and on the retina (*J. comp. Psychol.*, **19**, 149–154). [168]

44. Bartley, S. H., 1936. The relation of retinal illumination to the experience of movement (*J. exp. Psychol.*, **19**, 475–485). [204]

45. Bartley, S. H., 1938. Subjective flicker rate with relation to critical flicker frequency (*J. exp. Psychol.*, **22**, 388–394). [197]

46. Bartley, S. H., 1939. Some factors in brightness discrimination (*Psychol. Rev.*, **46**, 337–358). [171, 198]

47. Bartley, S. H., 1941. *Vision* (New York, Van Nostrand). [168, 171–175, 202, 205, 218]

Bartley, S. H., see also No. 78.

48. Bartley, S. H., and G. H. Bishop, 1940. Optic nerve response to retinal stimulation in the rabbit (*Proc. Soc. exp. Biol., N.Y.*, **44**, 39–41). [172, 195]

49. Bartley, S. H., and G. H. Bishop, 1942. Some features of the optic nerve discharge in the rabbit and cat (*J. cell. comp. Physiol.*, **19**, 79–93). [172, 195, 204]

50. Bash, K. W., 1939. An investigation into a possible organic basis for the hunger drive (*J. comp. Psychol.*, **28**, 109–134). [447]

51. Bash, K. W., 1939. Contribution to a theory of the hunger drive (*J. comp. Psychol.*, **28**, 137–160). [447, 449]

Bates, R. W., see Nos. 668, 669.

Baxter, R. E., see No. 810.

52. Bazett, H. C., 1934. Methods of investigation of sensation in man and the theoretical value of the results obtained (*Proc. Ass. Res. nerv. ment. Dis.*, **15**, 83–97). [271]

53. Bazett, H. C., B. McGlone, R. G. Williams, and H. M. Lufkin, 1932. Sensation. I. Depth, distribution and probable identification in the prepuce of sensory end-organs concerned in sensations of temperature and touch: thermometric conductivity (*Arch. Neurol. Psychiat.*, *Chicago*, **27**, 489–517). [271]

54. Beach, F. A., 1937. The neural basis of innate behavior. I. Effects of cortical lesions upon the maternal behavior pattern in the rat (*J. comp. Psychol.*, **24**, 393–440). [410]

55. Beach, F. A., 1938. Sex reversals in the mating pattern of the rat (*J. genet. Psychol.*, **53**, 329–334). [cf. 416]

56. Beach, F. A., 1938. The neural basis of innate behavior. II. Relative effects of partial decortication in adulthood and infancy upon the maternal behavior of the primiparous rat (*J. genet. Psychol.*, **53**, 109–148). [410]

57. Beach, F. A., 1940. Effects of cortical lesions upon the copulatory behavior of male rats (*J. comp. Psychol.*, **29**, 193–245). [435f.]

58. Beach, F. A., 1941. Effects of lesions to corpus striatum upon spontaneous activity in the male rat (*J. Neurophysiol.*, **4**, 191–195). [391]

59. Beach, F. A., 1941. Effects of brain lesions upon running activity in the male rat (*J. comp. Psychol.*, **31**, 145–178). [391]

60. Beach, F. A., 1942. Comparison of copulatory behavior of male rats raised in isolation, cohabitation, and segregation (*J. genet. Psychol.*, **60**, 121–136). [124, 417]

61. Beach, F. A., 1942. Execution of the complete masculine copulatory pattern by sexually receptive female rats (*J. genet. Psychol.*, **60**, 137–142). [cf. 416]

62. Beach, F. A., 1942. Central nervous mechanisms involved in the reproductive behavior of vertebrates (*Psychol. Bull.*, **39**, 200–226). [cf. 433–436]

63. Beach, F. A., 1942. Analysis of factors involved in the arousal, maintenance and manifestation of sexual excitement in male animals (*Psychosomat. Med.*, **4**, 173–198). [124, 418]

64. Beach, F. A., 1942. Analysis of the stimuli adequate to elicit mating behavior in the sexually inexperienced male rat (*J. comp. Psychol.*, **33**, 163–207). [124, 418]

Beck, A. [11]

65. Beitel, R. J., 1934. Spatial summation of subliminal stimuli in the human retina (*J. gen. Psychol.*, **10**, 311–327). [202]

66. Békésy, G. v., 1933. Ueber den Knall und die Theorie des Hörens (*Physik. Zsch.*, **34**, 577–582). [228]

67. Békésy, G. v., 1936. Zur Physik des Mittelohres und über das Hören bei Fehlerhaftem Trommelfell (*Akust. Zsch.*, **1**, 13–23). [228]

Bell, C. [14]

68. Bellows, R. T., 1939. Time factors in water drinking in dogs (*Amer. J. Physiol.*, **125**, 87–97). [442f.]

69. Bellows, R. T., and W. P. Van Wagenen, 1939. The effect of resection of the olfactory, gustatory and trigeminal nerves on water drinking in dogs without and with diabetes insipidus (*Amer. J. Physiol.*, **126**, 13–19). [cf. 443]

Berger, H. [11]

Bernard, C. [6, 11]

70. Best, C. H., and N. B. Taylor, 1940. *The physiological basis of medical practice* (Baltimore, Williams and Wilkins). [143, 316, 319, 321]

71. Betz, W., 1874. Anatomischer Nachweis zweier Gehirncentral (*Zbl. med. Wiss.*, **12**, 578–580, 594–599). [cf. 78, 336]

Bevin, S., see No. 390.

Billingsley, P. R., see No. 628.

72. Bingham, H. C., 1922. Visual perception of the chick (*Behav. Monogr.*, **4**, No. 4). [110]

73. Bingham, H. C., 1928. Sex development in apes (*Comp. Psychol. Monogr.*, **5**, No. 1). [417, 421]

74. Bishop, G. H., 1933. Cyclic changes in excitability of the optic pathway of the rabbit (*Amer. J. Physiol.*, **103**, 213–224). [174]

75. Bishop, G. H., 1933. Fiber groups in the optic nerve (*Amer. J. Physiol.*, **106**, 460–474). [172]

76. Bishop, G. H., 1935. Electrical responses accompanying activity of the optic pathway (*Arch. Ophthal.*, N. Y., **14**, 992–1019). [172]

77. Bishop, G. H., 1941. The relation of bioelectric potentials to cell functioning (*Annual Rev. Physiol.*, **3**, 1–20). [37, 57, 197]

Bishop, G. H., see also Nos. 48, 49, 364, 365, 366, 367.

78. Bishop, G. H., and S. H. Bartley, 1941. Activity in the optic system following stimulation by brief flashes of light (*Proc. Soc. exp. Biol., N.Y.*, **46**, 557–558). [173]

79. Bishop, G. H., and P. Heinbecker, 1933. Fiber distribution in optic and saphenous nerves (*Proc. Soc. exp. Biol., N.Y.*, **30**, 1312–1314). [59]

80. Bishop, G. H., and J. O'Leary, 1936. Components of the electrical response of the optic cortex of the rabbit (*Amer. J. Physiol.*, **117**, 292–308). [173]

81. Bishop, G. H., and J. O'Leary, 1938. Potential records from the optic cortex of the cat (*J. Neurophysiol.*, **1**, 391–404). [173]

82. Bissonnette, T. H., 1935. Modification of mammalian sexual cycles (*Biol. Bull., Wood's Hole*, **68**, 300–313). [419]

83. Bissonnette, T. H., 1936. Sexual photoperiodicity (*Quart. Rev. Biol.*, **11**, 371–386). [419]

Blair, E. A., see No. 237.

84. Blodgett, H. C., 1929. The effect of the introduction of reward upon the maze performance of rats (*Univ. Calif. Publ. Psychol.*, **4**, 113–134). [468]

Bloom, W., see No. 548.

Blum, M., see No. 601.

85. Bodansky, M., 1938. *Introduction to physiological chemistry* (New York, Wiley). [19, 43]

Bojar, S., see No. 711.

Boldrey, E., see No. 608.

Boling, J. L., see Nos. 159, 828.

86. Boling, J. L., W. C. Young, and E. W. Dempsey, 1938. Miscellaneous experiments on the estrogen-progesterone-induced heat in the spayed guinea pig (*Endocrinology*, **23**, 182–187). [427, 430]

Borgatti, see No. 589.

87. Boring, E. G., 1929. *A history of experimental psychology* (New York, Appleton-Century). [17]

88. Boring, E. G., 1935. The relation of the attributes of sensation to the dimensions of the stimulus (*Phil. Sci.*, 2, 236–245). [245]

89. Boring, E. G., H. S. Langfeld, and H. P. Weld, 1939. *Introduction to psychology* (New York, Wiley). [292f.]

90. Boring, E. G., 1942. *Sensation and perception in the history of experimental psychology* (New York, Appleton-Century). [17]

91. Boring, E. G., and S. S. Stevens, 1936. The nature of tonal brightness (*Proc. nat. Acad. Sci., Washington*, **22**, 514–521). [245]

92. Börnstein, W. S., 1940. Cortical representation of taste in man and monkey. I. Functional and anatomical relations of taste, olfaction, and somatic sensibility (*Yale J. Biol. Med.*, **12**, 719–736). [154f.]

93. Börnstein, W. S., 1940. Cortical representation of taste in man and the monkey. II. The localization of the cortical taste area in man and a method of measuring impairment of taste in man (*Yale J. Biol. Med.*, **13**, 133–156). [155]

94. Borovoski, V. M., 1936. The relation of the gull to its nest, eggs and young (*Refleksi, Instinkti, Naviki*, **2**, 139–174). [397]

Bray, C. W., see Nos. 801, 802, 803.

95. Breed, F. S., 1911. The development of certain instincts and habits in chicks (*Behav. Monogr.*, 1, No. 1). [123]

Brenner, C., see No. 671.

Brewer, E. D., see No. 232.

Brewster, R., see No. 827.

96. Brickner, R. M., 1936. *The intellectual functions of the frontal lobes; a study based upon observation of a man after partial bilateral frontal lobectomy* (New York, Macmillan). [561f.]

97. Bridgman, C., 1938. The absolute brightness threshold and the scotopic visibility curve of the cat's eye (Ph.D. thesis, Univ. Rochester). [105, 213]

Bridgman, C., see also No. 413.

Britton, S. W., see No. 131.

Broca, P. [9f., 16, 532]

98. Brogden, W. J., 1939. Unconditioned stimulus-substitution in the conditioning process (*Amer. J. Psychol.*, **52**, 46–55). [468]

99. Brogden, W. J., 1939. Sensory pre-conditioning (*J. exp. Psychol.*, **25**, 323–332). [468]

100. Brogden, W. J., 1940. Lateral cerebral dominance in the dog tested by the conditioning and extinction of forelimb flexion (*J. gen. Psychol.*, **23**, 387–392). [cf. 340]

101. Brogden, W. J., 1942. Non-alimentary components in the food-reinforcement of conditioned forelimb-flexion in food-satiated dogs (*J. exp. Psychol.*, **30**, 326–335). [cf. 468]

102. Brogden, W. J., and W. H. Gantt, 1937. Cerebellar conditioned reflexes (*Amer. J. Physiol.*, **119**, 277–278). [489]

103. Brogden, W. J., E. Girden, F. A. Mettler, and E. Culler, 1936. Acoustic value of the several components of the auditory system in cats (*Amer. J. Physiol.*, **116**, 252–261). [236]

104. Brogden, W. J., E. A. Lipman, and E. Culler, 1938. The role of incentive in conditioning and extinction (*Amer. J. Psychol.*, **51**, 109–118). [481]

105. Bromiley, R. B., and P. Bard, 1940. Unpublished results cited by Bard. [434]

106. Brooks, C. M., 1933. Studies on the cerebral cortex. II. Localized representation of hopping and placing reactions in the rat (*Amer. J. Physiol.*, **105**, 162–171). [325f.]

107. Brooks, C. M., 1937. The role of the cerebral cortex and of various sense organs in the excitation and execution of mating activity in the rabbit (*Amer. J. Physiol.*, **120**, 544–553). [418, 435]

108. Brooks, C. M., 1938. A study of the mechanism whereby coitus excites the ovulation-producing activity of the rabbit's pituitary (Amer. J. Physiol., **121**, 157–177). [418]

109. Browman, L. G., 1937. Light in its relation to activity and oestrus rhythms in the albino rat (*J. exp. Zool.*, **75**, 375–388). [426]

Brown, C. W., see Nos. 291, 292.

110. Brown, C. W., and E. E. Ghiselli, 1938. Subcortical mechanisms in learning. II. The maze (*J. comp. Psychol.*, **26**, 27–44). [499]

111. Brown, C. W., and E. E. Ghiselli, 1938. Subcortical mechanisms in learning. IV. Olfactory discrimination (*J. comp. Psychol.*, **26**, 109–120). [cf. 511]

112. Brown, C. W., and E. E. Ghiselli, 1938. Subcortical mechanisms in learning. VI. Pattern vision discrimination (*J. comp. Psychol.*, **26**, 287–300). [510f.]

113. Buchanan, E. F., and C. P. Richter, 1933. Abolition of bulbocapnine catatonia by cocaine (*Arch. Neurol. Psychiat.*, *Chicago*, **29**, 499–503). [345f.]

114. Bucy, P. C., 1933. Representation of ipsilateral extremities in the cerebral cortex (*Science*, **78**, 418). [538]

Bucy, P. C., see also Nos. 453, 454.

115. Bucy, P. C., and J. F. Fulton, 1933. Ipsilateral representation in the motor and premotor cortex of monkeys (*Brain*, **56**, 318–342). [538]

116. Bulatao, E., and A. J. Carlson, 1924. Influence of experimental changes in blood sugar level on gastric hunger contractions (*Amer. J. Physiol.*, **69**, 107–115). [448]

117. Bunch, C. C., 1929. Age variations in auditory acuity (*Arch. Otolaryngol.*, **9**, 625–636). [238f.]

Bunch, M. E., see No. 539.

118. Burckard, E., L. Dontcheff, and C. Kayser, 1933. Le rhythme nycthemeral chez le pigeon (*Ann. Physiol.*, **9**, 303–368). [378]

119. Burr, H. S., 1916. The effect of removal of the nasal placodes on Amblystoma embryos (*J. exp. Zool.*, **20**, 27–49). [132]

120. Calkins, M. W., 1925. *The persistent problems of philosophy* (New York, Macmillan). [357]

Cameron, D. E., see No. 377.

Camille, N., see No. 448.

121. Cannon, W. B., 1927. The James-Lange theory of emotions: a critical examination and an alternative theory (*Amer. J. Psychol.*, **39**, 106–124). [355f.]

122. Cannon, W. B., 1928. The mechanism of emotional disturbance of bodily function (*New Engl. J. Med.*, **198**, 877–884). [368, 370]

123. Cannon, W. B., 1929. *Bodily changes in pain, hunger, fear, and rage* (New York, Appleton). [89, 355]

124. Cannon, W. B., 1931. Again the James-Lange and the thalamic theories of emotion (*Psychol. Rev.*, **38**, 281–295). [369]

125. Cannon, W. B., 1932. *The wisdom of the body* (New York, Norton). [40, 91]

126. Cannon, W. B., 1934. Hunger and thirst. Pp. 247–263. In *A handbook of general experimental psychology* (C. Murchison, ed., Worcester, Clark Univ. Press). [40, 441, 448]

Cannon, W. B., see also No. 321.

127. Cannon, W. B., and A. Rosenbleuth, 1937. *Autonomic neuro-effector systems* (New York, Macmillan). [62, 93, 102, 309]

128. Cannon, W. B., and A. L. Washburn, 1912. An explanation of hunger (*Amer. J. Physiol.*, **29**, 441–454). [446]

129. Cantril, H., 1934. The roles of the situation and adrenalin in the induction of emotion (*Amer. J. Psychol.*, **46**, 568–579). [cf. 359]

130. Cantril, H., and W. A. Hunt, 1932. Emotional effects produced by the injection of adrenalin (*Amer. J. Psychol.*, **44**, 300–307). [cf. 359]

131. Carey, E. L., and S. W. Britton, 1931. The induction of precocious sexual maturity by corticoadrenal extract (*Amer. J. Physiol.*, **99**, 33–43). [419]

132. Carlson, A. J., 1912. The relation between the contractions of the empty stomach and the sensation of hunger (*Amer. J. Physiol.*, **31**, 175–192). [448]

133. Carlson, A. J., 1916. *The control of hunger in health and disease* (Chicago, Univ. Chicago Press) [448]
Carlson, A. J., see also Nos. 116, 528, 779.
134. Carmichael, L., 1928. A further experimental study of the development of behavior (*Psychol. Rev.*, **35**, 253–260). [124, 129]
135. Carmichael, L., 1941. The experimental embryology of mind (*Psychol. Bull.*, **38**, 1–28). [141]
Carmichael, L., see also Nos. 413, 783.
136. Carmichael, L., and G. F. J. Lehner, 1937. The development of temperature sensitivity during the fetal period (*J. genet. Psychol.*, **50**, 217–227). [129]
137. Carmichael, L., and M. F. Smith, 1939. Quantified pressure stimulation and the specificity and generality of response in fetal life (*J. genet. Psychol.*, **54**, 425–434). [127]
138. Carpenter, C. R., 1933. Psychobiological studies of social behavior in Aves. I. The effect of complete and incomplete gonadectomy on the primary sexual activity of the male pigeon (*J. comp. Psychol.*, **16**, 25–57). [428]
139. Carpenter, C. R., 1933. Psychobiological studies of social behavior in Aves. II. The effect of complete and incomplete gonadectomy on secondary sexual activity with histological studies (*J. comp. Psychol.*, **16**, 59–97). [415, 428]
140. Carpenter, C. R., 1942. Societies of monkeys and apes (*Biol. Symposia*, **8**, 177–204). [cf. 424]
141. Carpenter, C. R., 1942. Characteristics of social behavior in non-human primates (*Trans. N.Y. Acad. Sci.*, Series II, **4**, 248–258). [417]
142. Carpenter, C. R., 1942. Sexual behavior of free ranging rhesus monkeys (Maca mulatta). I. Specimens, procedures, and behavioral characteristics of estrus. II. Periodicity of estrus, homosexual, autoerotic and nonconformist behavior (*J. comp. Psychol.*, **33**, 113–162). [417]
143. Carpenter, R. L., 1932. Spinal-ganglion responses to the transplantation of differentiated limbs in Amblystoma larvae (*J. exp. Zool.*, **61**, 149–174). [131f.]
144. Carpenter, R. L., 1933. Spinal-ganglion responses to the transplantation of limbs after metamorphosis in Amblystoma punctatum (*J. exp. Zool.*, **64**, 287–301). [131f.]
Caton, R. [11]
Cattell, McK., see No. 11.
145. Cattell, McK., and H. Hoagland, 1931. Response of tactile receptors to intermittent stimulation (*J. Physiol.*, **72**, 392–404). [266]
Chappell, M. N., see No. 617.
146. Chase, A. M., 1937. An accessory photosensitive substance in visual purple regeneration (*Science*, **85**, 484). [169]
147. Chase, A. M., 1938. Photosensitive pigments from the retina of the frog (*Science*, **87**, 238). [169, 181]
Chase, A. M., see No. 358.
148. Child, C. M., 1921. *The origin and development of the nervous system* (Chicago, Univ. Chicago Press). [33, 524]
149. Child, C. M., 1924. *Physiological foundations of behavior* (New York, Holt). [31, 524]
Clark, A. B., see No. 772.
150. Clark, D., H. Hough, and H. G. Wolff, 1935. Experimental studies on headache: observations on histamine headache (*Proc. Ass. Res. nerv. ment. Dis.*, **15**, 417–436). [cf. 359]
151. Clark, D., J. Hughes, and H. S. Gasser, 1935. Afferent function in the group of nerve fibers of slowest conduction velocity (*Amer. J. Physiol.*, **114**, 69–76). [263–265]
152. Clark, S. L., and J. W. Ward, 1937. Electrical stimulation of the cortex cerebri of cats: responses elicitable in chronic experiments through implanted electrodes (*Arch. Neurol. Psychiat., Chicago*, **38**, 927–943). [cf. 350]
153. Clark, W. E. L., 1932. A morphological study of the lateral geniculate body (*Brit. J. Ophthal.*, **16**, 264–284). [298]
154. Clark, W. E. L., T. McKeown, and S. Zuckerman, 1939. Visual pathways concerned in gonadal stimulation in ferrets (*Proc. roy. Soc. London*, B-**126**, 449–468). [419]
155. Clauberg, C., and K. W. Schultze, 1934. Die Folgen der Sterilisierung und der Kastration bei Mann und Frau (*S. F. ärztl. Fot.*, **31**, 425). [428]
156. Coakley, J. D., 1939. Electric potentials in the medial geniculate body of the cat (*Amer. J. Physiol.*, **126**, 468). [237]
Coakley, J. D., see No. 198.
157. Cobb, S., 1941. *Foundations of neuropsychiatry* (Baltimore, Williams & Wilkins). [79, 318, 348f. 353]
158. Coghill, G. E., 1929. *Anatomy and the problem of behavior* (Cambridge Univ. Press). [125, 141]
Coleman, T. B., see No. 330.
159. Collins, V. J., J. L. Boling, E. W. Dempsey, and W. C. Young, 1938. Quantitative studies of experimentally induced sexual receptivity in the spayed guinea pig (*Endocrinology*, **23**, 188–196). [431]

160. Commins, W. D., and C. P. Stone, 1932. Effects of castration on the behavior of mammals (*Psychol. Bull.*, **29**, 493–508). [429]

Coppee, G. E., see No. 435.

161. Courten, H. C., 1902. Involuntary movements of the tongue (*Yale Psychol. Studies*, **10**, 93–96). [547]

162. Cowles, J. T., and H. W. Nissen, 1937. Reward-expectancy in delayed responses of chimpanzees (*J. comp. Psychol.*, **24**, 345–358). [472]

163. Crafts, L. W., T. C. Schneirla, E. E. Robinson, and R. W. Gilbert, 1938. *Recent experiments in psychology* (New York, Harper). [138, 181, 343, 497, 503, 506]

164. Crisler, G., 1930. Salivation is unnecessary for the establishment of the salivary conditioned reflex induced by morphine (*Amer. J. Physiol.*, **94**, 553–556). [486]

165. Critchley, N., 1937. Musicogenic epilepsy (*Brain*, **60**, 13–25). [351]

166. Crowe, S. J., S. R. Guild, and L. M. Polvogt, 1934. Observations on the pathology of high-tone deafness (*Johns Hopk. Hosp. Bull.*, **54**, 315–379). [239, 250]

167. Crozier, W. J., 1916. Regarding the existence of the "common chemical sense" in vertebrates (*J. comp. Neurol.*, **26**, 1–8). [152]

168. Crozier, W. J., 1916–18. Cell penetration by acids. I–IV. (*J. Biol. Chem.*, **24**, 255–279, **26**, 217–223, 225–230, **33**, 463–470). [153, 157]

169. Crozier, W. J., 1934. Chemoreception. Pp. 987–1036. In *A handbook of general experimental psychology* (C. Murchison, ed., Worcester, Clark Univ. Press). [160]

170. Crozier, W. J., 1939. Temperature and the critical intensity for response to visual flicker. II. (*Proc. nat. Acad. Sci.*, **25**, 78–82). [cf. 193]

171. Crozier, W. J., 1940. The theory of the visual threshold. I. Time and intensity (*Proc. nat. Acad. Sci.*, **26**, 54–60). [182]

172. Crozier, W. J., 1940. The theory of the visual threshold. II. On the kinetics of adaptation (*Proc. nat. Acad. Sci.*, **26**, 334–339). [185]

173. Crozier, W. J., 1940. On the law for minimal discrimination of intensities. IV. ΔI as a function of intensity (*Proc. nat. Acad. Sci.*, **26**, 382–389).

174. Crozier, W. J., 1940. On the relation between birth weight and litter size in mice (*J. gen. Physiol.*, **23**, 309–320). [cf 123ff.]

Crozier, W. J., see also Nos. 384, 385.

175. Crozier, W. J., and A. H. Holway, 1939. Theory and measurement of visual mechanisms. I. A visual discriminometer. II. Threshold stimulus intensity and retinal position (*J. gen. Physiol.*, **22**, 341–364). [190]

176. Crozier, W. J., and A. H. Holway, 1939. Theory and measurement of visual mechanisms. III. ΔI as a function of area, intensity, and wave-length for monocular and binocular stimulation (*J. gen. Physiol.*, **23**, 101–141). [191]

177. Crozier, W. J., and E. Wolf, 1939. The flicker-response contour for the crayfish. I. (*J. gen. Physiol.*, **23**, 1–10). [cf. 174, 193]

178. Crozier, W. J., and E. Wolf, 1939. The flicker-response contour for the crayfish. II. Retinal pigment and the theory of the asymmetry of the curve (*Biol. Bull.*, *Wood's Hole*, **77**, 126–134). [cf. 174, 193]

179. Crozier, W. J., and E. Wolf, 1939. The flicker response contour for the gecko (rod retina) (*J. gen. Physiol.*, **22**, 555–566). [175]

180. Crozier, W. J., and E. Wolf, 1939. Temperature and critical illumination for reaction to flickering light. IV. Anax nymphs (*J. gen. Physiol.*, **22**, 795–818). [cf. 193f.]

181. Crozier, W. J., and E. Wolf, 1939. Temperature and the critical intensity for response to visual flicker. III. On the theory of the visual response contour and the nature of visual duplexity (*Proc. nat. Acad. Sci.*, **25**, 171–175). [175]

182. Crozier, W. J., and E. Wolf, 1939. Specific constants for visual excitation. IV. On the nature of genetic differences (*Proc. nat. Acad. Sci.*, **25**, 176–179). [cf. 174]

183. Crozier, W. J., and E. Wolf, 1940. Temperature and critical illumination for reaction to flickering light. VI. Flash duration varied (*J. gen. Physiol.*, **23**, 531–549). [194f.]

184. Crozier, W. J., and E. Wolf, 1940. Reaction to visual flicker in the Newt Triturus (*J. gen. Physiol.*, **23**, 667–676). [175]

185. Crozier, W. J., and E. Wolf, 1940. The flicker response curve for Fundulus (*J. gen. Physiol.*, **23**, 677–694). [175]

186. Crozier, W. J., and E. Wolf, 1941. The flicker response contour for Phrynosoma (horned lizard, cone retina) (*J. gen. Physiol.*, **24**, 317–324). [175, 193]

187. Crozier, W. J., and E. Wolf, 1941. The simplex threshold contour for the zebra finch (*J. gen. Physiol.*, **24**, 625–633). [175, 193]

188. Crozier, W. J., and E. Wolf, 1941. Theory and measurement of visual mechanisms. IV. Critical intensities for visual flicker, monocular and binocular (*J. gen. Physiol.*, **24**, 505–534). [cf. 190]

189. Crozier, W. J., and E. Wolf, 1941. Theory and measurement of visual mechanisms. V. Flash duration and critical intensity for response to flicker (*J. gen. Physiol.*, **24,** 635–654). [194]

190. Crozier, W. J., and E. Wolf, 1941. Theory and measurement of visual mechanisms. VI. Wavelength and flash duration in flicker (*J. gen. Physiol.*, **25,** 89–110). [194f.]

191. Crozier, W. J., and E. Wolf, 1941. Theory and measurement of visual mechanisms. VII. The flicker response function outside the fovea (*J. gen. Physiol.*, **25,** 293–308). [193]

192. Crozier, W. J., and E. Wolf, 1941. Theory and measurement of visual mechanisms. VIII. The form of the flicker contour (*J. gen. Physiol.*, **25,** 369–379). [193]

193. Crozier, W. J., E. Wolf, and G. Zerrahn-Wolf, 1939. The flicker response function for the turtle Pseudemys (*J. gen. Physiol.*, **22,** 311–340). [193]

194. Crozier, W. J., E. Wolf, and G. Zerrahn-Wolf, 1939. The flicker response contour for the isopod Asellus (*J. gen. Physiol.*, **22,** 451–462). [cf. 174]

195. Cruze, W. W., 1935. Maturation and learning in chicks (*J. comp. Psychol.*, **19,** 371–409). [123]

196. Culler, E., 1935. An experimental study of tonal localization in the cochlea of the guinea pig (*Ann. Otol., etc., St. Louis*, **44,** 807–813). [231]

197. Culler, E., 1938. Recent advances in some concepts of conditioning (*Psychol. Rev.*, **45,** 134–153) [cf. 472]

Culler, E., see also Nos. 2, 3, 103, 104, 247, 301, 302, 552, 698.

198. Culler, E., J. D. Coakley, P. S. Shurrager, and H. W. Ades, 1939. Differential effects of curare upon higher and lower levels of the central nervous system (*Amer. J. Psychol.*, **52,** 266–273). [482]

199. Culler, E., and F. A. Mettler, 1924. Conditioned behavior in a decorticate dog (*J. comp. Psychol.*, **18,** 291–303). [481]

Dagnini, see No. 589.

200. Dallenbach, K. M., 1927. The temperature spots and end-organs (*Amer. J. Psychol.*, **39,** 402–427). [259, 271]

201. Dallenbach, K. M., 1939. Pain: history and present status (*Amer. J. Psychol.*, **52,** 331–347). [268]

Dallenbach, K. M., see also Nos. 16, 588.

202. Dandy, W. E., 1931. The effects of total removal of the left temporal lobe in a right-handed individual: localization of areas of the brain concerned with speech (*J. nerv. ment. Dis.,* **74,** 739–742). [531]

203. Dandy, W. E., 1933. Physiological studies following extirpation of the right cerebral hemisphere in man (*Johns Hopk. Hosp. Bull.*, **53,** 41–51). [531]

204. Daniel, R. S., 1939. The distribution of muscular action potentials during maze learning (*J. exp. Psychol.*, **24,** 621–629). [546]

Darwin, C. [8]

205. Davis, C. M., 1928. Self selection diet by newly weaned infants (*Amer. J. Dis. Child.*, **36,** 651–679). [451]

206. Davis, H., 1934. The physiological phenomena of audition. Pp. 962–986. In *A handbook of general experimental psychology* (C. Murchison, ed., Worcester, Clark Univ. Press). [254]

207. Davis, H., 1935. The electrical phenomena of the cochlea and the auditory nerve (*J. acoust. Soc. Amer.*, **6,** 205–215). [232]

Davis, H., see also Nos. 268, 732, 733.

208. Davis, H., A. J. Derbyshire, E. H. Kemp, M. H. Lurie, and M. Upton, 1935. Functional and histological changes in the cochlea of the guinea-pig resulting from prolonged stimulation (*J. gen. Psychol.*, **12,** 251–278). [229]

209. Davis, K. B., 1929. *Factors in the sex life of twenty-two hundred women* (New York, Harper). [424f.]

Davis, L. E., see No. 618.

Davis, W. A., see No. 316.

210. Dearborn, G. V. N., 1932. A case of congenital general pure analgesia (*J. nerv. ment. Dis.*, **75,** 612–615). [267]

D'Elseax, F., see No. 717.

Dempsey, E. W., see Nos. 86, 159, 828.

211. Dempsey, E. W., and D. M. Rioch, 1939. The localization in the brain stem of the oestrous responses of the female guinea pig (*J. Neurophysiol.*, **2,** 9–18). [434]

212. Dennis, W., 1929. The sensory control of the white rat in the maze habit (*J. genet. Psychol.*, **36,** 59–89). [503]

213. Dennis, W., and R. T. Sollenberger, 1934. Negative adaptation in the maze exploration of albino rats (*J. comp. Psychol.*, **18,** 197–206). [cf. 468]

Derbyshire, A. J., see No. 208.

214. **Derbyshire, A. J.,** B. Rempel, A. Forbes, and E. F. Lambert, 1936. The effect of anesthetics on action potentials in cerebral cortex of the cat (*Amer. J. Physiol.*, **116**, 577–596). [382]

Descartes, R. [2f., 12, 14]

215. **Detwiler, S. R.,** 1924. Experiments on the transplantation of limbs in the Amblystoma (*J. exp. Zool.*, **35**, 115–161). [131]

216. **Detwiler, S. R.,** 1936. *Neuroembryology* (New York, Macmillan). [132]

217. **Detwiler, S. R.,** 1936. Growth responses of spinal nerves to grafted brain tissue (*J. exp. Zool.*, **74**, 477–495). [131]

Dewey, J. [4]

Dille, J. M., see Nos. 458, 459.

218. **Dolley, D. H.,** 1913. The morphology of functional depression in nerve cells and its significance for the normal and abnormal physiology of the cell (*J. med. Res.*, **29**, 65–129). [47]

219. **Domm, L. G.,** and H. B. van Dyke, 1932. Precocious development of sexual characteristics in the fowl by daily injections of hebin. XXI. The male (*Proc. Soc. exp. Biol., N.Y.*, 30, 349. [420]

220. **Donaldson, H. H.,** 1924. *The rat* (Philadelphia, Wistar Institute).

Donnan, F. G., see No. 85. [19]

Dontcheff, L., see No. 118.

221. **Downey, J. E.,** 1933. Laterality of function (*Psychol. Bull.*, **30**, 109–142). [341]

222. **Driesch, H.,** 1910. Neue Versuche ueber die Entwicklung verschmolzener echinidenkeime (*Arch. f. Entw.-mech. d. Org.*, **30**, 8–23). [29]

223. **Dusser de Barenne, J. G.,** 1910. Die Strychninwirkung auf das Centralnervensystem (*Folia Neuro-Biol., Lpz.*, **4**, 467–474; **5**, 42–58, 342–359). [279]

224. **Dusser de Barenne, J. G.,** 1934. The disturbances after laminar thermocoagulation of the motor cerebral cortex (*Brain*, **57**, 517–526). [337]

Dusser de Barenne, J. G., see also No. 265.

225. **Dusser de Barenne, J. G.,** C. S. Marshall, W. S. McCulloch, and L. F. Nims, 1938. Observations on the pH of the arterial blood, the pH and the electrical activity of the cerebral cortex (*Amer. J. Physiol.*, **124**, 631–636). [352f.]

226. **Dworkin, S.,** J. Katzman, G. A. Hutchison, and J. R. McCabe, 1940. Hearing acuity of animals as measured by conditioning methods (*J. exp. Psychol.*, **26**, 281–298). [107]

227. **Ebbinghaus, H.,** 1885. *Ueber das Gedächtnis* (Leipzig, Duncker and Humblot). [466]

Eckert, J. F., see Nos. 655, 656.

Ectors, L., see No. 437.

Egan, J. P., see No. 734.

Elder, J. H., see No. 819.

228. **Elliott, M. H.,** 1928. The effect of change of reward on maze performance of rats (*Univ. Calif. Publ. Psychol.*, **4**, 19–30). [472f.]

229. **Ellson, D. G.,** 1941. Hallucinations produced by sensory conditioning (*J. exp. Psychol.*, **28**, 1–20). [468f.]

230. **Elsberg, C. A.,** 1935. The sense of smell. VIII. Olfactory fatigue. IX. A. Monorhinal, birhinal and bisynchronorhinal smell. B. Some facts regarding the psychophysiology of the olfactory sense (*Bull. neurol. Inst., N.Y.*, **4**, 479–499). [148]

231. **Elsberg, C. A.,** 1937. The sense of smell. XIV. The relation of the cerebral cortex to the olfactory impulse and the areas of the brain involved in fatigue of the sense of smell (*Bull. neurol. Inst., N.Y.*, **6**, 118–125). [152]

Elsberg, C. A., see also No. 617.

232. **Elsberg, C. A.,** and E. D. Brewer, 1935. The sense of smell. X. A detailed description of the technique of two olfactory tests used for the localization of supratentorial tumors of the brain. XI. The value of quantitative olfactory tests for the localization of supratentorial tumors of the brain. A preliminary report (*Bull. neurol. Inst., N.Y.*, **4**, 500–522). [147f., 152]

233. **Elsberg, C. A.,** and J. Stewart, 1938. Quantitative olfactory tests (*Arch. Neurol. Psychiat., Chicago*, **40**, 471–481). [cf. 152]

234. **Engle, E. T.,** 1929. The effect of daily transplants of the anterior lobe from gonadectomized rats on immature test animals (*Amer. J. Physiol.*, **88**, 101–106). [420]

235. **Erickson, M. R. H.,** 1940. Brain lesions and mental functions (*Yearb. nat. Soc. Stud. Educ.*, **39**, 106–108). [499]

236. **Erickson, S. C.,** 1939. The relative effect of a cerebral lesion upon learning, retention and transfer (*J. comp. Psychol.*, **27**, 373–391). [499]

237. **Erlanger, J.,** and E. A. Blair, 1931. The irritability changes in nerve in response to subthreshold shocks, and related phenomena, including relatively refractory phase (*Amer. J. Physiol.*, **99**, 108–128). [61]

238. Erlanger, J., and H. S. Gasser, 1937. *Electrical signs of nervous activity* (Philadelphia, Univ. Penn. Press). [69, 269]

239. Fearing, F., 1930. *Reflex action* (Baltimore, Williams & Wilkins). [17]

240. Feng, T. P., 1941. The local activity around the skeletal N-M junctions produced by nerve impulses. Pp. 121–152. In *Biological symposia III* (Lancaster, Jaques Cattell). [309]

241. Fernberger, S., *et al.*, 1941. Perception (*Psychol. Bull.*, **38**, 432–467).

242. Fields, P. E., 1931. Contributions to visual figure discrimination in the rat (*J. comp. Psychol.*, **18**, 123–193). [106]

243. Fields, P. E., 1932. Studies in concept formation. I. The development of the concept of triangularity by the white rat (*Comp. Psychol. Monogr.*, **9**, No. 2). [106, 110]
Fields, P. E., see also No. 497.

244. Finan, J. L., 1939. Effects of frontal lobe lesions on temporally organized behavior in monkeys (*J. Neurophysiol.*, **2**, 208–226). [cf. 556]

245. Finch, G., 1938. Salivary conditioning in atropinized dogs (*Amer. J. Physiol.*, **124**, 136–141). [486]

246. Finch, G., 1938. Pilocarpine conditioning (*Amer. J. Physiol.*, **124**, 679–682). [486]
Finch, G., see also No. 302.

247. Finch, G., and E. Culler, 1934. Effects of protracted exposure to a loud tone (*Science*, **80**, 41–42). [229]

248. Finley, C. B., 1941. Equivalent losses in accuracy of response after central and after peripheral sense deprivation (*J. comp. Psychol.*, **74**, 203–237). [501, 503]

249. Fjeld, H. A., 1934. The limits of learning ability in the rhesus monkey (*Genet. Psychol. Monogr.*, **15**, 369–537). [111]

250. Flechsig, P., 1876. *Die Leitungsbahnen im Gehirn und Rückenmark des Menschen auf Grund Entwickelungsgeschichtlicher Untersuchungen* (Leipzig, Wilhelm Engelmann). [141]
Flourens, M. J. P. [6–8, 15f.]

251. Foerster, O., 1933. The dermatomes in man (*Brain*, **56**, 1–39). [275]

252. Foerster, O., 1936. Symptomatologie der Erkrankungen des Grosshirns motorische Felder und Bahnen. In Bumke and Foerster (*Handb. Neurol.*, **6**, 1–448). [279]
Forbes, A., see No. 214.
Forbes, W. H., see No. 580.
Fountain, G., Jr., see No. 438.
Fox, J. C., Jr., see No. 287.

253. Fox, J. C., Jr., and W. J. German, 1936. Macular vision following cerebral resection (*Arch. Neurol. Psychiat.*, Chicago, **35**, 808–826). [530]
Frank, M., see No. 495.

254. Frank, R. T., 1929. *The female sex hormones* (Baltimore, Thomas). [428]

255. Franz, S. I., 1916. On certain fluctuations in cerebral function in aphasics (*J. exp. Psychol.*, **1**, 355–364). [cf. 541]

256. Freedberg, A. S., and L. H. Sloan, 1937. Association of carotid sinus reflexes with syncope and convulsions (*Arch. Neurol. Psychiat.*, Chicago, **38**, 761–774). [cf. 351]

257. Freeman, W., and J. W. Watts, 1942. *Psychosurgery* (Springfield, C. C. Thomas). [561, 563–567]

258. Frey, M. v., 1897. Beiträge zur Sinnesphysiologie der Haut (*Ber. sächs. Ges. Wiss.*, **49**, 462–468). [259, 265]

259. Frey, M. v., 1910. Der laugige Geruch (*Pflüg. Arch. ges. Physiol.*, **136**, 275–281). [cf. 157]

260. Freyburg, R. H., 1935. A study of the value of insulin in undernutrition (*Amer. J. med. Sci.*, **190**, 28). [448]

261. Fritsch, G., and E. Hitzig, 1870. Ueber die elektrische Erregbarkeit des Grosshirns (*Arch. Anat. Physiol., wiss. Med.*, **37**, 300–332). [10, 16, 335, 538]

262. Fulton, J. F., 1930. *Selected readings in the history of physiology* (Springfield, C. C. Thomas). [17]

263. Fulton, J. F., 1934. Forced grasping and groping in relation to the syndrome of the premotor area. A physiological analysis (*Arch. Neurol. Psychiat.*, Chicago, **31**, 221–235). [345]

264. Fulton, J. F., 1938. *Physiology of the nervous system* (New York, Oxford). [46, 62f., 69, 90, 102, 257, 275, 285, 291, 311, 316, 323, 325, 327, 329, 331f., 334, 336f., 344, 350, 353]
Fulton, J. F., see also Nos. 115, 439, 679, 720, 776.

265. Fulton, J. F., and J. G. Dusser de Barenne, 1933. The representation of the tail in the motor cortex of primates, with special reference to spider monkeys (*J. cell. comp. Physiol.*, **2**, 399–426). [335]

266. Fulton, J. F., C. F. Jacobsen, and M. A. Kennard, 1932. A note concerning the relation of the frontal lobes to posture and forced grasping in monkeys (*Brain*, **55**, 524–536). [cf. 339]

267. Fulton, J. F., and E. G. T. Liddell, 1925. Observations on ipsilateral contraction and "inhibitory" rhythm (*Proc. roy. Soc.*, **98B**, 214–227). [340]

Galambos, R., see Nos. 322, 561.

268. Galambos, R., and H. Davis, 1943. The response of single auditory-nerve fibers to acoustic stimulation (*J. Neurophysiol.*, **6**, 39–57). [234f.]

269. Galambos, R., and D. R. Griffin, 1942. Obstacle avoidance by flying bats: the cries of bats (*J. exp. Zool.*, **89**, 475–490). [399]

270. Gans, H. M., 1927. Studies on vigor. XIII. Effect of early castration on the voluntary activity of male albino rats (*Endocrinology*, **11**, 145–148). [429]

271. Gantt, W. H., 1937. Essential anatomical structures of the reflex arc for establishment of conditioned reflexes (*Amer. J. Physiol.*, **119**, 313–314). [486]

Gantt, W. H., see also Nos. 102, 433, 508, 526.

Gardner, M. B., see No. 724.

272. Gardner, W. J., 1933. Removal of the right cerebral hemisphere for infiltrating glioma. Report of a case (*J. Amer. med. Ass.*, **101**, 823–828). [531]

Gardner, W. U., see No. 15.

273. Gasser, H. S., 1934. Conduction in nerves in relation to fiber types (*Proc. Ass. Res. nerv. ment. Dis.*, **15**, 35–59). [261]

274. Gasser, H. S., 1935. Changes in nerve-potentials produced by rapidly repeated stimuli and their relation to the responsiveness of nerve to stimulation (*Amer. J. Physiol.*, **111**, 35–50). [353]

275. Gasser, H. S., 1937. The control of excitation in the nervous system (*Harvey Lectures*, **32**, 169–193). [66–68]

276. Gasser, H. S., 1937. Reciprocal innervation. Pp. 212–218. In *Jubilee volume in honor of Professor J. Demoor* (Liège, G. Thone). [66f.]

277. Gasser, H. S., 1938. Electrical signs of biological activity (*J. appl. Physics*, **9**, 88–96). [49f., 353, 520]

278. Gasser, H. S., 1938. Recruitment of nerve fibers (*Amer. J. Physiol.*, **121**, 193–202). [60]

279. Gasser, H. S., 1939. Axons as samples of nervous tissue (*J. Neurophysiol.*, **2**, 361–369). [53f., 60]

280. Gasser, H. S., 1941. The classification of nerve fibers (*Ohio J. Sci.*, **41**, 145–159). [58, 261f.]

Gasser, H. S., see also No. 151.

281. Gasser, H. S., and H. T. Graham, 1933. Potentials produced in the spinal cord by stimulation of dorsal roots (*Amer. J. Physiol.*, **102**, 303–320). [66]

282. Gasser, H. S., and H. Grundfest, 1936. Action and excitability in mammalian A fibers (*Amer. J. Physiol.*, **117**, 113–133). [53f.]

283. Gasser, H. S., and H. Grundfest, 1939. Axon diameters in relation to the spike dimensions and the conduction velocity in mammalian A fibers (*Amer. J. Physiol.*, **127**, 393–414). [51]

284. Gellerman, L. W., 1931. The double alternation problem (*J. genet. Psychol.*, **39**, 50–72, 197–226, 359–392). [110, 113]

285. Gellerman, L. W., 1933. Form discrimination in chimpanzees and two-year-old children (*J. genet. Psychol.*, **42**, 1–50). [110]

286. Gerard, R. W., 1938. Brain metabolism and circulation (*Proc. Ass. Res. nerv. ment. Dis.*, **18**, 316–345). [100]

German, W. J., see Nos. 253, 679.

287. German, W. J., and J. C. Fox, Jr., 1934. Observations following unilateral lobectomies (*Res. Publ. Ass. nerv. ment. Dis.*, **13**, 378–434). [530]

288. Ghiselli, E. E., 1937. Encephalization of brightness discrimination in mammals (*Science*, **86**, 618–619). [cf. 214]

289. Ghiselli, E. E., 1937. The superior colliculus in vision (*J. comp. Neurol.*, **67**, 451–467). [cf. 214]

290. Ghiselli, E. E., 1938. Mass action and equipotentiality of the cerebral cortex in brightness discrimination (*J. comp. Psychol.*, **25**, 273–290). [cf. 500]

Ghiselli, E. E., see also Nos. 110, 111, 112.

291. Ghiselli, E. E., and C. W. Brown, 1938. Subcortical mechanisms in learning. III. Brightness discrimination (*J. comp. Psychol.*, **26**, 93–107). [508, 511]

292. Ghiselli, E. E., and C. W. Brown, 1938. Subcortical mechanisms in learning. VII. The effect of cerebral injury upon the relative distribution of errors in a spatial maze (*J. comp. Psychol.*, **26**, 301–309). [499]

Gibbs, E. L., see No. 294.

293. Gibbs, F. A., 1937. Effect on the electroencephalogram of certain drugs which influence nervous activity (*Arch. int. Med.*, **60**, 154–166). [382]

294. Gibbs, F. A., and E. L. Gibbs, 1936. The convulsion threshold of various parts of the cat's brain (*Arch. Neurol. Psychiat., Chicago*, **35**, 109–116). [cf. 350]

Gilbert, R. W., see No. 163.

295. Gilchrist, F. G., 1929. The determination of the neural plate in urodeles (*Quart. Rev. Biol.*, **4**, 544–561). [31]

296. Girden, E., 1940. The role of the auditory area of the cortex (*Amer. J. Psychol.*, **53**, 371–383). [237, 517]

297. Girden, E., 1940. Cerebral mechanisms in conditioning under curare (*Amer. J. Psychol.*, **53**, 397–406). [483]

298. Girden, E., 1942. The dissociation of blood pressure conditioned responses under erythroidine (*J. exp. Psychol.*, **31**, 219–231). [cf. 483f.]

299. Girden, E., 1942. The dissociation of pupillary conditioned reflexes under erythroidine and curare (*J. exp. Psychol.*, **31**, 322–332). [483]

300. Girden, E., 1943. Role of the response mechanism in learning and in 'excited emotion' (*Amer. J. Psychol.*, **56**, 1–20). [cf. 482f.]
Girden, E., see also No. 103.

301. Girden, E., and E. Culler, 1937. Conditioned responses in curarized striate muscle in dogs (*J. comp. Psychol.*, **23**, 261–274). [482]

302. Girden, E., F. A. Mettler, G. Finch, and E. Culler, 1936. Conditioned responses in a decorticate dog to acoustic, thermal, and tactile stimulation (*J. comp. Psychol.*, **21**, 367–385). [481]

303. Goldscheider, A., 1911. Beiträge zur Lehre von der Hautsensibilität (*Zsch. klin. Med.*, **74**, 270–296). [259, 269]

304. Goldscheider, A., 1917. Weitere Mitteilungen zur Physiologie der Sinnesnerven der Haut (*Pflüg. Arch. ges. Physiol.*, **168**, 36–88). [259, 269]

305. Goldstein, K., 1939. *The organism* (New York, American Book). [533]

306. Goldstein, K., 1940. *Human nature in the light of psychopathology* (Cambridge, Harvard Univ. Press). [528, 533f.]
Gould, J., see No. 562.

307. Gould, J., and C. T. Morgan, 1942. Auditory sensitivity in the rat (*J. comp. Psychol.*, **34**, 321–329). [107]

308. Graham, C. H., 1932. The relation of nerve response and retinal potential to number of sense cells illuminated in an eye lacking lateral connections (*J. cell. comp. Physiol.*, **2**, 295–310). [202]

309. Graham, C. H., 1934. Some neural correlations. Pp. 829–879. In *A handbook of general experimental psychology* (C. Murchison, ed., Worcester, Clark Univ. Press). [218]

310. Graham, C. H., and R. Granit, 1931. Comparative studies on the peripheral and central retina. VI. Inhibition, summation, and synchronization of impulses in the retina (*Amer. J. Physiol.*, **98**, 664–673). [203]

311. Graham, C. H., and H. K. Hartline, 1935. The response of single visual sense-cells to lights of different wave-lengths (*J. gen. Physiol.*, **18**, 917–931). [209f.]

312. Graham, C. H., and L. A. Riggs, 1935. The visibility curve of the white rat as determined by the electrical retinal response to lights of different wave lengths (*J. gen. Physiol.*, **12**, 279–295). [170]
Graham, H. T., see No. 281.

313. Graham, J. R., and H. G. Wolff, 1938. Mechanism of migraine headache and action of ergotamine tartrate (*Arch. Neurol. Psychiat., Chicago*, **39**, 737–763). [360]

314. Granit, R., 1930. Comparative studies on the peripheral and central retina. I. On interaction between distant areas in the human eye (*Amer. J. Physiol.*, **94**, 41–50). [202]

315. Granit, R., 1933. Components of the retinal action potential in mammals and their relation to the discharge in the optic nerve (*J. Physiol.*, **77**, 207–238). [170f.]
Granit, R., see also No. 310.

316. Granit, R., and W. A. Davis, 1931. Comparative studies on the peripheral and central retina. IV. Temporal summation of subliminal visual stimuli and the time course of the excitatory after-effect (*Amer. J. Physiol.*, **98**, 644–653). [202f.]

317. Granit, R., and P. P. Therman, 1935. Excitation and inhibition in the retina and in the optic nerve (*J. Physiol.*, **83**, 359–381). [196]

318. Greene, C., 1926. The physiology of spawning migration (*Physiol. Rev.*, **6**, 201–241). [cf. 402]

319. Gregersen, M. I., 1931. Observations on the quantitative changes in salivary flow during dehydration (*Amer. J. Physiol.*, **97**, 107–116). [cf. 441]

320. Gregersen, M. I., 1932. Conditions affecting the daily water intake of dogs as registered continuously by a potometer (*Amer. J. Physiol.*, **102**, 344–349). [445]

321. Gregersen, M. I., and W. B. Cannon, 1932. The effect of extirpation of the salivary glands on the water intake of dogs while panting (*Amer. J. Physiol.*, **102**, 336–343). [445]
Griffin, A. M., see No. 811.
Griffin, D. R., see Nos. 269, 615.

322. Griffin, D. R., and R. Galambos, 1941. The sensory basis of obstacle avoidance by flying bats (*J. exp. Zool.*, **86**, 481–506). [399]
Grundfest, H., see Nos. 282, 283.
Gudernatsch, F., see No. 85. [36]

323. Guild, S. R., 1919. War deafness and its prevention—report of the labyrinths of the animals used in testing of preventive measures (*J. Lab. clin. Med.*, **4**, 153–180). [229]

Guild, S. R., see No. 166.

324. Guilford, J. P., and E. M. Lovewell, 1936. The touch spots and the intensity of the stimulus (*J. gen. Psychol.*, **15**, 149–159). [260]

325. Guyer, M. F., 1941. *Animal biology* (New York, Harper). [22, 25]

Hagquist, C. W., see No. 828.

Haig, C., see No. 358.

326. Hall, C. S., 1934. Emotional behavior in the rat. I. Defecation and urination as measures of individual differences in emotionality (*J. comp. Psychol.*, **18**, 385–403). [365]

327. Hall, C. S., 1938. The inheritance of emotionality (*Sigma Xi Quart.*, **26**, 17–27). [365]

Hall, M. [6, 14]

Haller, A. v. [12]

328. Hamburger, V., 1929. Experimentlle Beiträge zur Entwicklungsphysiologie der Nervenbahnen in der Frosch-extremität (*Roux' Arch.*, **119**, 47–99). [132]

329. Hamburger, V., 1934. The effects of wing bud extirpation on the development of the central nervous system in chick embryo (*J. exp. Zool.*, **68**, 449–494). [131]

330. Hamilton, W. F., and T. B. Coleman, 1933. Trichromatic vision in pigeons as illustrated by the spectral hue discrimination curve (*J. comp. Psychol.*, **15**, 183–191). [105]

331. Harlow, H. F., 1936. The neuro-physiological correlates of learning and intelligence (*Psychol. Bull* **33**, 479–525). [532]

332. Harlow, H. F., 1940. The effects of incomplete curare paralysis upon formation and elicitation of conditioned responses in cats (*J. genet. Psychol.*, **56**, 273–282). [482f]

333. Harlow, H. F., and R. Stagner, 1933. Effect of complete striate muscle paralysis upon the learning process (*J. exp. Psychol.*, **16**, 283–294). [482]

334. Harlow, H. F., and P. H. Settlage, 1936. The effect of application of anaesthetic agents on circumscribed motor and sensory areas of the cortex (*J. Psychol.*, **2**, 193–200). [483]

335. Harlow, H. F., and P. H. Settlage, 1939. The effect of curarization of the fore part of the body upon the retention of conditioned responses in cats (*J. comp. Psychol.*, **27**, 45–48). [483]

336. Harrison, R. G., 1907. Experiments in transplanting limbs and their bearing upon the problems of the development of nerves (*J. exp. Zool.*, **4**, 239–281). [130]

337. Harrison, R. G., 1929. Correlation in the development and growth of the eye studied by means of heteroplastic transplantation (*Arch. Entw.-mech.*, **120**, 1). [132]

Hartley, D. [4]

338. Hartline, H. K., 1937. The discharge of impulses in the optic nerve fibers of the eye of the Pectan irradians (*Amer. J. Physiol.*, **119**, 328). [173]

339. Hartline, H. K., 1938. The response of single optic nerve fibers of the vertebrate eye to illumination of the retina (*Amer. J. Physiol.*, **121**, 400–415). [173]

Hartline, H. K., see also No. 311.

Hartman, C. G., see Nos. 31, 657.

340. Hartridge, H., 1934. Theories of hearing. Pp. 924–961. In *A handbook of general experimental psychology* (C. Murchison, ed., Worcester, Clark Univ. Press). [254]

341. Hasama, B., 1934. Ueber die elektrischen Begleiterscheinungen an der Riechsphäre bei der Geruchsempfindung (*Pflüg. Arch. ges. Physiol.*, **234**, 748–755). [151]

342. Hasama, B., 1935. Hirnrinderregung durch Reizung des peripheren Geschmacksorgans im Aktionsstrombild (*Pflüg. Arch. ges. Physiol.*, **236**, 36–44). [151]

Havermann, E. C., see No. 768.

Hawkes, C. D., see Nos. 658, 659.

343. Head, H., 1920. *Studies in neurology* (London, Frowde, Hodder and Stoughton). [362]

344. Head, H., 1923–1924. The conception of nervous and mental energy (*Brit. J. Psychol.*, **12**, 126–147). [542]

345. Head, H., 1926. *Aphasia and kindred disorders of speech* (London, Macmillan). [528, 531–533]

346. Heathers, G. L., 1940. The avoidance of repetition of a maze reaction in the rat as a function of the time interval between trials (*J. Psychol.*, **10**, 359–380). [551]

347. Hebb, D. O., 1937. The innate organization of visual activity. II. Transfer of response in the discrimination of brightness and size by rats reared in total darkness (*J. comp. Psychol.*, **24**, 277–299). [397]

348. Hebb, D. O., 1939. Intelligence in man after large removals of cerebral tissue: report of four left frontal lobe cases (*J. gen. Psychol.*, **21**, 73–87). [539f.]

349. Hebb, D. O., 1939. Intelligence in man after large removals of cerebral tissue: defects following right temporal lobectomy (*J. gen. Psychol.*, **21**, 437–446). [539f.]

350. Hebb, D. O., 1941. Human intelligence after removal of cerebral tissue from the right frontal lobe (*J. gen. Psychol.*, **25**, 257–265). [539f.]

351. Hebb, D. O., 1942. The effect of early and late brain injury upon test scores and the nature of normal adult intelligence (*Proc. Amer. Philos. Soc.*, **85**, 275–292). [539f.]

352. Hebb, D. O., and W. Penfield, 1940. Human behavior after extensive bilateral removal from the frontal lobes (*Arch. Neurol. Psychiat.*, *Chicago*, **44**, 421–438). [539f.]

353. Hecht, S., 1921. Photochemistry of visual purple. I. The kinetics of the decomposition of visual purple by light. II. The effect of temperature on the bleaching of visual purple by light (*J. gen. Physiol.*, **3**, 1–3, 285–290). [169]

354. Hecht, S., 1927. The kinetics of dark adaptation (*J. gen. Physiol.*, **10**, 781–809). [185]

355. Hecht, S., 1934. The nature of the photoreceptor process. Pp. 704–828. In *A handbook o. general experimental psychology* (C. Murchison, ed., Worcester, Clark Univ. Press). [184, 199f, 218, 274]

356. Hecht, S., 1935. A theory of visual intensity discrimination (*J. gen. Physiol.*, **18**, 767–789). [192]

357. Hecht, S., 1938. The photochemical basis of vision (*J. appl. Physics*, **9**, 156–164). [182f., 274]

358. Hecht, S., C. Haig, and A. M. Chase, 1937. The influence of light adaptation on subsequent dark adaptation of the eye (*J. gen. Physiol.*, **20**, 831–850). [cf. 185]

359. Hecht, S., and J. Mandelbaum, 1938. Rod-cone dark adaptation and vitamin A (*Science*, **88**, 219–221). [186]

360. Hecht, S., and E. U. Mintz, 1939. The visibility of single lines at various illuminations and the retinal basis of visual resolution (*J. gen. Physiol.*, **22**, 593–612). [200]

361. Hecht, S., J. C. Peskin, and M. Patt, 1938. Intensity discrimination in the human eye. II. The relation between ΔI/I and intensity for different parts of the spectrum (*J. gen. Physiol.*, **22**, 7–19). [192]

362. Hecht, S., S. Shlaer, and M. H. Pirenne, 1942. Energy, quanta, and vision (*J. gen. Physiol.*, **25**, 819–840). [181]

363. Hecht, S., and R. E. Williams, 1922. The visibility of monochromatic radio-action and the absorption spectrum of visual purple (*J. gen. Physiol.*, **5**, 1–34). [180]

Heinbecker, P., see No. 79.

364. Heinbecker, P., G. H. Bishop, and J. O'Leary, 1932. Allocation of function to specific fiber types in peripheral nerves (*Proc. Soc. exp. Biol.*, *N.Y.*, **30**, 304–305). [263]

365. Heinbecker, P., G. H. Bishop, and J. O'Leary, 1933. Pain and touch fibers in peripheral nerves (*Arch. Neurol. Psychiat.*, *Chicago*, **29**, 771–789). [262, 265]

366. Heinbecker, P., G. H. Bishop, and J. O'Leary, 1934. Analysis of sensation in terms of the nerve impulse (*Arch. Neurol. Psychiat.*, *Chicago*, **31**, 34–53). [265, 267]

367. Heinbecker, P., G. H. Bishop, and J. O'Leary, 1936. Functional and histological studies of somatic and autonomic nerves of man (*Arch. Neurol. Psychiat.*, *Chicago*, **35**, 1233–1255). [267]

368. Heiser, F., 1932. Stimulus temperature and thermal sensation (*Arch. Psychol.*, *N.H*, **21**, No. 138). [260]

Helmholtz, H. L. F. v. [13]

369. Hemmingsen, A. M., and N. B. Krarup, 1937. Rhythmic diurnal variations in the oestrous phenomena of the rat and their susceptibility to light and dark (*K. danske vidensk. Selsk. Skr.*, **13**, No. 7, Pp. 61). [426]

370. Henning, H., 1924. *Der Geruch* (Leipzig, Barth). [149–151, 158, 160]

371. Henschen, S. E., 1890–1894. *Klinische und anatomische Beiträge zur Pathologie des Gehirns* (Upsala, Almquist and Wiksell). [528f.]

372. Hering, E., 1920. *Grundzüge der Lehre vom Lichtsinn* (Berlin, Springer). [207]

373. Herrick, C. J., 1926. *Brains of rats and men* (Chicago, Univ. Chicago Press). [122]

374. Herrick, C. J., 1931. *Introduction to neurology* (Philadelphia, Saunders). [45, 145]

375. Hertz, M., 1931. Die Organization des Optischen Feldes bei der Biene III (*Zeit. vergl. Physiol.*, **14**, 629–674). [106]

Hess, W., see No. 503.

376. Hilgard, E. R., and D. G. Marquis, 1940. *Conditioning and learning* (New York, Appleton-Century). [457, 467, 472, 475, 479, 489f., 521]

Hines, M., see Nos. 660, 661, 662.

Hisaw, F. L., see No. 15.

Hitzig, E., see No. 261.

Hoagland, H., see Nos. 11, 145.

377. Hoagland, H., D. E. Cameron, and M. A. Rubin, 1938. Emotion in man as tested by the delta index of the electroencephalogram. I. (*J. gen. Psychol.*, **19**, 227–245). II. Simultaneous records from cortex and from a region near the hypothalamus (*J. gen. Psychol.*, **19**, 245–261). [373]

378. Hodgkin, A. L., 1938. The subthreshold potentials in a crustacean nerve fiber (*Proc. roy. Soc. London*, **126**, 87–121). [49f.]

379. Hoelzel, F., 1927. Central factors in hunger (*Amer. J. Physiol.*, **82**, 665–671). [446]

380. Holmes, G., 1917. The symptoms of acute cerebellar injuries due to gun-shot injuries (*Brain*, **40**, 461–535). [334]

381. Holmes, G., 1922. The Croonian lectures on the clinical symptoms of cerebellar disease and their interpretation (*Lancet*, **1**, 1177–1182, 1231–1237, **2**, 59–65, 111–115). [334]

382. Holt, E. B., 1931. *Animal drive and the learning process* (New York, Holt). [136, 520]

Holt, L. E., see No. 663.

383. Holtfreter, see No. 85. [30]

Holway, A. H., see Nos. 175, 176.

384. Holway, A. H., and W. J. Crozier, 1937. Differential sensitivity for somesthetic pressure (*Psychol. Rec.*, **1**, 170–176). [270]

385. Holway, A. H., and W. J. Crozier, 1937. The significance of area for differential sensitivity in somesthetic pressure (*Psychol. Rec.*, **1**, 178–184). [270]

386. Holway, A. H., and L. Hurvich, 1937. Differential gustatory sensitivity to salt (*Amer. J. Psychol.*, **49**, 37–48). [156]

387. Hooker, D., 1936. Early fetal activity in mammals (*Yale J. Biol. Med.*, **8**, 579–602). [126]

388. Hoskins, R. G., 1933. *Tides of life* (New York, Norton). [36]

389. Hoskins, R. G., 1941. *Endocrinology* (New York, Norton). [429]

390. Hoskins, R. G., H. M. Levine, and S. Bevin, 1939. The relationship of the male sex hormone to the level of bodily vigor in senility (*Endocrinology*, **25**, 143). [431]

Hough, H., see No. 150.

391. Howell, W. H., 1934. *A textbook of physiology* (Philadelphia, Saunders). [162, 528]

Hughes, J., see No. 151.

392. Hull, C. L., 1934. Learning. II. The factor of the conditioned reflex. Pp. 382–455. In *A handbook of general experimental psychology* (C. Murchison, ed., Worcester, Clark Univ. Press). [467]

393. Hunt, J. McV., 1941. The effects of infant feeding-frustration upon adult hoarding behavior (*J. abnorm. (soc.) Psychol.*, **36**, 338–360). [403]

Hunt, W. A., see Nos. 130, 471.

394. Hunt, W. A., and C. Landis, 1936. The overt behavior pattern in startle (*J. exp. Psychol.*, **19**, 309–315). [367]

395. Hunter, W. S., 1913. The delayed reaction in animals and children (*Behav. Monogr.*, **2**, No. 1). [113]

396. Hunter, W. S., 1929. The sensory control of the maze habit in the white rat (*J. genet. Psychol.*, **36**, 505–537). [113, 545]

397. Hunter, W. S., 1930. A consideration of Lashley's theory of the equipotentiality of cerebral action (*J. gen. Psychol.*, **3**, 455–468). [cf. 500]

398. Hunter, W. S., 1930. A further consideration of the sensory control of the maze habit in the white rat (*J. genet. Psychol.*, **38**, 3–19). [cf. 502]

399. Hunter, W. S., 1931. Lashley on "cerebral control versus reflexology" (*J. gen. Psychol.*, **5**, 230–234). [cf. 500–504]

Hunter, W. S., see also No. 623.

Hurvich, L., see No. 386.

Hutchison, G. A., see No. 226.

Ingram, W. R., see No. 629.

400. Ingvar, S., 1920. Reactions of cells to the galvanic current in tissue cultures (*Proc. Soc. exp. Biol.*, *N.Y.*, **17**, 198). [32]

Ivy, A. C., see No. 687.

Jackson, T. A., see No. 407.

401. Jacobsen, C. F., 1931. A study of cerebral function in learning. The frontal lobes (*J. comp. Neurol.*, **52**, 271–340). [554–556]

402. Jacobsen, C. F., 1932. Influence of motor and premotor area lesions upon the retention of skilled movements in monkeys and chimpanzees (*Proc. Ass. Res. nerv. ment. Dis.*, **13**, 225–247). [339, 495]

403. Jacobsen, C. F., 1935. Functions of the frontal association areas in primates (*Arch. Neurol. Psychiat.*, *Chicago*, **33**, 558–569). [554–556]

404. Jacobsen, C. F., 1936. Studies of cerebral function in primates (*Comp. Psychol. Monogr.*, **13**, No. 63). [391, 495, 554–556]

405. Jacobsen, C. F., 1939. The effects of extirpations on higher brain processes (*Physiol. Rev.*, **19**, 303–322). [391, 517]

Jacobsen, C. F., see No. 266.

406. Jacobsen, C. F., and H. W. Nissen, 1937. Studies of cerebral function in primates. IV. The effects of frontal lobe lesions on the delayed alternation habit in monkeys (*J. comp. Psychol.*, **23**, 101–112). [555f.]

407. Jacobsen, C. F., J. B. Wolfe, and T. A. Jackson, 1935. An experimental analysis of the functions of the frontal association areas in primates (*J. nerv. ment. Dis.*, **82**, 1–14). [554f]

408. Jacobson, E., 1932. The electrophysiology of mental activities (*Amer. J. Psychol.*, **44**, 677–694). [548f.]

409. James, W., 1894. The physical basis of the emotions (*Psychol. Rev.*, **1**, 516–529). [355f.]

410. James, W. T., 1941. An experiment on transfer of a conditioned avoiding reaction under laboratory conditions to a similar situation under kennel conditions (*J. comp. Psychol.*, **32**, 341–351). [cf. 478]

411. James, W. T., 1941. Experimental observations indicating the significance of work on conditioned motor reactions (*J. comp. Psychol.*, **32**, 353–366). [cf. 467–470]

412. Jasper, H. H., 1937. Electrical signs of cortical activity (*Psychol. Bull.*, **34**, 411–481). [57]

413. Jasper, H. H., C. S. Bridgman, and L. Carmichael, 1937. An ontogenetic study of cerebral electrical potentials in the guinea pig (*J. exp. Psychol.*, **21**, 63–71). [126f., 138]

414. Jasper, H. H., and E. T. Raney, 1937. The physiology of lateral cerebral dominance (*Psychol. Bull.*, **34**, 151–165). [cf. 340–342]

Jeghers, H., see No. 773.

415. Jenkins, T. N., 1927. A standard problem box of multiple complexity for use in comparative studies (*J. comp. Psychol.*, **7**, 129–144). [111]

416. Jenkins, W. L., 1937. Studies in thermal sensitivity. I. Adaptation with a series of small circular stimulators (*J. exp. Psychol.*, **21**, 670–679). [270]

417. Jenkins, W. L., 1938. Studies in thermal sensitivity. 2. Adaptation with a series of small rectangular stimulators. 3. Adaptation with a series of small annular stimulators. 4. Minor contributions. 5. The reactions of untrained subjects to simultaneous warm-cold stimulation. 6. The reactions of untrained subjects to simultaneous warm-cold-electric shock (*J. exp. Psychol.*, **22**, 84–89, 164–177, 178–185; **23**, 451–461, 564–572). [270]

418. Jenkins, W. L., 1938. Studies in thermal sensitivity. 7. Further synthetic evidence against the Alrutz theory. 8. Analytic evidence against the Alrutz theory (*J. exp. Psychol.*, **22**, 411–416, **23**, 417–422). [270, 274]

419. Jenkins, W. L., 1938. A critical examination of Nafe's theory of thermal sensitivity (*Amer. J. Psychol.*, **51**, 424–429). [260, 270, 272]

420. Jenkins, W. L., 1939. Studies in thermal sensitivity. 12. Part-whole relations in seriatim cold-mapping (*J. exp. Psychol.*, **25**, 373–384). [260]

Jenkins, W. L., see also No. 749.

421. Jenkins, W. L., and L. J. Stone, 1941. Recent research in cutaneous sensitivity. II. Touch and the neural basis of the skin senses (*Psychol. Bull.*, **38**, 69–91). [282]

422. Johnson, H. M., 1926. An essay toward an adequate explanation of sleep (*Psychol. Bull.*, **23**, 141–142). [382]

423. Johnson, H. M., and T. H. Swan, 1930. Sleep (*Psychol. Bull.*, **27**, 1–39). [cf. 375–380]

424. Johnson, H. M., T. H. Swan, and G. E. Weigand, 1930. In what positions do healthy people sleep? (*J. Amer. med. Ass.*, **94**, 2058–2068). [376]

Johnson, O., see No. 566.

Jones, R. C., see No. 735.

425. Jones, R. C., S. S. Stevens, and M. H. Lurie, 1940. Three mechanisms of hearing by electrical stimulation (*J. acoust. Soc. Amer.*, **12**, 281–290). [254]

426. Kappauf, W. E. The effect of removal of the visual cortex upon flicker discrimination in the cat (unpublished). [213]

Kappauf, W. E., see also No. 711.

427. Kappers, C. U. A., 1921. On the structural laws in the nervous system. The principles of neurobiotaxis (*Brain*, **44**, 125). [32]

428. Kappers, C. U. A., G. C. Huber, and E. C. Crosby, 1936. *The comparative anatomy of the nervous system of vertebrates, including man* (New York, Macmillan). [32]

Karbe, M., see No. 751.

Karn, H. W., see Nos. 602, 603.

429. Karnosh, L. J., 1935. Clinical aspects of frontal lobe disease (*J. Indiana Med. Ass.*, **28**, 568). [562]

430. Karplus, J. P., and A. Kreidl, 1914. Ueber total Extirpationen einer und beider Grosshirnhemisphären an Affen (Macacus rhesus) [*Arch. Anat. Physiol.* (Physiol. Abt.), 155–212]. [383]

431. Katz, B., 1937. Experimental evidence for a non-conducted response of nerve to subthreshold stimulation (*Proc. roy. Soc.*, **124B**, 244–276). [49]

432. Katz, B., and O. H. Schmidt, 1940. Electric interaction between two adjacent nerve fibers (*J. Physiol.*, **97**, 471–488). [197]

433. Katzenelbogen, S., R. B. Loucks, and W. H. Gantt, 1939. An attempt to condition gastric secretion to histamin (*Amer. J. Physiol.*, **128**, 10–12). [486]

Katzman, J., see No. 226.

Kaufmann, M. R., see No. 717.

Kayser, C., see No. 118.

434. Kellogg, W. N., 1939. "Positive" and "negative" conditioning, without contraction of the essential muscles during the period of training (*Psychol. Bull.*, **36**, 575). [486]

Kemp, E. H., see No. 208.

435. Kemp, E. H., G. E. Coppee, and E. H. Robinson, 1937. Electric responses of the brain stem to unilateral auditory stimulation (*Amer. J. Physiol.*, **120**, 304–315). [235]

436. Kemp, E. H., and E. H. Robinson, 1937. Electrical responses of the brain stem to bilateral auditory stimulation (*Amer. J. Physiol.*, **120**, 316–322). [235]

Kennard, M. A., see No. 266.

437. Kennard, M. A., and L. Ectors, 1938. Forced circling movements in monkeys following lesions of the frontal lobes (*J. Neurophysiol.*, **1**, 45–54). [cf. 391–395]

438. Kennard, M. A., S. Spencer, and G. Fountain, Jr., 1941. Hyperactivity in monkeys following lesions of the frontal lobes (*J. Neurophysiol.*, **4**, 512–524). [394]

439. Kennard, M. A., H. R. Viets, and J. F. Fulton, 1934. The syndrome of the pre-motor cortex in man: impairment of skilled movements, forced grasping, spasticity and vasomotor disturbance (*Brain*, **57**, 69–84). [339]

440. Kennedy, J. L., 1939. The effects of complete and partial occipital lobectomy upon the thresholds of visual real movement in the cat (*J. genet. Psychol.*, **54**, 119–149). [215, 509]

441. Kiesow, F., 1933. Sulla localizzazione di sensazioni cutanee pure di tatto e di dolore nonchè di impressioni tattile e dolorose composte (*Arch. ital. Psicol.*, **10**, 201–244). [268]

442. Kinder, E. F., 1927. A study of nest-building activity of the albino rat (*J. exp. Zool.*, **47**, 117–161). [407]

King, C. G., see Nos. 602, 603.

443. Kirk, S. A., 1936. Extra-striate functions in the discrimination of complex visual patterns (*J. comp. Psychol.*, **21**, 146–159). [510, 518]

444. Kleemeier, R. W., 1942. Fixation and regression in the rat (*Psychol. Monogr.*, **54**, No. 4). [cf. 559]

445. Kleist, K., 1934. Kriegsverletzungen des Gehirns in ihrer Bedeutung für die Hirnlokalisation und Hirnpathologie (*Hanbk. ärtzt. Erfahr. Weltkriege*, Leipzig, Barth, **4**, 343–1408). [528]

446. Kleitman, N., 1927. The influence of starvation on the rate of secretion of saliva elicited by pilocarpine, and its bearing on conditioned salivation (*Amer. J. Physiol.*, **82**, 686–692). [486f.]

447. Kleitman, N., 1939. *Sleep and wakefulness as alternating phases in the cycle of existence* (Chicago, Univ. Chicago Press). [376–379, 381–385, 395, 404]

448. Kleitman, N., and N. Camille, 1932. Studies on the physiology of sleep. VI. Behavior of decorticated dogs (*Amer. J. Physiol.*, **100**, 474–480). [383f.]

449. Klüver, H., 1933. *Behavior mechanisms in monkeys* (Chicago, Univ. Chicago Press). [477]

450. Klüver, H., 1936. An analysis of the effects of the removal of the occipital lobes in monkeys (*J. Psychol.*, **2**, 49–61). [cf. 215, 217, 509]

451. Klüver, H., 1937. Certain effects of lesions of the occipital lobes in macaques (*J. Psychol.*, **4**, 383–401). [536]

452. Klüver, H. (ed.), 1942. Visual mechanisms. (*Biological Symposia*, VII, Lancaster, Jaques Cattell). [536, cf. 212–218, 509]

453. Klüver, H., and P. C. Bucy, 1938. An analysis of certain effects of bilateral temporal lobectomy in the rhesus monkey, with special reference to "psychic blindness" (*J. Psychol.*, **5**, 33–54). [cf. 530]

454. Klüver, H., and P. C. Bucy, 1939. Preliminary analysis of functions of the temporal lobes in monkeys (*Arch. Neurol. Psychiat., Chicago*, **42**, 979–1000). [cf. 530]

455. Köhler, W., 1920. *Die physischen Gestalten in Ruhe und im stationären Zustand* (Erlangen, Weltkriesverlag). [519]

456. Köhler, W., 1925. *The mentality of apes* (New York, Harcourt Brace). [466, 471]

457. Köhler, W., 1940. *Dynamics in psychology* (New York, Liveright). [519]

458. Koppanyi, T., and J. M. Dille, 1935. Remarks on the distribution of barbiturates in the brain (*J. Pharmacol. exp. Therap.*, **54**, 84–86). [382]

459. Koppanyi, T., J. M. Dille, and A. Krop, 1934. Studies on the barbiturates. VIII. Distribution of barbiturates in the brain (*J. Pharmacol. exp. Therap.*, **52**, 121–128). [382]

Krarup, N. B., see No. 369.

460. Krechevsky, I., 1932. "Hypotheses" in rats (*Psychol. Rev.*, **39**, 516–532). [471, 503]

461. Krechevsky, I., 1935. Brain mechanisms and "hypotheses" (*J. comp. Psychol.*, **19**, 425–468). [493]

462. Krechevsky, I., 1937. Brain mechanisms and variability (*J. comp. Psychol.*, **23**, 121–138, 139–164, 351–364). [494]

463. Krechevsky, I., 1938. Brain mechanisms and Umweg behavior (*J. comp. Psychol.*, **25**, 147–174). [494]

Kreidl, A., see No. 430.

Krop, A., see No. 459.

Kryter, K. D., see No. 506.

464. Kun, H., 1934. Psychische Feminierung und Hermaphrodisierung von Männchen durch weibliches Sexualhormon (*Endokrinology*, **13**, 311–323). [432]

465. Kuntz, A., 1934. *The autonomic nervous system*, 2 ed. (Philadelphia, Lea and Febiger). [cf. 363f.]

466. Kuntz, A., 1942. *Neuroanatomy* (Philadelphia, Lea and Febiger). [77, 102, 277, 288]

467. Kuo, Z. Y., 1924. A psychology without heredity (*Psychol. Rev.*, **31**, 427–448). [cf. 136]

468. Kuo, Z. Y., 1932. Ontogeny of embryonic behavior in Aves. V. The reflex concept in the light of embryonic behavior in birds (*Psychol. Rev.*, **39**, 499–515). [126]

469. Ladd, G. T., and R. S. Woodworth, 1911. *Elements of physiological psychology* (New York, Scribner).

Lahr, E. L., see Nos. 668, 669.

Lambert, E. F., see No. 214.

470. Landis, C., 1934. The expressions of emotion. Pp. 312–351. In *A handbook of general experimental psychology* (C. Murchison, ed., Worcester, Clark Univ. Press). [359]

Landis, C., see also No. 394.

471. Landis, C., and W. A. Hunt, 1932. Adrenalin and emotion (*Psychol. Rev.*, **39**, 467–485). [cf. 359]

472. Langworthy, O. R., and C. P. Richter, 1939. Increases in spontaneous activity aroused by frontal lobe lesions in cats (*Amer. J. Physiol.*, **126**, 158–161). [391, 393]

473. Lasereff, P., 1928. *Theorie ionique de l'excitation des tissus vivants* (Coll. Monogr. scient. étrang). [157f.]

474. Lashley, K. S., 1917. The accuracy of movement in the absence of excitation from the moving organ (*Amer. J. Physiol.*, **43**, 169–194). [cf. 549]

475. Lashley, K. S., 1924. Studies of cerebral function in learning. V. The retention of motor habits after destruction of the so-called motor areas in primates (*Arch. Neurol. Psychiat.*, *Chicago*, **12**, 249–276). [342, 478]

476. Lashley, K. S., 1924. Studies of cerebral function in learning. VI. The theory that synaptic resistance is reduced by the passage of the nerve impulse (*Psychol. Rev.*, **31**, 369–375). [cf. 520]

477. Lashley, K. S., 1926. Studies of cerebral function in learning. VII. The relation between cerebral mass, learning and retention (*J. comp. Neurol.*, **41**, 1–58). [500]

478. Lashley, K. S., 1929. *Brain mechanisms and intelligence* (Chicago, Univ. Chicago Press). [29, 214, 491, 497, 498, 504, 508, 515, 523–525, 553]

479. Lashley, K. S., 1930. Basic neural mechanisms in behavior (*Psychol. Rev.*, **37**, 1–24). [500]

480. Lashley, K. S., 1930. The mechanism of vision. I. A method for rapid analysis of pattern-vision in the rat (*J. genet. Psychol.*, **37**, 353–460). [106]

481. Lashley, K. S., 1933. Integrative functions of the cerebral cortex (*Psychol. Rev.*, **13**, 1–42). [215, 500, 516, 519]

482. Lashley, K. S., 1934. Nervous mechanisms in learning. Pp. 456–496. In *A handbook of general experimental psychology* (C. Murchison, ed., Worcester, Clark Univ. Press). [108f., 122, 214f., 504, 549f.]

483. Lashley, K. S., 1935. Studies of cerebral function in learning. XI. The behavior of the rat in latch box situations (*Comp. Psychol. Monogr.*, **11**, No. 52). [491f.]

484. Lashley, K. S., 1937. Functional determinants of cerebral localization (*Arch. Neurol. Psychiat.*, *Chicago*, **38**, 371–387). [500]

485. Lashley, K. S., 1938. The thalamus and emotion (*Psychol. Rev.*, **45**, 42–61). [361f.]

486. Lashley, K. S., 1938. The mechanism of vision. XV. Preliminary studies of the rat's capacity for detail vision (*J. gen. Psychol.*, **18**, 123–193). [215, 471]

487. Lashley, K. S., 1938. An experimental analysis of instinctive behavior (*Psychol. Rev.*, **45**, 445–471). [436]

488. Lashley, K. S., 1938. Factors limiting recovery after central nervous lesions (*J. nerv. ment. Dis.*, **88**, 733–755). [493, 516, 518, 536–542]

489. Lashley, K. S., 1939. The mechanism of vision. XVI. The functioning of small remnants of the visual cortex (*J. comp. Neurol.*, **70**, 45–67). [510, 516]

490. Lashley, K. S., 1941. Coalescence of neurology and psychology (*Proc. Amer. Philos. Soc.*, **84**, 461–470).

491. Lashley, K. S., 1941. Thalamo-cortical connections of the rat's brain (*J. comp. Neurol.*, **75**, 67–121). [cf. 502]

492. Lashley, K. S., 1942. The problem of cerebral organization in vision (*Biol. Symposia*, VII. Lancaster, Jaques Cattell). [479]

493. Lashley, K. S., 1942. An examination of the "continuity theory" as applied to discriminative learning (*J. gen. Psychol.*, **26**, 241–265). [467, 471, 472]
494. Lashley, K. S., and J. Ball, 1929. Spinal conduction and kinesthetic sensitivity in the maze habit (*J. comp. Psychol.*, **9**, 71–105). [545]
495. Lashley, K. S., and M. Frank, 1934. The mechanism of vision. X. Postoperative disturbances of habits based on detail vision in the rate after lesions in the cerebral visual areas (*J. comp. Psychol.*, **17**, 355–391). [507]
496. Lashley, K. S., and L. E. Wiley, 1933. Studies of cerebral function in learning. IX. Mass action in relation to the number of elements in the problem to be learned (*J. comp. Neurol.*, **57**, 3–49). [cf. 497f., 500]
497. Lathan, C., and P. E. Fields, 1936. A report on the test-retest performances of 38 college students and 27 white rats on the identical 25-choice elevated maze (*J. genet. Psychol.*, **49**, 283–296). [109].
498. Layman, J. D., 1936. The avian visual system. I. Cerebral functions of the domestic fowl in in pattern vision (*Comp. Psychol. Monogr.*, **12**, No. 58). [121, 212, 516]
499. Lehmann, J. E., 1937. The effects of changes in pH on the action of mammalian A nerve fibers (*Amer. J. Physiol.*, **118**, 600–612). [54f.]
500. Lehmann, J. E., 1937. The effect of changes in the potassium-calcium balance on the action of mammalian A nerve fibers (*Amer. J. Physiol.*, **118**, 613–619). [55, 57]
501. Lehmann, J. E., 1937. The effects of asphyxia on mammalian A fibers (*Amer. J. Physiol.*, **119**, 111–120). [56]
    Lehner, G.F.J., see No. 136.
    Leibnitz, G. W. [3]
    Levine, H. M., see No. 390.
502. Levine, J., 1941. Studies on the interrelation of central nervous structures in binocular vision (Ph.D. thesis, Harvard University). [105, 515]
503. Lewis, T., and W. Hess, 1933. Pain derived from the skin and the mechanism of its production (*Clin. Sci.*, **1**, 39–61). [268]
504. Lewis, T., G. W. Pickering, and P. Rothschild, 1931. Central paralysis arising out of arrested blood flow to the limb, including notes on a form of tingling (*Heart*, **16**, 1–32). [262]
505. Licklider, J. C. R., 1942. Frequency-localization in the auditory cortex of the cat (Ph.D. thesis, University of Rochester). [237]
506. Licklider, J. C. R., and K. D. Kryter, 1942. Frequency-localization in the auditory cortex of the monkey (*Fed. Proc. Amer. Soc. exp. Biol.*, **1**, 51). [237]
    Liddell, E. G. T., see No. 267.
507. Liddell, H. S., 1934. The conditioned reflex. Pp. 247–296. In F. A. Moss, *Comparative psychology* (New York, Prentice Hall). [467, 559]
508. Light, J. S., and W. H. Gantt, 1936. Essential part of reflex arc for establishment of conditioned reflex. Formation of conditioned reflex after exclusion of motor peripheral end (*J. comp. Psychol.*, **21**, 19–36). [485f.]
509. Lillie, R. S., 1922. Transmission of physiological influence in protoplasmic systems, especially nerve (*Physiol. Rev.*, **2**, 1–37). [49]
510. Lindley, S. B., 1930. The maze-learning ability of anosmic and blind anosmic rats (*J. genet. Psychol.*, **37**, 245–267). [545[
511. Lindsley, D. B., 1938. Foci of activity of the alpha rhythm in the human electro-encephalogram (*J. exp. Psychol.*, **23**, 159–171). [139]
512. Lindsley, D. B., 1939. A longitudinal study of the occipital alpha rhythm in normal children: frequency and amplitude standards (*J. genet. Psychol.*, **55**, 197–213). [cf. 140]
513. Lipman, E. A., 1940. Comparative exploration of the auditory cortex in the dog by conditioning and electrical methods (*Psychol. Bull.*, **37**, 497). [237]
    Lipman, E. A., see also No. 104.
    Locke, J. [3, 6]
514. Loewi, O., 1921. Ueber humorale Übertragbarkeit der Herznervenwirkung (*Arch. ges. Physiol.*, **189**, 239–242). [93]
515. Lorente de No, R., 1934. Studies on the structure of the cerebral cortex. II. Continuation of the study of the ammonic system (*J. Psychol. Neurol., Lpz.*, **46**, 113–177). [166]
516. Lorente de No, R., 1935. The synaptic delay of motoneurones (*Amer. J. Physiol.*, **111**, 272–282). [65]
517. Lorente de No, R., 1935. Facilitation of motoneurones (*Amer. J. Physiol.*, **113**, 505–523). [66]
518. Lorente de No, R., 1935. The summation of impulses transmitted to the motoneurones through different synapses (*Amer. J. Physiol.*, **113**, 524–528). [66]
519. Lorente de No, R., 1938. Limits of variation of the synaptic delay (*J. Neurophysiol.*, **1**, 187–194). [65]
520. Lorente de No, R., 1938. Analysis of the activity of the chains of internuncial neurons (*J. Neurophysiol.*, **1**, 207–244). [64, 166]

521. Lorente de No, R., 1938. The cerebral cortex: architecture, intracortical connections and motor projections. In J. F. Fulton, *Physiology of the nervous system* (New York, Oxford). [64, 165f.]

Lotze, R. H. [14]

522. Loucks, R. B., 1931. Efficacy of the rat's motor cortex in delayed alternation (*J. comp. Neurol.*, **53**, 511–567). [551]

523. Loucks, R. B., 1935. The experimental delimitation of neural structures essential for learning: the attempt to condition striped muscle responses with faradization of the sigmoid gyri (*J. Psychol.*, **1**, 5–44). [488]

524. Loucks, R. B., 1937. Humoral conditioning in mammals (*J. Psychol.*, **4**, 295–307). [488]

525. Loucks, R. B., 1938. Studies of neural structures essential for learning. II. The conditioning of salivary and striped muscle responses to faradization of cortical sensory elements, and the action of sleep upon such mechanisms (*J. comp. Psychol.*, **25**, 315–332). [488]

Loucks, R. B., see also No. 433.

526. Loucks, R. B., and W. H. Gantt, 1938. The conditioning of striped muscle responses based upon faradic stimulation of dorsal roots and dorsal columns of the spinal cord (*J. comp. Psychol.*, **25**, 415–426). [487]

Lovewell, E. M., see No. 324.

Lucas, K. [11]

527. Luciani, L., 1891. *Il cervelleto. Nuovi studi di fisiologia normale e patologica* (Florence, Monnier). [330]

Luckhardt, A. B., see No. 689.

528. Luckhardt, A. B., and A. J. Carlson, 1915. Contributions to the physiology of the stomach. XVII. On the chemical control of the gastric hunger mechanism (*Amer. J. Physiol.*, **36**, 37–46). [449]

Lufkin, H. M., see No. 53.

Lurie, M. H., see Nos. 208, 425, 733.

529. Lush, J. L., 1930. Nervous goats (*J. Hered.*, **21**, 242–247). [350]

Magendie, F. [14]

530. Maier, N. R. F., 1932. The effect of cerebral destruction on reasoning and learning in rats (*J. comp. Neurol.*, **54**, 45–75). [553]

531. Maier, N. R. F., 1932. Cortical destruction in the posterior part of the brain and its effect on reasoning in rats (*J. comp. Neurol.*, **56**, 179–214). [553]

532. Maier, N. R. F., 1939. *Studies of abnormal behavior in the rat* (New York, Harper). [351, 372, 559]

533. Maier, N. R. F., and T. C. Schneirla, 1935. *Principles of animal psychology* (New York, McGraw-Hill). [122, 502, 553]

534. Maier, N. R. F., and T. C. Schneirla, 1942. Mechanisms in conditioning (*Psychol. Rev.*, **49**, 117–134). [469, 488]

535. Malmo, R. B., 1940. Effects of removal of the visual cortex on brightness discrimination and spectral brightness distribution in the rhesus monkey (*Psychol. Bull.*, **37**, 497–498). [213]

536. Malmo, R. B., 1942. Interference factors in delayed response in monkeys after removal of frontal lobes (*J. Neurophysiol.*, **5**, 295–308). [556]

Mandelbaum, J., see No. 359.

537. Mandelbaum, J., and E. U. Mintz, 1941. The sensitivities of the color receptors as measured by dark adaptation (*Amer. J. Ophthal.*, **24**, 1241–1253). [208, 210f.]

538. Mangold, O., and H. Spemann, 1927. Ueber Induktion von Medullarplatte durch Medullarplatte in jüngern Kein, ein Beispiel homogenetischer oder assimilatorischer Induktion (*Arch. entwick. Organismen*, **3**, 341–422). [30]

539. Margolin, S. E., and M. E. Bunch, 1940. The relationship between age and the strength of hunger motivation (*Comp. Psychol. Monogr.*, **16**, No. 83).

540. Marquis, D. G., 1934. Effects of removal of the visual cortex in mammals with observations on the retention of light discrimination in dogs (*Res. Publ. Ass. Res. nerv. ment. Dis.*, **13**, 558–592). [215, 484]

541. Marquis, D. G., 1935. Phylogenetic interpretation of the functions of the visual cortex (*Arch. Neurol. Psychiat.*, Chicago, **33**, 807–815). [121, 217]

Marquis, D. G., see also No. 376.

Marshall, C. S., see No. 225.

542. Marshall, F. H. A., 1936. Further observations on the incidence of the breeding seasons and the factors controlling Sexual periodicity. (*Trans. roy. Soc. Lond.*, **226B**, 413–428). [426]

543. Marshall, W. H., C. N. Woolsey, and P. Bard, 1937. Cortical representation of tactile sensibility as indicated by cortical potentials (*Science*, **85**, 388–390). [280]

544. Matthews, B. H. C., 1931. The response of a muscle spindle during active contraction of a muscle (*J. Physiol.*, **72**, 153–174). [307]

545. Matthews, B. H. C., 1933. Nerve endings in mammalian muscle (*J. Physiol.*, **78**, 1–53). [286]

Matthews, R., see Nos. 12, 13.

Maurer, S., see No. 760.

546. Max, L. W., 1935. An experimental study of the motor theory of consciousness. III. Action-current responses in deaf-mutes during sleep, sensory stimulation and dreams (*J. comp. Psychol.*, **19**, 469–486). [549]

547. Max, L. W., 1937. Experimental study of the motor theory of consciousness. IV. Action-current responses in the deaf during awakening, kinaesthetic imagery and abstract thinking (*J. comp. Psychol.*, **24**, 301–344). [549]

548. Maximov, A. A., and W. Bloom, 1941. *A textbook of histology*, 4 ed. (Philadelphia, Saunders). [35]

549. Mead, L. C., 1939. Thresholds of visual intensity-discrimination in phylogeny (*Amer. J. Psychol.*, **52**, 465–467). [106]

550. Mead, L. C., 1939. The curve of visual intensity discrimination in the cat before and after removal of the striate area of the cortex (Ph.D. thesis, University of Rochester). [214, 508]

551. Mead, L. C., 1942. Visual brightness discrimination in the cat as a function of illumination (*J. genet. Psychol.*, **60**, 223–257; also personal communication). [214]

Mettler, C. C., see No. 552.

Mettler, F. A., see Nos. 2, 3, 103, 199, 302.

552. Mettler, F. A., C. C. Mettler, and E. Culler, 1935. Effects of total removal of the cerebral cortex (*Arch. Neurol. Psychiat., Chicago*, **34**, 1238–1249). [cf. 481]

553. Meyer, M., 1908. The nervousness correlates of pleasantness and unpleasantness (*Psychol. Rev.*, **15**, 201–216, 292–322). [357]

Mintz, E. U., see Nos. 360, 537.

554. Mitchell, P. H., 1938. *A textbook of general physiology*, 3 ed. (New York, McGraw-Hill). [116, 154, 224]

555. Monakow, C. v., 1914. *Die Lokalization im Grosshirn* (Wiesbaden, Bergmann). [537]

556. Montgomery, M. F., 1931. The role of the salivary glands in the thirst mechanism (*Amer. J. Physiol.*, **96**, 221–227). [441]

Moore, E. M., see No. 829.

557. Morgan, C. T., 1937. The nature of discrimination of movement in the cat, with preliminary observations concerning its relation to the visual area of the cortex (M.A. thesis, University of Rochester). [215, 509]

558. Morgan, C. T., 1939. The dark adaptation curve of normal and A-avitaminotic rats (Ph.D. thesis, University of Rochester). [184]

559. Morgan, C. T., 1941. The latency of audiogenic seizures (*J. comp. Psychol.*, **32**, No. 2). [351]

560. Morgan, C. T., 1942. Studies in vision. II. Dark adaptation in normal and A-avitaminotic rats (*J. genet. Psychol.*, **60**, 109–119). [187]

Morgan, C. T., see also Nos. 1, 307, 727, 728, 736.

561. Morgan, C. T., and R. Galambos, 1942. Production of audiogenic seizures in rats by tones of low frequency (*Amer. J. Psychol.*, **55**, 555–559). [351]

562. Morgan, C. T., and J. Gould, 1941. Acoustical determinants of the "neurotic pattern" in rats (*Psychol. Rec.*, **4**, 258–267). [351, 372]

563. Morgan, C. T., and J. D. Morgan, 1939. Auditory induction of abnormal behavior in the rat (*J. comp. Psychol.*, **27**, 505–508). [351]

564. Morgan, C. T., and J. D. Morgan, 1940. Studies in hunger. I. The effects of insulin upon the rat's rate of eating (*J. genet. Psychol.*, **56**, 137–147). [448]

565. Morgan, C. T., and J. D. Morgan, 1940. Studies in hunger. II. The relation of gastric denervation and dietary sugar to the effect of insulin upon food-intake in the rat (*J. genet. Psychol.*, **57**, 153–163). [447, 449]

566. Morgan, C. T., E. Stellar, and O. Johnson, 1943. Food-deprivation and hoarding in rats (*J. comp. Psychol.*, in press). [402f.]

567. Morgan, C. T., and H. Waldman, 1941. "Conflict" and audiogenic seizures (*J. comp. Psychol.*, **31**, 1–11). [351]

568. Morgan, C. T., and W. M. Wood, 1943. Cortical localization of symbolic processes in the rat. II. The effect of cortical lesions upon delayed alternation (*J. Neurophysiol.*, **6**, 173–180). [552]

Morgan, J. D., see Nos. 563, 564, 565.

Morgan, J. J. B., see No. 785.

569. Moss, F. A., ed., 1934. *Comparative psychology* (New York, Prentice-Hall). [107]

570. Mott, F. W., and C. S. Sherrington, 1895. Experiments upon the influence of sensory nerve upon movement and nutrition of the limbs. Preliminary communication (*Proc. roy. Soc.*, **57**, 481–488). [340]

571. Muenzinger, K. F., and A. E. Reynolds, 1936. Color vision in white rats. I. Sensitivity to red (*J. genet. Psychol.*, **48**, 58–71). [105]

572. Mulinos, M. G., 1933. The gastric hunger mechanism. IV. The influence of experimental alterations in blood sugar concentration on the gastric hunger contractions (*Amer. J. Physiol.,* **104,** 371–378). [448]

Müller, J. [6, 12f.]

Munk, H. [17]

573. Munn, N. L., 1930. Visual pattern discrimination in the white rat (*J. comp. Psychol.,* **10,** 145–166). [106]

574. Munn, N. L., 1931. The relative efficacy of form and background in the chick's discrimination of visual patterns (*J. comp. Psychol.,* **12,** 41–75). [106]

575. Munn, N. L., 1938. *Psychological development* (Boston, Houghton Mifflin). [113, 122, 141, 503, 543, 551]

McBride, K. E., see No. 788.

McCabe, J. R., see No. 226.

576. McCord, F., 1941. The effect of frustration on hoarding in rats (*J. comp. Psychol.,* **32,** 531–541). [404]

577. McCrea, E. D., B. H. McSwiney, and J. S. B. Stopford, 1926. Effects of the section of the vagi nerves on the motor activity of the stomach (*Quart. J. exp. Physiol.,* **16,** 195–203). [448]

McCulloch, T. L., see No. 591.

578. McCulloch, W. S., 1938. Irreversibility of conduction in the reflex arc (*Science,* **87,** 65–66). [65]

McCulloch, W. S., see also Nos. 225, 617.

579. McDougall, W., 1926. The hypothesis of inhibition by drainage (*Psychol. Rev.,* **33,** 370–374). [523]

580. McFarland, R. A., and W. H. Forbes, 1940. The effects of variations in the concentration of oxygen and of glucose on dark adaptation (*J. gen. Physiol.,* **24,** 69–98). [187f.]

581. McFarland, R. A., and M. H. Halperin, 1940. The relation between foveal visual acuity and illumination under reduced oxygen tension (*J. gen. Physiol.,* **23,** 613–630). [cf. 188]

582. McGeoch, J. A., 1942. *The psychology of human learning* (New York, Longmans). [457, 479]

McGlone, B., see No. 53.

583. McGraw, M. B., 1935. *Growth: a study of Johnny and Jimmy* (New York, Appleton-Century). [141]

McKeown, T., see No. 154.

McSwiney, B. H., see No. 577.

584. Nafe, J. P., 1929. A quantitative theory of feeling (*J. gen. Psychol.,* **2,** 199–211). [358]

585. Nafe, J. P., 1934. The pressure, pain, and temperature senses. Pp. 1037–1085. In *A handbook of general experimental psychology* (C. Murchison, ed., Worcester, Clark Univ. Press). [256, 259, 264, 266f., 270f., 282]

586. Neet, C. C., 1933. Visual pattern discrimination in the Macacus Rhesus monkey (*J. genet. Psychol.,* **43,** 163–196). [110]

587. Neff, W. D., 1940. An experimental investigation of hearing following partial section of the eighth nerve (*Psychol. Bull.,* **37,** 527–528; also personal communication). [240, 250]

588. Neff, W. S., and K. M. Dallenbach, 1936. The chronaxy of pressure and pain (*Amer. J. Psychol.,* **48,** 632–637). [265]

589. Neri, V., Borgatti, Dagnini, and Scaglietti, 1934. Recherches expérimentales sur le mécanisme par lequel l'excitation d'infundibulum produit le sommeil (*Rev. Neurol.,* **41,** 909–912). [381]

Newman, E. B., see Nos. 737, 739.

590. Newman, H. H., 1929. Mental and physical traits of identical twins reared apart (*J. Hered.,* **20,** 49–64, 97–104, 153–166). [341]

Nims, L. F., see No. 225.

Nissen, H. W., see Nos. 162, 406.

591. Nissen, H. W., and T. L. McCulloch, 1937. Equated and non-equated stimulus situations in discrimination learning by chimpanzees. III. (*J. comp. Psychol.,* **23,** 377–381). [105]

O'Leary, J., see Nos. 80, 81, 364, 365, 366, 367.

592. Olmsted, J. M. D., 1921. Effects of cutting the lingual nerve of the dog (*J. comp. Neurol.,* **33,** 149–154). [153]

593. Olmsted, J. M. D., 1922. Taste fibers and the chorda tympani nerve (*J. comp. Neurol.,* **34,** 337–341). [153]

Ornstein, L. S., see No. 688.

594. Orr, D. W., and W. F. Windle, 1934. The development of behavior in chick embryos: the appearance of somatic movements (*J. comp. Neurol.,* **60,** 271–285). [126]

595. Orton, S. T., 1930. Familial occurrence of disorders in acquisition of language (*Eugenics,* **3,** 140–146). [341]

596. Orton, S. T., 1937. *Reading, writing, and speech problems in children* (New York, Norton). [341]

597. Parker, G. H., 1919. *The elementary nervous system* (Philadelphia, Lippincott). [23, 25, 33]

598. Parker, G. H., 1922. *Smell, taste, and allied senses in the vertebrates* (Philadelphia, Lippincott). [154, 160]

599. Parker, G. H., and R. E. Sheldon, 1913. The sense of smell in fishes (*Bull. Bur. Fish.*, **32**, 33–46). [108]

Paterson, A. S., see No. 664.

600. Paterson, A. S. and C. P. Richter, 1933. Action of scopolamine and carbon dioxide on catalepsy produced by bulbocapnine (*Arch. Neurol. Psychiat., Chicago*, **29**, 231–240). [cf. 345]

Patt, M., see No. 361.

601. Patton, H. D., M. Blum, and T. C. Ruch, 1943. Thalamic localization of the taste pathway in Macaca mulatta (*J. Neurophysiol.*, to be published). [155]

602. Patton, R. A., H. W. Karn, and C. G. King, 1941. Studies on the nutritional basis of abnormal behavior in albino rats. I. The effect of vitamin B1 and vitamin B-complex deficiency on convulsive seizures (*J. comp. Psychol.*, **32**, 543–556). [352f.]

603. Patton, R. A., H. W. Karn, and C. G. King, 1942. Studies on the nutritional basis of abnormal behavior in albino rats. II. Further analysis of the effects of inanition and vitamin B1 on convulsive seizures (*J. comp. Psychol.*, **33**, 253–258). [352]

604. Pavlov, I. P., 1923. The identity of inhibition with sleep and hypnosis (*Scient. Monthly*, **17**, 603–608). [382]

605. Pavlov, I. P., 1923. Die Charackteristik der Rindenmasse der Grosshirnhemisphären, vom Standpunkte der Erregbarkeitsveränderungen ihrer einzelnen Punkte (*Schweiz. Arch. Neurol. Psychiat.*, **13**, 568–574). [523]

606. Pavlov, I. P., 1927. *Conditioned reflexes. An investigation of the physiological activity of the cerebral cortex* (New York, Oxford). [466f., 481, 523]

607. Pavlov, I. P., 1928. *Lectures on conditioned reflexes* (New York, International). [466f.]

Pecher, C., see No. 77. [301, 307]

Penfield, W. G., see No. 352.

608. Penfield, W. G., and E. Boldrey, 1937. Somatic motor and sensory representation in the cerebral cortex of man as studied by electrical stimulation (*Brain*, **60**, 389–443). [279f., 336f.]

609. Pennington, L. A., 1937. The function of the brain in auditory localization. II. The effect of cortical operation upon original learning (*J. comp. Neurol.*, **66**, 415–442). [511]

Peskin, J. C., see No. 361.

Peterson, B. M., see No. 712.

610. Peterson, G. M., 1934. Mechanisms of handedness in the rat (*Comp. Psychol. Monogr.*, **9**, No. 6). [341]

611. Peterson, G. M., 1938. The influence of cerebral destruction upon the handedness of the rat in the latch box (*J. comp. Psychol.*, **26**, 445–459). [341]

612. Pfaffmann, C., 1941. Gustatory afferent impulses (*J. cell. comp. Physiol.*, **17**, 243–258). [160]

Pflüger, E. [14]

613. Pick, A., 1913. *Die agrammatischen Sprachstörungen* (Berlin, Julius Springer). [534]

614. Pick, E. P., 1928. Pharmakologie des vegetativen Nervensystems (*Deut. Zsch. Nervenh.*, **106**, 238–268, 304–319). [382]

Pickering, G. W., see No. 504.

615. Pierce, G. W., and D. R. Griffin, 1938. Experimental determination of supersonic notes emitted by bats (*J. Mammal.*, **19**, 454–455). [cf. 399]

616. Pieron, H., 1913. *Le problème physiologique du sommeil* (Paris, Masson et Cie). [381]

617. Pike, F. H., C. A. Elsberg, W. S. McCulloch, and M. N. Chappell, 1931. The problem of localization in experimentally induced convulsions (*Proc. Ass. Rev. nerv. ment. Dis.*, **7**, 203). [cf. 350]

Pirenne, M. H., see No. 362.

618. Pollock, L. J., and L. E. Davis, 1924. Studies in decerebration. II. An acute decerebrate preparation (*Arch. Neurol. Psychiat., Chicago*, **12**, 288–293). [319, 352]

619. Poltyrev, S. S., and G. P. Zeliony, 1930. Grosshirnrinde und Assoziations-funktion (*Z. Biol.*, **90**, 157–160). [481]

Polvogt, L. M., see No. 166.

620. Polyak, S. L., 1941. *The retina* (Chicago, Univ. Chicago Press). [163, 165, 206f.]

621. Poppelreuter, W., 1917. *Die psychischen Schädigungen durch Kopfschuss* (Leipzig, Voss). [218]

622. Potter, R. H., Jr., 1943. The effect of ablation of the striate cortex of the rat upon the retention of a conditioned response to a change in the intensity of illumination (Honors thesis, Harvard University). [cf. 510]

623. Prosser, C. L., and W. S. Hunter, 1936. The extinction of startle responses and spinal reflexes in the white rat (*Amer. J. Physiol.*, **117**, 609–618). [485]

Quigley, J. P., see No. 754.

624. Rademaker, G. G. J., 1937. Experimentelle Physiologie des Hirnstammes (Mit Ausnahme der vegetativen Funktionen). In Bumke and Foerster (*Handbuch der Neurol.*, **2**, 187–234). [331]

Raney, E. T., see No. 414.

625. Ranson, S. W., 1931. Cutaneous sensory fibers and sensory conduction (*Arch. Neurol. Psychiat., Chicago*, **26**, 1122–1144). [cf. 263f.]

626. Ranson, S. W., 1939. Somnolence caused by hypothalamic lesions in the monkey (*Arch. Neurol. Psychiat., Chicago*, **41**, 1–23). [383]

627. Ranson, S. W., 1941. *Anatomy of the nervous system* (Philadelphia, Saunders). [145]

628. Ranson, S. W., and P. R. Billingsley, 1916. Vasomotor reactions from stimulation of the floor of the fourth ventricle. Studies in vasomotor reflex arcs. III. (*Amer. J. Physiol.*, **41**, 85–90). [265]

629. Ranson, S. W., and W. R. Ingram, 1932. Catalepsy caused by lesions between the mammillary bodies and third nerve in the cat (*Amer. J. Physiol.*, **101**, 690–696). [383]

630. Rashevsky, N., 1937. Mathematical biophysics of conditioning (*Psychometrika*, **2**, 199–209). [522]

631. Rashevsky, N., 1938. *Mathematical biophysics: Physicomathematical foundations of biology* (Chicago, Univ. Chicago Press). [522]

632. Ray, B. S., and H. G. Wolff, 1940. Experimental studies on headache: pain-sensitive structures of the head (*Arch. Surg., Chicago*, **41**, 813–856). [cf. 359f.]

633. Ray, J. J., 1936. The generalizing ability of dull, bright, and superior children (*Peabody Coll. Contrib. Educ.*, No. 175). [110]

Rayson, G. G., see No. 712.

634. Reeves, C. D., 1919. Discrimination of lights of different wave length by fish (*Behav. Monogr.*, **4**, No. 3). [105]

Rempel, B., see No. 214.

Reynolds, A. E., see No. 571.

Rhoades, R. P., see No. 817.

635. Richter, C. P., 1922. A behavioristic study of the activity of the rat (*Comp. Psychol. Monogr.*, **1**, 1–55). [440, 447]

636. Richter, C. P., 1927. Animal behavior and internal drives (*Quart. Rev. Biol.*, **2**, 307–343). [386f.]

637. Richter, C. P., 1931. The grasping reflex in the new-born monkey (*Arch. Neurol. Psychiat., Chicago*, **26**, 784–790). [345]

638. Richter, C. P., 1933. The role played by the thyroid gland in the production of gross body activity (*Endocrinology*, **17**, 73–87). [390]

639. Richter, C. P., 1933. The effect of early gonadectomy on the gross body activity of rats (*Endocrinology*, **17**, 445–450). [388, 429]

640. Richter, C. P., 1933. Cyclical phenomena produced in rats by section of the pituitary stalk and their possible relation to pseudo-pregnancy (*Amer. J. Physiol.*, **106**, 80–89). [426]

641. Richter, C. P., 1934. Pregnancy urine given by mouth to gonadectomized rats: its effect on spontaneous activity and on the reproductive tract (*Amer. J. Physiol.*, **110**, 499–512). [cf. 389]

642. Richter, C. P., 1934. The grasp reflex of the new-born infant (*Amer. J. Dis. Childr.*, **48**, 327–332). [345]

643. Richter, C. P., 1935. The primacy of polyuria in diabetes insipidus (*Amer. J. Physiol.*, **112**, 481–487). [444]

644. Richter, C. P., 1936. The spontaneous activity of adrenalectomized rats treated with replacement and other therapy (*Endocrinology*, **20**, 657–666). [cf. 389f.]

645. Richter, C. P., 1937. Hypophyseal control of behavior (*Cold Spring Harbor Symposia on Quant. Biol.*, **5**, 258–268). [390, 406–409]

646. Richter, C. P., 1938. Factors determining voluntary ingestion of water in normals and in individuals with maximum diabetes insipidus (*Amer. J. Physiol.*, **122**, 668–675). [445]

647. Richter, C. P., 1939. Mineral appetite of parathyroidectomized rats (*Amer. J. med. Sci.*, **198**, 9–16). [cf. 454f.]

648. Richter, C. P., 1941. Behavior and endocrine regulators of the internal environment (*Endocrinology*, **28**, 193–195).

649. Richter, C. P., 1941. The internal environment and behavior. V. Internal secretions (*Amer. J. Psychiat.*, **97**, 878–893). [444, 454]

650. Richter, C. P., 1941. Alcohol as a food (*Quart. J. Stud. Alco.*, **1**, 650–666).

651. Richter, C. P., 1942. Physiological psychology (*Ann. Rev. Physiol.*, **4**, 561–574). [451]

Richter, C. P., see also Nos. 113, 472.

652. Richter, C. P., and B. Barelare, 1939. Further observations on the carbohydrate, fat, and protein appetite of vitamin B deficient rats (*Amer. J. Physiol.*, **127**, 199–210). [451]

653. Richter, C. P., and K. H. Campbell, 1940. Taste thresholds and taste preference of rats for five common sugars (*J. Nutrition*, **20**, 31–46).

654. Richter, C. P., and K. H. Campbell, 1940. Alcohol taste thresholds and concentrations of solution preferred by rats (*Science*, **91**, 507–508).

655. Richter, C. P., and J. F. Eckert, 1935. Further evidence for the primacy of polyuria in diabetes insipidus (*Amer. J. Physiol.*, **113**, 578–581). [cf. 444]

656. Richter, C. P., and J. F. Eckert. 1939. Mineral appetite of parathyroidectomized rats (*Amer. J. med. Sci.*, **198**, 9–16). [cf. 454f.]

657. Richter, C. P., and C. G. Hartman, 1934. The effect of injection of amniotin on the spontaneous activity of gonadectomized rats (*Amer. J. Physiol.*, **108**, 136–143). [389]

658. Richter, C. P., and C. D. Hawkes, 1939. Increased spontaneous activity and food-intake produced in rats by removal of the frontal poles of the brain (*J. Neurol. Psychiat.*, Chicago, **2**, 231–242). [391]

659. Richter, C. P., and C. D. Hawkes, 1941. The dependence of the carbohydrate, fat and protein appetite of rats on the various components of the vitamin B complex (*Amer. J. Physiol.*, **131**, 639–649). [456]

660. Richter, C. P., and M. Hines, 1932. Experimental production of the grasp reflex in adult monkeys by lesions of the frontal lobes (*Amer. J. Physiol.*, **101**, 87–88). [345]

661. Richter, C. P., and M. Hines, 1934. The production of the "grasp reflex" in adult macaques by experimental frontal lobe lesions (*Res. Publ. Ass. Res. nerv. ment. Dis.*, **13**, 211–224). [345]

662. Richter, C. P., and M. Hines, 1938. Increased spontaneous activity produced in monkeys by brain lesions (*Brain*, **61**, 1–16). [391]

663. Richter, C. P., L. E. Holt, and B. Barelare, 1937. Vitamin B1 craving in rats (*Science*, **86**, 354–355).

664. Richter, C. P., and A. S. Paterson, 1931. Bulbocapnine catalepsy and the grasp reflex (*J. Pharmacol. exp. Therap.*, **43**, 677–691). [345]

665. Richter, C. P., and E. C. H. Schmidt, 1939. Behavior and anatomical changes produced in rats by pancreatectomy (*Endocrinology*, **25**, 698–706). [453]

666. Richter, C. P., and E. C. H. Schmidt, 1941. Increased fat and decreased carbohydrate appetite of pancreatomized rats (*Endocrinology*, **28**, 179–192). [cf. 455]

667. Riddle, O., 1935. Contemplating the hormones (*Endocrinology*, **19**, 1–13).

668. Riddle, O., R. W. Bates, and E. L. Lahr, 1935. Prolactin induces broodiness in fowl (*Amer. J. Physiol.*, **111**, 352–360). [411]

669. Riddle, O., E. L. Lahr, and R. W. Bates, 1935. Maternal behavior induced in virgin rats by prolactin (*Proc. Soc. exp. Biol.*, N.Y., **32**,, 730–734). [cf. 411]

670. Riggs, L. A., 1937. Dark adaptation in the frog eye as determined by the electrical response of the retina (*J. cell. comp. Physiol.*, **9**, 491–510). [187]

Riggs, L. A., see also No. 312.

Rioch, D. M., see Nos. 41, 211.

671. Rioch, D. M., and C. Brenner, 1938. Experiments on the striatum and rhinencephalon (*J. comp. Neurol.*, **68**, 491–507). [151]

Robinson, E. E., see No. 163.

Robinson, E. H., see Nos. 435, 436.

672. Rogers, F. T., 1922. Studies of the brain stem. VI. An experimental study of the corpus striatum of the pigeon as related to various instinctive types of behavior (*J. comp. Neurol.*, **35**, 21–60). [435]

Rolando, L. [10]

673. Root, W. S., and P. Bard, 1937. Erection in the cat following removal of lumbo-sacral segments (*Amer. J. Physiol.*, **119**, 392–393). [419]

Rosenblueth, A., see No. 127.

Rothschild, P., see No. 504.

674. Roule, L., 1933. *Fishes: their journeys and migrations* (New York, Norton). [401]

675. Rowan, W., 1931. *The riddle of migration* (Baltimore, Williams and Wilkins). [cf. 400f.]

676. Rowan, W., 1938. Light and seasonal reproduction in animals (*Biol. Rev.*, **13**, 374–402). [419]

677. Roy, S., 1936. An experimental study of certain qualities of the sense of touch (*Indian J. Psychol.*, **11**, 157–189). [260]

Rubin, M. A., see No. 377.

678. Ruch, T. C., 1935. Cortical localization of somatic sensibility. The effect of precentral, postcentral and posterior parietal lesions upon the performance of monkeys trained to discriminate weights (*Proc. Ass. Res. nerv. ment. Dis.*, **15**, 289–330). [281, 289f., 512]

Ruch, T. C., see also No. 601.

679. Ruch, T. C., J. F. Fulton, and W. J. German, 1938. Sensory discrimination in monkey, chimpanzee and man after lesions of the parietal lobe (*Arch. Neurol. Psychiat.*, Chicago, **39**, 919–937). [290, 513]

680. Ruch, T. C., and H. A. Shenkin, 1943. The relation of area 13 of the orbital surface of the frontal lobe to hyperactivity and hyperphagia in monkeys (*J. Neurophysiol.*, **6**, 349–360). [394f.]

681. Ruckmick, C. A., 1936. *The psychology of feeling and emotion* (New York, McGraw-Hill). [363, 374]

682. Rylander, G., 1939. *Personality changes after operations on the frontal lobes* (London, Oxford). [562]

683. Rylander, G., 1941. Brain surgery and psychiatry (*Acat. chir. Scandinav.*, 85, 213). [562]
684. Sanford, F. H., 1942. Speech and personality (*Psychol. Bull.*, **39**, 811–845).
    Scaglietti, see No. 589.
685. Scharrer, E., 1939. The functional significance of the capillary bed in the brain of the opossum (*Anat. Rec.*, **75**, 319–340). [99]
686. Schilder, P., 1934. Localization of the body image (postural model of the body) (*Res. Publ. Ass. nerv. ment. Dis.*, **13**, 466–484). [534f.]
    Schmidt, E. C. H., see Nos. 665, 666.
    Schmitt, O. H., see No. 432.
687. Schnedorf, J. G., and A. C. Ivy, 1929. An examination of the hypnotoxin theory of sleep (*Amer. J. Physiol.*, **125**, 491–505). [381]
    Schneirla, T. C., see Nos. 163, 534.
688. Schouten, J. F., and L. S. Ornstein, 1939. Measurements on direct and indirect adaptation by means of a binocular method (*J. opt. Soc. Amer.*, **29**, 168–182). [183]
    Schultz, F. W., see No. 807.
    Schultze, K. W., see No. 155.
    Scott, C. C., see No. 689.
689. Scott, W. W., C. C. Scott, and A. B. Luckhardt, 1938. Observations on the blood sugar level before, during, and after hunger periods in humans (*Amer. J. Physiol.*, **123**, 243–247). [448]
    Settlage, P. H., see Nos. 333, 334, 335.
690. Seward, J. P., 1940. Studies on the reproductive activities of the guinea pig. III. The effect of androgenic hormone on sex drive in males and females (*J. comp. Psychol.*, **30**, 435–449). [430f.]
691. Seward, J. P., 1941. The hormonal induction of behavior (*Psychol. Rev.*, **48**, 302–315). [433]
    Sheard, N. M., see No. 789.
    Sheldon, R. E., see No. 599.
    Shenkin, H. A., see No. 680.
692. Sherrington, C. S., 1893. Experiments in the examination of the peripheral distribution of the fibres of the posterior roots of some spinal nerves (*Philos. Trans.*, **184B**, 641–763). [274]
693. Sherrington, C. S., 1898. Decerebrate rigidity, and reflex coordination of movements (*J. Physiol.*, **22**, 319–332). [320]
694. Sherrington, C. S., 1906. *The integrative action of the nervous system* (London, Constable). [14f., 65]
695. Sherrington, C. S., 1909. On plastic tonus and proprioceptive reflexes (*Quart. J. exp. Physiol.*, **2**, 109–156). [344]
    Sherrington, C. S., see also No. 570.
696. Shapiro, H. A., 1937. Effect of testosterone proprionate on mating (*Nature*, **139**, 588). [420]
697. Shirley, M., 1929. Spontaneous activity (*Psychol. Bull.*, **26**, 341–365). [395]
    Shlaer, S., see No. 362.
    Shurrager, H. C., see No. 699.
    Shurrager, P. S., see No. 198.
698. Shurrager, P. S., and E. Culler, 1938. Phenomena allied to conditioning in the spinal dog (*Amer. J. Physiol.*, **123**, 186–187). [485]
699. Shurrager, P. S., and H. C. Shurrager, 1941. Converting a spinal CR into a reflex (*J. exp. Psychol.*, **29**, 217–224). [485]
    Sloan, L. H., see No. 256.
700. Slonaker, J. R., 1924. The effect of pubescence, oestruation and menopause on the voluntary activity in albino rats (*Amer. J. Physiol.*, **68**, 294–315). [387, 422]
701. Slonaker, J. R., 1935. Sex drives in rats (*Amer. J. Physiol.*, **112**, 176–181). [422]
702. Smith, D. E., 1939. Cerebral localization in somaesthetic discrimination in the rat (*J. comp. Psychol.*, **28**, 161–188). [282, 511]
703. Smith, J. R., 1938. The electroencephalogram during normal infancy and childhood (*J. gen. Psychol.*, **53**, 431–453, 455–469, 471–482). [138]
704. Smith, J. R., 1941. The frequency growth of the human alpha rhythms during normal infancy and childhood (*J. Psychol.*, **11**, 177–198). [138–140]
705. Smith, K. U., 1937. The postoperative effects of removal of the striate cortex upon certain unlearned visually controlled reactions in the cat (*J. genet. Psychol.*, **50**, 137–156). [215, 328, 484]
706. Smith, K. U., 1937. Visual discrimination in the cat. V. The postoperative effects of removal of the striate cortex upon intensity discrimination (*J. genet. Psychol.*, **51**, 329–369). [214f.]
707. Smith, K. U., 1938. Visual discrimination in the cat. VI. The relation between pattern vision and visual acuity and the optic projection centers of the nervous system (*J. genet. Psychol.*, **53**, 251–272). [215, 325]

708. Smith, K. U., 1940. The neural centers concerned in the mediation of apparent movement vision (*J. exp. Psychol.*, **26**, 443–466). [216]

709. Smith, K. U., 1941. The effect of partial and complete decortication upon the extinction of optic nystagmus (*J. gen. Psychol.*, **25**, 3–18). [325]

710. Smith, K. U., and A. J. Akelaitis, 1942. Studies on the corpus callosum. I. Laterality in behavior and bilateral motor organization in man before and after section of the corpus callosum (*Arch. Neurol. Psychiat., Chicago*, **47**, 519–543). [cf. 342]

711. Smith, K. U., W. E. Kappauf, and S. Bojar, 1940. The functions of the visual cortex in optic nystagmus at different velocities of movement in the visual field (*J. gen. Psychol.*, **22**, 341–357). [216, 325]

712. Smith, K. U., B. M. Peterson, and G. G. Rayson, 1941. Spontaneous activity in guinea pigs following removal of the frontal areas of the cortex (*J. gen. Psychol.*, **24**, 439–445). [cf. 391–395]

713. Smith, K. U., and J. Warkentin, 1939. The central neural organization of optic functions related to minimum visible acuity (*J. genet. Psychol.*, **55**, 177–195).

Smith, M. F., see No. 137.

714. Smith, P. E., 1926. Hastening development of female genital system by daily homeoplastic pituitary transplants (*Proc. Soc. exp. Biol., N.Y.*, **24**, 131–132).

715. Smith, P. E., 1927. The induction of precocious sexual maturity by pituitary homeotransplants (*Amer. J. Physiol.*, **80**, 114–125). [420]

716. Smith, P. E., 1940. (Ed.) *Bailey's textbook of histology* (Baltimore, Williams and Wilkins). [223]

Snow, W. B., see No. 725.

Sollenberger, R. T., see No. 213.

717. Solomon, H. C., M. R. Kaufmann, and D'Elseax, F., 1931. Some effects of the inhalation of carbon dioxide and oxygen, and of intravenous sodium amytal on certain neuropsychiatric conditions (*Amer. J. Psychiat.*, **10**, 761–769). [346]

718. Speidel, C. C., 1933. Studies of living nerves. II. Activities of ameboid growth cones, sheath cells, and myelin segments, as revealed by prolonged observation of individual nerve fibers in frog tadpoles (*Amer. J. Anat.*, **52**, 1–79). [32]

719. Spemann, H., 1938. *Embryonic development and induction* (New Haven, Yale Univ. Press). [30, 33]

Spemann, H., see also No. 538.

720. Spence, K. W., and J. F. Fulton, 1936. The effects of occipital lobectomy on vision in chimpanzee (*Brain*, **59**, 35–50). [217]

Spencer, S., see No. 438.

721. Sperry, R. W., 1940. The functional results of muscle transposition in the hind limb of the rat (*J. comp. Neurol.*, **73**, 379–404). [135f.]

722. Sperry, R. W., 1941. The effect of crossing nerves to antagonistic muscles in the hind limb of the rat (*J. comp. Neurol.*, **75**, 1–20). [135f.]

723. Sperry, R. W., 1942. Transplantation of motor nerves and muscles in the forelimb of the rat (*J. comp. Neurol.*, **76**, 283–321). [135f.]

Spurzheim, G. [15]

724. Steinberg, J. C., and M. B. Gardner, 1937. The dependence of hearing impairment on sound intensity (*J. acoust. Soc. Amer.*, **9**, 11–23). [245f.]

725. Steinberg, J. C., and W. B. Snow, 1934. Physical factors in auditory experience (*Bell System Tech. J.*, **13**, 245–259). [248]

726. Steinhardt, J., 1936. Intensity discrimination in the human eye. I. The relation of $\Delta I/I$ to intensity (*J. gen. Physiol.*, **20**, 185–209). [cf. 191f.]

Stellar, E., see No. 566.

727. Stellar, E., C. T. Morgan, and M. Yarosh, 1942. Cortical localization of symbolic processes in the rat (*J. comp. Psychol.*, **34**, 107–126). [504, 552]

728. Stellar, E., and C. T. Morgan, 1943. The effect of cortical lesions upon kinesthetic discrimination in the rat (unpublished). [289]

729. Stevens, S. S., 1934. The attributes of tones (*Proc. nat. Acad. Sci.*, **20**, 457–459). [245]

730. Stevens, S. S., 1935. The relation of pitch to intensity (*J. acoust. Soc. Amer.*, **6**, 150–154). [240]

731. Stevens, S. S., 1937. On hearing by electrical stimulation (*J. acoust. Soc. Amer.*, **8**, 191–195). [254]

Stevens, S. S., see also Nos. 91, 425.

732. Stevens, S. S., and H. Davis, 1938. *Hearing: its psychology and physiology* (New York, Wiley). [220, 226f., 229, 232, 241, 243f., 246, 248, 254, 307]

733. Stevens, S. S., H. Davis, and M. H. Lurie, 1935. The localization of pitch perception on the basilar membrane (*J. gen. Psychol.*, **13**, 297–315). [229, 230, 233, 238, 242]

734. Stevens, S. S., and J. P. Egan, 1941. Diplacusis in "normal" ears (*Psychol. Bull.*, **38**, 548). [252f.]

735. Stevens, S. S., and R. C. Jones, 1939. The mechanism of hearing by electrical stimulation (*J. acoust. Soc. Amer.*, **10**, 261–269). [254]

736. Stevens, S. S., C. T. Morgan, and J. Volkmann, 1941. Theory of the neural quantum in the discrimination of loudness and pitch (*Amer. J. Psychol.*, **54**, 315–335). [cf. 241]

737. Stevens, S. S., and E. B. Newman, 1936. On the nature of aural harmonics (*Proc. nat. Acad. Sci.*, **22**, 668–672). [247]

738. Stevens, S. S., and J. Volkmann, 1940. The relation of pitch to frequency: a revised scale (*Amer. J. Psychol.*, **53**, 329–353). [241, 244, 303]

739. Stevens, S. S., J. Volkmann, and E. B. Newman, 1937. A scale for the measurement of the psychological magnitude pitch (*J. acoust. Soc. Amer.*, **8**, 186–190). [303]

Stewart, J., see No. 233.

740. Stone, C. P., 1923. Further study of sensory functions in the activation of sexual behavior in the young male albino rat (*J. comp. Psychol.*, **3**, 469–473). [cf. 418]

741. Stone, C. P., 1924. The awakening of copulatory ability in the male albino rat (*Amer. J. Physiol.*, **68**, 407–424). [124, 420]

742. Stone, C. P., 1925. The effects of cerebral destruction on the sexual behavior of rabbits. I. The olfactory bulbs (*Amer. J. Physiol.*, **71**, 430–435). [435]

743. Stone, C. P., 1925. The effects of cerebral destruction on the sexual behavior of rabbits. II. Frontal and parietal lesions (*Amer. J. Physiol.*, **72**, 372–385).

744. Stone, C. P., 1926. The initial copulatory response of female rats reared in isolation from the age of 20 days to puberty (*J. comp. Psychol.*, **6**, 78–83). [124]

745. Stone, C. P., 1926. The effects of cerebral destruction upon the sexual behavior of male rabbits. III. The frontal, parietal, and occipital regions (*J. comp. Psychol.*, 6, 435–448). [cf. 435f.]

746. Stone, C. P., 1927. The retention of copulatory ability in male rats following castration (*J. comp. Psychol.*, **7**, 369–387). [428]

747. Stone, C. P., 1939. Sex drive. Pp. 1213–1262. In *Sex and internal secretions*, eds., E. Allen, C. H. Danforth, and E. A. Doisy (Baltimore, Williams and Wilkins). [389, 397, 417, 420, 424, 428, 431, 436]

Stone, C. P., see also No. 160.

748. Stone, C. P., and R. G. Barker, 1934. Spontaneous activity, direct and indirect measures of sexual drive in adult male rats (*Proc. Soc. exp. Biol.*, *N.Y.*, **32**, 195–199). [388, 389]

Stone, L. J., see No. 421.

749. Stone, L. J., and W. L. Jenkins, 1940. Recent research in cutaneous sensitivity. I. Pain and temperature (*Psychol. Bull.*, **37**, 285–311). [268, 282]

Stopford, J. S. B., see No. 577.

750. Strughold, H., 1923. Die Wirkung der Kampfstoffe Diphenylarsinchlorid (Blaukreuzstoff) und Äthylarsindichlorid auf die Haut des Menschen (*Zsch. Biol.*, **78**, 195–230). [269]

751. Strughold, H., and M. Karbe, 1925. Vitale Färbung des Auges und experimentelle Untersuchung der gefärbten Nervenelement (*Zsch. Biol.*, **83**, 297–308). [271]

Swan, T. H., see Nos. 423, 424.

752. Swann, H. G., 1934. The function of the brain in olfaction. II. The results of destruction of olfactory and other nervous structures upon the discrimination of odors (*J. comp. Neurol.*, **59**, 175–201). [151]

Sweet, W. H., see No. 22.

753. Szymanski, J. S., 1918. Aktivität und Ruhe bei Tieren und Menschen (*Zeit. allgem. Physiol.*, **18**, 105–162). [376]

Taylor, N. B., see No. 70.

754. Templeton, R. D., and J. P. Quigley, 1930. The action of insulin on motility of the gastro-intestinal tract. II. (*Amer. J. Physiol.*, **91**, 467–474.) [449]

755. Ten Cate, J., 1934. Akustische und optische Reaktionen der Katzen nach teilweisen und totalen Extirpationen des Neopalliums (*Arch. néerl. Physiol.*, **19**, 191–264). [cf. 325]

Therman, P. P., see No. 317.

756. Thorson, A. M., 1925. The relation of tongue movements to internal speech (*J. exp. Psychol.*, **8**, 1–32). [547f., 550]

757. Tinklepaugh, O. L., 1928. An experimental study of representative factors in monkeys (*J. comp. Psychol.*, **8**, 197–236). [472]

758. Tinklepaugh, O. L., 1933. The nature of periods of sex desire in woman and their relation to ovulation (*Amer. J. Obst. Gynecol.*, **26**, 335). [425]

759. Tryon, R. C., 1939. Studies in individual differences in maze learning. VI. Disproof of sensory components: experimental effects of stimulus variation (*J. comp. Psychol.*, **28**, 361–415). [544]

760. Tsai, L. S., and S. Maurer, 1930. Right handedness in white rats (*Science*, **72**, 436–438). [341]

761. Tsang, Y. C., 1934. The functions of the visual areas of the cerebral cortex of the rat in the learning and retention of the maze. I. (*Comp. Psychol. Monogr.*, **10**, No. 50). [500f.]

762. Tsang, Y. C., 1936. The functions of the visual areas of the cerebral cortex of the rat in the learning and retention of the maze. II. (*Comp. Psychol. Monogr.*, **12**, No. 57). [500f.]

763. Tsang, Y. C., 1937. Maze learning in rats hemidecorticated in infancy (*J. comp. Psychol.*, **24**, 221–254). [539]

764. Tsang, Y. C., 1937. Visual sensitivity of rats deprived of visual cortex in infancy (*J. comp. Psychol.*, **24**, 255–262). [539]

765. Tsang, Y. C., 1938. Hunger motivation in gastrectomized rats (*J. comp. Psychol.*, **26**, 1–17). [447]

766. Twitty, V. C., 1932. Influence of the eye on the growth of its associated structures, studied by means of heteroplastic transplantation (*J. exp. Zool.*, **61**, 333–374). [132]

Upton, M., see No. 208.

Van Dyke, H. B., see No. 219.

Van Wagenen, W. P., see No. 69.

Viets, H. R., see No. 439.

Volkmann, J., see Nos. 736, 738, 739.

Volta, A. [10]

767. Wada, T., 1922. Experimental study of hunger in its relation to activity (*Arch. Psychol.*, **8**, 1–65). [387, 447]

768. Wagoner, K. S., and E. C. Havermann, 1936. III. The effect of thermal stimulation in one hand upon the temperature limen in the contralateral hand (*J. Psychol.*, **2**, 441–449). [272]

769. Wald, G., 1935. Carotenoids in the visual cycle (*J. gen. Physiol.*, **19**, 351–373). [169]

770. Wald, G., 1938. Area and visual threshold (*J. gen. Physiol.*, **21**, 269–287). [189, 270]

771. Wald, G., 1941. The visual systems of euryhaline fishes (*J. gen. Physiol.*, **25**, 235–245). [105]

772. Wald, G., and A. B. Clark, 1937. Visual adaptation and chemistry of the rods (*J. gen. Physiol.*, **21**, 93–105). [185]

773. Wald, G. H., Jeghers, and J. Arminio, 1938. An experiment in human dietary night-blindness (*Amer. J. Physiol.*, **123**, 732–746). [cf. 186f.]

Waldman, H., see No. 567.

774. Walker, A. E., 1938. *The primate thalamus* (Chicago, Univ. Chicago Press). [83, 288]

775. Walker, A. E., 1940. A cytoarchitectural study of the prefrontal area of the macque monkey (*J. comp. Neurol.*, **73**, 59–86). [cf. 560–567]

776. Walker, A. E., and J. F. Fulton, 1938. Hemidecortication in chimpanzee, baboon, macaque, potto, cat and coati: A study in encephalization (*J. nerv. ment. Dis.*, **87**, 677–700). [281, 289]

777. Wang, G. H., 1923. Relation between "spontaneous" activity and oestrus cycle in the white rat (*Comp. Psychol. Monogr.*, **2**, No. 6). [387, 422]

778. Wang, G. H., 1924. A sexual activity rhythm in the female rat (*Amer. Nat.*, **58**, 36–42). [422]

779. Wangensteen, O. H., and A. J. Carlson, 1931. Hunger sensations in a patient after total gastrectomy (*Proc. Soc. exp. Biol., N.Y.*, **28**, 545–547). [cf. 447]

780. Ward, H., 1921. Some of the factors controlling the migration and spawning of the Alaska Red Salmon (*Ecol.*, **2**, 235–254). [402]

Ward, J. W., see No. 152.

781. Warkentin, J., 1937. The visual acuity of some vertebrates (*Psychol. Bull.*, **34**, 793). [106, 129]

782. Warkentin, J., 1938. A genetic study of vision in animals (Ph.D. thesis, University of Rochester).

Warkentin, J., see also No. 713.

783. Warren, H. C., and L. Carmichael, 1930. *Elements of human psychology* (Boston, Houghton Mifflin). [162]

Washburn, A. L., see No. 128.

784. Watson, J. B., 1929. *Psychology from the standpoint of a behaviorist* (Philadelphia, Lippincott). [5]

Watson, J. B. [5]

785. Watson, J. B., and J. J. B. Morgan, 1917. Emotional reactions and psychological experimentation (*Amer. J. Psychol.*, **28**, 163–174). [366]

786. Watterston, D., 1923. The sensory activities of the skin for touch and temperature (*Brain*, **46**, 200–208). [269]

Watts, J. W., see No. 257.

787. Weber, E. H., 1846. Der Tastsinn und das Gemeingefühl (R. Wagner's *Handwörterbuch der Phsyiol.*, III, ii, 481–588). [255]

Weigand, G. E., see No. 424.

788. Weisenberg, T., and K. E. McBride, 1935. *Aphasia* (New York, Commonwealth Fund). [527, 529–534, 540, 542]

789. Weiss, P., 1931. Das Resonanzprinzip der Nerventätigkeit (*Arch. ges. Physiol.*, **226**, 600–658). [134]

790. Weiss, P., 1935. Homologous function in supernumerary limbs after elimination of sensory control (*Proc. Soc. exp. Biol., N.Y.*, **33**, 30–32). [133]

791. Weiss, P., 1935.   Unmodifiability of locomotor coordination in amphibia, demonstrated by the reverse functioning of mutually exchanged right and left limbs (*Proc. Soc. exp. Biol., N.Y.*, **33**, 241–242).   [133]

792. Weiss, P., 1936.   Selectivity controlling the central-peripheral relations in the nervous system (*Biol. Rev.*, **11**, 494–531).   [32, 134]

793. Weiss, P., 1937.   Further experimental investigations on the phenomenon of homologous response in transplanted amphibian limbs (*J. comp. Neurol.*, **66**, 181–210, 481–536, 537–548, **67**, 269–315).   [133]

794. Weiss, P., 1939.   *Principles of development* (New York, Holt).   [32f., 133f., 351, 520]

795. Weiss, P., 1940.   Functional properties of isolated spinal cord grafts in larval amphibians (*Proc. Soc. exp. Biol., N.Y.*, **44**, 350–352).   [137, 349]

796. Weiss, P., 1941.   Further experiments with deplanted and deranged nerve centers in amphibians (*Proc. Soc. exp. Biol.*, **46**, 14–15).   [137]

797. Weiss, P., 1941.   Autonomous versus reflexogenous activity of the central nervous system (*Proc. Amer. phil. Soc.*, **84**, 53–64).   [131]

798. Weiss, P., 1941.   Self-differentiation of the basic patterns of coordination (*Comp. Psychol. Monogr.*, **17**, No. 88).   [141]

799. Wendt, G. R., 1936.   An interpretation of inhibition of conditioned reflexes as competition between reaction systems (*Psychol. Rev.*, **43**, 258–281).   [474]

800. Wever, E. G., 1939.   The electrical responses of the ear (*Psychol. Bull.*, **36**, 143–186).   [233]

801. Wever, E. G., and C. W. Bray, 1930.   Action currents in the auditory nerve in response to acoustical stimulation (*Proc. nat. Acad. Sci.*, **16**, 344–350).   [233]

802. Wever, E. G., and C. W. Bray, 1936.   The perception of low tones and the resonance-volley theory (*J. Psychol.*, **3**, 101–114).   [250, 252]

803. Wever, E. G., and C. W. Bray, 1936.   Hearing in the pigeon, as studied by the electrical responses of the inner ear (*J. comp. Psychol.*, **22**, 353–364).   [107]

804. Wiersma, C. A. J., 1941.   The efferent innervation of muscle. Pp. 259–290.   In *Biological symposia III* (Lancaster, Jaques Cattell).   [309f.]

805. Wiesner, B. P., and N. M. Sheard, 1933.   Sex behavior in hypophysectomized male rats (*Nature*, **132**, 641).   [429]

806. Wiggers, H. C., 1937.   The functions of the intra-aural muscles (*Amer. J. Physiol.*, **120**, 781–797).   [227]

807. Wilder, C. E., 1937.   Selection of rachitic and antirachitic diets in the rat (*J. comp. Psychol.*, **24**, 547–577).   [452]

Wiley, L. E., see No. 496.

Williams, R. E., see No. 363.

Williams, R. G., see No. 53.

808. Willier, B. H., 1939.   The embryonic development of sex. Pp. 64–143.   In *Sex and internal secretions*, eds., E. Allen, C. H. Danforth, and E. A. Doisy (Baltimore, Williams & Wilkins).   [413]

Wilson, M. T., see No. 829.

809. Windle, W. F., 1940.   *Physiology of the fetus: origin and extent of function in prenatal life* (Philadelphia, Saunders).

Windle, W. F., see also No. 594.

810. Windle, W. F., and R. E. Baxter, 1936.   Development of reflex mechanisms in the spinal cord of albino rat embryos.   Correlations between structure and function, and comparisons with the cat and chick (*J. comp. Neurol.*, **63**, 189–210).   [126]

811. Windle, W. F., and A. M. Griffin, 1931.   Observations on embryonic and fetal movements of the cat (*J. comp. Neurol.*, **52**, 149–188).   [126]

Wittenborn, J. R., see No. 825.

812. Wolcott, R. H., 1940.   *Animal biology* (New York, McGraw-Hill).   [27]

Wolf, E., see Nos. 177–194.

813. Wolfe, J., 1939.   An exploratory study in food storing in rats (*J. comp. Psychol.*, **28**, 97–108).   [402]

Wolfe, J. B., see No. 407.

814. Wolff, H. G., 1941.   Mechanisms of headache (*Arch. Neurol. Psychiat., Chicago*, **46**, 1096–1098).   [cf. 359f.]

Wolff, H. G., see also Nos. 150, 313, 632.

Wood, W. M., see No. 568.

815. Woodworth, R. S., 1938.   *Experimental psychology* (New York, Holt).   [158]

Woodworth, R. S., see also No. 469.

Woolsey, C. N., see No. 543.

Wundt, W. [4, 6]

816. Wyczoikowski, A., 1913. Theoretical and experimental studies on the mechanism of speech (*Psychol. Rev.*, **20**, 448–458). [547]

Yamagiwa, K., see No. 14.

Yarosh, M., see No. 727.

817. Yeakel, E. H., and R. P. Rhoades, 1941. A comparison of the body and endocrine gland (adrenal, thyroid and pituitary) weights of emotion and nonemotional rats (*Endocrinology*, **28**, 337–340). [365]

818. Yerkes, R. M., 1940. Social behavior of chimpanzees: dominance between mates, in relation to sexual status (*J. comp. Psychol.*, **30**, 147–186). [424]

819. Yerkes, R. M., and J. H. Elder, 1936. Oestrus, receptivity, and mating in the chimpanzee (*Comp. Psychol. Monogr.*, **13**, No. 65). [423f.]

820. Young, A. C., 1941. Action potentials of skeletal muscle. Pp. 153–160. In *Biological symposia III* (Lancaster, Jaques Cattell). [309]

821. Young, P. T., 1936. *Motivation of behavior* (New York, Wiley). [479]

822. Young, P. T., 1938. Preferences and demands of the white rat for food (*J. comp. Psychol.*, **26**, 545–588). [cf. 451–455]

823. Young, P. T., 1940. Reversal of food preferences of the white rat through controlled pre-feeding (*J. gen. Psychol.*, **22**, 33–66). [451]

824. Young, P. T., 1941. The experimental analysis of appetite (*Psychol. Bull.*, **38**, 129–164). [450]

825. Young, P. T., and J. R. Wittenborn, 1940. Food preferences of rachitic and normal rats (*J. comp. Psychol.*, **30**,261–275). [cf. 452]

Young, T. [13]

826. Young, W. C., 1937. The vaginal smear picture, sexual receptivity and the time of ovulation in the guinea pig (*Anat. Rec.*, 67, 305). [422]

Young, W. C., see also Nos. 86, 159.

827. Young, W. C., and R. Brewster, 1939. The hormonal induction of homosexual behavior in the spayed female guinea pig (*Psychosomat. Med.*, **1**, 449–460). [430, 432]

828. Young, W. C., E. W. Dempsey, C. W. Hagquist, and J. L. Boling, 1939. Sexual behavior and sexual receptivity in the female guinea pig (*J. comp. Psychol.*, **27**, 49–68). [426, 430]

Zeliony, G. P., see No. 619.

Zerrahn-Wolfe, G., see Nos. 193, 194.

829. Zigler, M. J., E. M. Moore, and M. T. Wilson, 934. Comparative accuracy in the localization of cutaneous pressure and pain (*Amer. J. Psychol.*, **46**, 47–58). [268]

Zuckerman, S., see No. 154.

830. Zwaardemaker, H., 1925. *L'odorat* (Paris, Doin). [147, 150f.]

SUBJECT INDEX

A

A fiber, 59, 262–264, 276, 286*f.*
A wave, 170–173, 195
Abducens nerve, 73*f.*
Absolute refractory period, 52
Absolute threshold
  area, 189–191
  binocular summation, 190*f.*
  light adaptation, 182*f.*
  retinal summation, 202
  time, 181*f.*
  vision, 179–183
Abstraction, 109, 478
Accommodation, 329
Acetylcholine, 93–95
Acidosis
  activity, 390
  headache, 360
Acoustic reflex, 227
Acoustics (*see* Hearing)
Acromegaly, 39
Action potential, 47–51
  after-potentials, 49–51
  cerebral, 138–140
  decay, 52
  local process, 48*f.*
  muscle, 309*f.*
  spike potential, 48*f.*
  summation, 52
  symbolic processes, 548*f.*
  (*See also* Excitability curve; Nervous
    impulse)
Activity, 385–395
  adrenalin, 37
  castration, 429
  c.m.s., 461
  drives, 385–388
  endocrine basis, 388–391
  estrus cycle, 422
  frontal areas, 391–395
  hunger, 386*f.*
  neural control, 391–395
  sexual drive, 387*f.*

Activity, sleep, 375–377
  spontaneous, 137
Acuity
  visual, 199–201
Adaptation
  color, 209–211
  dark, 183–189
  light, 185
  olfactory, 148
  pain, 268
  principle of, 475
  skin senses, 259
Adaptive behavior, 457–479
  phylogenesis, 108–114
    complexity of elements, 110–112
    concept formation, 109*f.*
    delayed reaction, 112–114
    learning, 108*f.*
    theories, 457*f.*
    (*See also* Learning; Motivation)
Adjustors, 25
Adrenal gland
  activity, 389*f.*
  androgenic hormones, 38
  cortex, 37*f.*
  cortin, 37*f.*
  hibernation, 405
  medulla, 37
  sexual behavior, 429
  sexual development, 419*f.*
Adrenalin, 37, 365
Adrenalin-like substance
  neurohumoral transmission, 93*f.*
Adrenergic, 94
After-discharge, 66, 311
After-potentials, 51, 309*f.*
Age
  memory, 539*f.*
Agnosia, 527, 534
Agraphia, 527
Alexia, 527
All-or-none law, 50, 301
Alpha adaptation, 183

601